Protozoology

by

R. P. HALL
New York University

Englewood Cliffs, N. J.
PRENTICE-HALL, INC.

PRENTICE-HALL ANIMAL SCIENCE SERIES

H. Burr Steinbach, *Editor*

Current printing (last digit):
13 12 11 10 9 8 7 6 5 4

PRINTED IN THE UNITED STATES OF AMERICA

ACKNOWLEDGMENTS

The writer is much indebted to several colleagues for their patience in reading portions of the manuscript and for their helpful suggestions, and also to the many investigators whose contributions of reprints have greatly eased the task of reviewing the literature.

R. P. HALL

Contents

I

General Morphology of the Protozoa

THE PROTOZOA include a variety of microorganisms which, by general agreement of protozoologists, are currently assigned to the phylum. More specific characterization of the Protozoa is difficult and even the name of the phylum, as applied to the groups it conventionally includes, is not entirely appropriate. Many flagellates—those usually listed as Phytomastigoda, Phytomastigina, or Phytomastigophora—are commonly considered algae by botanists. Also, the Mycetozoida (Mycetozoa)

1

of protozoologists are nothing else than the slime-molds of botanists, and the Sarcosporidia, usually considered Sporozoa, are believed by some workers to be molds.

This situation, which suggests that protozoologists are unable to distinguish animals from plants, is somewhat disconcerting to those who favor consistency in taxonomy. Consequently, various taxonomic reforms have been suggested. The old term, *Protista,* recalls such an effort by Haeckel, but the Protista were only a heterogeneous collection of microorganisms with the plant and animal labels obscured. A more positive reform was proposed by Calkins (17) in his decision to eliminate the chlorophyll-bearing flagellates from the Phylum Protozoa. On the face of it, the proposal seemed to be an admission that zoologists had been in error in laying claim to the "Phytomastigophora." However, some of the more interesting colorless phytoflagellates were saved from a botanical fate by arbitrary transfer to the "Zoomastigophora." The resulting mixtures could not be justified on the basis of sound taxonomic criteria; hence, this innovation has not been generally accepted. The basic classification of Copeland (33) recognizes a separate Kingdom Protoctista which includes the Protozoa and various groups of algae and fungi. While this suggestion sidesteps the problem of deciding which Protozoa are animals and which are plants, it seems to imply that such Protozoa as the ciliates are more closely related to the red algae and related organisms than they are to the Kingdom Animalia.

At present, many protozoologists continue to list the phytoflagellates and slime-molds as Protozoa, although they realize that botanists have no objections to placing these groups in the plant kingdom. While the current practice is a bit confusing taxonomically, there is the advantage that botanists and protozoologists can legitimately maintain equal interest in these groups which apparently represent mergers of the plant and animal kingdoms.

From the morphological standpoint, Protozoa are often referred to as *unicellular* animals, in contrast to the multicellular Metazoa. The small size and simple structure of many Protozoa tend to justify this designation. On the other hand, some Protozoa are not so small and are measurable in millimeters, or even centimeters, instead of microns. Furthermore, the uninucleate condition is far from universal. Many species possess more than one nucleus, and the numbers range from two to many hundreds. Examples are found in each of the major taxonomic groups. Structural complexity often extends beyond a mere increase in number of nuclei. Mycetozoan protoplasm, as noted in *Physarum* (167), is traversed by channels through which a liquid, containing many granules, flows back and forth in a sort of primitive circulatory system. Multiplicity of flagellar units is associated with multinuclearity in Mastigophora. The result may be many nucleo-flagellar units (karyomastigonts), as in certain Calonymphidae (Fig. 1. 10, D). In addition to normally multinucleate Protozoa, many species are uninucleate in one phase of the life-cycle and multinucleate in another.

Such structural diversity has led protozoologists into difficulties with the Cell Theory. Dobell (45), who suggested that Protozoa are *non-cellular* organisms, was one of the first to revolt against strict application of the Cell Theory to this group. Such an interpretation has appealed to some zoologists. A different concept, favored by Kofoid (138) for example, is that some Protozoa are unicellular while others are multicellular. Protozoan "multicellularity" is considered analogous to metazoan multicellularity as seen in syncytial tissues. According to this view, the Protozoa are the phylum in which multicellularity originated in animals.

The evolutionary transition from Protozoa to Metazoa involved differentiation beyond the separation of reproductive and somatic cells. Hyman (98) has stressed the characteristic establishment of an axis along which morphological and physiological differentiation has occurred. Such colonial types as *Volvox,* in spite of their specialized somatic and reproductive "cells," are usually considered Protozoa. The distinction is mainly one of degree, since *Volvox* has several attributes of an organism in the metazoan sense. The colony moves as a unit, with apparently coordinated flagellar activity, and exhibits some degree of polarity with functional differentiation. The colony may produce daughter colonies asexually or it may develop gametes. The zygote develops into a young colony in a manner not unlike that in which a fertilized egg produces a young metazoan individual. The Myxosporida, another exceptional group, show somatic differentiation in that some cells produce spore-membranes while others give rise to the polar capsules of the myxosporidian spore. In other words, the separation of Protozoa from Metazoa in borderline cases may involve somewhat arbitrary decisions influenced to some extent by factors of taxonomic convenience.

VARIATIONS IN FORM OF
THE BODY

Protozoa range from approximately spherical forms to bizarre shapes not readily explained on a functional basis. Symmetry is often poorly defined. Most active swimmers show spiral torsion in some degree and this tendency toward asymmetry is presumably correlated with the usual spiral course in locomotion (62, 136). However, universal symmetry and radial symmetry may be noted in various floating and sessile species, respectively, and bilateral symmetry is apparent in such genera as *Giardia* and *Octomitus*. In Protozoa which are not spherical, form of the body may be rather characteristic of a given species under particular conditions. However, form is often relatively constant rather than absolutely so, and within specific limits, may be modified by environmental conditions and activities of the organism. Even the nature and quantity of the available food may influence form as well as size of the body. Such a relationship is striking in *Tetrahymena vorax* (Fig. 1. 1) when strains are fed on different diets (118). In addition to the usual variations, attrib-

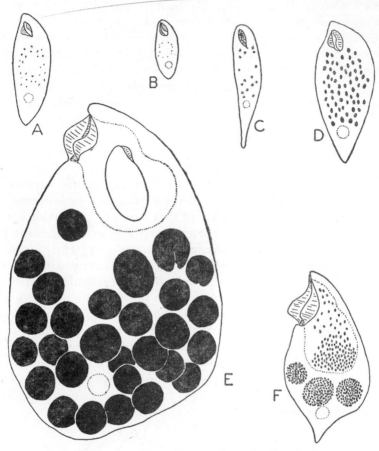

Fig. 1. 1. Influence of diet on form and size in *Tetrahymena vorax*. A. Organism from young broth culture (saprozoic nutrition). B. Specimen from older broth culture. C. A ciliate fed on *Aerobacter cloacae*. D. A ciliate fed on killed *Tetrahymena geleii*. E. A large carnivore from a culture fed living *T. geleii*. F. A carnivore after transfer to a culture of living yeast. Ingested food, peristomial area, and contractile vacuole are indicated diagrammatically but cilia are not shown. x450 (after Kidder, Lilly, and Claff).

utable to environmental or inherent factors, dimorphic and polymorphic life-cycles include two or more different morphological stages. *Naegleria gruberi* (Chapter V), for example, exhibits both flagellate and amoeboid stages. Although adaptive trends may be assumed, specific correlation of form with habitat is impossible in many instances. Yet certain generalizations are permissible for sessile, floating, swimming, and creeping types. Floating types, free from the usual stresses of locomotor activity, often approach a spherical form. Active swimmers are usually elongated, with a major axis more or less parallel to the path of locomotion. Creeping

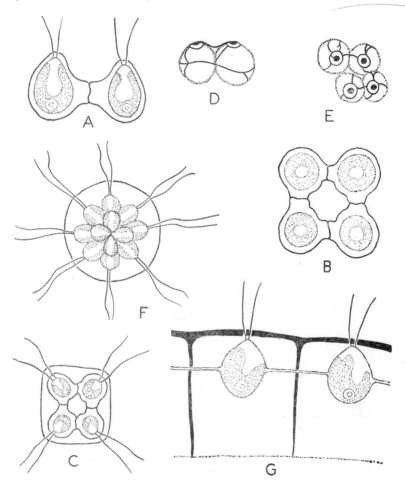

Fig. 1. 2. A-C. *Gonium sociale:* side view (A); surface view (B); colony with superficial continuous matrix (C); x900 (after Pascher). D, E. *Gonium* sp., portions of colonies showing supposed protoplasmic connections impregnated with silver; x760 (after Klein). F. *Syncrypta volvox;* x580 (after Stein). G. Protoplasmic connections of somatic flagellates in *Volvox;* x1800 (after Janet).

forms are frequently flattened and may show differentiated dorsal and ventral surfaces. Sessile ciliates and flagellates are often more or less conical, attached to the substratum directly or by a secreted stalk.

In individual Protozoa, form of the body may be maintained by a thickened cortex (the differentiated outer zone of cytoplasm), by various secreted layers (pellicle, theca, lorica, test, and shell of particular groups), and by internal structures such as radiolarian skeletons. The gross morphology of protozoan aggregates and colonies depends upon the means by which the individual organisms are bound together.

COLONIAL ORGANIZATION

The usual colony consists of similar organisms joined together in some particular pattern so that the form of the mature colony is characteristic of the genus or species. As a rule, any member of the colony may undergo fission or budding. In the Phytomonadida, this is true in *Gonium*, *Pandorina*, and *Platydorina* but apparently not in *Eudorina*, *Pleodorina*, and *Volvox*. However, flagellates isolated from colonies of

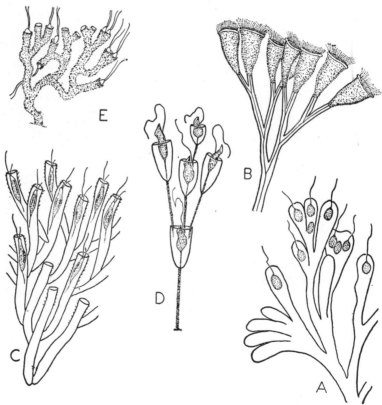

Fig. 1. 3. Arboroid colonies. A. *Phalansterium digitatum,* branching matrix; x290 (after Lemmermann). B. *Zoothamnium adamsi,* portion of colony showing stalk with continuous branching fibril; diagrammatic (after Stokes). C. *Hyalobryon ramosum,* loricate type; x720 (after Awerinzew). D. *Poteriodendron petiolatum;* each lorica with stalk; x290 (after Lemmermann). E. *Cladomonas fruticulosa* with continuous branching "lorica"; x290 (after Lemmermann).

Eudorina, Gonium, and *Pandorina* may undergo fission and produce daughter colonies (11). The component flagellates of the *Volvox* colony are differentiated into somatic and reproductive individuals and the former are believed to lose their reproductive ability when the colony reaches maturity.

Protozoan colonies are usually classified on the basis of their organization. *Spheroid* and *discoid* colonies, containing a matrix secreted by the associated organisms during development of the colony, are represented by such ciliates as *Ophrydium* and various flagellates—*Syncrypta, Gonium, Pandorina, Volvox,* and others. In *Gonium sociale,* for example, the matrix shows two components (Fig. 1. 2, C), a "cell wall" enclosing each flagellate and a continuous outer gelatinous layer. In some specimens (Fig. 1. 2, A, B) the outer layer is lacking. Each flagellate in the *Volvox* colony is enclosed in a thin cell wall and a thick outer sheath. Except in *V. aureus,* the boundaries of the individual sheaths are readily distinguished. The flagellates appear to be joined by protoplasmic strands in certain species of *Volvox* (Fig. 1. 2, G) and apparently also in *Eudorina, Gonium,* and *Pandorina* (11). Dried colonies of *Gonium* (Fig. 1. 2, D, E), after silver impregnation, show "silver-line" connections between adjacent flagellates (131).

In *arboroid* colonies (Fig. 1. 3), the individual organisms are arranged in a branching pattern. Stalks are characteristic of many arboroid colonies. In different species, each organism may have its own stem which is attached to a common stalk, or each stalk of the framework may bear more than one organism. Such stalks may be gelatinous or sometimes solid and relatively firm, and in certain cases they are elastic tubes containing contractile fibrils. In other arboroid types, colonial organization is maintained by attachment of one lorica to another (Fig. 1. 3, C, D), or by a continuous tubular "lorica" in which the organisms are located at the tips of the branches (Fig. 1. 3, E).

NON-COLONIAL GROUPINGS

Certain other aggregates are not colonies in the strict sense. So-called *catenoid* colonies have been described in dinoflagellates (Fig. 1. 4, D) and certain astomatous ciliates (Fig. 1. 4, C). These chains arise in repeated fission without prompt separation of daughter organisms and are temporary groupings rather than true colonies. *Palmella* stages (Fig. 1. 4, A) of certain flagellates develop in much the same manner as spheroid and discoid colonies. However, the palmella does not show a well defined range in size, the number of organisms varies with size of the mass, and the flagellates lack flagella. The term, *gleocystis* stage, is sometimes applied to similar aggregates in which an individual gelatinous layer surrounds each organism (Fig. 1. 4, B).

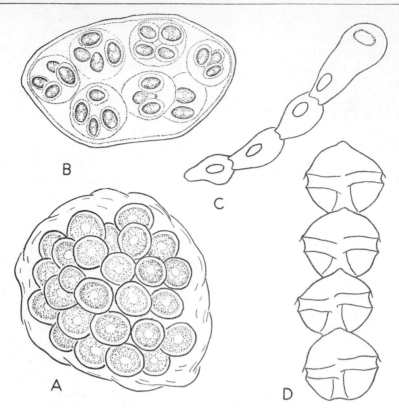

Fig. 1. 4. A. Palmella stage, as seen in *Haematococcus* and related Phytomonadida; diagrammatic (after Wollenweber). B. Gleocystis stage, as found in various Chlamydomonadidae; diagrammatic (after Goroschankin). C. Chain ("catenoid colony") of *Haptophrya michiganensis;* x90 (after Bush). D. Chain formed in fission of *Gonyaulax catenella;* x580 (after Whedon and Kofoid).

CORTEX, SECRETED COVERINGS, AND SKELETONS

No well developed cortex is apparent in simple flagellates or typical amoebae. The superficial cytoplasmic layer of *Amoeba proteus* is formed from, and gives rise to endoplasm continuously during amoeboid activity and thus lacks the relative permanence of the cortex in more specialized Protozoa. However, some amoeboid organisms have a thin pellicle similar to that of *Amoeba verrucosa*. In this species, the pellicle maintains itself under mechanical stress in microdissection (96).

At the other extreme, the relatively thick cortex of a ciliate may contain basal granules, fibrils, myonemes, mitochondria, and other inclusions, and sometimes trichocysts. Although often flexible, the layer is at least firm enough to maintain a typical body form in the swimming ciliate. The pellicle covering the surface of ciliates seems to be a distinct layer, and *Blepharisma undulans* is said to shed its pellicle after treatment with strychnine. The cilia are withdrawn and the body retracted, leaving a space beneath the pellicle, and the ciliate later emerges through the old cytostomal area or the region of the posterior contractile vacuole (169).

Surface layers of flagellates range from a delicate periplast or pellicle, similar to that of certain amoebae, to thick tests or shells. The flexible

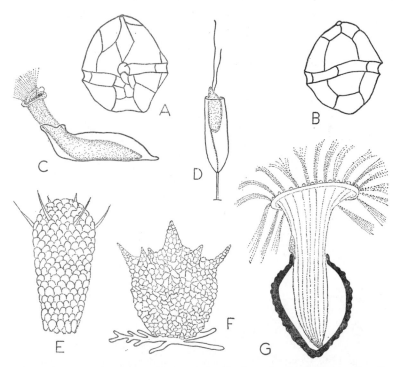

Fig. 1. 5. A, B. Ventral and dorsal thecal plates in *Gonyaulax acatenella;* x560 (after Whedon and Kofoid). C. *Vaginicola longicollis,* optical section of lorica; x140 (after Penard). D. *Stokesiella lepteca,* stalked lorica; x1060 (after Stokes). E. Test of *Euglypha alveolata;* x350 (after Leidy). F. *Difflugia corona;* x135 (after Leidy). G. *Tintinnopsis nucula,* optical section of lorica; diagrammatic; x570 (after Campbell).

periplast of many Euglenida permits a characteristic euglenoid movement ("metaboly"), but tends to maintain a characteristic form in the swimming flagellate. This periplast presumably is a secreted layer, since it becomes separated from the underlying cytoplasm in plasmolysis (22). Thickened pellicular layers, as seen in *Lepocinclis* and *Phacus,* may be so firm that the body shows little change in shape. Such membranes are often decorated with ridges, papillae or other markings.

The *theca* of many Phytomonadida and Dinoflagellida is a secreted covering applied directly to the surface of the body and is comparable to the thick cell wall found in higher plants. The flagella emerge through pores in the theca. A theca may be somewhat flexible, allowing slight changes in form, or it may be rigid. The firmness imparted by cellulose or pectins is sometimes increased by impregnation with inorganic salts to produce a hard covering, as in *Phacotus, Trachelomonas,* and some of the dinoflagellates. The theca of many dinoflagellates is differentiated into a number of plates (Fig. 1. 5, A, B), the pattern varying with the species.

Lorica, test, and *shell* are terms applied to coverings which often fit less closely than the theca and hence are less comparable to the typical cell wall of plants. A lorica (Fig. 1. 5, C, D) is usually a tubular or vase-like structure with an opening through which the anterior part of the

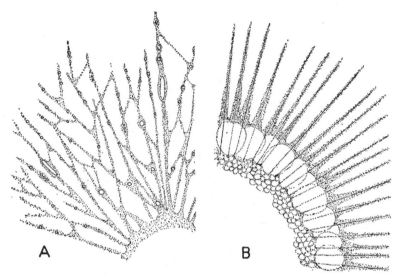

Fig. 1. 6. Groups of myxopodia (A) and axopodia (B); diagrammatic.

body or its appendages can be extended. The base of the lorica, in sessile species, may be attached directly to the substratum or may end in a stalk. In colonial types (Fig. 1. 3, C, D), one lorica may be attached to another directly or by means of a stalk. A lorica may be composed entirely of secreted material or may be reinforced with diatom shells, sand grains, or other foreign particles.

The tests (or shells) of many Sarcodina vary widely in form and composition. Some appear to be homogeneous. Others consist mainly of separate elements cemented together, as in *Euglypha* and *Difflugia* (Fig. 1. 5, E, F). The test of *Euglypha* is composed of plates, formed within the body prior to fission; that of *Difflugia* is made of sand grains embedded in a secreted cement. The comparable arenaceous tests of certain Foraminiferida (Chapter V) are built of sand grains, discarded tests, sponge spicules, or other materials cemented together over a thin chitinous test. The composition of other foramiferan tests varies from group to group. That of the Allogromiidae is typically chitinous, while the majority of the multichambered tests are calcareous. Siliceous tests also have been reported in a few Foraminiferida. In many species at least, the foraminiferan test is not really external; instead, it is normally enclosed within a thin layer of cytoplasm.

The simplest skeletons of Radiolarida are represented by scattered siliceous spicules, while the more complicated types are structures unique among the Protozoa (Chapter V). In the Acantharina long spines radiate in definite patterns from the center of the body. To these elements is often added a lattice-work shell, joining and supported by the spines. Siliceous skeletons of other Radiolarida are quite varied in structure. Spherical types may be composed of several concentric lattice-work shells, and sometimes of spicules in addition. Bilateral types, conical forms, and other departures from radial symmetry are fairly common.

PSEUDOPODIA

Pseudopodia are temporary organelles which can be retracted and formed anew, depending upon activities of the organism. Four major types may be distinguished—*lobopodia, filopodia, myxopodia,* and *axopodia.*

Lobopodia, which have relatively dense outer layers and more fluid inner zones, are relatively broad pseudopodia with rounded tips. Short or slender lobopodia may be hyaline, but larger ones usually show a clear ectoplasm enclosing a granular endoplasm. Lobopodia are characteristic of amoebae, certain flagellates, and certain testate rhizopods (Fig. 1. 5, F).

Filopodia are slender hyaline pseudopodia which taper from base to pointed tip and also tend to branch and anastomose. In addition, filopodia may fuse locally to produce thin webs of cytoplasm. The absence of circulating granules helps to distinguish filopodial from myxopodial nets.

Myxopodia (rhizopodia, or reticulopodia), characteristic of the Foraminiferida, are filamentous structures (Fig. 1. 6, A) which branch and anastomose into complex networks often covering a wide area. Such nets are efficient food-traps and are fairly effective locomotor organelles. In addition, the digestive activities of myxopodia are usually marked in Foraminiferida (Chapter V). The comparatively dense inner zone of the myxopodium has been considered fibrillar in structure (198). The fluidity of the outer layer is indicated by the active circulation of cytoplasmic granules, as illustrated by *Elphidium (Polystomella) crispum* (103).

Axopodia (Fig. 1. 6, B) tend to radiate singly from the surface of more or less spherical organisms (Heliozoida, Radiolarida). The axial filament of a typical axopodium has been described as a fibrillar tube enclosing a homogeneous core (193, 195). In contrast to the axial filament, the outer cytoplasm is a sol, as indicated by the movement of inclusions. Axial filaments may converge in a *central granule* (*Acanthocystis* and related genera) or they may end separately in the cytoplasm (*Actinosphaerium*).

FLAGELLA AND ASSOCIATED STRUCTURES

Flagella

These organelles are found in Mastigophora and in flagellate stages of Sarcodina and Sporozoa. A typical flagellum is composed of a *sheath,* which may be circular, elliptical, or flattened in cross-section, and an inner *axoneme.* The latter, according to some workers, is the active portion of the flagellum while the sheath is merely protective. Others think that the axoneme is only an elastic support for a contractile sheath. The axoneme arises from a granule, the *blepharoplast,* and may or may not extend beyond the sheath as a distal end-piece (Fig. 1. 7, F). A terminal knob (Fig. 1. 7, H), instead of a filament, is evident in silver preparations of *Trypanosoma rhodesiense* (127). The anterior flagella of *Hexamitus pulcher* (130) also are unusual in that they arise from external rod-like structures (Fig. 1. 7, E) of uncertain significance.

The finer structure of the flagellum[1] is incompletely known, although investigations with the electron microscope (13, 56, 180, 199) have supplemented earlier observations. The axoneme may be composed of one, two (*Astasia, Euglena*), three (*Peranema*), or perhaps more fibrils, while the sheath apparently contains a spirally coiled filament in certain species.

The sheath in some flagella shows lateral filaments (Fig. 1. 7, A, C), the *mastigonemes* (43) or "Flimmer," the nature of which is uncertain. Although observed in living *Mallomonas acaroides* in dark-field (217), they may be artifacts (173) or may represent fibrils of the sheath which are frayed out laterally under certain conditions (180). At any rate, such filaments appear consistently in some species and not in others. In the *stichonematic* flagellum (43), a single row of filaments extends along one side of the sheath (Fig. 1. 7, A), as in *Astasia* and *Euglena* (13). In the *pantonematic* type there are two or more rows of mastigonemes. Only a terminal filament is present in the *acronematic,* or "lash" flagellum (174), while the *pantacronematic* type shows both a terminal filament and one or more rows of mastigonemes. A *simple* type, found in Cryptomonadida and Dinoflagellida (174), shows neither terminal filament nor mastigonemes. These characteristics of the flagellum seem to be constant within various groups and may furnish significant information in studies on taxonomy and phylogeny (174, 217).

In the majority of flagellates, the flagellum extends forward from its

[1] This subject has been reviewed in several papers (13, 174, 180, 217).

origin, whereas a *trailing* flagellum (Fig. 1. 9, F) arises anteriorly but is trailed posteriorly in swimming. A trailing flagellum may be of the conventional type, or it may be ribbon-like as in *Macrotrichomonas pulchra* (126). The *undulating membrane* of *Trichomonas* and related genera (Fig. 1. 7, G, I) contains a marginal flagellum which originates in an anterior blepharoplast and extends posteriorly, sometimes beyond the end

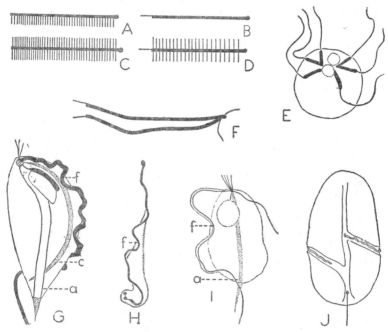

Fig. 1. 7. A-D. Deflandre's types of flagella: stichonematic (A), acronematic (B), pantonematic (C), pantacronematic (D). E. *Hexamitus pulcher*, flagella with rod-like basal portions; protargol; x3460 (after Kirby and Honigberg). F. Acronematic flagella of *Monocercomonoides pilleata;* protargol; x3960 (after Kirby and Honigberg). G. Ribbon-like flagellum of undulating membrane in *Tritrichomonas muris;* protargol; x2810 (after Kirby and Honigberg). H. Terminal knob on flagellum of *Trypanosoma brucei;* protargol; x1790 (after Kirby). I. Undulating membrane in *Pentatrichomonas hominis;* x2660 (after Wenrich). J. Axial flagellum and ribbon-like transverse flagellum of *Gyrodinium dorsum* x470 (after Kofoid and Swezy). Key: *a*, axostyle; *c*, costa; *f*, flagellum in undulating membrane.

of the membrane. This marginal flagellum is sometimes ribbon-like, as in *Tritrichomonas muris* (130). The undulating membrane of *Trypanosoma* originates near the posterior end of the body and extends to the anterior end (Fig. 1. 7, H).

The majority of species have only one or two flagella. More than four are rare in free-living flagellates, although not in parasites. When several flagella are present, they may differ in size, structure, and activity. *Pentatrichomonas hominis* (Fig. 1. 7, I), for instance, has four relatively short anterior flagella, a longer fifth flagellum, and an undulating membrane. A typical dinoflagellate (Fig. 1. 7, J) has a *transverse* flagellum, lying in a spiral groove (the girdle), and an *axial* (or *longitudinal*) flagellum extending posteriorly from a lateral or postero-lateral origin.

Axostyles

The axostyle (Fig. 1. 8) varies from a filament to a thick hyaline rod, usually joined to a blepharoplast and extending posteriorly along the major axis of the body. The axostyle may end in the body or may project externally, sometimes tapering to a filament which may serve for attachment to the host (124). The anterior end is often expanded into a

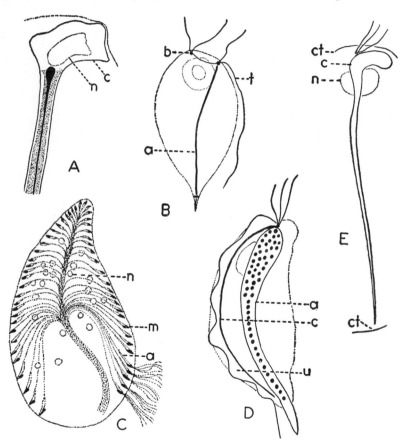

Fig. 1. 8. Axostyles. A. Capitulum and anterior portion of axostyle in *Hyperdevescovina insignita;* x1800 (after Kirby). B. Slender axostyle in *Monocercomonoides pilleata;* x3600 (after Kirby and Honigberg). C. Multiple axostyles of *Snyderella tabogae;* diagrammatic; x350 (after Kirby). D. *Tritrichomonas augusta,* axostyle with inclusions; x1950 (after Kofoid and Swezy). E. Axostyle with capitulum in *Bullanympha silvestri;* x750 (after Kirby). Key: *a,* axostyle; *b,* blepharoplast; *c,* capitulum; *ct,* cortex; *m,* mastigont; *n,* nucleus; *t,* trailing flagellum; *u,* undulating membrane.

capitulum (Fig. 1. 8, A, E). Many multinucleate species contain a number of axostyles, one for each mastigont, and the distal portions of the axostyles form a bundle extending posteriorly as in *Snyderella* (Fig. 1. 8, C).

Staining reactions of the axostyle vary in different species. Iron-hematoxylin stains the axostyle of *Monocercomonoides pilleata* (Fig. 1. 8, B) but not that of certain other flagellates. The organelle appears homogeneous in some species, shows a sheath and a core in others (Fig. 1. 8, A), and sometimes contains stainable granules (Fig. 1. 8, D). The axostyle of *Trichomonas termopsidis* (124) is stained brown in iodine solution.

Costa, cresta, pelta, and aciculum

The *costa* (Fig. 1. 7, G; 1. 8, D) arises from a blepharoplast and extends along the base of the undulating membrane in various tricho-

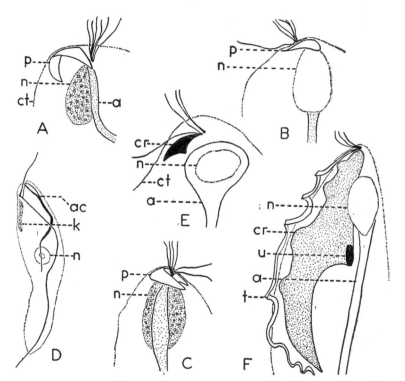

Fig. 1. 9. A-C. Pelta, different views, *Hexamastix citelli;* x6500 (after Kirby and Honigberg). D. Aciculum of *Cryptobia helicis;* kinetoplast indicated diagrammatically; x5330 (after Kozloff). E. Cresta, small type, *Caduceia kofoidi;* x3060 (after Kirby). F. Large cresta, *Macrotrichomonas emersoni;* shelf-like unguis attached; trailing flagellum ribbon-like; x1425 (after Kirby). Key: *a,* axostyle; *ac,* aciculum; *cr,* cresta; *ct,* cortex; *k,* kinetoplast; *n,* nucleus; *p,* pelta; *t,* trailing flagellum; *u,* unguis.

monad flagellates. The function of the costa is uncertain, although it may add firmness to the cytoplasm underlying the undulating membrane.

The *cresta* (Fig. 1. 9, E, F), possibly a homologue of the costa, is present in *Macrotrichomonas* and related genera. This organelle is a somewhat triangular membrane, often visible in the living organism and apparently capable of independent movement (125). The broad anterior end is usually joined to a blepharoplast, while the rest of the cresta extends posteriorly with its outer margin near the periplast. The length, in different species, ranges from about 1.5μ to almost that of the body. A trailing flagellum, sometimes loosely adherent to the periplast anteriorly, may parallel the cresta (Fig. 1. 9, F) and thus simulate the relationship between the undulating membrane and the costa.

The *pelta* (Fig. 1. 9, A, C), demonstrable by the Bodian silver technique, is a crescentic membrane lying anterior to and separate from the blepharoplasts in certain flagellates. The pelta may be homologous with a membranous extension of the axostylar capitulum in certain devescovinid flagellates (128).

The *aciculum* (Fig. 1. 9, D) of *Cryptobia helicis*, a needle-like structure lying opposite the kinetoplast and extending approximately to the origin of the anterior flagellum, is detectable in living material but is best demonstrated by the Bodian silver technique (141).

The parabasal apparatus

In many parasitic and a few free-living flagellates a parabasal apparatus, an organelle of unknown function, forms part of the mastigont (Fig. 1. 10). The simplest type is a small compact body, often attached by a rhizoplast to a blepharoplast. At the other extreme, the apparatus may be a large branched structure or may be composed of separate elements.

The index of refraction of the parabasal body is approximately that of the cytoplasm and vital staining is rather slow (71); consequently, the organelle is not readily seen in the living flagellate. The apparent internal structure may vary with the species as well as with methods of fixation and staining (47, 123).

The parabasal apparatus of free-living flagellates shows little variety (Fig. 1. 10, H, L, N-P). One or two small parabasal bodies have been described in several species; one or more long slender bodies, in certain others. In the tetranucleate *Polykrikos schwartzi* (27), each band-like parabasal body is attached to a ring encircling the intracytoplasmic portion of an axial flagellum. The parabasal body of *Codosiga elegans* (196) is of special interest because it closely resembles a structure (Fig. 1. 10, M) described in choanocytes of calcareous sponges (218).

Among parasitic flagellates, the complexity of the parabasal apparatus varies widely. The small *kinetoplast* of *Trypanosoma brucei* (Fig. 1. 10,

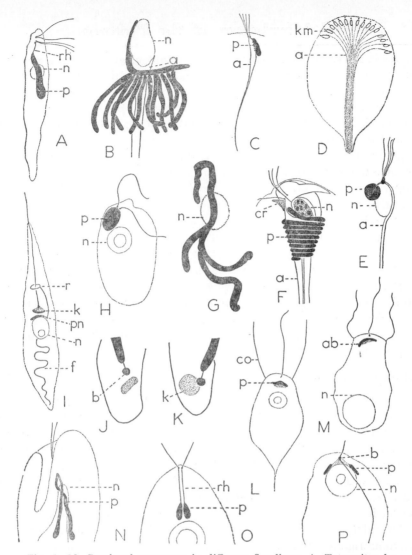

Fig. 1. 10. Parabasal apparatus in different flagellates. A. *Tetramitus bufonis;* x2200 (after Duboscq and Grassé). B. *Pseudodevescovina uniflagellata;* x1100 (after Kirby). C. Single mastigont of *Snyderella tabogae* (see Fig. 1. 8, C); diagrammatic (after Kirby). D. *Stephanonympha nelumbium,* diagrammatic optical section showing karyomastigonts; x750 (after Kirby). E. Karyomastigont of *S. nelumbium;* x1870 approx. (after Kirby). F. *Hyperdevescovina torquata;* x1050 (after Kirby). G. *Macrotrichomonas ramosa;* x1360 (after Kirby). H. *Bodo caudatus;* x3600 (after Hollande). I. *Leptomonas ctenocephali;* diagrammatic (after A. and M. Lwoff). J. *Trypanosoma brucei,* kinetoplast seen on edge; protargol; diagrammatic (after Kirby). K. *T. brucei,* surface view of kinetoplast (after Kirby). L. *Codosiga elegans,* a choanoflagellate; diagrammatic (after de Saedeleer). M. Choanocyte of a sponge, *Clathrina coriacea;* diagrammatic (after Volkonsky). N. *Chilomonas paramecium;* x2850 (after Hollande). O. *Polytoma uvella;* diagrammatic (after Volkonsky). P. *Cercobodo heimi;* x3450 approx. (after Hollande). Key: *a,* axostyle; *ab,* apical body; *b,* blepharoplast; *co,* collar; *cr,* cresta; *f,* parabasal filament; *k,* kinetoplast; *km,* karyomastigont; *n,* nucleus; *p,* parabasal apparatus; *pn,* paranuclear body; *r,* periflagellar ring; *rh,* rhizoplast.

J, K) is fairly typical of the Trypanosomidae, although the mastigont of *Leptomonas ctenocephali* (151) is less simple. In addition to the kinetoplast, a periflagellar ring in *L. ctenocephali* gives rise to a long parabasal filament (Fig. 1. 10, I). A simple elongated parabasal body is found in certain uninucleate Trichomonadidae (Fig. 1. 10, A) and in each complete mastigont of such multinucleate genera as *Stephanonympha, Calonympha,* and *Snyderella* (Fig. 1. 10, C-E). In certain flagellates a long parabasal body is coiled around the axostyle (Fig. 1. 10, F), while the apparatus of *Macrotrichomonas ramosa* (126) is branched (Fig. 1. 10, G) and that of *Pseudodevescovina uniflagellata* is compound (Fig. 1. 10, B). A complex apparatus, often including many separate elements, occurs also in various Hypermastigida (47).

The special term, *kinetoplast* (127), has been applied to the parabasal body of trypanosomes and related flagellates. This usage seems justified. Kinetoplasts are Feulgen-positive (104, 152, 188, 192) and are demonstrable by methods of fixation and staining which are unsatisfactory for the trichomonad parabasal body. Furthermore, the kinetoplast divides in fission whereas this is rarely the case in other types of parabasal apparatus.

Multiple karyomastigonts and mastigonts

The kinetic elements of many multinucleate flagellates have increased in number along with their nuclei. Each flagellar unit (*mastigont*) is associated with a nucleus in *Coronympha* and *Stephanonympha* (Fig. 1. 10, D). Such flagellates thus contain a number of *karyomastigonts,* each composed of a nucleus and associated blepharoplasts, flagella, parabasal body, and axostyle. This appears to be the primitive condition in such flagellates. Two sets of flagella are associated with each of the four nuclei in *Polykrikos schwartzi* (25); the flagellar apparatus has doubled independently of the nucleus without otherwise disrupting the basic karyomastigont (Fig. 4. 20, G). *Calonympha* represents an intermediate condition showing both karyomastigonts and mastigonts, the latter being far more numerous. A degree of specialization rare in flagellates—independence of nucleus and mastigont—is represented by *Snyderella tabogae* (Fig. 1. 8, C), in which the several dozen nuclei are all dissociated from the hundreds of mastigonts.

CILIA AND THEIR DERIVATIVES

Cilia are structurally similar to flagella but are shorter and more restricted in movement and are generally present in greater numbers. *Prorodon teres,* for example, is equipped with about 11,600 cilia (231). A cilium, like the flagellum, apparently consists of a *sheath* and an *axoneme* ending in a *basal granule.* A "sensory" component has been described as a thin argentophilic layer covering the axial filament and tapering distally to a granular "end-organ" (132). Electron micrographs indicate that the unfixed, dehydrated axoneme is composed of fibrils in *Paramecium*, whereas a sheath is suggested merely by possible remnants of an enveloping layer (102, 199).

In certain ciliates an accessory "ciliary corpuscle" (30) is attached to the basal granule; in some instances, the accessory body may be mitochondrial in nature (26). Two accessory granules have been reported in certain ciliates (132). A slender fibril, the *ciliary rootlet,* extends inward from the basal granule in some ciliates, but is said to be absent in certain primitive species (29). From many of the basal granules in *Opalina obtrigonoidea* (Fig. 1. 11, G), fibrils extend dorso-ventrally through the cytoplasm to end in basal granules on the opposite side of the body (34). Whether these fibrils are homologous with the ciliary rootlets of other ciliates is uncertain.

Cilia lie in meridional or spiral rows in the less specialized ciliates. Although such a pattern is usually rather constant within a species, changes from spiral to meridional to spiral, and even a reversal of the spirals, occur in certain species with complex life-cycles (150). Individual cilia, in ciliates with sculptured pellicles, may emerge from grooves, from the margins of such grooves, or from individual pits in different cases.

The simple cilium is the primitive locomotor structure in ciliates. Many species possess compound organelles which have arisen by fusion of cilia in longitudinal or transverse rows, or in tufts. Such organelles are known as *undulating membranes, membranelles* and *cirri.* An undulating membrane, formed by the fusion of one or more longitudinal rows of cilia, lies in the peristome (oral "groove") of various species. Rippling movements of the membrane drive particles to the cytostome. This organelle may not be permanent in quite the same sense that cilia are so considered, since the membrane of *Blepharisma undulans* may break up, spontaneously or after injury, into individual cilia. The cilia eventually fuse again into an undulating membrane (24). Membranelles, which are more or less triangular flaps formed by fusion of two or more transverse rows of cilia, are found especially in the peristomial area (Fig. 1. 15, H). Each membranelle of *Spirostomum ambiguum* contains a double row of cilia whose basal granules end in a plate parallel to the surface of the body (Fig. 1. 11, E). A basal lamella, extending inward from the plate, tapers to an end-thread which joins a basal fibril in the endoplasm (8). Cirri, characteristic of the Hypotrichina, consist of tufts of cilia probably embedded in a matrix (Fig. 1. 11, C, D). The number of cilia varies with the size of the cirrus—in *Oxytricha fallax,* for example, three or more in the small marginal cirri and 8-18 in the ventral, frontal, and anal cirri (146).

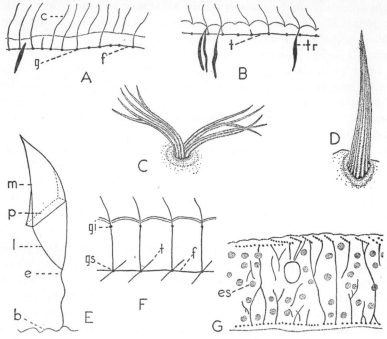

Fig. 1. 11. A. Longitudinal fibril joining basal granules in *Entorhipidium echini;* longitudinal section of cortex; x1890 (after Lynch). B. Transverse connecting fibrils in *E. echini;* cross-section of cortex; x1800 (after Lynch). C. Frayed cirrus of *Oxytricha fallax* showing component cilia; x2025 (after Lund). D. cirrus of *O. fallax;* x1725 (after Lund). E. A membranelle of *Spirostomum ambiguum;* diagrammatic (after Bishop). F. Basal granules and connecting fibrils in *Tillina canalifera;* diagrammatic (after Turner). G. Dorso-ventral fibrils joining basal granules in *Opalina obtrigonoidea;* longitudinal section; x1100 (after Cosgrove). Key: *b,* basal fibril; *c,* cilium; *e,* end-thread; *es,* endoplasmic spherule; *f,* longitudinal fibril; *g,* basal granule; *gi,* primary basal granule; *gs,* secondary basal granule; *l,* basal lamella; *m,* membranelle; *p,* basal plate; *t,* transverse fibril; *tr,* trichocyst.

FIBRILLAR SYSTEMS

The basal granules in each longitudinal row of cilia are joined by a fibril. Transverse fibrils may also link the basal granules in some species (Fig. 1. 11, A, B). *Tillina canalifera* (123) is unusual in that longitudinal and transverse fibrils join secondary basal granules, which in turn are connected by rhizoplasts to superficial *primary* basal granules from which the cilia arise (Fig. 1. 11, F). In *Opalina obtrigonoidea,* oblique fibrils join basal granules in different longitudinal rows but longitudinal fibrils cannot be detected (34). This situation suggests possible modification of the primitive symmetry during the evolution of opalinid ciliates.

The longitudinal fibrils in certain ciliates seem to be morphologically independent (29). In other species, the fibrils are joined in complex fibrillar systems (64, 132, 211) referred to as *neuromotor apparatus,* *silver-line system, neuroneme system,* and *infraciliature* by different workers. These "systems" have been demonstrated by various techniques, so that it is difficult to correlate each one with all the others. In general, however, the neuromotor system seems to be both endoplasmic and ectoplasmic while the other fibrillar systems occupy a superficial position.

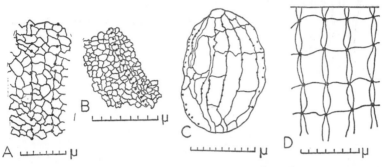

Fig. 1. 12. Silver-line systems (after Klein). A. *Prorodon teres;* narrow-mesh type with some orientation of fibrils. B. Primitive narrow-mesh type. C. Striation-system in *Cyclidium glaucoma.* D. Double striation-system in *Cinetochilum margaritaceum.*

Neuromotor apparatus

The neuromotor system of *Euplotes* (79, 209, 212, 238) includes a relatively small number of fibrils (Fig. 1. 13, G). Those from the anal cirri converge anteriorly in a "motorium," from which a membranelle fibril passes anteriorly and to the left, and then posteriorly beneath the peristomial membranelles. In addition, groups of fibrils extend from the basal plates of the frontal and ventral cirri into the endoplasm. Although the first and second frontal cirri are joined by such fibrils, no interconnections have been demonstrated for the other cirri (79). A comparable neuromotor apparatus has been described in other ciliates (211).

Silver-line system

The observations of Klein (132, 134) and others have revealed a *silver-line system* in many ciliates. The name of the system is derived from Klein's technique, in which reduced silver is deposited on superficial structures. The argentophilic "silver-lines" are assumed to be plastic structures having the capacity to grow, split, undergo resorption, and then reappear (132).

The primitive system is a narrow-mesh (0.75-1.0μ) network containing the basal granules (Fig. 1. 12, B). The fibrils themselves extend through the interstices of the ectoplasmic alveoli. Since a narrow-mesh network has been reported in *Dileptus, Oxytricha, Epalxis, Spirostomum, Stentor,*

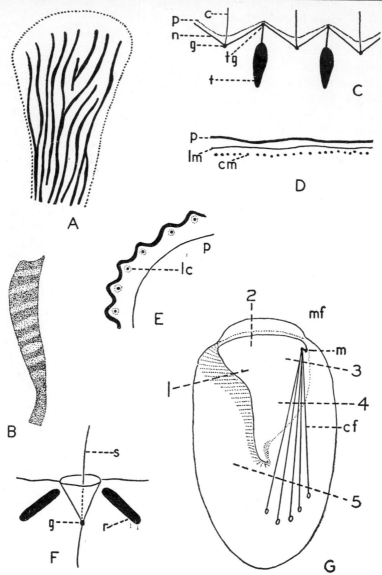

Fig. 1. 13. A. Myonemes in anterior half of *Stentor coeruleus;* diagrammatic (after Dierks). B. Portion of a myoneme (*S. coeruleus*) showing cross-striations; diagrammatic (after Dierks). C. A neuroneme in *Paramecium;* diagrammatic (after Gelei). D-E. Myonemes in *Monocystis agilis,* longitudinal and transverse sections; diagrammatic (after Roskin and Levinson). F. Sensory bristle of *Euplotes patella;* diagrammatic (after Hammond). G. Neuromotor system of *Euplotes (patella) eurystomum,* showing major fibrils and incisions made in microdissection; x680 (after Taylor). Key: *c,* cilium; *cf,* anal-cirrus fibril; *cm,* circular myoneme; *g,* basal granule; *lc,* longitudinal canal containing myoneme; *lm,* longitudinal myoneme; *m,* motorium; *mf,* fibril to membranelles; *n,* neuroneme; *p,* pellicle; *r,* rodlet of "rosette"; *s,* "sensory" fibril; *t,* trichocyst; *tg,* trichocyst-granule; 1-5, approximate planes of incisions in Taylor's operations.

and also in *Podophrya* (Suctorea), this primitive system obviously is not limited to unspecialized ciliates.

Specialization of the silver-line system involves first an increase in diameter of the mesh, so that a single mesh comes to enclose a group of ectoplasmic alveoli. As the mesh widens, the silver-lines decrease in number and begin to parallel the rows of basal granules (Fig. 1. 12, A). In meridional ciliation, the system may be reduced to *meridians* bearing the basal granules and sometimes joined by transverse commissures (Fig. 1. 12, C)—so-called *striation-systems*. Each meridian is sometimes double (Fig. 1. 12, D). Or the silver-line may be a bundle of fibrils. In *Colpidium colpoda* (132), each meridian is said to split just behind the cytostome into primary and secondary meridians. The basal granules lie very close together in the fused anterior meridians. Posteriorly, the basal granules in the primary meridians are spaced at fairly short and rather regular intervals; those in the secondary meridians, at longer and more irregular intervals.

In addition to the basal granules of cilia, the silver-line system includes *trichocyst-granules* and *protrichocyst-granules,* all three types being considered "'relator-granules" which relate the corresponding structures to the silver-lines. The protrichocyst-granules also have been considered tectin-granules (12), which presumably are extruded through secretory pores in the pellicle (65). The relator-granules, especially the basal granules, may persist after their organelles have disappeared in phylogeny, and thus represent persistent traces of much more primitive conditions (132).

Both the fibrils and the relator-granules are said to lie at the same level in the ectoplasm (132). However, the network ("indirect system" of Klein) apparently does not occupy the same plane as the basal granules and longitudinal fibrils in *Paramecium caudatum,* since the latter are not in focus in photomicrographs which show the network clearly (67). Lund (145) concluded that the peripheral "network" in *P. multimicronucleatum* represents pellicular ridges upon which silver is deposited in dried specimens. The correlation between pellicular markings and the silver-line pattern also has been stressed by Jacobson (100). Therefore, the exact nature of Klein's superficial network remains uncertain. The silver-line meridians, which join the basal granules, appear to be subpellicular.

Neuroneme system

This system (64, 67), demonstrable by the techniques of Gelei and Horvath (68), joins the basal granules and possibly corresponds to the meridians of Klein. In sectioned material, the neuronemes of *Paramecium caudatum* (Fig. 1. 13, C) appear as zigzag lines joining the basal granules to the more superficial trichocyst-granules (64). The neuronemes are not continuous with the superficial silver-line network of Klein.

Infraciliary network

This system lies at the level of the basal granules or somewhat deeper, between the alveolar and the inner ectoplasmic layers (62). Neither the basal granules nor the trichocysts are directly connected with this system, and no connection with the outer network has been observed. The longitudinal fibrils of the infraciliary system generally follow the pattern of the ciliary rows.

The infraciliature

The basal fibril, or kinetodesma, of Chatton's infraciliature is considered to be separate from the ciliary meridian of Klein. The silver-line fibril is said to lie on the left of the basal granules while the kinetodesma lies on the right (26, 29, 214). However, such regularity in position of the silver-line is not apparent in some of Klein's figures, and in ciliates showing "circular fibrils" in the silver-lines, basal granules may lie on the circular fibril or may be enclosed by it (133).

Sensory bristles

So-called sensory bristles, apparently associated with the fibrillar systems of certain ciliates, are well developed on the dorsal surface of *Euplotes* (79, 212). Each bristle arises from a granule at the base of a pit which is surrounded by a "rosette" of rodlets (Fig. 1. 13, F). On the ventral surface, two or three similar rosettes without bristles lie near the base of each cirrus. Analogous structures, supposedly sensory in function, have been described in *Didinium* and certain other genera (63).

Significance of fibrillar systems

According to various workers, the fibrillar systems of ciliates are contractile fibrils, supporting or skeletal structures, organizers in the onto-genetic development of related organelles (134), coordinating systems, and delicate circulatory systems for transporting such materials as nucleo-proteins to the basal granules and trichocysts (86).

Except for whatever support these hypotheses may derive from mor-phological relationships, the data bearing on functions of fibrillar systems are meager. The results of microdissection suggest a coordinating func-tion in *Euplotes* (209). The adoral membranelles in this hypotrich are important in swimming, while the anal cirri play a major part in creep-ing. Cutting the membranelle-fibril (Fig. 1. 13, G) destroyed coordination of the membranelles so that swimming movements were abnormal. Sever-ing the fibrils to the anal cirri affected both creeping and swimming, while destruction of the motorium disturbed the coordination of the anal cirri and membranelles. Incisions not severing the neuromotor fibrils failed to modify swimming or creeping movements. Similar experiments

(236) indicate that coordination of the ciliary beat in *Paramecium* is dependent upon impulses transmitted longitudinally through the ectoplasm. These findings seem to eliminate Klein's superficial network as a coordinating system in *Paramecium* and suggest, instead, such a function for the longitudinal fibrils (superficial fibrils of the neuromotor apparatus, neuronemes of Gelei, kinetodesmas of Chatton and possibly the silver-meridians of Klein). More recently, it has been concluded that the cortical localization of acetycholinesterase in *Tetrahymena pyriformis* supports the hypothesis that conduction by the fibrillar system is similar to conduction along nerve fibres (201a).

Silver-line system of flagellates

Among the dinoflagellates, *Polykrikos schwartzi* (28) and such gymnodinioid types as *Gyrodinium pavillardi* and *Gymnodinium splendens* show an argentophilic surface network, while impregnation merely blackens the sutures of the thecal plates in peridinioid species (6). Impregnation of *Gonium, Eudorina,* and *Volvox* (Fig. 1. 2, D, E) demonstrates silver-lines in the individual flagellates (131), while the silver-lines of various Euglenida (106, 131) apparently correspond to the pellicular striations visible in living material. In addition, the flagella of Pyronymphidae (105), as well as the pellicular ridges and the margin of the undulating membrane in *Trypanosoma rotatorium* (106), are impregnated with silver.

MYONEMES AND CONTRACTILE STALKS

Myonemes are well developed in various large ciliates which are capable of changing form rapidly. The band-like and cross-striated myonemes of *Stentor coeruleus* (44) extend from the posterior end of the body to the adoral zone, sometimes branching to follow the rows of cilia (Fig. 1. 13, A, B). Posteriorly, the myonemes turn inward and anteriorly as a bundle which finally branches into fibrils that disappear in the endoplasm. Among the flagellates, swimming of the medusa-like *Leptodiscus* and *Craspedotella* is attributed to myonemes which bring about rhythmic contractions of the body (177). Pellicular ridges in such large trypanosomes as *Trypanosoma rotatorium* have been considered myonemes, but their contractile nature is uncertain. Some of the larger gregarines apparently possess both circular and longitudinal myonemes (Fig. 1. 13, D, E) enclosed in individual ectoplasmic canals (194). Many Protozoa have no myonemes but the absence of such structures does not eliminate contractility. This fundamental property is exhibited by many species which seem to show no appropriate differentiations at the microscopic level.

Well developed myonemes (stalk-muscles, or spasmonemes) are found also in the stalks of certain ciliates. The stalk-muscle of *Zoothamnium* extends spirally within a sheath continuous with the protoplasm of the body. Between the sheath and the surface of the stalk, there is a matrix filled with elastic fibrils which arise from a differentiated area, the *scopula,* in the aboral body wall (182). The stalk-muscle extends almost to the base of the stalk, where it is attached by a fibrillar bundle to the basal disc. The individual stalk-muscles of the *Carchesium* colony are attached to the bases of their own stalks, so that each stalk-muscle contracts independently.

TRICHOCYSTS AND NEMATOCYSTS

Trichocysts are cortical structures reported in certain ciliates and flagellates. Trichocyst-bearing Holotrichida are represented by several dozen genera. In addition, trichocysts have been reported in some Heterotrichina (e.g., *Blepharisma*) and in *Strombidium* among the Oli-

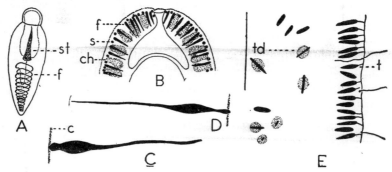

Fig. 1. 14. A. Nematocyst of *Polykrikos;* x1450 (after Kofoid and Swezy). B. Fusiform and spherical trichocysts of *Gonyostomum semen;* diagrammatic (after Chadefaud). C, D. Trichocysts of *Dileptus anser* before and after discharge; x3080 (after Hayes). E. Developing and mature trichocysts in *Paramecium caudatum;* diagrammatic; x1280 (after Jacobson). Key: *c,* cortex; *ch,* chromatophore; *f,* fibril (A), fusiform trichocyst (B); *s,* spherical trichocyst; *st,* stylet; *t,* trichocyst; *td,* developing trichocyst.

gotrichina (200). Trichocysts may be widely scattered over the body (*Paramecium*), limited to the peristomial area (*Dileptus*), or borne on tentacles or papillae (*Actinobolina, Legendrea*). Development of trichocysts from macronuclear granules has been reported. However, this phenomenon has not been confirmed (100), although developing trichocysts (Fig. 1. 14, E) appear in the cytoplasm of *Frontonia leucas* and *Paramecium caudatum.* The outgrowth of trichocysts from "trichocystosomes," granules produced by division of basal granules, also has been reported (150). So-called protrichocysts of various ciliates have been interpreted also as deposits of tectin, used in formation of the cyst membrane or the lorica (12, 200).

The trichocysts of *Dileptus gigas* (215) show no internal organization and form no detectable structures upon discharge. These trichocysts (*toxicysts*), which change shape during contortions of the ciliate and become almost spherical under pressure of a coverslip, are believed to contain a fluid. Comparable trichocysts are found in the tips of retractile tentacles in *Actinobolina* (225), and the flask-shaped trichocysts of *Conchophthirius mytili* (116) also may be similar to those of *D. gigas*.

Trichocysts of certain other ciliates are discharged as recognizable structures. Such is the case in *Legendrea, Frontonia, Paramecium, Prorodon,* and *Dileptus anser*. In electron micrographs (101, 102), discharged trichocysts of *Paramecium* show a pointed tip resembling a golf tee, and a transversely striated shaft. The trichocyst of *Dileptus anser* consists of a thread-like extension into the cytoplasm and a bulbous portion which tapers to a subpellicular granule (Fig. 1. 14, C). Upon discharge (Fig. 1. 14, D), the positions of these components are reversed, the trichocyst-granule adhering to the pellicle (81). Discharge apparently involves turning the trichocyst inside out.

Trichocysts have been interpreted as offensive and defensive weapons and as organelles of attachment. Under artificial stimulation, trichocysts of *Entorhipidium pilatum* are often expelled from the body but they sometimes backfire into the endoplasm (148). Therefore, the behavior of trichocysts under artificial conditions should be interpreted cautiously. A protective function is often suggested but has not been adequately demonstrated in *Paramecium*. Another suggestion for *Paramecium* (197) is that the trichocyst, which hardens after extrusion so that only the tip remains sticky, serves in anchoring the ciliates. The stimulus to natural discharge, in which only a portion of the trichocyst is discharged, is said to be contact with solid objects. In contrast to the trichocysts of *Paramecium,* those of *Dileptus gigas* apparently are offensive and defensive weapons. They paralyze some organisms, induce cytolysis of others, and cause vigorous reactions in additional Protozoa (215). Paralysis of flagellates and small ciliates is produced by trichocysts of *Dileptus anser,* and even large rotifers react vigorously (81). Contact of rotifers with the tentacles of *Actinobolina vorax* also may be followed by paralysis (225).

Trichocysts have been reported in various flagellates (77). Two types have been described in *Gonyostomum* (Fig. 1. 14, B)—spindle-shaped trichocysts and small spherical ones, both distributed in the cortex. The former become long filaments when discharged; the latter give rise to short delicate filaments (21). The "trichocysts" of *Chilomonas,* represented by refractile bodies lining the pharyngeal groove, are discharged as long slender threads. Another type, possibly represented by small cortical inclusions, gives rise to short thin filaments. Filamentous structures also have been interpreted as discharged trichocysts in species of *Polykrikos, Peridinium, Diplopsalis,* and *Ceratium* (142).

Certain subcuticular inclusions of Euglenida—the cortical globules of *Euglena archaeoplastidiata,* which are expelled and stained brown in iodine solution (22), and the rod-like bodies beneath the pellicular striations of *Peranema trichophorum* (23)—also have been homologized with trichocysts of ciliates. These inclusions are demonstrable by mitochondrial techniques in *Peranema trichophorum* (74). It has been suggested (88) that such subcuticular bodies of Euglenida are merely substances accumulated for the secretion of cyst membranes and similar layers.

Among the dinoflagellates, *Polykrikos* and *Nematodinium* contain nematocysts resembling those of coelenterates (27, 136). The similarity is so close that some workers have considered such nematocysts (Fig. 1. 14, A) to be foreign bodies ingested by the flagellates. However, this interpretation is not supported by the regular occurrence of nematocysts in certain species and their absence in others feeding on the same plankton. The nematocysts lie free in the cytoplasm and nothing is known about their possible discharge under natural conditions.

THE CYTOSTOME AND ASSOCIATED STRUCTURES

The ingestion of solid food by organisms with a well developed cortex usually occurs through a *cytostome,* which often opens into a *cytopharynx.* The area leading to or surrounding the cytostome often forms a specialized *peristome* in ciliates. Although a typical cytostome and cytopharynx ("gullet") are to be expected only in holozoic organisms with a well differentiated body wall, interestingly similar structures occur in certain amoebae (Fig. 1. 15, C, E, F)—*Amoeba vespertilio* and *Hartmanella* sp. (99), and also *Dientamoeba fragilis* (230), and *Entamoeba muris* (227). Aside from their greater permanence, the cytostome and cytopharynx of various flagellates represent little advance beyond the condition seen in these amoebae. In ciliates, however, the peristomial area may be equipped with an undulating membrane, a row of membranelles, or differentiated zones of cilia.

The peristome of *Paramecium multimicronucleatum* (Fig. 1. 15, G) is lined with cilia, while the pharynx is equipped with a dorsal zone of long cilia and the *penniculus,* a band of closely set cilia extending spirally from an antero-dorsal origin to the ventral pharyngeal wall. Activity of these specialized cilia drives particles into a zone of *paraoesophageal fibrils* which are continued from the wall of the cytopharynx into the endoplasm as the *postoesophageal fibrils.* When enough particles are trapped, a food vacuole develops as a bulge in the dorsal wall of the gullet. After separation from the gullet, the vacuole is guided into the endoplasm by the surrounding postoesophageal fibrils which exert a sort of "peristaltic" effect (147). The peristomial area, or "oral groove," serves

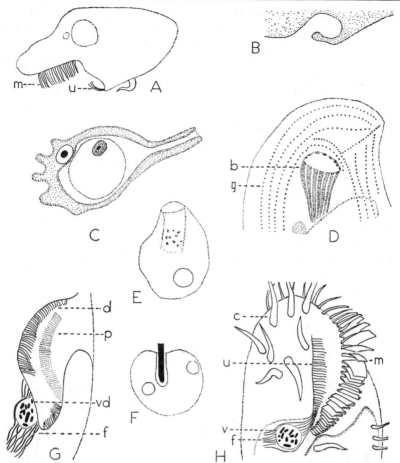

Fig. 1. 15. A. Section across the peristome of *Oxytricha fallax;* x1225 (after Lund). B. Section through the middle of the peristome in *Euplotes aediculatus;* x445 (after Pierson). C. Gullet-like structure in *Amoeba iuvenalis* after ingestion of a flagellate; diagrammatic (after Ivanič). D. Pharyngeal-basket in *Chilodonella labiata;* diagrammatic (after MacDougall). E, F. Gullet-like structures in *Dientamoeba fragilis;* x1930 (after Wenrich). G. Gullet (peristomial area) in *Paramecium multimicronucleatum;* diagrammatic; x670 (after Lund). H. Peristome of *Stylonychia;* diagrammatic; x720 (after Lund). Key: *b*, pharyngeal-basket; *c*, cirrus; *d*, dorsal cilia; *f*, postoesophageal fibrils; *g*, basal granule of cilium; *m*, row of membranelles; *p*, basal granules of penniculus; *u*, undulating membrane; *v*, food vacuole; *vd*, developing food vacuole.

as a scoop which directs water toward the cytostome. The cytostome and associated structures in *Paramecium* thus form an efficient mechanism for concentrating small particles and delivering them to the food vacuole.

In *Oxytricha* (146) and *Stylonychia* (147) the left margin of the peristome bears a row of adoral membranelles, while an undulating membrane extends along much of the right peristomial wall (Fig. 1. 15, A,

H). In addition, dorsal and lateral fibrils extend forward in the peristomial cortex and, by their contractions, produce undulations of the cortex near the cytostome. Both sets extend, as the *postoesophageal fibrils*, past the base of the pharynx and deep into the cytoplasm, their movements guiding each newly formed food vacuole, much as in *Paramecium*.

The small undulating membrane and the lack of cytostomal fibrils

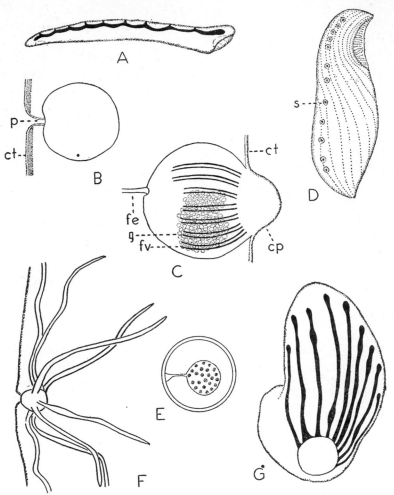

Fig. 1. 16. A. Contractile tube of *Haptophrya michiganensis;* x100 (after MacLennan). B. Contractile vacuole and pore in *Eudiplodinium maggii;* x830 (after MacLennan). C. "Sensory" vacuole of *Blepharoprosthium;* diagrammatic (after Dogiel). D. Row of "statocysts" in *Loxodes rostrum;* body cilia omitted; x160 (after Penard). E. Single "statocyst" of *L. striatus;* diagrammatic (after Penard). F. Contractile vacuole and canals in *Paramecium multimicronucleatum;* x720 (after King). G. Contractile vacuole and canals in *Tillina canalifera,* diagrammatic (after Turner). Key: *cp,* pellicular cap; *ct,* cortex; *fe,* endoplasmic fibril; *fv,* fibrils at surface of vacuole; *g,* granules in vacuole; *s,* "statocyst."

suggest that *Euplotes harpa,* and perhaps other Euplotidae, cannot concentrate small food particles very efficiently (147), although the peristomial area is partially enclosed ventrally by an extension of the right peristomial wall (Fig. 1. 15, B). In cultures, *E. harpa* thrives best on food particles larger than bacteria (147).

In such ciliates as *Chilodonella* and *Prorodon* the pharynx is surrounded by a conical or cylindrical "pharyngeal basket" (Fig. 1. 15, D) which undergoes dilation during ingestion (179). The basket is composed of rods which are probably protein in nature (153) and, in certain species, may represent fused bundles of slender trichites (179). Convergence and apparent fusion of the rods posteriorly may be noted, as in *Chilodonella* (153). There are circumpharyngeal trichites in *Spathidium* (235) and *Didinium* (179) also, although a compact basket is lacking. The paralysis of small ciliates after contact with the cytostomal region of *S. spathula* (235) suggests that the trichites function much like trichocysts of certain other ciliates.

The pharyngeal-rod apparatus ("Staborgan") of *Peranema* and similar holozoic Euglenida (Chapter IV) includes two longitudinal rods extending posteriorly from the cytostome and a smaller curved element at the rim of the cytostome (23). The conical "siphon" of *Entosiphon* (23) is possibly a derivative of the rod-apparatus but its homologies are uncertain.

VACUOLES OF PROTOZOA

Contractile vacuoles

Contractile vacuoles, characteristic of fresh-water species, are absent in most parasitic and marine Protozoa. The position, number, and accessory structures of the contractile vacuoles vary in different Protozoa. In such genera as *Amoeba,* the position of the vacuole changes with movements of the organism. Differentiation of the cortical layer is generally accompanied by a relatively fixed position of the contractile vacuole.

The origin of a new vacuole after discharge (systole) usually involves the appearance of a few minute vacuoles in the area where the new contractile vacuole will develop. These small vacuoles fuse into a single larger one. Later increase in volume (diastole) of the contractile vacuole involves various processes. In certain ciliates, the young vacuole is fed by one or more canals (Fig. 1. 16, F, G). The newly formed vacuole in *Spirostomum ambiguum* (42), for example, fuses with a long canal which in turn receives fluid by fusion with small vacuoles. The new vacuole in *Paramecium multimicronucleatum* (119) is fed in similar fashion by several canals. Growth of the new vacuole in *Amoeba* (80), *Euplotes* (210), and many other Protozoa depends, to some extent at least, upon fusion with smaller vacuoles. In fact, growth of the vacuole in spurts, instead of a steady increase in volume, suggests that fluid enters the contractile vacuole of *Amoeba proteus* almost entirely through the fusion with accessory vacuoles (161). In *Eudiplodinium*, however, growth of the vacuole in late diastole apparently is not dependent upon accessory vacuoles, and the vacuolar membrane presumably is responsible for the segregation of fluid (161).

Systole usually involves discharge of the contents directly to the outside of the body, but there are exceptions. The vacuoles of Euglenida empty into the reservoir ("gullet"); those of *Epistylis* and related ciliates (55) empty into the pharynx, often termed the "vestibule" in view of its several functions. The point of discharge is often a differentiated pore as in *Paramecium* (119) and the Ophryoscolecidae (154). Except during systole, this pore is sealed by a membrane (Fig. 1. 16, B, F) apparently derived from the wall of the preceding vacuole.

A long contractile tube (Fig. 1. 16, A), instead of a contractile vacuole, extends throughout most of the body between the endoplasm and dorsal ectoplasm in *Haptophrya* (160). This tube is an apparently permanent structure which is divided in binary fission. Excretory canals extend to dorsal pores, which vary in number with length of the ciliate. Systole involves one or more waves of contraction, but the wall of the tube does not collapse completely, and does not disappear. After systole, small vacuoles appear in the wall of the tube and then fuse to form a continuous lumen.

Sensory vacuoles

A supposedly sensory vacuole, located anteriorly under a pellicular cap (Fig. 1. 16, C), occurs in parasitic ciliates belonging to the families Bütschliidae and Paraisotrichidae (46). Fibrils on the wall of the vacuole converge toward the pellicular cap, while the vacuolar cavity contains a number of granules ("statoliths"). Superficially similar vacuoles (Fig. 1. 16, D, E), forming a row near the aboral surface of the body, have been described in *Loxodes*. These vacuoles ("Müller's vesicles") have been interpreted both as statocysts (179) and as "excretion-vacuoles" (187).

Vacuoles in flotation

Cytoplasmic vacuoles may play an important part in flotation. In Radiolarida (Chapter V), the foamy outer cytoplasm (*calymma*) is filled with vacuoles which maintain the organisms at a particular depth in the ocean. Under appropriate stimulation, collapse of the vacuoles and retraction of pseudopodia increase the specific gravity and the organisms sink. When new vacuoles develop in the calymma, the organisms rise again. An analogous phenomenon has been described in *Arcella* (10). The appearance of gas bubbles in the peripheral cytoplasm, supposedly induced by reduction in oxygen tension of the medium, causes the organism to rise toward the surface. Perhaps the zone of vacuoles beneath the theca of *Ceratium* (53) also functions in flotation.

CHROMATOPHORES, PIGMENTS, PYRENOIDS, PHOTORECEPTORS

Chromatophores

Chromatophores, found in many phytoflagellates, vary in number, size, color, and form in different groups. Some flagellates contain one large cup-shaped chromatophore, or an H-type in which two large lobes are joined by a connective (Fig. 1. 17, A, E, F, I). The chromatophores in *Peridinium umbonatum* form an anastomosing network with lobes extending into the endoplasm (Fig. 1. 17, J). Some of the Euglenidae contain many small flattened chromatophores arranged in a peripheral layer (Fig. 1. 17, G).

Pigment-free leucoplasts, homologous with chromatophores, have been reported in *Polytoma* (219) and *Polytomella* (185). Since Pringsheim (183) has pointed out that peripheral mitochondrial networks have sometimes been interpreted as leucoplasts, the status of leucoplast-bearing species requires further investigation.

Pyrenoids

These structures (Fig. 1. 17, B, C, J, L), which are usually associated with chromatophores, vary from solid bodies to aggregates of granules, around which starch or paramylum may accumulate. Each pyrenoid in *Euglena americana* (Fig. 1. 17, L), for example, consists of two plano-convex masses adherent to the chromatophore and covered by paramylum (88). The extraplastidial "pyrenoids" of certain Cryptomonadida are termed *amphosomes* by Hollande (88), who believes that homologous structures are unknown in other flagellates. The amphosome of *Cryptomonas dangeardii* (Fig. 1. 17, N) consists of two chromophilic plates separated by chromophobic material, and is sometimes surrounded by starch grains. The functional significance of the amphosome is unknown.

Pyrenoids have been interpreted as reserves of protein, as structures involved in the synthesis of polysaccharides, and even as intracellular symbiotes. The second assumption is consistent with the frequent occurrence of starch or similar materials immediately surrounding the pyrenoids. According to various reports, pyrenoids may be resorbed occasionally, they may be reduced in number during formation of cysts and zygotes, and they may arise by division or be formed *de novo*. Such apparent variations in behavior are of little assistance in functional interpretations.

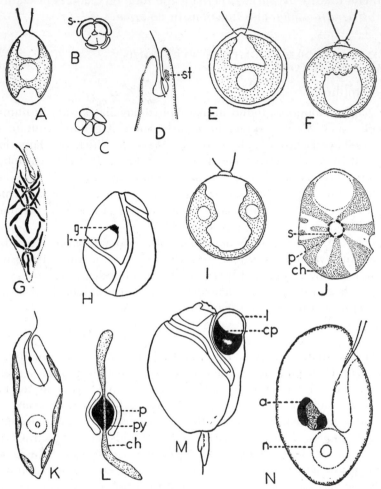

Fig. 1. 17. A, E, F, I. Chromatophores in *Chlamydomonas aglöeformis, C. umbonata, C. inversa* and *C. bicocca;* diagrammatic (after Pascher). B, C. Compound pyrenoids of *Pyramidomonas montana,* with and without starch deposits; x1200 (after Geitler). D. Granular stigma of *Euglena;* diagrammatic. G. Chromatophores in *Euglena geniculata* (?); x1500 (after Hollande). H. Ocellus with granular pigment in *Protopsis neapolitana;* x550 (after Kofoid and Swezy). J. Chromatophore "network" in *Peridinium umbonatum;* diagrammatic optical section (after Geitler). K. Peripheral chromatophores in *Colacium vesiculosum;* x1380 (after Johnson). L. A chromatophore with pyrenoid and paramylum shell in *Euglena americana;* diagrammatic (after Hollande). M. Ocellus with pigment-cup in *Erythropsis cornuta;* x320 (after Kofoid and Swezy). N. Amphosome in *Cryptomonas dangeardii;* chromatophores omitted; x2700 (after Hollande). Key: *a,* amphosome; *ch,* chromatophore; *cp,* pigment-cup; *g,* granular pigment; *l,* lens; *n,* nucleus; *p,* paramylum; *py,* pyrenoid; *s,* starch; *st,* stigma.

Pigments

The pigments of chromatophores vary in different groups of the phytoflagellates, and may have some phylogenetic as well as taxonomic significance. Chlorophyll of one variety or another presumably is always present although the green color may be masked by other pigments to produce shades of greenish-yellow, yellow, brown, and rarely blue. Blue chromatophores have been reported (143) in *Cyanomonas coeruleus, Chroomonas setoniensis, Cyanomastix morgani,* and *Gymnodinium limneticum.*

In addition to the pigments of chromatophores, various red, yellow, violet, brown, blue, and green pigments are found in the cytoplasm of certain Protozoa, many of them species without chromatophores. The blue-green granules ("stentorin") of *Stentor coeruleus,* which contain lipoproteins and resemble mitochondria, lie mainly in longitudinal ectoplasmic bands. These granules usually disappear after 24-48 hours of starvation (223). The pink pigment of *Blepharisma undulans,* which is also peripheral (169), is bleached after exposure to light, and is regenerated in darkness (69). This pigment is quite toxic to species of *Paramecium,* various other ciliates, and also to rotifers (70).

Chromatographic techniques (18, 204, 205, 206) have been used in the identification of certain pigments. In Dinoflagellida, chlorophylls *a* and *c,* β-carotene ("yellow haematochrome"), and several xanthophylls (dinoxanthin, diadinoxanthin, neodinoxanthin, peridinin) have been distinguished. Peridinin, which may be limited to dinoflagellates among the Protozoa, is possible identical with sulcatoxanthin isolated from certain sea anemones and probably derived from their symbiotic algae (82). Chrysomonadida contain chlorophyll *a* (but apparently no chlorophyll *b*), β-carotene and the xanthophyll, lutein. Euglenida contain chlorophylls *a* and *b,* β-carotene and also red haematochrome (euglenarhodon), a xanthophyll closely related to the astacene of Crustacea. Phytomonadida contain chlorophylls *a* and *b* and, in such species as *Haematococcus pluvialis,* a red haematochrome similar to that of Euglenida.

The functional significance of most protozoan pigments is unknown. The absorption of energy in photosynthesis is, of course, dependent mainly upon the chlorophylls, of which chlorophyll *a* is probably most important. However, carotenoid pigments also may serve in absorbing the predominantly blue-green light of low intensity received by marine species in fairly deep water (50, 205). The red pigment of *Euglena rubra* may be protective in reflecting light from the red end of the spectrum. This species thrives in shallow water reaching a temperature of 35-45° in bright sunlight. Under such conditions the pigment forms a layer just outside the chromatophores (107). In the laboratory, peripheral migration of the pigment occurs at temperatures of 30-40° in either dark-

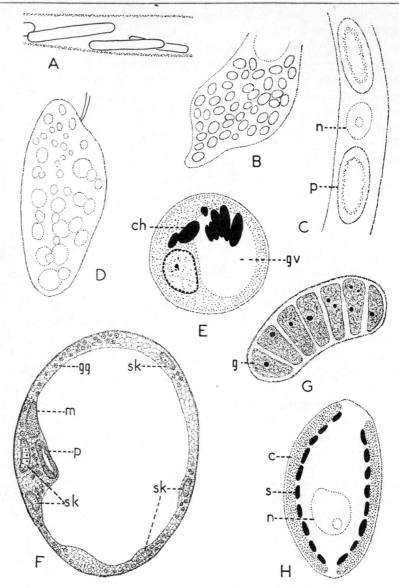

Fig. 1. 18. A. Bacilliform paramylum bodies in *Euglena acus;* x750
(after Deflandre). B. Small paramylum bodies of *Distigma proteus;* x3640
(after Hollande). C. Paramylum bodies (*p*) of *Euglena spirogyra;* x850
(after Dangeard). D. Polysaccharide reserves in *Chilomonas paramecium;*
x4500 (after Hollande). E. Chromatoid bodies and glycogen "vacuole" in
Entamoeba invadens; x2350 (after Geiman and Ratcliffe). F. Skeletal plates
and glycogen granules in cross-section of *Polyplastron multivesiculatum;*
diagrammatic; endoplasm omitted (after MacLennan). G. Cross-section of
right dorsal skeletal plate, *P. multivesiculatum;* x4720 (after MacLennan).
H. Starch grains at surface of chromatophore in *Cryptomonas ovata;* x2250
(after Hollande). Key: *c,* chromatophore; *ch,* chromatoid body; *g,* glycogen blocks; *gg,* glycogen granule; *gv,* glycogen "vacuole"; *m,* macronucleus; *n,* nucleus; *p,* pharynx; *s,* starch; *sk,* skeletal plate.

ness or light and also after irradiation with infrared or visible light. With the effects of temperature controlled, light from the blue end of the spectrum is more effective than that of longer wave lengths (108). The accumulation of a similar red pigment in *Haematococcus pluvialis* has been attributed to the exhaustion of nitrogenous or other foods. Massive production of this pigment occurs also in young cultures exposed to light in a medium containing acetate; salts of butyric and certain other acids show no such effect (152). In acetate-free medium, intensely red "haematocyst" stages are commonly developed in bright sunlight but not in dim light (52).

Photoreceptors

A *stigma* is characteristic of many chlorophyll-bearing flagellates, and occurs also in certain colorless phytoflagellates. The stigma of Euglenida is typically a flattened mass of reddish granules embedded in a matrix (Fig. 1. 17, D), whereas a granular organization is not apparent in typical phytomonad and chrysomonad flagellates. The stigma of *Volvox* and related colonial types is said to contain a concave mass of pigment and a hyaline lens (164). The stigma is usually located near the anterior end of the flagellate, but lies near the middle of the body in some species. The typical position in Euglenida (Fig. 1. 17, D) is near the wall of the reservoir.

Certain dinoflagellates (Pouchetiidae) possess an *ocellus* composed of a hyaline lens and a dark mass of pigment (*melanosome*) partially covering the lens. In certain species the melanosome can be extended over the surface of the lens or contracted toward the base (Fig. 1. 17, M). The melanosome may be homogeneous except for a core of red pigment at the base of the lens, or may be merely a loose aggregate of granules as in *Protopsis neapolitana* (Fig. 1. 17, H).

CYTOPLASMIC INCLUSIONS

Cytoplasmic food reserves

Foods of various kinds are frequently stored in the cytoplasm of Protozoa and, in any one species, the amount and type of reserves may vary with environmental conditions. Starch is the major reserve in young cultures of *Polytoma uvella;* lipids predominate after 15-30 days (220). In *P. uvella,* and probably in Protozoa generally, less food is stored in rapidly growing than in slowly growing cultures.

Polysaccharide reserves of phytoflagellates occur as granules or as larger bodies sometimes of characteristic shape and size. Synthesis of these carbohydrates is not dependent upon chlorophyll and may be expected in both colorless and pigmented species. The supposed presence of colorless "chromatophores" (leucoplasts) in non-pigmented phytoflagellates has been questioned (183). *Paramylum* (or "paramylon") of Euglenida occurs mainly as refractile endoplasmic bodies (Fig. 1. 18, A-C), but may be found also at the surface of the pyrenoid (Fig. 1. 17, L) in chlorophyll-bearing species. In addition, glycogen-like inclusions occur in *Euglena* (22) and *Peranema* (23). The *leucosin* of Chrysomonadida (Chapter IV) is stored as bodies (Fig. 4. 1, D-F) which are often relatively large. Starch may be deposited as fine granules or larger bodies in Cryptomonadida, Phytomonadida, and Dinoflagellida. Starch grains are deposited on the inner surface of the chromatophore in *Cryptomonas ovata* (Fig. 1. 18, H), while the reserves of *Chilomonas,* which are composed of β-amylose and amylopectin (97), are scattered refractile bodies (Fig. 1. 18, D). In Phytomonadida and Dinoflagellida, starch occurs both as scattered granules and as deposits around pyrenoids.

Glycogen, or a similar material, is common in groups other than the phytoflagellates. Little is known about the chemical nature of these inclusions. Such reserves are distributed as fine granules in *Paramecium* (186), but may be concentrated posteriorly in *Stentor* (222, 240). In the Ophryoscolecidae, the skeletal plates (Fig. 1. 18, F, G) contain much of the glycogen (155), although cytoplasmic granules may occur also (154). Glycogen or paraglycogen is generally deposited during heavy feeding and consumed in starvation, as traced in *Stentor* (222, 223). Such reserves also may be deposited before encystment—as in *Dileptus* (207), *Ichthyophthirius* (156), and certain Endamoebidae—and consumed before excystment. The paraglycogen of *Ichthyophthirius* is formed as small granules within a mitochondrial sphere which disappears after the paraglycogen mass reaches a diameter of 5-6μ. (156). A similar development has been observed in gregarines (109), whereas glycogen is deposited in association with the parabasal body of *Cryptobia helicis* (48).

Lipids are probably stored by most, if not all, Protozoa, under certain conditions. The accumulation of fat in *Stentor* has been attributed to low oxygen tensions (240), and stored lipids are characteristic of old rather than young cultures of *Polytoma uvella* (220). Lipids may be distributed through the endoplasm or else concentrated in one region as in *Anoplophrya* (51). In *Stentor coeruleus* (223), these inclusions vary from small granules to bodies as large as the macronuclear nodes. So-called *bodies of Maupas,* believed to contain at least some lipids, occur in various Cryptomonadida as two refractile ellipsoidal inclusions (88). In *Ichthyophthirius,* the fatty acids and glycerol which reach the cytoplasm are first segregated into globules within which neutral fat is formed (156). A similar process has been described in *Opalina* (114).

Protein reserves have been described as basophilic granules, metachromatic granules, chromatoid bodies, albuminoid reserves, and chromidia. Such reserves occur as scattered granules through the endoplasm, they may be stored in peripheral globules in *Opalina* (115), or they may be deposited as fairly large masses. Chromatoid bodies (Fig. 1. 18, E), representing the third condition, are refractile inclusions present in young cysts in certain Endamoebidae. Little is known about the origin of protein reserves. However, protein granules are extruded from the macronucleus of *Ichthyophthirius multifiliis* after the ciliates invade a host and begin to feed (156). Similar achromatic bodies in the macronucleus of *Blepharisma undulans* also have been interpreted as protein reserves (239). The chromatoid bodies of *Entamoeba histolytica* on the other hand, are formed by the coalescence of clear vacuoles which appear in the cytoplasm (90). Dietary factors may influence the synthesis of protein reserves. Storage of protein granules in *Polytoma uvella,* for example, is extensive in a medium containing butyrate, but is much less noticeable with acetate (220).

Volutin granules, known in many Protozoa, presumably should be considered nitrogenous reserves (158). Although the term has been used rather loosely, volutin may be considered metachromatic material which is Feulgen-negative but is stainable by a modified technique which omits preliminary hydrolysis (158, 188). The disappearance of volutin in trypanosomes and haemogregarines after digestion with ribonuclease indicates that the granules contain ribonucleic acid (5). Such granules are resorbed in old cultures and during induced starvation of *Polytoma uvella* (220); they accumulate during active feeding of *Oxymonas dimorpha* and decrease in the motile phase (32), and are apparently a reserve food in *Pelomyxa carolinensis* (233).

Crystalline inclusions are found in various species. The crystals of *Amoeba proteus* apparently contain amino acids, presumably derived from digested food (165, 166), but the composition of such inclusions in many other Protozoa remains to be determined. As traced in *Paramecium bursaria* (232), crystals accumulate during holozoic feeding and then disappear gradually as the supply of bacteria in the culture is exhausted and the ciliates become increasingly dependent upon their symbiotic algae.

Chromidia

Originally, chromidia were defined as granules derived from the nucleus. Certain "generative" chromidia were considered extranuclear chromatin granules with a potential ability to form aggregates and develop into nuclei. In other cases, extrusion of chromidia from the nucleus was believed to be a means of restoring a normal nucleo-cytoplasmic ratio. In more recent literature, a variety of inclusions—probably including mitochondria, volutin granules and protein granules ("albuminoid reserves")—have been referred to as chromidia. Since the older chromidial theories are no longer accepted, and the identities of the more modern "chromidia" are so varied, it seems advisable to drop the term as a designation for cytoplasmic inclusions of Protozoa.

Mitochondria

Mitochondria (or chondriosomes), which seem to be generally present in Protozoa, were observed as early as 1910 in *Chilomonas, Cryptomonas,* and *Noctiluca* (54). Subsequently, mitochondria have been described in many species (76, 77, 158). Mitochondria are to be expected in Protozoa during the active phase of the life-cycle, but may be absent in the cyst, as reported for *Ichthyophthirius multifiliis,* in which the mitochondria disappear rapidly after encystment (156, 159). Reportedly mitochondria-free sporozoites of *Monocystis* (94) may be an analogous case. In addition, mitochrondria have not been found in active stages of a marine amoeba, *Flabellula mira* (89).

Mitochondria may occur as granules, short rods, filaments, or filamentous networks. The form is more or less characteristic of a species, although some variation may be expected. Filamentous mitochondria (Fig. 1. 19, A), apparently less common than other types, have been described in *Chlorogonium, Chlamydomonas,* and *Polytoma.* Such filaments are often anastomosed in a superficial network. Mitochondrial nets also have been observed in green and colorless strains of *Euglena gracilis* (95). Similar networks, which occasionally break up into short rods, occur in *Glenodinium sociale* and other dinoflagellates (7). These inclusions are usually stainable vitally with Janus green B, although the reaction may be less intense than that of metazoan mitochondria. Good results have also been reported with Janus red (91). Special fixatives, such as the chromate-osmic mixtures, are advisable for good permanent preparations.

The cytoplasmic distribution of mitochondria varies with the species. Random cytoplasmic distribution (Fig. 1. 19, B) is common, but aggregation around food vacuoles is sometimes noted (166). The mitochondria of *Chilomonas* (Fig. 1. 19, D) and *Cryptomonas,* as well as those of Phytomonadida and Euglenida, are believed by Hollande (88) to be entirely peripheral. Certain endoplasmic inclusions of these flagellates, previously interpreted as mitochondria after demonstration with mitochondrial techniques (76, 77), are said to be cytoplasmic vacuoles. Peripheral mitochondria of ciliates may be oriented in rows, as in *Nyctotherus cordiformis* (93). Association of peripheral mitochondria with the basal granules has been described in *Colpidium colpoda* and other ciliates (26), but this is not the case in *Tillina canalifera* (213). Mitochondria of *Bursaria truncatella* are mostly peripheral during conjugation but are scattered through the cytoplasm in other phases of the life-cycle (181).

Various functions have been assigned to the mitochondria. Morphogenetic interpretations include a mitochondrial origin of pyrenoids (20) and the derivation of Golgi material, parabasal bodies, blepharoplasts, and the stigma from mitochondria (1). Supposed physiological activities

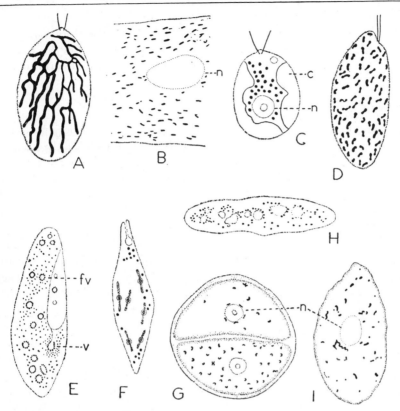

Fig. 1. 19. A. Mitochondrial network in *Polytoma uvella;* x2700 (after Hollande). B. Mitochondria and one nucleus in *Protoopalina hylarum;* diagrammatic (after Richardson and Horning). C. Granules stained with neutral red in *Chlamydomonas variabilis;* x1170 (after Dangeard). D. Mitochondria in *Chilomonas paramecium;* x2700 (after Hollande). E. Neutral-red granules in *Paramecium caudatum;* x310 (after Dunihue). F. Neutral-red granules in *Euglena polymorpha;* x635 (after Dangeard). G. Osmiophilic inclusions in associated "gametocytes" of *Gregarina cuneata;* x635 (after Joyet-Lavergne). H. Osmiophilic inclusions in *P. caudatum;* x245 (after Dunihue). I. Osmiophilic inclusions in *Protoopalina hylarum;* diagrammatic (after Richardson and Horning). Key: *c,* chromatophore; *fv,* food vacuole; *n,* nucleus; *v,* developing food vacuole.

are even more varied: association with the deposition of lipids in gregarines (112); a causative role in amoeboid movement (19); mitochondrial origin of digestive enzymes (92); transportation of waste products to contractile vacuoles (165); transportation of enzymes to food vacuoles and of digested materials away from the vacuoles (166); and association with the deposition of paraglycogen (156). A belief that protozoan mitochondria are involved in oxidations is in accord with the demonstration that mitochondria contain most of the succinic dehydrogenase in liver cells (87). Joyet-Lavergne (113) reported the capacity of mitochondria in gregarines to oxidize leuco-derivatives of various dyes, and suggested that such oxidations are effected partly with the aid of glutathione and vitamin A, previously detected in mitochondria (35, 111). The localization of cytochrome oxidase in mitochondria also has been determined for *Stentor coeruleus* (224).

Vacuome

The term, *vacuome,* was introduced as a collective designation for the vacuoles in plant cells (36). According to later views (72), the vacuome is distinct from the mitochondria and shows several characteristic properties. It may be stained vitally with dilute solutions of neutral red and certain other dyes which do not stain mitochondria. Furthermore, the vacuome is not reliably demonstrated by mitochondrial techniques, although often impregnated by Golgi methods.

Cytoplasmic inclusions of Protozoa were probably first referred to as a vacuome by Dangeard (37), although neutral-red-stainable granules had been described much earlier. The vacuome, in microorganisms generally, consists of small globules or granules rather than obvious vacuoles (39). The reverse is true in higher plants. The vacuome of Protozoa includes small inclusions (Fig. 1. 19, C, E, F) which are distinguishable from mitochondria in vital staining with mixtures of neutral red and Janus green B. In certain species, it is evident that the elements of the vacuome are normal inclusions of the living organism. The available data (76, 77, 158) suggest that a vacuome is generally present in Protozoa, although apparently lacking in *Conchophthirius mytili* (116) and disappearing during encystment of *Ichthyophthirius multifiliis* (156). Elements of the vacuome are scattered through the endoplasm in many species. In certain gregarines (110), however, the distribution varies in different stages of the life-cycle. Adhesion of neutral-red granules to newly formed food vacuoles (Fig. 1. 19, E) also occurs in certain ciliates.

The ability to segregate neutral red apparently is not limited to one type of inclusions. Dangeard (38) stained not only the usual vacuome but also the cortical "mucous granules" (sometimes called trichocysts) in certain Euglenida. Bush (16) also found two types of neutral-red granules in *Haptophrya michiganensis.* Food vacuoles of Protozoa also are stainable with neutral red but they are usually not considered a part of the vacuome, in view of their different origin and behavior.

Guilliermond (72) has pointed out that the vacuome of plants functions in segregation and storage of metabolic products, and should be considered a part of the deutoplasm, or paraplasm, rather than living protoplasm. The vacuome may have comparable functions in Protozoa. As shown by micro-incineration, the vacuome of *Paramecium caudatum* segregates appreciable quantities of minerals (162), and the number of neutral-red granules decreases in this species during starvation (49). The vacuome of *Opalina* is said to serve for the storage of proteins (114). In addition, the vacuome contains volutin in *Chilomonas paramecium* (59), *Peranema trichophorum* (23), *Polytoma uvella* (219), and species of *Euglena* (22, 178).

The neutral-red granules which collect on the food-vacuole in certain ciliates (Fig. 1. 19, E) have been called *digestive granules*. Prowazek (184) suggested that they enter the food-vacuoles of *Paramecium aurelia* and participate in digestion. Similar conclusions have been reported for *P. caudatum* (192), *Vorticella* (218), and *Tetrahymena pyriformis* (221). Both Koehring (135) and Dunihue (49), while confirming aggregation at the surface, have denied that the neutral-red granules penetrate the food-vacuole in *Paramecium*. Such granules apparently get into food-vacuoles of *Ichthyophthirius* without penetrating a membrane. The granules collect on a freshly formed food-vacuole, a new membrane is developed around the mass, and the original vacuolar membrane then disappears (156). Although no such relationship has been detected in certain other ciliates (75, 78), the behavior of these inclusions in *Paramecium* and *Ichthyophthirius* may justify their designation as digestive granules.

Osmiophilic inclusions and organelles

A number of osmiophilic structures and inclusions have been interpreted as protozoan Golgi material. The nature of such material is undoubtedly varied, and complete agreement has not been reached in regard to the identity of protozoan Golgi apparatus.[2] Even a single species has sometimes been credited with two or more kinds of Golgi material. This situation is not surprising because the Golgi techniques are not absolutely specific. Furthermore, selection of the appropriate inclusions is handicapped by the lack of a precise concept of protozoan "Golgi material" and specific criteria for identifying such material.[3]

Protozoan Golgi material apparently was first described as osmiophilic rings and crescents in *Monocystis ascidiae* (84). Comparable inclusions (Fig. 1. 19, G-I) have been reported subsequently in many species of Mastigophora, Sarcodina, Sporozoa, and Ciliatea. The distribution and relative number of such "Golgi bodies" apparently vary within a species. Golgi material may even disappear in the cyst and arise *de novo* after excystment, as in *Ichthyophthirius* (157) and *Protoopalina* (189). Young

[2] This subject has been discussed in several reviews (76, 77, 83, 121, 158, 202, 208).

[3] This situation in protozoan cytology merely reflects the unstable position of "Golgi material" in metazoan cytology. Some workers maintain that ". . . the Golgi apparatus is a gross artifact" (176). According to another view, "a tissue lacking the full complement of Golgi substance would be unable to function normally" (237). Likewise, the statement that "efforts to demonstrate a Golgi apparatus in living, or fresh, somatic cells have been unsuccessful" (175), may be contrasted with the conclusion that "the Golgi apparatus can be seen in most, and perhaps all, living animal cells" (237).

stages of *Monocystis agilis* contain comparatively few Golgi bodies; the older stages show more numerous inclusions (85). Changes in cytoplasmic distribution also occur at different stages in the life-cycles of gregarines (109).

The parabasal apparatus of flagellates has been homologized with metazoan Golgi material (48). The stigma of *Euglena* also has been considered Golgi apparatus (71) on the basis of its supposed homology with the parabasal body of certain other flagellates. Mangenot (163) has objected that the stigma is more probably a modified plastid and that impregnation has no significance beyond the fact that carotenoid pigments will reduce osmium tetroxide. The endoplasmic spherules of *Opalina* also have been considered equivalent to the parabasal apparatus of flagellates and hence to represent Golgi bodies (122). However, the endoplasmic spherules are distinct from the Golgi material described in *Protoopalina* (189). Even the recognition of authentic parabasal bodies as Golgi material has been opposed on several grounds (123, 208).

Inclusions superficially resembling Golgi networks have been described. A simple "net" was produced in *Plasmodium praecox* by the fusion of osmiophilic globules (35). A more complicated net, supposedly arising from the food vacuole, has been reported in *Entamoeba gingivalis* (19), while the Golgi apparatus of *Peranema trichophorum* (14) has been pictured as fibrils resembling the silver-line systems of certain euglenoid flagellates.

The membrane of the contractile vacuole, which is osmiophilic in *Chilomonas paramecium* and certain ciliates (51, 170, 171), also has been considered Golgi apparatus. Gatenby and Singh (58) have extended this concept to the wall of the reservoir (gullet) in *Copromonas subtilis* (Euglenida). If the wall of the contractile vacuole is to be homologized with the Golgi apparatus, it probably should be osmiophilic in Protozoa generally. Such is not the case, since the contractile vacuole of various ciliates and flagellates is not osmiophilic (15, 75, 84, 168).

Another suggestion (35, 75, 110) is that neutral-red granules may be recognized as Golgi material because elements of the vacuome are impregnated by Golgi techniques in a number of species. Sound objections to this generalization have arisen. Attempts to impregnate the neutral-red granules of several species by the usual Golgi methods have failed (16, 40, 124, 139, 154, 157, 213). Furthermore, the osmiophilic bodies of certain gregarines move toward the centripetal pole in the ultracentrifuge, whereas the neutral-red granules are not noticeably displaced (40). Also, the neutral-red granules of *Paramecium* (120) and *Ichthyophthirius* (159) remain stratified with the food vacuoles, although other cytoplasmic inclusions are displaced. The significance of the results obtained with the ultracentrifuge is uncertain. In the case of metazoan Golgi bodies, the centrifuge frequently separates chromophilic and chromophobic substances (190), sends the chromophilic elements to either the centrifugal pole (191) or to the centripetal pole (3), sometimes stratifies the Golgi bodies in different zones (237), and sometimes separates the "vacuome" and the Golgi bodies (237).

NUCLEI OF PROTOZOA

Under the general term, *nucleus,* are included the micronucleus and the macronucleus of ciliates and the vesicular nuclei of other Pro-

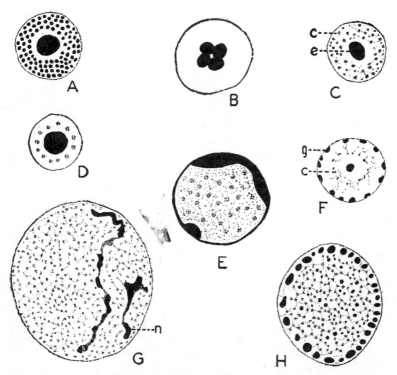

Fig. 1. 20. Nuclei. A. *Heteronema acus;* x4290 (after Loefer). B. Multiple endosomes in *H. acus;* chromatin omitted; x3740 (after Loefer). C. *Haematococcus pluvialis;* x3280 (after Elliott). D. *Iodamoeba bütschlii;* x4000 (after Wenrich). E. *Chilomastix magna;* x9360 (after Kirby and Honigberg). F. *Entamoeba histolytica;* x3900 (after Wenrich). G. *Zelleriella elliptica;* x2340 (after Chen). H. *Pelomyxa carolinensis;* x2070 (after Kudo). Key: *c,* chromatin; *e,* endosome; *g,* peripheral "chromatin" granules; *n,* nucleolus.

tozoa. On the basis of nuclear equipment, two types of Protozoa may thus be recognized. In one group, the nuclei in binucleate and multinucleate species are of the same kind, so far as structure can be determined and functions inferred. In Ciliophora, with the apparent exception of the Protociliatia,[4] nuclei are differentiated into micronuclei and macronuclei which differ in size, in structure, and in behavior during fission and conjugation.

Vesicular nuclei

The vesicular nuclei of Mastigophora, Sarcodina, and Sporozoa vary so much in structure that morphological classifications are necessarily arbitrary. However, it is possible to recognize two general types—those with an *endosome* and those without. In the endosome-type (Fig. 1. 20, A-D, F) the chromatin lies between the nuclear membrane and a more or less central body, the endosome. The endosome apparently does not contribute directly, at least in a morphological sense, to the formation of chromosomes. A negative Feulgen reaction, indicating the absence of desoxyribonucleic acid, has been reported for the endosome in Euglenida, Phytomonadida and trypanosomes (104) and in *Entamoeba coli, E. histolytica, Endolimax nana,* and *Iodamoeba bütschlii* (228). In encysted *Giardia lamblia,* however, the endosome is intensely Feulgen-positive (144). The endosome of *Entamoeba muris* also gives a positive reaction (226). The nucleus in *Entamoeba* (Fig. 1. 20, F) contains a small endosome and relatively little chromatin; that of *Endolimax* and *Iodamoeba* (Fig. 1. 20, D), a large endosome and a small amount of chromatin. The well defined peripheral granules, adherent to the nuclear membrane and commonly considered chromatin granules, are Feulgen-negative in *Entamoeba muris* (226), *E. coli,* and *E. histolytica* (228). The discovery that the chromosomes develop from a zone of minute Feulgen-positive "granules" around the endosome of these amoebae emphasizes the need for critical study of the smaller protozoan nuclei. The nucleus of Euglenida (Fig. 1. 20, A, B) contains abundant Feulgen-positive chromatin and a rather large endosome which is sometimes fragmented. The endosome disappears early in mitosis in the Endamoebidae and phytomonad flagellates, but it persists and undergoes division in Euglenida and such dinoflagellates as *Oxyrrhis marina* (73).

Nuclei without endosomes (Fig. 1. 20, E, G, H) may contain several nucleoli which often disappear in mitosis, although they persist in *Zelleriella* (31). The chromatin is usually distributed throughout the nucleus and its appearance may suggest some sort of a nuclear framework or "network." Such nuclei are characteristic of many Heliozoida, Radiolarida, Hypermastigida, Dinoflagellida, opalinid ciliates, and Sporozoa.

---

[4] Although Konsuloff (140) has maintained that the Feulgen-negative endoplasmic spherules of Opalinidae are macronuclei, this interpretation has not been accepted. Furthermore, Metcalf's "macrochromosomes," supposedly homologous with the macronuclear chromatin of other ciliates, are merely Feulgen-negative nucleoli (31).

Nuclear dimorphism

The Ciliophora are unique in that all species, except the supposedly primitive opalinids, have both micronuclei and macronuclei—unless *Stephanopogon mesnili* (149) is another valid exception. In *S. mesnili,* all of the nuclei are similar in size and structure, and their division closely resembles that of the micronucleus in typical ciliates. Perhaps this case is analogous to that of *Dileptus* (81, 216), discussed below. In the typical ciliates, more than one micronucleus or macronucleus may be characteristic of a species and the number of each type sometimes varies independently. *Stentor coeruleus,* for example, may show 10-42 micronuclei distributed irregularly along the 7-23 links of the macronuclear chain (201). Both types of nuclei have a common origin from the synkaryon formed in conjugation. The division-products of the synkaryon, presumably identical cytologically and genetically, undergo divergent metamorphosis in conjugation. A developing micronucleus undergoes reduction in size and often a decrease in staining capacity. The developing macronucleus increases in size, undergoes changes in internal structure and may show extensive changes in form before reorganization is completed. The nature of the changes involved in the development of macronuclei is still unknown. On the basis of genetic data (203), it has been suggested that the macronucleus is a compound nucleus composed of many units, each with its own diploid set of genes. At each fission, the macronucleus divides amitotically, contributing approximately half of its units to each daughter ciliate. Subsequently, the normal number of units is restored by mitotic processes within each reorganizing macronucleus. This theory is interesting, but adequate morphological grounds for such an interpretation are lacking. The ciliate micronucleus, in contrast to the macronucleus, undergoes mitosis during reproduction of the organism.

Macronuclei vary considerably in form, size and number. The simplest are spherical to ovoid bodies (Fig. 1. 21, C) containing many densely staining granules perhaps embedded in an achromatic framework (159). The macronucleus of *Paramecium* is stretched in the ultracentrifuge and the contents are stratified in two zones, the chromatin granules apparently being denser than the achromatic substance (120). The Feulgen technique indicates that different types of granules are stainable with hematoxylin. Uniformly small granules, scattered through the macronucleus of certain ciliates, are Feulgen-positive; certain larger granules give a negative reaction (57, 104, 156). The staining capacity of these Feulgen-positive granules in *Stentor coeruleus* is not affected by ribonuclease (223).

Macronuclei are not always compact. The macronucleus of *Euplotes*

(Fig. 1. 21, B) and that of *Vorticella* wind through much of the endoplasm, while that of *Conchophthirius caryoclada* (117) is irregularly lobate (Fig. 1. 21, A). The two slender macronuclei of *Spathidium spathula* (235) extend nearly the length of the ciliate and may sometimes be joined posteriorly. In various species of *Spirostomum* and *Stentor* (Fig. 1. 21, F)

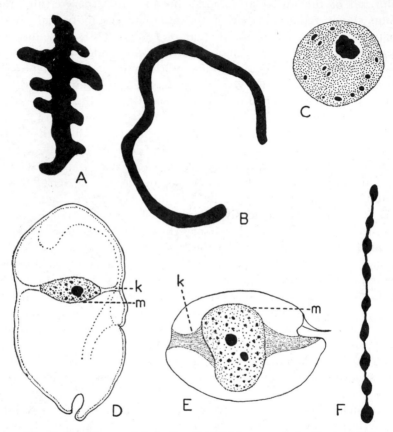

Fig. 1. 21. Macronuclei. A. *Conchophthirius caryoclada;* diagrammatic; x440 (after Kidder). B. *Euplotes;* diagrammatic; x460 (after Turner). C. *Ichthyophthirius multifiliis;* x630 (after MacLennan). D, E. *Nyctotherus gyoeryanus,* longitudinal and transverse sections; karyophore attached to macronucleus; diagrammatic (after Grassé). F. *Stentor* type; diagrammatic. Key: *k,* karyophore; *m,* macronucleus.

there is a chain of macronuclear nodes joined by filaments. In certain ciliates, the macronucleus is suspended from the cortex by a fibrillar "karyophore" (Fig. 1. 21, D, E).

The significance of nuclear dimorphism remains uncertain. It is usually assumed that the macronucleus is involved in metabolic activities. In this connection, the extensive resorption of the macronucleus during starvation of *Stentor coeruleus* (223) is of interest. The micronucleus is supposedly concerned mainly with reproduction and sexual phenomena and therefore is primarily of genetic interest. The occurrence of apparently amicronucleate strains in several species—*Oxytricha hymenostoma* (41), *Oxytricha fallax, Urostyla grandis* (234), and *Tillina magna* (4), among others—suggests that the micronucleus is not actually essential to growth and fission. Observations on the regeneration of fragments (2) indicate that the macronucleus is essential for complete regeneration of ciliates. The importance of the micronucleus apparently varies with the species. Some species fail to grow, or even to regenerate, without a micronucleus, while macronucleate fragments containing no micronuclei have given rise to amicronucleate races in other species—*Stentor coeruleus* (201) and *Oxytricha fallax* (9), for example.

Dispersed nuclei

So-called dispersed nuclei have been described in certain Protozoa, although the older accounts have not been confirmed in more recent investigations and such interpretations were undoubtedly based upon inadequate cytological techniques. However, the ciliate *Dileptus* has been cited for many years as an example in which chromatin granules, scattered through the endoplasm, are the substitute for a nucleus. The condition in *Dileptus gigas* has been analyzed by Visscher (216). During postconjugant reorganization the synkaryon divides into two nuclei, one of which produces 32-64 micronuclei, and the other a comparable number of macronuclei. The latter eventually divide further into the many scattered macronuclear derivatives characteristic of the normal ciliate. The nuclear apparatus of *Dileptus anser* (81) may include as many as 200 small macronuclei measuring 2-3µ and containing fine Feulgen-positive granules. A few of the macronuclei can usually be found in division at almost any time, but they all seem to divide almost simultaneously just before binary fission.

LITERATURE CITED

1. Alexeieff, A. 1928. *Arch. f. Protistenk.* **60**: 268.
2. Balamuth, W. 1940. *Quart. Rev. Biol.* **15**: 290.
3. Beams, H. W. and R. L. King 1935. *Proc. Roy. Soc. London, B,* **118**: 264.
4. Beers, C. D. 1946. *Biol. Bull.* **91**: 256.
5. Berghe, L. van den 1946. *J. Parasit.* **32**: 465.
6. Biecheler, B. 1934. *C. R. Soc. Biol.* **115**: 1039.
7. ——— 1934. *C. R. Ac. Sci.* **199**: 1241.
8. Bishop, A. 1927. *Quart. J. Micr. Sci.* **71**: 147.
9. Bishop, E. L. 1943. *J. Morph.* **72**: 441.
10. Bles, E. J. 1929. *Quart. J. Micr. Sci.* **72**: 527.
11. Bock, F. 1926. *Arch. f. Protistenk.* **56**: 321.
12. Bresslau, E. 1922. *Zentralbl. f. Bakt., Orig.* **89**: 87.
13. Brown, H. P. 1945. *Ohio J. Sci.* **45**: 247.
14. Brown, V. E. 1930. *Quart. J. Micr. Sci.* **73**: 403.
15. Browne, K. M. R. 1938. *J. Roy. Micr. Soc.* **58**: 188.
16. Bush, M. 1934. *Univ. Calif. Publ. Zool.* **39**: 251.

17. Calkins, G. N. 1933. *The Biology of the Protozoa* (Philadelphia: Lea & Febiger).
18. Carter, P. W., I. M. Heilbron and B. Lythgoe 1939. *Proc. Roy. Soc. London, B,* **128**: 82.
19. Causey, D. 1925. *Univ. Calif. Publ. Zool.* **28**: 1.
20. —— 1926. *Univ. Calif. Publ. Zool.* **28**: 217.
21. Chadefaud, M. 1937. *C. R. Ac. Sci.* **204**: 1688.
22. —— 1937. *Le Botaniste* **28**: 85.
23. —— 1938. *Rev. Algol.* **11**: 189.
24. Chambers, R. and J. A. Dawson 1925. *Biol. Bull.* **48**: 240.
25. Chatton, E. 1930. *Arch. Zool. Ital.* **16**: 169.
26. —— and S. Brachon 1935. *C. R. Soc. Biol.* **118**: 958.
27. —— and P. Grassé 1929. *C. R. Soc. Biol.* **100**: 281.
28. —— and R. Hovasse 1934. *C. R. Soc. Biol.* **115**: 1036.
29. —— and A. Lwoff 1935. *C. R. Soc. Biol.* **118**: 1068.
30. ——, ——, M. Lwoff and J.-L. Monod 1931. *Bull. Soc. Zool. France* **56**: 367.
31. Chen, T.-T. 1948. *J. Morph.* **83**: 281.
32. Connell, F. C. 1930. *Univ. Calif. Publ. Zool.* **36**: 51.
33. Copeland, H. F. 1947. *Amer. Nat.* **81**: 340.
34. Cosgrove, W. B. 1947. *J. Parasit.* **33**: 351.
35. Cowdry, E. W. and G. H. Scott 1928. *Arch. Inst. Pasteur Tunis* **17**: 233.
36. Dangeard, P. 1918. *C. R. Ac. Sci.* **169**: 1005.
37. —— 1923. *C. R. Ac. Sci.* **177**: 978.
38. —— 1928. *Ann. Protistol.* **1**: 69.
39. Dangeard, P. A. 1929. *Le Botaniste* **21**: 281.
40. Daniels, M. L. 1938. *Quart. J. Micr. Sci.* **80**: 293.
41. Dawson, J. A. 1920. *J. Exp. Zool.* **30**: 129.
42. Day, H. C. 1930. *Physiol. Zool.* **3**: 56.
43. Deflandre, G. 1934. *Ann. Protistol.* **4**: 31.
44. Dierks, K. 1926. *Arch. f. Protistenk.* **54**: 1.
45. Dobell, C. C. 1911. *Arch. f. Protistenk.* **23**: 269.
46. Dogiel, V. 1929. *Arch. f. Protistenk.* **68**: 319.
47. Duboscq, O. and P. Grassé 1926. *C. R. Soc. Biol.* **96**: 33.
48. —— and —— 1933. *Arch. Zool. Exp. Gén.* **73**: 381.
49. Dunihue, F. W. 1931. *Arch. f. Protistenk.* **75**: 476.
50. Dutton, H. J. and W. M. Manning 1941. *Amer. J. Bot.* **28**: 516.
51. Eksemplarskaja, E. V. 1931. *Arch. f. Protistenk.* **73**: 147.
52. Elliott, A. M. 1934. *Arch. f. Protistenk.* **82**: 250.
53. Entz, G., Jr. 1927. *Arch. f. Protistenk.* **58**: 344.
54. Fauré-Fremiet, E. 1910. *Arch. Anat. Micr.* **11**: 457.
55. —— 1925. *C. R. Soc. Biol.* **93**: 500.
56. Foster, E., M. B. Baylor, N. A. Meinkoth and G. L. Clark 1947. *Biol. Bull.* **93**: 114.
57. Garnjobst, L. 1937. *Arch. f. Protistenk.* **89**: 317.
58. Gatenby, J. B. and B. N. Singh 1938. *Quart. J. Micr. Sci.* **80**: 567.
59. —— and J. D. Smyth 1940. *Quart J. Micr. Sci.* **81**: 595.
60. Geitler, L. 1926. *Arch. f. Protistenk.* **53**: 343.
61. —— 1926. *Arch. f. Protistenk.* **56**: 128.
62. Gelei, G. v. 1937. *Arch. f. Protistenk.* **89**: 133.
63. Gelei, J. v. 1933. *Arch. f. Protistenk.* **80**: 116.
64. —— 1936. *C. R. XII Congr. Intern. Zool. Lisbon,* p. 174.
65. —— 1937. *Biol. Zentralbl.* **57**: 175.
66. —— 1937. *Arch. f. Protistenk.* **88**: 314.
67. —— 1937. *Arch. f. Protistenk.* **90**: 165.
68. —— and P. Horvath 1931. *Ztschr. wiss. mikr. Tech.* **48**: 9.
69. Giese, A. C. 1938. *Trans. Amer. Micr. Soc.* **57**: 77.
70. —— 1949. *Biol. Bull.* **97**: 145.
71. Grassé, P. P. 1926. *Arch. Zool. Exp. Gén.* **65**: 345.
72. Guilliermond, A. 1934. *Ztschr. wiss. Mikr. u. mikr. Tech.* **51**: 203.
73. Hall, R. P. 1925. *Univ. Calif. Publ. Zool.* **26**: 281.
74. —— 1929. *J. Morph.* **48**: 105.

75. —— 1931. *Ztschr. Zellforsch. mikr. Anat.* **13**: 770.
76. —— 1936. *Botan. Rev.* **2**: 85.
77. —— 1946. *Botan. Rev.* **12**: 515.
78. —— and F. W. Dunihue 1931. *Trans. Amer. Micr. Soc.* **50**: 196.
79. Hammond, D. M. 1937. *Quart. J. Micr. Sci.* **79**: 507.
80. Haye, A. 1930. *Arch. f. Protistenk.* **70**: 1.
81. Hayes, M. L. 1938. *Trans. Amer. Micr. Soc.* **57**: 11.
82. Heilbron, I., H. Jackson and R. N. Jones 1935. *Biochem. J.* **29**: 1384.
83. Hill, J. C. 1933. *J. Roy. Micr. Soc.* **53**: 227.
84. Hirschler, J. 1914. *Anat. Anz.* **47**: 289.
85. —— 1927. *Ztschr. Zellforsch. mikr. Anat.* **5**: 704.
86. Hofker, J. 1928. *Tijdschr. Nederl. Dierk. Ver.*, Ser. 3, **1**: 34.
87. Hogeboom, G. H., W. C. Schneider and G. E. Pallade 1948. *J. Biol. Chem.* **172**: 619.
88. Hollande, A. 1942. *Arch. Zool. Exp. Gén.* **83**: 1.
89. Hopkins, D. L. 1938. *Biodynamica*, No. **34**.
90. —— and K. L. Warner 1946. *J. Parasit.* **32**: 175.
91. Horning, E. S. 1926. *Austral. J. Exp. Biol. Med. Sci.* **3**: 89.
92. —— 1927. *Austral. J. Exp. Biol. Med. Sci.* **4**: 69.
93. —— 1927. *Austral. J. Exp. Biol. Med. Sci.* **4**: 187.
94. —— 1929. *Quart. J. Micr. Sci.* **73**: 135.
95. Hovasse, R. 1948. *New Phytol.* **47**: 68.
96. Howland, R. B. 1924. *J. Exp. Zool.* **40**: 263.
97. Hutchens, J. O., B. Podolsky and M. F. Morales 1948. *J. Cell. Comp. Physiol.* **32**: 117.
98. Hyman, L. H. 1942. *Biol. Symp.* **8**: 27.
99. Ivanič, M. 1933. *Arch. f. Protistenk.* **79**: 200.
100. Jacobson, I. 1931. *Arch. f. Protistenk.* **75**: 31.
101. Jakus, M. A. 1945. *J. Exp. Zool.* **100**: 457.
102. —— and C. E. Hall 1946. *Biol. Bull.* **91**: 141.
103. Jepps, M. W. 1942. *J. Mar. Biol. Assoc.* **25**: 607.
104. Jirovec, O. 1927. *Arch. f. Protistenk.* **59**: 550.
105. —— 1931. *Arch. f. Protistenk.* **73**: 47.
106. —— 1933. *Arch. f. Protistenk.* **81**: 195.
107. Johnson, L. P. 1939. *Trans. Amer. Micr. Soc.* **58**: 42.
108. —— and T. L. Jahn 1942. *Physiol. Zool.* **15**: 89.
109. Joyet-Lavergne, P. 1926. *Arch. Anat. Micr.* **22**: 1.
110. —— 1926. *C. R. Soc. Biol.* **94**: 830.
111. —— 1927. *C. R. Ac. Sci.* **184**: 1587.
112. —— 1927. *C. R. Soc. Biol.* **97**: 327.
113. —— 1932. *C. R. Soc. Biol.* **110**: 552.
114. Kedrowsky, B. 1931. *Ztschr. Zellforsch. mikr. Anat.* **12**: 666.
115. —— 1931. *Ztschr. Zellforsch. mikr. Anat.* **13**: 1.
116. Kidder, G. W. 1933. *Arch. f. Protistenk.* **79**: 1.
117. —— 1933. *Biol. Bull.* **65**: 175.
118. ——, D. M. Lilly and C. L. Claff 1940. *Biol. Bull.* **78**: 9.
119. King, R. L. 1935. *J. Morph.* **58**: 555.
120. —— and H. W. Beams 1937. *J. Morph.* **61**: 27.
121. King, S. D. 1927. *J. Roy. Micr. Soc.* **48**: 342.
122. —— and J. B. Gatenby 1926. *Quart. J. Micr. Sci.* **70**: 217.
123. Kirby, H. 1931. *Trans. Amer. Micr. Soc.* **50**: 189.
124. —— 1931. *Univ. Calif. Publ. Zool.* **36**: 171.
125. —— 1936. *Quart. J. Micr. Sci.* **79**: 309.
126. —— 1942. *Univ. Calif. Publ. Zool.* **45**: 93.
127. —— 1944. *J. Morph.* **75**: 361.
128. —— 1947. *J. Parasit.* **33**: 214.
129. —— 1949. *Univ. Calif. Publ. Zool.* **45**: 319.
130. —— and B. Honigberg 1949. *Univ. Calif. Publ. Zool.* **53**: 315.
131. Klein, B. M. 1930. *Arch. f. Protistenk.* **72**: 404.
132. —— 1932. *Ergebn. d. Biol.* **8**: 75.

133. ——— 1933. *Arch. f. Protistenk.* **79**: 146.
134. ——— 1943. *Ann. Naturhistor. Mus. Wien* **53**: 156.
135. Koehring, V. 1930. *J. Morph.* **49**: 45.
136. Kofoid, C. A. 1907. *Zool. Anz.* **31**: 291.
137. ——— 1910. *Proc. 4th Intern. Zool. Congr.*, p. 928.
138. ——— 1941. "The Life Cycle of the Protozoa" in *Protozoa in Biological Research* (New York: Columbia University Press), p. 565.
139. ——— and M. Bush 1936. *Bull. Mus. Nat. Hist. Belg.* **12**: 1.
140. Konsuloff, S. 1931. *Arch. f. Protistenk.* **73**: 311.
141. Kozloff, E. N. 1948. *J. Morph.* **83**: 253.
142. Krüger, F. 1934. *Arch. f. Protistenk.* **83**: 321.
143. Lackey, J. B. 1936. *Biol. Bull.* **71**: 492.
144. Lucas, M. S. 1930. *Proc. Soc. Exp. Biol. Med.* **27**: 258.
145. Lund, E. E. 1933. *Univ. Calif. Publ. Zool.* **39**: 35.
146. ——— 1935. *J. Morph.* **58**: 257.
147. ——— 1941. *J. Morph.* **69**: 563.
148. Lynch, J. E. 1929. *Univ. Calif. Publ. Zool.* **33**: 27.
149. Lwoff, A. 1936. *Arch. Zool. Exp. Gén.* **78**: 117.
150. ——— 1950. *Problems of Morphogenesis in Ciliates: the Kinetosomes in Development, Reproduction and Evolution* (New York: J. Wiley & Sons).
151. ——— and M. Lwoff 1931. *Bull. Biol. Fr. Belg.* **45**: 170.
152. Lwoff, M. and A. Lwoff 1930. *C. R. Soc. Biol.* **105**: 454.
153. MacDougall, M. S. 1936. *Bull. Biol. Fr. Belg.* **70**: 308.
154. MacLennan, R. F. 1933. *Univ. Calif. Publ. Zool.* **39**: 205.
155. ——— 1934. *Arch. f. Protistenk.* **81**: 412.
156. ——— 1936. *Arch. f. Protistenk.* **86**: 404.
157. ——— 1940. *Trans. Amer. Micr. Soc.* **59**: 149.
158. ——— 1941. "Cytoplasmic inclusions" in *Protozoa in Biological Research* (New York: Columbia University Press), p. 111.
159. ——— 1943. *J. Morph.* **72**: 1.
160. ——— 1944. *Trans. Amer. Micr. Soc.* **43**: 187.
161. ——— 1944. *Physiol. Zool.* **17**: 260.
162. ——— and H. K. Murer 1934. *J. Morph.* **55**: 421.
163. Mangenot, G. 1926. *C. R. Soc. Biol.* **94**: 577.
164. Mast, S. O. 1928. *Arch. f. Protistenk.* **60**: 197.
165. ——— and W. L. Doyle 1935. *Arch. f. Protistenk.* **86**: 155.
166. ——— and ——— 1935. *Arch. f. Protistenk.* **86**: 278.
167. Moore, A. R. 1935. *J. Cell. Comp. Physiol.* **7**: 113.
168. Moore, I. 1934. *J. Exp. Zool.* **69**: 59.
169. Nadler, E. J. 1929. *Biol. Bull.* **56**: 327.
170. Nassonov, D. 1924. *Arch. mikr. Anat. Entwickl.* **103**: 437.
171. ——— 1925. *Ztschr. Zellforsch. mikr. Anat.* **2**: 87.
172. Nierenstein, E. 1905. *Ztschr. allg. Physiol.* **5**: 434.
173. Owen, H. M. 1947. *Trans. Micr. Soc.* **66**: 50.
174. ——— 1949. *Trans. Amer. Micr. Soc.* **68**: 261.
175. Palade, G. E. and A. Claude 1949. *J. Morph.* **85**: 35.
176. ——— and ——— 1949. *J. Morph.* **85**: 71.
177. Pascher, A. 1917. *Biol. Zentralbl.* **37**: 241.
178. Patten, R. and H. W. Beams 1936. *Quart. J. Micr. Sci.* **78**: 615.
179. Penard, E. 1922. *Études sur les infusoires d'eau douce* (Genève Georg).
180. Pitelka, D. R. 1949. *Univ. Calif. Publ. Zool.* **53**: 377.
181. Poljansky, G. 1934. *Arch. f. Protistenk.* **81**: 420.
182. Precht, H. 1935. *Arch. f. Protistenk.* **85**: 234.
183. Pringsheim, E. G. 1948. *New Phytol.* **47**: 52.
184. Prowazek, S. v. 1897. *Ztschr. wiss. Zool.* **63**: 187.
185. Rabinovich, D. 1938. *C. R. Soc. Biol.* **128**: 168.
186. Rammelmeyer, H. 1925. *Arch. f. Protistenk.* **51**: 184.
187. Reichenow, E. 1927. *Lehrbuch der Protozoenkunde,* beg. F. Doflein, I Teil (Jena G. Fischer).

188. ——— 1928. *Arch. f. Protistenk.* **61**: 144.
189. Richardson, K. C. and E. S. Horning 1931. *J. Morph.* **52**: 27.
190. Richter, K. M. 1940. *J. Morph.* **67**: 489.
191. Ries, E. 1938. *Arch. Exp. Zellforsch.* **22**: 569.
192. Robertson, M. 1927. *Parasitol.* **19**: 375.
193. Roskin, G. 1925. *Arch. f. Protistenk.* **52**: 207.
194. ——— and L. B. Levinson 1929. *Arch. f. Protistenk.* **66**: 355.
195. Rumantzew, A. and E. Wermel 1925. *Arch. f. Protistenk.* **52**: 217.
196. Saedeleer, H. de 1930. *C. R. Soc. Biol.* **103**: 160.
197. Saunders, J. T. 1925. *Biol. Rev.* **1**: 249.
198. Schmidt, W. J. 1929. *Protoplasma* **7**: 353.
199. Schmitt, F. O., C. E. Hall and M. A. Jakus 1943. *Biol. Symp.* **10**: 261.
200. Schneider, W. 1930. *Arch. f. Protistenk.* **72**: 482.
201. Schwartz, V. 1935. *Arch. f. Protistenk.* **85**: 100.
201a. Seaman, G. R. 1951. *Proc. Soc. Exp. Biol. Med.* **76**: 169.
202. Smyth, J. D. 1944. *Biol. Rev.* **19**: 94.
203. Sonneborn, T. M. 1945. *Ann. Missouri Bot. Gard.* **32**: 213.
204. Strain, H. H. and W. M. Manning 1942. *J. Biol. Chem.* **144**: 625.
205. ———, ——— and G. Hardin 1943. *J. Biol. Chem.* **148**: 655.
206. ———, ——— and ——— 1944. *Biol. Bull.* **86**: 169.
207. Studitsky, A. N. 1930. *Arch. f. Protistenk.* **70**: 155.
208. Subramaniam, M. K. and R. G. Aiyar 1937. *Proc. Indian Acad. Sci.* **6**: 1.
209. Taylor, C. V. 1920. *Univ. Calif. Publ. Zool.* **19**: 403.
210. ——— 1923. *J. Exp. Zool.* **37**: 259.
211. ———"Fibrillar Systems in Ciliates" in *Protozoa in Biological Research* (New York: Columbia Univ. Press), p. 191.
212. Turner, J. P. 1933. *Biol. Bull.* **64**: 53.
213. ——— 1940. *Arch. f. Protistenk.* **93**: 255.
214. Villeneuve-Brachon, S. 1940. *Arch. Zool. Exp. Gén.* **82**: 1.
215. Visscher, J. P. 1923. *Biol. Bull.* **45**: 113.
216. ——— 1927. *J. Morph.* **44**: 383.
217. Vlk, W. 1938. *Arch. f. Protistenk.* **90**: 448.
218. Volkonsky, M. 1929. *C. R. Soc. Biol.* **101**: 133.
219. ——— 1930. *C. R. Soc. Biol.* **105**: 619.
220. ——— 1930. *C. R. Soc. Biol.* **105**: 624.
221. ——— 1933. *Bull. Biol. Fr. Belg.* **67**: 135.
222. Weisz, P. B. 1948. *J. Exp. Zool.* **108**: 263.
223. ——— 1949. *J. Morph.* **84**: 335.
224. ——— 1950. *J. Morph.* **86**: 177.
225. Wenrich, D. H. 1929. *Biol. Bull.* **56**: 390.
226. ——— 1940. *J. Morph.* **66**: 215.
227. ——— 1941. *Biol. Bull.* **81**: 324.
228. ——— 1941. *J. Parasit.* **27**: 1.
229. ——— 1944. *Amer. J. Trop. Med.* **24**: 39.
230. ——— 1944. *J. Parasit.* **30**: 322.
231. Wetzel, A. 1925. *Arch. f. Protistenk.* **51**: 209.
232. Wichterman, R. 1948. *Anat. Rec.* **101** (suppl.): 97.
233. Wilber, C. G. 1945. *Trans. Amer. Micr. Soc.* **64**: 289.
234. Woodruff, L. L. 1921. *J. Exp. Zool.* **34**: 329.
235. ——— and H. Spencer 1922. *J. Exp. Zool.* **35**: 189.
236. Worley, L. G. 1934. *J. Cell. Comp. Physiol.* **5**: 53.
237. ——— 1946. *Ann. N. Y. Acad. Sci.* **47**: 1.
238. Yocom, H. B. 1918. *Univ. Calif. Publ. Zool.* **18**: 337.
239. Young, D. 1939. *J. Morph.* **64**: 297.
240. Zhinkin, L. 1930. *Ztschr. Morph. Ökol. Tiere* **18**: 217.

II

Reproduction and Life-Cycles

IN MANY PROTOZOA, reproduction occurs at frequent intervals, with relatively short periods of growth intervening under favorable conditions. In other cases, growth may extend over a period of several to many days, so that reproduction occurs at comparatively long intervals. Depending upon the species, reproduction may or may not be preceded regularly by sexual phenomena. Of the species which do show sexual activity, some normally undergo syngamy as a prelude to a reproductive phase while others show sporadic sexual activity.

METHODS OF REPRODUCTION

The less complex Protozoa reproduce either by binary fission or by simple budding. In either case, the nucleus undergoes mitosis; or mitosis of the micronucleus and "amitosis" of the macronucleus occur in Ciliophora. Cytoplasmic division is approximately equal in fission, unequal in budding.

Although reproduction in uninucleate species is comparable in some respects to cell division in higher organisms, the structural specialization of many Protozoa introduces complications. The new organisms must be equipped with various organelles, the nature of which varies with the species. Parental organelles such as flagella are often inherited equally or unequally by the daughter organisms which later produce enough new structures to complete their equipment. Even the paraglycogen reserves of *Stentor coeruleus,* normally stored posteriorly, are shifted to the middle

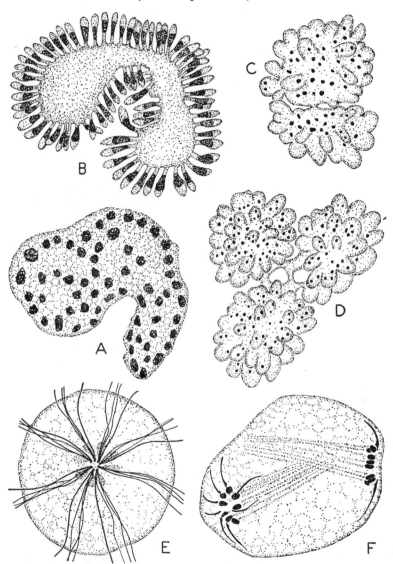

Fig. 2. 1. A. Multinucleate stage (schizont) of *Ovivora thalassemae;* superficial section; x1000 (after Mackinnon and Ray). B. Schizogony in *O. thalassemae;* x1000 (after Mackinnon and Ray). C, D. Plasmotomy in *Pelomyxa carolinensis;* division into two and three individuals; x40 (after Kudo). E, F. *Coronympha octonaria;* x1650 (after Kirby); vegetative stage showing nuclei and flagellar groups (E); nuclear groups at end of telophase, just before plasmotomy (F).

of the body and then shared between the daughter organisms in transverse fission (238). Blepharoplasts, basal granules, kinetoplasts, and sometimes chromatophores and pyrenoids, are self-reproducing. Their duplication during fission fills the needs of the daughter organisms. Other structures, including the cirri of certain ciliates and the parabasal apparatus of certain flagellates, undergo resorption so that each daughter organism must develop a set of its own—in the case of cirri, apparently by outgrowth from inherited basal granules. The resorption of parental structures is sometimes extensive. Reproduction may thus involve dedifferentiation of the old body as well as the differentiation of new structures in the developing daughter organisms. The beginning of differentiation, in two new centers of organization within the parental body, possibly supplies the stimulus for subsequent dedifferentiation.

Reproduction of multinucleate Protozoa, or of multinucleate stages in the life-cycle, may involve either budding or fission. In many Sporozoa a young uninucleate stage grows, with repeated mitoses, into a multinucleate plasmodium (Fig. 2. 1, A) which then reproduces by *schizogony*. Essentially, schizogony is multiple budding in which separation of uninucleate buds from a residual mass of protoplasm is completed within a short time (Fig. 2. 1, B). Certain multinucleate Protozoa normally divide into several organisms, each of which receives some of the parental nuclei. This process, not necessarily synchronized with nuclear division, is known as *plasmotomy*. Both schizogony and plasmotomy have been described in *Coelosporidium* (119), while plasmotomy is characteristic of *Pelomyxa* (158). In the latter (Fig. 2. 1, C, D), plasmotomy produces 2-6 smaller organisms, among which the parental nuclei are distributed at random. Less variation is characteristic of *Coronympha octonaria* (151), in which all eight nuclei usually undergo mitosis and the daughter nuclei separate in groups of eight before plasmotomy occurs (Fig. 2. 1, E, F).

Binary fission

In Mastigophora, fission may occur in the active stage, within a cyst, or in non-flagellated palmella stages (Fig. 2. 2, K). The plane of fission is most frequently longitudinal and the division-furrow usually appears first at the anterior end (Fig. 2. 2, I). Among the dinoflagellates, however, fission is often oblique and may be almost transverse in late stages (Fig. 2. 2, A-H). *Spirotrichonympha bispira* divides transversely, although related species undergo longitudinal fission (61). Mitosis in Trichomonadida is commonly followed by migration of the karyomastigonts to opposite sides of the body and fission is then completed by cytoplasmic constriction (Fig. 2. 2, J).

Cytoplasmic structures[1] may undergo division, resorption followed by origin *de novo*, or partial resorption followed by growth and differentia-

---

[1] The literature on several groups of flagellates has been reviewed by Kirby (152).

tion. Duplication of blepharoplasts, apparently by division, is characteristic of fission in the flagellate stage. The behavior of blepharoplasts in non-flagellated stages of Phytomastigophorea is mostly unknown, although they persist as division-centers in *Eudorina illinoisiensis* (117). The fate of other cytoplasmic structures in fission seems to be variable.

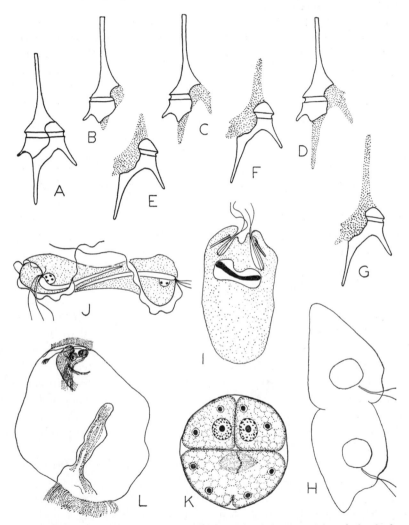

Fig. 2. 2. A-G. Fission and regeneration of missing portions of the body and theca in *Ceratium hirundinella;* diagrammatic (after Entz). H. Late fission in *Oxyrrhis marina;* nuclei and flagella indicated diagrammatically; x1400 (after Hall). I. *Heteronema acus;* division of body starting at anterior end; endosomes shown, chromosomes omitted; x1395 (after Loefer). J. Late fission in *Tritrichomonas augusta;* x1305 (after Kofoid and Swezy). K. Fission in palmella stage of *Haematococcus pluvialis;* x1815 (after Elliott). L. Early fission in a lophomonad flagellate; nucleus divided and new sets of organelles developing; old organelles degenerating; diagrammatic; x125 (after Kirby).

The stigma divides in *Chlamydomonas nasuta* (140), whereas the old stigma passes to one daughter flagellate in *Platydorina caudata* (228). Division of the chromatophores has been reported in certain Euglenida (115). Division of pyrenoids has been described in *Eudorina illinoisiensis* (117); resorption of the old pyrenoid and differentiation of new ones occur in *Chlamydomonas nasuta* (140).

Flagella probably do not split in fission and the few reports of such a process are based upon inadequate evidence. Retention of the old flagella has been described most frequently. In biflagellate and multi-flagellate species, each daughter organism may receive one or more of the original flagella and develop the necessary new ones, as in *Heteronema* (163) and *Trichonympha* (152). However, flagellar resorption occurs in *Monas* (210) and in Phytomonadida which divide within a parental theca. The old flagella and associated structures also degenerate in *Lophomonas* and related genera (Fig. 2. 2, L). The axostyle of trichomonad flagellates, the pharyngeal-rod apparatus of *Heteronema* (163), the siphon of *Entosiphon* (115), and the cresta of devescovinid flagellates (152) undergo resorption, whereas the costa of trichomonads apparently is retained by one of the daughter flagellates. The kinetoplast of Trypanosomidae divides but parabasal bodies of other flagellates usually do not. One of the exceptions is *Chilomonas paramecium* in which each daughter receives part of the old parabasal apparatus (115). Parabasal bodies are sometimes retained intact, as in *Barbulanympha laurabuda* (66); or partial or complete resorption may occur. Although complete resorption of the parabasal body sometimes occurs in *Trichomonas termopsidis* and various devescovinid flagellates, a portion often remains attached to its blepharoplast. In these cases, the parabasal of one daughter is regenerated from the persisting fragment while that of the other is differentiated *de novo* (152).

The rigid theca of *Ceratium* (Fig. 2. 2, A-G) and related dinoflagellates is divided in fission and the missing portions are regenerated. On the other hand, such testate flagellates as *Trachelomonas volvocina* usually undergo fission within the test, one daughter emerging to produce a new test (99).

The simpler Sarcodina often show little of cytological interest aside from division of the nucleus. However, the cytoplasmic changes in *Amoeba proteus* (39, 162) indicate that the physical aspects of fission are not particularly simple (Fig. 2. 3, A-C). The presence of a shell complicates reproduction of many Sarcodina. In primitive genera (*Cochliopodium, Pseudodifflugia*), the simple test is divided in fission. *Euglypha alveolata* secretes reserve shell-plates and stores them (Fig. 2. 3, D) until the next fission, when they are passed to one of the daughter organisms. The other retains the old test. In typical Foraminiferida, schizogony has replaced binary fission.

Fission in ciliates is typically transverse (Fig. 2. 4, H) and, in at least

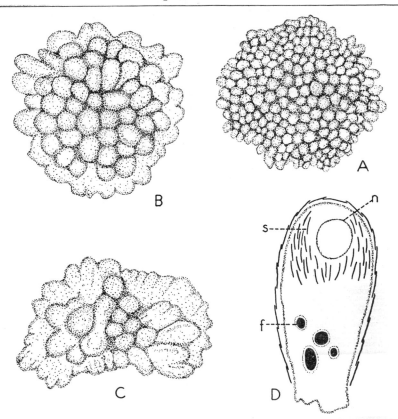

Fig. 2. 3. A-C. Surface changes during fission in *Amoeba proteus;* early division (A); stage with nucleus in anaphase (B); shortly before constriction of the body (C); diagrammatic (after Chalkley and Daniel). D. Reserve shell-plates stored in *Euglypha;* x810 (after Hall and Loefer). Key: *f*, ingested food; *n*, nucleus; *s*, reserve shell-plates.

certain species, there seems to be a definite division-plane which is not displaced by amputations just before fission (256). However, the plane of fission in Peritrichida passes from the oral to the aboral end and is morphologically longitudinal (Fig. 2. 4, A-C). The plane of fission in Opalinidae also is oblique or almost longitudinal. *Cyathodinium piriforme* (Fig. 2. 4, D-F) is unusual, in that the plane of fission passes through the originally longitudinal axis of the body but separates the posterior ends of the daughter ciliates in late fission (164).

Reorganization in ciliates is often striking, and may involve macronuclei as well as cytoplasmic structures. The old cirri are resorbed in *Uronychia* (229), dedifferentiation of the peristomial area occurs in *Bursaria* (212), and resorption of the peristomial membranelles in *Fabrea* (79). In *Chilodonella uncinatus* (165), the old pharyngeal basket, cytostome, and many body cilia are resorbed. On the other hand, *Euplotes* (107),

Colpidium, Glaucoma (49), and *Stentor* (238) retain the peristomial organelles. Division of the parental cytostome and peristome occurs in *Cyclochaeta astropectinis* (51) and possibly in other peritrichs.

The infraciliature shows genetic continuity through multiplication of basal granules, as traced in *Chilodonella* (49), Foettingeriidae (48), *Opalina* (42), and *Ichthyophthirius* (71), among others. In *Tetrahymena* and similar ciliates (Fig. 2. 4, G, H), the development of a new mouth for the posterior daughter involves the multiplication of basal granules at a particular level in the stomatogenous row. These basal granules later give rise to membranelles of the new peristomial area. The continuity of basal

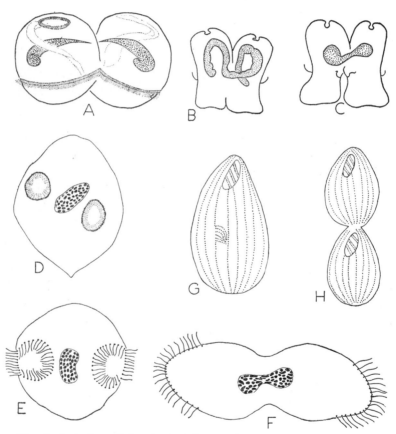

Fig. 2. 4. A. Late fission in *Opisthonecta henneguyi,* x410 (after Kofoid and Rosenberg). B, C. Fission in *Scyphidia ameiuri;* ciliation not shown; diagrammatic (after Thompson, Kirkegaard and Jahn). D-F. Fission in *Cyathodinium piriforme* (after Lucas); two new sets of cilia move into the transverse axis (D, E), and posterior ends of daughter organisms are separated in fission (F); D, E, x1220; F, x1160. G, H. Fission in a hypothetical ciliate similar to *Tetrahymena;* basal granules (indicated diagrammatically) multiply in a particular region of the stomatogenous row (G) and become organized into new adoral membranes (H).

granules is especially striking in *Podophrya fixa,* which shows the usual ciliated larva and non-ciliated adult of the Suctorea. Basal granules persist in the adult, and during reproduction, those in the cortex of the bud multiply and form rows from which the cilia of the larva arise (50a). All the cilia, and apparently their basal granules also, are resorbed in *Cyathodinium* (164). New infraciliatures appear as endoplasmic units which migrate to opposite surfaces of the body, where cilia then arise from the new basal granules (Fig. 2. 4, D, E). This process resembles the formation of new mastigonts in *Lophomonas.*

Budding and schizogony

In simple budding nuclear division is accompanied by unequal division of the cytoplasm. Budding in ciliates is typically external, while both internal and external budding occur in Suctorea. In internal budding of *Tokophrya lemnarum* (Fig. 2. 5), a slit-like cavity appears in the endoplasm during division of the micronucleus, and is gradually extended to cut out a spheroidal mass of cytoplasm following division of the macro-

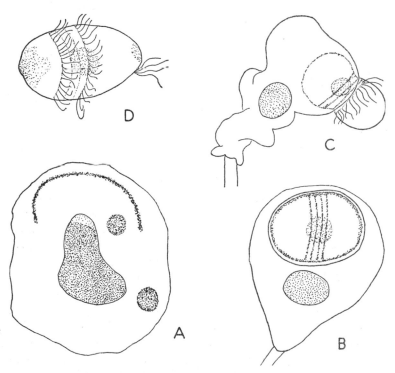

Fig. 2. 5. Internal budding in *Tokophrya lemnarum;* tentacles not shown (after Noble). A. Cytoplasmic cleft developing; macronucleus dividing and micronuclear division completed; x1050. B. Completely separated bud enclosed in pouch; ciliary bands developing; x660. C. Expulsion of bud from brood pouch; x660. D. Ciliated larval stage; x715.

nucleus. After differentiation of cilia, the larva begins to rotate within the brood pouch. Increasingly vigorous contractions of the parent finally expel the larva (196). The development of sporoblasts in various Cnidosporidea (Chapter VI) also may be considered a form of internal budding.

In certain other Protozoa, budding may follow a series of nuclear divisions. *Tritrichomonas augusta,* although usually reproducing by fission, sometimes develops into a somatella which undergoes budding (Fig. 2. 14, F, G). A similar process in *Colacium vesiculosum* (Fig. 2. 14, A, B) involves a multinucleate stage without flagella or reservoirs. These structures appear in each bud before it is separated from the parental somatella (134).

Schizogony, involving the production of several to many buds more or less simultaneously, is characteristic of certain Protozoa. This process is especially efficient in many Sporozoa in which the plasmodium (Fig. 2. 1, A) often contains many nuclei before schizogony (Fig. 2. 1, B). A schizont of *Eimeria bovis,* for example, may produce as many as 170,000 merozoites (108).

NUCLEAR DIVISION

Although mitosis has been reported in most species which have been studied carefully, the small size of many nuclei has made it difficult to interpret the structure of chromosomes in early mitosis and in the interphase. The interphase chromatin of Cryptomonadida (115) and *Zelleriella elliptica* (Fig. 1. 19, G) has been described as fine granules dispersed on a network; that of *Pelomyxa carolinensis* (Fig. 2. 7, A), as Feulgen-positive granules and short filaments. The Feulgen-positive interphase chromatin of Euglenida, according to different reports (115), ranges from periendosomal granules to a continuous spireme which in optical section simulates separate granules. Actually, it has been impossible to find stages suggesting an achromatic network containing chromatin granules in some of the Euglenida and Dinoflagellida. Instead, beaded chromosomes seem to persist through vegetative stages. In general, however, chromosomes of the later prophases seem to develop from some sort of a "reticulum" and, in such favorable material as *Pamphagus hyalinus* (17), the process has been traced in living material. In certain species of *Entamoeba* (Fig. 1. 20, F) and in *Naegleria gruberi* (207), the chromosomes develop from a finely granular or reticular zone of Feulgen-positive material around the endosome. The persisting "peripheral chromatin" granules, apparently adherent to the nuclear membrane in *Entamoeba,* may give rise to chromosome-like bodies perhaps analogous to the nucleoli of *Zelleriella* (58). Interpretations are even more difficult in *Endamoeba blattae* because the interphase nucleus is Feulgen-negative, although Feulgen-positive chromosomes appear in mitosis (177).

The origin of chromosomes from an endosome or a karyosome, in nuclei supposedly containing no interphase "chromatin granules," has been reported in certain Protozoa. In some of these, such as *Endolimax nana,* periendosomal material has been demonstrated in more recent investigations (240). Furthermore, Noble (200) reports a functional separation of endosomal granules and periendosomal chromatin in *Entamoeba gingivalis,* in spite of their intermingling during early prophases. However, the interphase precursors of the chromosomes have not yet been identified with certainty in many Protozoa and much remains to be learned about the earliest stages of mitosis in most species.

The observations of Cleveland (63) on *Holomastigotoides* have shown that the chromosomes persist as such throughout the mitotic cycle. The diagrammatically clear behavior of the chromosomes in this genus supplies a logical pattern for interpreting mitosis in smaller nuclei. Each chromosome consists of a coiled *chromonema* embedded in a matrix. Only the matrix is distinguished in heavily stained preparations, but both components can be detected with phase-contrast microscopy and also by ordinary microscopy in suitably stained preparations. The disappearance of major coiling and the apparent lengthening of each chromonema, as the chromosomal matrix disappears late in mitosis, result in long twisted filaments. This stage, in small nuclei containing a number of chromosomes, would suggest the interphase "reticulum" described in various species. If the uncoiled chromosomes are very slender, optical sections of a small nucleus might suggest a granular organization of the chromatin. Origin of chromosomes from such a "granular" or "reticular" interphase, in the light of chromosomal behavior in *Holomastigotoides,* may involve only a condensation of preexisting chromosomes. Each chromonema becomes more and more tightly coiled (in the "major coils" of Cleveland) as a new matrix is developed. The result is the more or less compact chromosome of the later prophases. According to Cleveland, duplication of each chromonema occurs before the development of the new matrix.

Eumitosis and paramitosis

Differences in chromosomal behavior and the structure of the achromatic division-figure have formed the bases for various classifications of protozoan mitoses. Among these systems, that of Bělař (20) has the advantage of simplicity in recognizing two general types, *eumitosis* and *paramitosis.*

Characteristic features of *eumitosis* are longitudinal splitting of the chromosomes, the development of compact prophase chromosomes, and the appearance of an equatorial belt of chromosomes within the spindle. Many protozoan mitoses can be fitted into such a scheme.

Nuclear division in *Dimorpha mutans* (Fig. 2. 6) is representative. Mitosis is initiated by division of the centrosome, and the subsequent development of an amphiaster is accompanied by the formation of short chromosomes from the interphase chromatin. The nucleus moves into the spindle, the nuclear membrane is said to disappear, and the chromosomes form an equatorial plate. Additional examples are found in *Actinophrys* (18), *Pelomyxa* (Fig. 2. 7), and *Zelleriella* (58).

In paramitosis, condensation of the prophase chromosomes is less marked and a typical equatorial plate is not developed. In *Aggregata eberthi* (Fig. 2. 8, A-D), only one end of each chromosome extends into

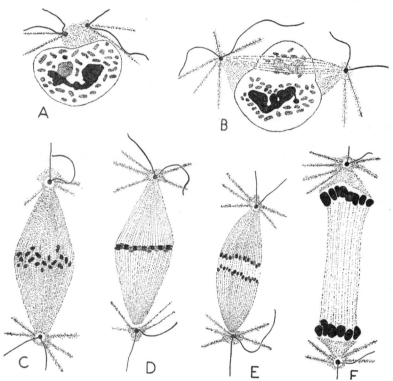

Fig. 2. 6. Mitosis in *Dimorpha mutans;* eumitotic type; basal portions of flagella and a few axopodia are indicated at the poles of the division-figure; x3135 (after Bělař).

the equatorial zone of the spindle. Since the daughter chromosomes separate before they are shortened, later stages of mitosis suggest transverse division of long chromosomes. Long chromosomes persist also in certain Radiolarida (20), Dinoflagellida (29, 106), Euglenida (3, 115, 157), and in *Teratonympha* (Fig. 2. 8, E, F).

The picture presented during separation of the daughter chromosomes depends upon the position of the centromeres and the length of the chromosomes. Terminal centromeres (Fig. 2. 10, H), which have been demonstrated in *Holomastigotoides* (63), probably occur in *Aggregata*

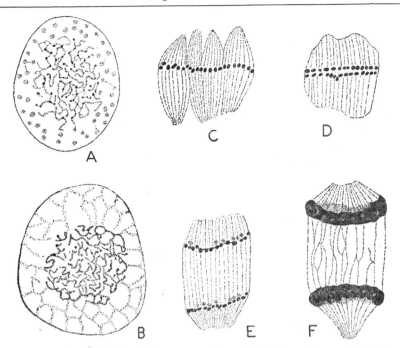

Fig. 2. 7. Mitosis in *Pelomyxa carolinensis.* A. Interphase; x2300. B. Early prophase; x2300. C. Late prophase; x2645. D, E. Separation of daughter chromosomes; x2990. F. Clumping of chromosomes in late anaphase; x2990 (after Kudo).

and in Euglenida and Dinoflagellida. The appearance of V-shaped daughter chromosomes during anaphases, as described in *Pleurotricha lanceolata* (173), would suggest median instead of terminal centromeres.

Persistence of the nuclear membrane throughout mitosis is characteristic of many Protozoa. However, a large portion of the old membrane is discarded after division of the nucleus in *Holomastigotoides* (63) and disappearance of the membrane in the prophase has been described in *Dimorpha mutans* (20).

The micronucleus of ciliates

The small size of the micronucleus increases the difficulty of interpreting chromosomal behavior. Longitudinal splitting of the chromosomes has been reported in some species and transverse division in others, but decisions are difficult for the almost spherical chromosomes found in certain ciliates. Longitudinal splitting has been described in *Pleurotricha* (173), *Stylonychia* (119a), *Conchophthirius* (144), and in pregamic divisions in *Euplotes* (234). In the last three cases, members of each pair of daughter chromosomes slip past each other toward the poles of the spindle (Fig. 2. 9).

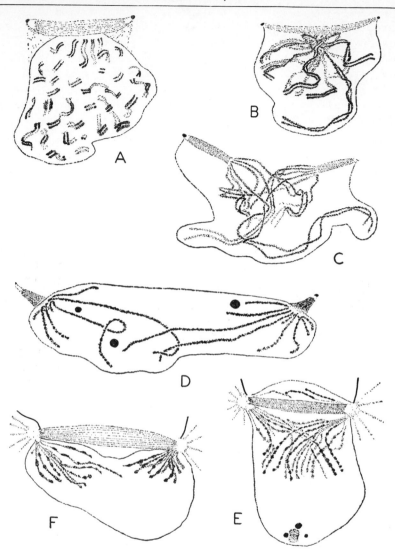

Fig. 2. 8. A-D. Mitosis in *Aggregata eberthi;* paramitotic type; x3790 (after Bělař). E, F. Long chromosomes in the dividing nucleus of *Teratonympha;* x2400 (after Cleveland).

The achromatic figure

Both extranuclear and intranuclear achromatic figures have been described in Protozoa. The extranuclear figure is sometimes represented merely by the centrosomes and a *paradesmose* (156) which ranges from a delicate fibril to a bundle of fibrils in different species (Fig. 2. 10, A-G). The fibrillar paradesmose, as seen in *Gigantomonas,* differs mainly in degree from the extranuclear spindle of *Pseudotrichonympha* and similar types (Fig. 2. 10, I, J). Comparable extranuclear spindles occur in certain dinoflagellates (29, 195) and in *Aggregata* (20). Since the nuclear membrane persists in such forms as *Pseudotrichonympha,* some of the astral rays, during development of the spindle, make connections with the centromeres at the nuclear membrane. Each chromosome in *Holomastigotoides* (Fig. 2. 10, H), for example, ends in a terminal centromere which remains anchored to the nuclear membrane. Duplication of the centromere parallels that of the chromonema. In some of the Hypermastigida, development of the spindle and its connections with the chromosomes has been followed in living flagellates. Pulls exerted on the achromatic figure

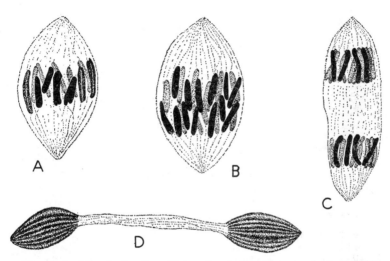

Fig. 2. 9. Mitosis in the ciliate, *Conchophthirius anodontae;* x3995 (after Kidder). A. Longitudinal splitting of the chromosomes. B, C. Separation of daughter chromosomes. D. Nuclear division nearly completed.

cause corresponding movements of the chromosomes; when the tension is released, the fibrils and chromosomes snap back into place (59).

Intranuclear figures have been described in the micronuclei of ciliates, in *Actinophrys* (18), *Monocystis* (184), and *Euglypha* (120), among others (Fig. 2. 11, E-L). In some of these cases, the spindle ends in centrosomes which seem to be embedded in the nuclear membrane or else adherent to it. An intranuclear spindle is typical of the dividing micronucleus (Fig. 2. 11, E, F), although little is known about division-centers in ciliates. The spindle sometimes extends into achromatic masses ("polar caps") which may or may not contain "centrioles." Only a granule has been described at each pole in certain ciliates, and even the granules seem to be missing in others.

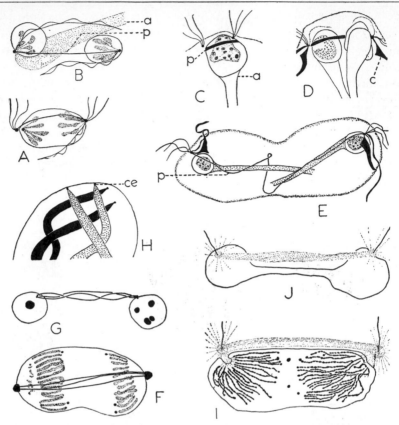

Fig. 2. 10. A, B. Paradesmose in *Tritrichomonas augusta;* x2390 (after Kofoid and Swezy). C-E. Paradesmose in *Metadevescovina cuspidata;* early division (C), x2160; nucleus divided and other organelles duplicated (D), x1800; later stage with very long paradesmose (E), x1440 (after Kirby). F, G. Fibrillar paradesmose in *Gigantomonas herculea;* late anaphase (F), x1710; nuclear division completed (G), x725 (after Kirby). H. Centromeres in *Holomastigotoides;* portions of chromosomes indicated diagrammatically; x1260 (after Cleveland). I, J. Extranuclear spindle in *Pseudotrichonympha;* chromosomes moving toward poles (I), x935; later stage (J), chromosomes not shown, x735 (after Cleveland). Key: *a,* axostyle; *c,* cresta; *ce,* centromere; *p,* paradesmose.

The significance of the persisting endosome in Euglenida and certain dinoflagellates (Fig. 2. 11, A-D) is uncertain. Although this structure occupies an axial position and is divided in mitosis, there is no good evidence that the endosome is analogous to an intranuclear spindle.

The macronucleus

The simpler macronuclei often divide by mere elongation and constriction into approximately equal parts, although unequal division occurs occasionally (71). Division of the compact macronucleus is not always simple, however. A regular elimination of material (Fig. 2. 12) from the macronucleus during division, or from the daughter nuclei afterward, has been described in such genera as *Ancistruma* (142), *Colpoda* (145), *Tillina* (14), *Chilodonella* (167), *Colpidium, Glaucoma,* and *Urocentrum* (146). The significance of this process is unknown.

Ciliates with more than one macronucleus and those with long beaded or band-like macronuclei may show more complicated nuclear changes.

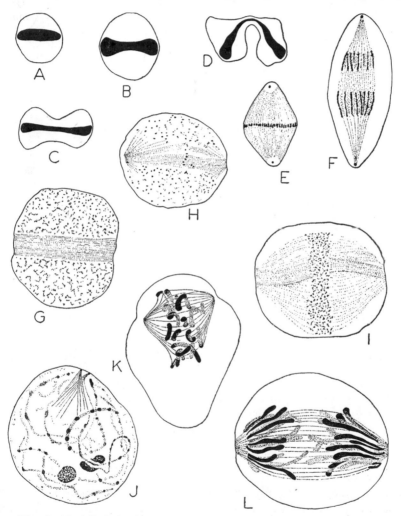

Fig. 2. 11. A-D. Behavior of the endosome during mitosis in *Heteronema acus;* A, B, D, x2890; C, x2270 (after Loefer). E. Intranuclear spindle, micronucleus of *Stentor coeruleus;* x2365 (after Mulsow). F. Intranuclear spindle, micronucleus of *Stylonychia pustulata;* x1730 (after Ivanič). G-I. Intranuclear spindle in *Oxymonas grandis;* x1330 (after Cleveland). J-L. Intranuclear spindle in *Pyrsonympha;* early stage in development (J), x2920; later stages (K, L), x1985 (after Cleveland).

The C-shaped macronucleus of *Euplotes* (Fig. 2. 13, A-D) is shortened and thickened, and undergoes changes in staining reactions which suggest progressive internal changes. The two macronuclei of *Stylonychia pustulata* (227) fuse into a single body which then divides. The macronuclear chains of *Spirostomum, Stentor,* and *Blepharisma* also undergo

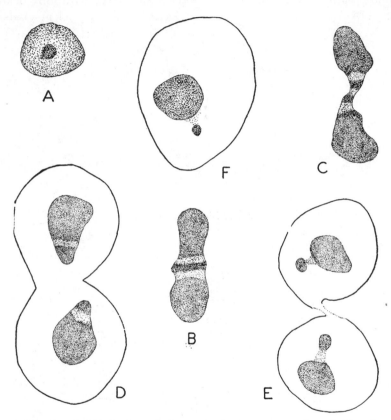

Fig. 2. 12. Elimination of chromatin during macronuclear division in *Colpidium colpoda.* A. Central chromatin mass evident just before division. B-E. Stages in division. F. Separation of discarded mass from a daughter macronucleus. A-E, x510; F, x700 (after Kidder and Diller).

extensive condensation. In *Spirostomum ambiguum* (22) and *Stentor coeruleus* (238) the macronuclear nodes gradually fuse into a compact central body, which then undergoes moderate elongation and a final constriction (Fig. 2. 13, E-I). In *Blepharisma undulans,* the anterior and posterior macronuclear nodes fuse into two masses, while the middle nodes gradually disappear. The anterior and posterior masses then fuse into one body which elongates and undergoes division (238, 255).

LIFE-CYCLES

General features

The simple life-cycles of many species include only an active phase and a cyst. With the cyst apparently eliminated, the "cycle" reaches the limit of simplicity in such types as *Entamoeba gingivalis* and *Pentatricho-monas hominis*. Other modifications of this basic pattern include: (a) the development of two or more stages in the active phase; (b) the introduction of sexual phenomena, which may appear in a sexual phase alternating with an asexual phase in the cycle.

Two or more active stages occur in the life-cycles of many Protozoa. In addition, immature and adult forms of a single organism may be quite

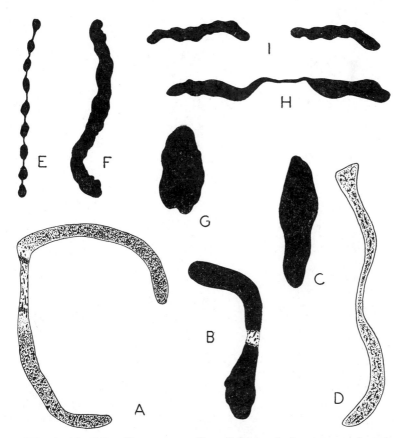

Fig. 2. 13. A-D. Changes preceding division of the macronucleus in *Euplotes;* stages in condensation (A-C); elongation just before division (D); x485 (after Turner). E-I. Division of the macronucleus in *Stentor coeruleus;* diagrammatic (after Weisz).

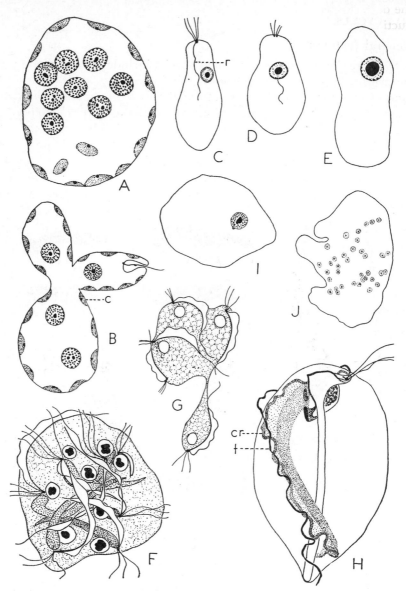

Fig. 2. 14. A, B. Somatella and reproduction by budding in *Colacium vesiculosum* (after Johnson); A, x1840; B, x1380. C-E. Metamorphosis of flagellate into amoeboid stage in *Tetramitus rostratus;* x2080 (after Bunting). F, G. Somatella and formation of bud in *Tritrichomonas augusta;* F, x2100; G, x1200 (after Kofoid and Swezy). H-J. *Gigantomonas herculea,* flagellate stage (H), x1000; uninucleate amoeboid stage (I), x385; multinucleate amoeboid stage (J), x135; diagrammatic (after Kirby). Key: *c*, chromatophore; *cr*, cresta; *r*, rhizostyle; *t*, trailing flagellum.

different in appearance and behavior. Examples include the ciliated larva and non-ciliated adult of Suctorea and the stalkless telotroch and the stalked adult of vorticellid ciliates. Dimorphism sometimes involves the alternation of amoeboid and flagellate stages (Fig. 2. 14, C-E; H-J). The flagellate stage may be temporary, as in *Naegleria;* or it may be the dominant stage, as in *Tetramitus* and certain Chrysomonadida. The flagellate, *Gigantomonas herculea,* shows amoeboid-flagellate dimorphism in which reproduction is limited to the amoeboid phase. Reproductive stages in *Haematococcus* and related genera also are typically non-flagellated. The dominant phase in *Colacium* (134) is a non-flagellated form which occasionally produces flagellate buds (Fig. 2. 14, A, B). Dimorphism also may involve the alternation of a gamete-producing stage and one which undergoes asexual reproduction, as in Foraminiferida. Life-cycles characterized by more than two active stages are found in certain Trypanosomidae, in many Sporozoa, and in some of the Ciliophora.

Protozoan life-cycles may be considered adaptive in that they represent responses to changes in the environment, and perhaps favor, or insure survival when such changes occur. Occurrence of a cycle as such probably is dependent directly upon the environment. This seems evident in parasitic species which must reach a susceptible host in order to complete the cycle, or in many instances even to survive for more than a short time. Within a suitable host, there is often reasonable security during completion of a life-cycle, but establishment in a host does not necessarily insure independence of external conditions. For example, the development of *Plasmodium vivax* in the mosquito may be retarded or prevented by unfavorable temperatures. A modification of environmental conditions may induce a marked change in the cycle, in parasitic as well as free-living species. Maintenance of *Plasmodium gallinaceum* in chick-tissue cultures has caused a normal stock to lose its ability to produce pigmented erythrocytic stages. Chicks inoculated from such cultures always died from exoerythrocytic infections, always without showing normally pigmented erythrocytic stages, and often without any erythrocytic parasites at all (160). In some cases it has been possible to eliminate cyclic changes by strict control of environmental conditions, as in the prevention of conjugation and encystment in ciliates by Woodruff, Beers, and others. Such elimination of cyclic changes does not necessarily mean that the particular life-cycles have no significance. Since a given cycle presumably adapts a species to changing environments it may normally encounter, a perfectly uniform environment may fail to evoke the cycle.

Cysts

Encysted stages, in which the organism is enclosed within a cyst membrane, are a common feature of protozoan life-cycles. On the basis of apparent functions, *protective* and *reproductive* cysts have been distinguished.

Protective cysts may be developed directly from active stages, from zygotes in *Volvox* and Gregarinida, or from sporoblasts (division-products of the zygote) in Coccidia. Such cysts usually possess rather firm walls (Fig. 2. 15, A-D), the composition of which varies from group to group.

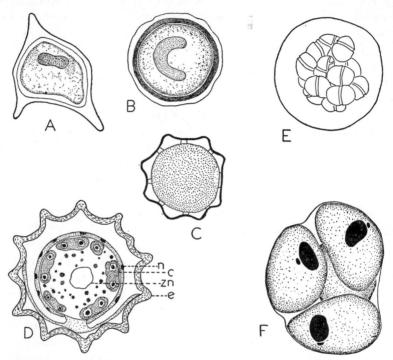

Fig. 2. 15. A. Cyst of *Ceratium hirundinella;* x385 (after Hall). B. Protective cyst of *Didinium nasutum;* outer (ectocyst) and inner (mesocyst) membranes evident; x310 (after Beers). C. Protective cyst of *Bursaria truncatella;* x135 (after Beers). D. Encysted zygote of *Volvox globator;* diagrammatic (after Janet). E. Reproductive cyst in *Gyrodinium* sp.; x240 (after Kofoid and Swezy). F. Reproductive cyst in *Colpoda cucullus;* x735 (after Kidder and Claff). Key: *c,* chromatophore; *e,* developing ectocyst; *n,* nucleus in syncytial layer enclosing zygote; *zn,* nucleus of zygote.

The cyst membranes of many ciliates are probably composed largely of proteins (172), although the inner membrane (endocyst) may be carbohydrate in nature (100). In Endamoebidae and *Giardia,* the properties of the cyst wall resemble those of keratins (155). Siliceous cyst walls are characteristic of Chrysomonadida, and walls composed largely of sand grains are produced in *Difflugia* (203). Many of the thick-walled cysts show spines, ridges, or other surface markings. A compound cyst wall (Fig. 2. 16, C), composed of two or more membranes, is not uncommon.

In such cases one of the membranes—the ectocyst of *Bursaria* (16), the mesocyst of *Didinium* (12), the outer membrane of *Volvox* (122)—is often thicker and more rigid than the others. This heavy membrane may be continuous like the others, or it may, as in *Bursaria* (Fig. 2. 17, A), contain an "emergence-pore" closed by a thin membrane. The two-layered cyst of *Naegleria* contains several analogous pores (207). Double or multiple resting cysts are sometimes produced in Colpodidae. The double cyst of *Tillina magna* shows only one ectocyst, but each of the contained ciliates has its own mesocyst and endocyst (11).

The protective qualities of cysts vary with the species. Dried cysts of *Colpoda cucullus* have remained viable for more than five years (69). Cysts of *Naegleria gruberi* also withstand drying (207). Drying at room temperature prolongs the life of protective cysts of *Stylonethes sterkii* but kills those of *Euplotes taylori* (90). Cysts of *Didinium nasutum* do not survive desiccation although they have remained viable for ten years in sealed containers of hay infusion (10). Cysts of Endamoebidae also do not survive drying. However, cysts of *Entamoeba histolytica,* kept moist under refrigeration, have remained viable for 46 days (245). *Woodruffia metabolica* produces two types of resting cysts, a stable one which resists desiccation, and an unstable type which does not (136). Resistance of protective cysts to unfavorable temperatures is sometimes striking. Thoroughly dried cysts of *Colpoda* have resisted exposure to dry heat at 100° for three hours (23), and immersion in liquid air for 13.5 hours (230).

Reproductive cysts are those in which fission, budding, and sometimes gametogenesis and syngamy occur in different species. However, reproductive activities are not limited entirely to reproductive cysts, since mitosis occurs in the protective cysts of *Giardia* and various Endamoebidae. The wall of the reproductive cyst, although sometimes compound, is usually thin and has relatively little protective value. Such cysts are known in various dinoflagellates (Fig. 2. 15, E) and in certain free-living and parasitic ciliates. Fission within a cyst is characteristic of *Colpoda cucullus* and related species (Fig. 2. 15, F). A similar cyst serves also for attachment of *Ichthyophthirius multifiliis* to the substratum (172). The gametocyst of gregarines probably should be included in this type. Cysts which are presumably of the reproductive type have been referred to as "feeding cysts" in certain dinoflagellates, because they are formed after the organisms ingest a large amount of food.

Encystment

Precystic changes in the organism usually precede secretion of a cyst wall. Material for the membrane sometimes accumulates as globules in the peripheral cytoplasm. Food vacuoles may be eliminated, as in Endamoebidae, and cytoplasmic reserves such as starch or glycogen are often stored in abundance. Since cysts usually approach a spherical form, there is a corresponding change in shape of the body. In such genera as *Euplotes* (90), softening of the pellicle must precede this change in form. Partial or complete resorption of locomotor organelles is common. As traced in *Woodruffia metabolica,* the cilia begin to shorten as the organism rounds up, and shortening is completed after 22-24 hours. The endocyst is not secreted until after the cilia have disappeared (136). Encystment apparently involves some loss of water, with a corresponding increase in density of the protoplasm. The resistance to desiccation, noted in stable cysts but not in unstable cysts of *W. metabolica,* is attributed to a lower water content of the former (136).

The occurrence of encystment has been correlated with various environmental changes. Encystment of *Euplotes taylori* seems to be related to evaporation of the culture medium (90), while *Bursaria truncatella* encysts when transferred singly or in groups to food-free spring water (16). Encystment of *Didinium nasutum* is induced by crowding, either with or without a food supply (15). *Colpoda* (*duodenaria*) *steinii* encysts when starved, and the percentage of cysts increases with the number of organisms present. Encystment of this ciliate has been attributed to the inactivation of essential enzyme systems by metabolic products (231). The lack of materials for synthesis of such enzymes should produce the same effect, and encystment of *C. steinii* in pure culture has followed elimination of thiamine, pyridoxine, nicotinamide, or pantothenic acid from the standard medium, or the omission of foods known to contain several B-vitamins (91). An abundance of food has been considered essential for encystment of some species, but such a food supply would favor rapid multiplication with subsequent crowding. Encystment of ciliates also has been related to an unusually low or high pH of the medium (68), although *Didinium nasutum* encysts most frequently within the range favorable to growth (7).

The varied data on encystment obviously hinder selection of any one factor as the key to this process. However, such a theory as that of Taylor and Strickland (231) lends itself to possible correlation with several environmental changes. The inactivation of a critical enzyme system might result from accumulation of metabolic poisons—induction by waste products and by crowding. Inactivation might be accelerated by a deficiency of materials for synthesizing such enzymes—induction by starvation and crowding. Also, the inactivation of an enzyme system might occur more rapidly at one pH than at another.

Excystment

Excystment often includes the regeneration of peripheral organelles as well as a certain amount of internal reorganization. Rupture of the cyst membranes may involve two different mechanisms. The more important seems to be the absorption of water by the protoplasm early in excystment. The resulting increase in volume forcibly ruptures rigid membranes. In ciliates, the absorbed water may accumulate in a large excystment-vacuole (Fig. 2. 16, A), apparently identical with the contractile vacuole of *Euplotes taylori* (90) and *Didinium nasutum* (12), or in a number of vacuoles as in *Tillina magna* (11). The second mechanism involves the secretion of enzymes which digest the endocyst and perhaps other flexible membranes. This enzymatic action, first described in *Colpoda cucullus* (100), probably occurs also in *Tillina* and *Didinium*.

The first signs of excystment in *Didinium nasutum* (Fig. 2. 16) are the

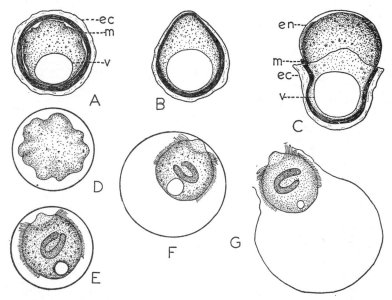

Fig. 2. 16. Excystment in *Didinium nasutum;* x275 (after Beers). A. Appearance of excystment-vacuole. B. Ectocyst and mesocyst almost ruptured. C. Endocyst protruding from ruptured outer membranes. D. Organism after discharge of excystment-vacuole. E, F. Active ciliate in endocyst, which increases in diameter. G. Escape of ciliate. Key: *ec,* ectocyst; *en,* endocyst; *m,* mesocyst; *v,* excystment-vacuole.

beginning of cyclosis and the appearance of a small posterior vacuole. When the vacuole grows to about half the volume of the body, a bulge appears at the opposite pole of the cyst. A little later, the mesocyst and ectocyst are ruptured and the organism slips out, still within the endocyst. The ciliate soon becomes very active within the endocyst, which gradually increases in diameter. The membrane becomes thinner and thinner, and finally seems to dissolve in the medium. Excystment is completed within four hours. At emergence, the meridionally arranged cilia extend from the anterior ciliary girdle about halfway to the posterior end of the body. Later on, the posterior cilia of the longitudinal rows develop into a posterior girdle, while the intermediate cilia disappear. The primitive ciliary pattern of Holotrichida is thus recapitulated to some extent during excystment of *D. nasutum* (12).

Excystment of *Bursaria truncatella* (Fig. 2. 17) is strikingly different. Cyclosis begins early, and a hyaline area of cytoplasm just beneath the emergence-pore becomes more apparent. After a time, the opercular mem-

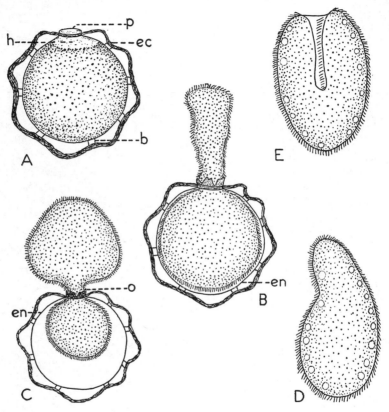

Fig. 2. 17. Excystment in *Bursaria truncatella;* x200 (after Beers). A. Appearance of a "hyaline cap" in the cytoplasm. B, C. Emergence of the ciliate through the ruptured opercular membrane. D. Young excysted ciliate. E. Older stage with developing peristomial membranelles. Key: *b,* "bridge" joining endocyst and ectocyst; *ec,* ectocyst; *en,* endocyst; *h,* hyaline cap; *o,* opercular membrane; *p,* emergence-pore.

brane bulges outward, and then breaks suddenly as a column of cytoplasm erupts through the pore. The endoplasm streams into the protruded part of the body and ciliary activity, which now increases, tends to move the body through the pore in repeated thrusts. Emergence is completed, posterior end first, and the immature organism swims away. During the next hour the peristomial groove and membranelles are differentiated, and the adult form is gradually assumed (16).

The physiological aspects of excystment are probably no less compli-cated than the morphological changes. Excystment of *Colpoda steinii* involves several stages. In an initial phase, the length of which is in-fluenced by temperature but not by oxygen tension, essential organic substances are absorbed from the medium. The activities of three later periods, distinguishable by varying susceptibility of the cysts to X-rays, are influenced by oxygen tension but not by organic components of the medium (25). Weyer (241) suggested that excystment of *Gastrostyla steinii* is induced solely by organic substances elaborated by bacteria in the medium. Excystment of *Didinium nasutum,* in various media, de-pends upon the presence of living bacteria. Previously bacterized culture fluids are inactive after being heated or filtered to remove the bacteria (13). *Entamoeba histolytica* will excyst in the absence of living bacteria, but only at a low oxidation-reduction potential (216).

Barker and Taylor (5) apparently were the first to show that excyst-ment can be induced specifically by adding certain animal or plant ex-tracts to basal media. Some substance or group of substances was active for *Colpoda steinii* in dilutions as high as 1: 100,000,000. In attempts to isolate these factors, two concentrates from hay extract were found to be active separately, and also to show complementary effects in combinations (232). The activity of hay extracts was next related to salts of organic acids (acetic, citric, fumaric, malic, and tartaric), the effectiveness of which was quadrupled by a co-factor prepared from hay and replaceable by certain sugars in dilute solutions (105). Two crystalline substances, prepared from corn leaves, proved active at concentrations of 2.0-4.0 x 10^{-8} gm/ml in the presence of suitable co-factors. The co-factors, pre-pared from corn extract and essentially inactive themselves, could be replaced in part by a sugar solution and certain combinations of thiamine, nicotinic acid, nicotinamide, adenylic acid, citrate, and malate (206). A later report (226) indicates that potassium ions, not replaceable by so-dium ions, are essential to excystment of *C. steinii*. Several vitamins pro-duced no significant effect, although certain carbon sources (citrate, glutamate, malate, and propionate) and adenosine triphosphate showed some activity.

Requirements for excystment are less complex in certain other ciliates. Distilled water induces excystment of *Tillina magna* (11) and *Colpoda cucullus* (147), and dilution of the original medium is effective for *Euplotes taylori* (89).

SEXUAL PHENOMENA

Varieties of sexual phenomena

Although sexual processes are not necessarily a prerequisite to reproduction as they so commonly are in Metazoa, and although many

Protozoa undergo such activity at irregular intervals, the life-cycles of certain species cannot be completed without syngamy. For example, the mosquito phase of the life-cycle in *Plasmodium* must be initiated by gametogenesis and syngamy. The same thing is true for the formation of spores (protective cysts) in *Eimeria* and related genera.

Various kinds of sexual phenomena have been described in Protozoa. *Syngamy,* in which two gametes fuse completely to form a zygote, may involve gametes which are similar in appearance (*isogamy*), or are of two types (*anisogamy*). *Pedogamy* appears to be an unusual type of syngamy in which the two gametes are not more than one or two cell-generations removed from a single gametocyte. *Autogamy* involves the formation of two gametic nuclei, and their subsequent fusion to form a synkaryon (zygotic nucleus) within a single organism. *Parthenogenesis,* or the development of a gamete without syngamy, has been reported but its status in Protozoa is uncertain. Typical *conjugation* involves the exchange of haploid pronuclei (gametic nuclei) between two paired organisms, the formation of a synkaryon in each, and then nuclear reorganization.

Meiosis in relation to the life-cycle

A reduction of the chromosomes to the haploid number may occur in gametogenesis (*gametic meiosis*), in an early division of the zygote

TABLE 2. 1. TYPES OF MEIOSIS IN PROTOZOA

Gametic	Zygotic
Mastigophora	Mastigophora
Notila proteus (65a)	*Euconympha imla* (65b)
Paradinium poucheti (40)	*Glenodinium lubiniensiforme* (74)
	Oxymonas doroaxostylus (64)
Sarcodina	Phytomonadida (202, 213, 213a, 257)
Actinophrys sol (18)	*Saccinobaculus ambloaxostylus* (65)
Foraminiferida (185, 186, 187, 188)	*Trichonympha* (62)
Gregarinida	Gregarinida
Monocystis spp. (36, 184, 190)	*Actinocephalus parvus* (237)
Urospora lagidis (189)	*Apolocystis elongata* (204)
	Diplocystis schneideri (121)
Haemosporidia	*Gregarina blattarum* (225)
	Stylocephalus longicollis (103)
Plasmodium falciparum, *P. vivax*,	*Zygosoma globosum* (197)
probably gametic (168)	
Cnidosporidia	Coccidia
Ceratomyxa blennius (198)	*Adelea ovata* (102)
Guyenotia sphaerulosa (194)	*Adelina cryptoceri* (254)
Myxidium gasterostei (199)	*A. deronis* (112)
M. incurvatum (193)	*Aggregata eberthi* (76, 77)
Myxobolus guyenoti (192)	*Karyolysus zuluetei* (209)
Sphaeromyxa sabrazesi (193)	*Klossia helicina* (191)
Triactinomyxon ignotum, *T. legeri* (169)	*Ovivora thalassemae* (170)
Tetractinomyxon intermedium (118)	
Zschokkella rovignensis (92)	

(*zygotic meiosis*), or in one of the pregamic divisions in conjugation (*conjugant meiosis*). The type of meiosis varies in different Protozoa (Table 2. 1). Available data indicate that the Heliozoida, Foraminiferida, Cnidosporidia, and Ciliophora are diploid throughout most of the life-cycle. Among the Mycetozoida, some of the Plasmodiophorina are said to be predominantly haploid. Nuclear fusion, supposedly occurring at the end of the vegetative phase, may be followed immediately by meiosis (116, 236). In such cases, meiosis might be considered zygotic, although the uninucleate haploid products promptly encyst, becoming "spores." Some of the Eumycetozoina are believed to undergo syngamy just before development of the plasmodium begins, and presumably are diploid throughout the vegetative phase. In such cases, meiosis apparently precedes the formation of "spores," which give rise to the gametes after excystment. The Coccidia and a number of the Gregarinida are haploid organisms, although a few of the gregarines seem to be diploid. Among the flagellates, gametic meiosis has been reported in two species, and zygotic meiosis in a number of others.

Syngamy

In addition to many established cases of syngamy (Table 2. 1) in Protozoa, a number of descriptions need confirmation. The lack of critical evidence does not in itself justify dismissal of such reports. Syngamy in Zoomastigophorea was described occasionally in the older literature but most protozoologists remained unconvinced. The investigations of Cleveland (62, 64, 65, 65a, 65b) have supplied cytological evidence that was previously lacking. Certain descriptions of syngamy in trypanosomes (86, 87) do not approach the cytological standards set by Cleveland. However, the trypanosomes are not particularly favorable material for studying chromosomal behavior and the accumulation of adequate evidence will be correspondingly difficult.

The status of sexual phenomena in Phytomastigophorea other than the Phytomonadida remains uncertain. A fairly recent description (21) of syngamy in *Euglena* has not been confirmed, and the often cited case of "*Copromonas subtilis*" (75) is questionable. In "*C. subtilis*" the so-called reduction-divisions involved the extrusion of small granules ("polar bodies") from the nucleus, whereas meiosis, as demonstrated in many Protozoa, is a genuine nuclear division. Other reports of syngamy in Euglenida also offer inadequate evidence. Among the Dinoflagellida, syngamy has been reported in *Ceratium hirundinella* (85), *Coccodinium mesnili* (41) and *Noctiluca milaris* (104). Syngamy and formation of zygotes have been described in *Glenodinium lubiniensiforme,* a heterothallic species which apparently undergoes zygotic meiosis (74). These accounts receive additional support from a brief account of meiosis in *Paradinium poucheti* (40).

Among the Sarcodina, descriptions of syngamy have been published for several Testacida (203) and Amoebida. Careful studies of chromosomal behavior have not been reported. Some supposed instances of syngamy in Amoebida have appeared in peculiar life-cycles which seem to be eliminated by the use of pure-line cultures (135) and the occurrence of sexual phenomena in this order is still unproven.

Although isogamy has been reported in some Sarcodina, gregarines and Phytomonadida, certain of these examples involve gametes which are similar in size and form but are distinguishable by vital staining or other means. Mühl (183) noted that members of each pair, in syzygy of certain gregarines, show different staining reactions with neutral red. These observations have since been confirmed and extended (138). Such differences in staining reactions have been related to differences in oxidation-reduction potentials of the two gametocytes, which may differ also in the quantity and distribution of cytoplasmic inclusions (138, 139).

Physiological differentiation of similar gametes also has been reported in Chlamydomonadidae. Species of *Chlamydomonas* may be homothallic (synoecious) or heterothallic (heteroecious). In homothallic species a single culture will develop gametes of both "sexes." Every motile flagellate in such a culture is a potential gamete capable of uniting with a flagellate of the opposite sex in the same culture. As observed in the laboratory, syngamy occurs in heterothallic species only when two cultures containing gametes of opposite sexes are mixed under favorable conditions. Moewus (180, 181, 182) has attributed such differentiation to specific substances produced by *Chlamydomonas*.[2] The original assumptions were based upon certain effects produced by fluids from cultures. (1) A *motility factor* in culture fluid stimulates rapid formation of flagella upon addition to a culture containing palmella stages. (2) *Termones* determine the sex of the gametes derived from palmella stages in heterothallic races. Gynotermones cause production of female gametes; androtermones, the production of male gametes. (3) *Gamones,* concerned mainly with mutual attraction of the gametes, modify sexually inactive flagellates so that they can undergo syngamy. Androgamones from male cultures cause agglutination of female gametes under favorable conditions; gynogamones from female cultures have a comparable effect on male gametes.

Spectroscopic analysis of active substances, concentrated from large volumes of culture filtrates, indicated that they were carotenoid derivatives. In subsequent tests, the effects of culture filtrates were more or less duplicated by certain derivatives of protocrocin. Accordingly, it was assumed that protocrocin, synthesized by the flagellates, is broken down in the presence of light in a series of reactions, each controlled by a particular gene. The products include picrocrocin, which in turn yields

---

[2] The work of Moewus and his colleagues has been reviewed by Sonneborn (220, 221).

safranal and glucose, and crocin, which is decomposed into gentiobiose and *cis-* and *trans*-dimethylcrocetin esters. Crocin (or a related glycoside of crocetin) seems to be the motility factor, active for *C. eugametos* in dilutions as high as 4×10^{-15}. The action of gynotermones was duplicated

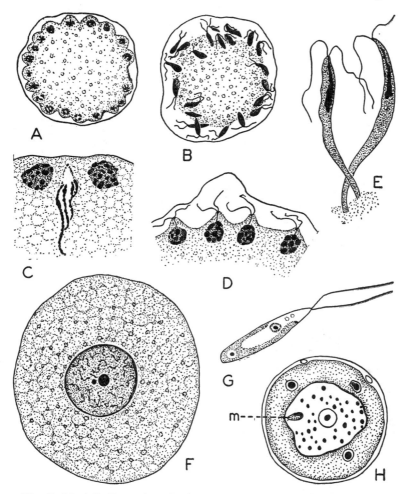

Fig. 2. 18. A-E. Formation of microgametes in *Ovivora thalassemae;* A, B, x1000; C-E, x2690 (after Mackinnon and Ray). F. Female gametocyte of *O. thalassemae;* x900 (after Mackinnon and Ray). G. Microgamete of *Volvox aureus;* x1900 (after Janet). H. Macrogamete of *Volvox globator* shortly after entrance of the microgamete (*m*); diagrammatic (after Janet).

by picrocrocin; that of androtermones, by safranal. The gamones were believed to be mixtures of the *cis-* and *trans*-crocetin esters and the intensity of "maleness" or "femaleness" exhibited by gametes was attributed to the *cis-/trans-* ratio in a given mixture.

The behavior of certain American stocks of *Chlamydomonas* differs to some extent from that reported by Moewus. Strains of *C. reinhardi, C. minutissima,* and *C. intermedia,* for example, become motile and develop sexual activity in darkness as well as in light (214, 215). However, light seems to be required for clumping and pairing of *C. moewusi* (161).

Prior to the work of Moewus, Schreiber (213) had described + and — strains in *Gonium* and *Pandorina,* mixtures of different clones producing zygotes in some combinations but not in others. Tests with lines started from division-products of zygotes indicated that differentiation occurred in the first or second postzygotic fission.

Aside from such biochemical differentiation of similar gametes, the development of minor structural differences apparently preceded the evolution of marked gametic dimorphism. Among the gregarines, for example, primitive anisogamy may involve differences in size of the nuclei, differences in shape, and slight differences in size of the gametes. This trend culminated in the development of small microgametes, resembling spermatozoa in their low cytoplasmic content, and relatively large macro-gametes containing appreciable amounts of stored food. Such extreme differentiation is characteristic of certain Sporozoa (Coccidia, Haemo-sporidia) and *Volvox* (Fig. 2. 18).

Pedogamy

In this process, attributed to *Actinophrys* and *Actinosphaerium,* a single organism encysts and then divides into two or more "gametocytes." After meiosis occurs, the resulting gametes undergo syngamy. In repeat-ing earlier observations on *Actinophrys sol,* Bělař (18) described a reduc-tional division in each gametocyte, followed by degeneration of one of the two haploid nuclei. Fusion of the uninucleate gametes was then fol-lowed by encystment of the zygote. The occurrence of syngamy in Helio-zoida seems unquestionable but the validity of "pedogamy" may be less certain. It has been suggested that, as in certain Foraminiferida (185), two associated "gametocytes" secrete a common cyst membrane. However, such an interpretation is not supported by Bělař's data.

Autogamy

The older literature (109) contains numerous descriptions of au-togamy. In a typical account, the nucleus of an encysted amoeba divides and each daughter nucleus undergoes meiosis. The haploid nuclei then fuse in pairs. Or, fusion may be preceded by degeneration of all except two haploid nuclei, so that only one synkaryon is produced. Believing that such cases are open to more plausible explanations, protozoologists generally had considered autogamy a highly dubious process.

The question was reopened by Diller's (70) report of autogamy in *Paramecium aurelia.* Autogamy, followed by meiosis of the synkaryon, was reported shortly afterward in *Phacus pyrum* (157), although this account has not been confirmed. Diller's observations on *P. aurelia* have been followed by descriptions of autogamy in *P. bursaria* (53) and *P. trichium* (72). Cases of autogamy in which ciliates form a conjugant pair but fail to exchange pronuclei have been referred to as *cytogamy* in *P. caudatum* (243). In addition, certain genetic data (Chapter IX) agree with the cytological evidence for autogamy in *Paramecium*. Up to a certain point, nuclear behavior in autogamy parallels that in conjugation. Maturation divisions are normal and pronuclei are formed. Instead of reciprocal transfer, however, fusion of two pronuclei occurs within the same ciliate. It is uncertain whether autogamy is a normal process in its own right or merely abortive conjugation. Chen (55) has found that, in conjugating trios of *P. bursaria,* a small area of cytoplasmic contact will initiate autogamy in the odd member which is left out of the normal pairing.

Conjugation

The onset of conjugation in mass cultures of certain ciliates is indicated by a tendency for the organisms to adhere on contact, sometimes forming clumps containing many individuals. The nature of this mating reaction is uncertain, although such a process suggests that the ciliates develop sticky surfaces. This initial reaction in *Paramecium bursaria* (126) seems to involve chance contact which leads to clumping. In general, such a preliminary reaction seems to be independent of later pairing and may be insignificant, or may not occur at all, in certain clones of *P. bursaria* and in various other ciliates. The stalked conjugant of *Vorticella microstoma* seems to exert some sort of attraction for motile microconjugants passing within a distance of a millimeter (88).

Clumping in *P. bursaria* is followed, after a half hour or so, by gradual breaking up of the aggregates. At the end of several hours, only pairs and single ciliates remain as a rule. Groups of three or four persist occasionally, but only two members of each group are properly paired for conjugation (55). Pairing seems to depend upon favorable conditions and may be influenced by temperature and intensity of light.

The positions assumed by the paired conjugants (Fig. 2. 19) and the extent of cytoplasmic fusion vary with the species. Contact commonly involves the peristomial areas of the two conjugants. However, fusion at the posterior ends occurs in *Ancistrocoma myae* (154), and fusion of oral to aboral surface in *Kidderia mytili* (141). Among the Peritrichida, the microconjugant becomes attached near the aboral end of the body in *Opisthonecta* (211) and *Vorticella,* but near the oral end in *Scyphidia* (233). In certain Apostomina, conjugants in lateral contact undergo repeated fission to produce chains and conjugation then proceeds between corresponding members of the chains (47). The extent of fusion in conjugation apparently is influenced by the nature of the body wall. In ciliates with a firm cuticle, fusion, or sometimes merely adhesion, may involve a limited area of the body such as the left margin of the peristome in *Euplotes* (234).

As a rule, the micronucleus undergoes three pregamic divisions (Fig.

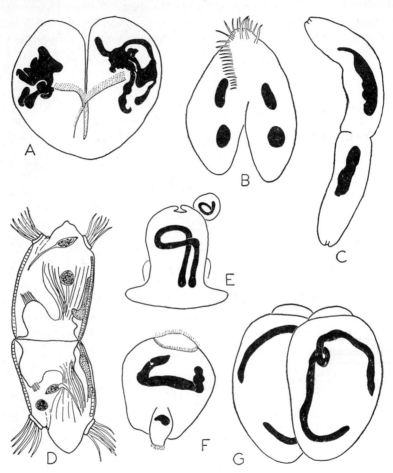

Fig. 2. 19. Pairing in conjugation. A. *Nyctotherus cordiformis;* x430 (after Wichterman). B. *Pleurotricha lanceolata;* x275 (after Manwell). C. *Ancistrocoma myae,* fusion of posterior ends; x2395 (after Kofoid and Bush). D. *Cycloposthium bipalmatum,* adoral organelles omitted; diagrammatic (after Dogiel). E. *Scyphidia ameirui;* diagrammatic (after Thompson, Kirkegaard and Jahn). F. *Vorticella microstoma;* x700 (after Finley). G. *Euplotes (patella) eurystomus;* x346 (after Turner).

41, A-D). More commonly the second, but sometimes the first (101) of these, is reductional. However, exceptions to the usual pattern have been noted. The third pregamic division is sometimes omitted in *Paramecium trichium* (72), and micronuclei may even be exchanged just after the first division (73). When several or many micronuclei are present, the number participating in the pregamic divisions varies with the species. Only one of the many micronuclei undergoes the first division in *Dileptus gigas* (235), but two or more may do so in other species. Comparable differences in nuclear behavior have also been reported for the second and third divisions. Furthermore, variation may occur within a single species. For instance, 2-5 (and possibly 1-5) products of the second pregamic division may complete the third division in *Paramecium aurelia* (70). In

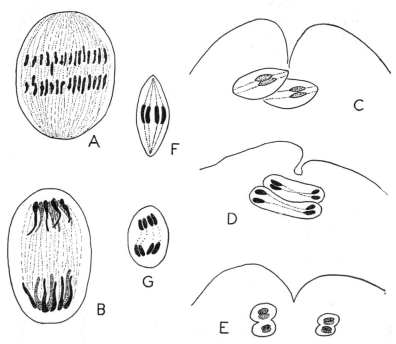

Fig. 2. 20. A. First pregamic division, early anaphase, *Kidderia mytili;* x1875 (after Kidder). B. Late anaphase, second pregamic (reductional) division, *K. mytili;* x2100 (after Kidder). C-G. *Chilodonella uncinatus;* nuclei just before the third pregamic division (C); late third division (D); fusion of pronuclei (E); first division of the synkaryon (F, G); diagrammatic (after MacDougall).

any case, the nuclei which do not undergo a particular division in the series soon degenerate.

In typical conjugation the third pregamic division produces two or more *pronuclei.* One of these, a migratory pronucleus, passes into the opposite conjugant and fuses with a stationary pronucleus to form a synkaryon (Fig. 2. 20, E). The actual exchange of pronuclei, which has been questioned occasionally, is supported by recent cytological and genetic data and has been observed in living specimens of *Paramecium bursaria* (244).

Fusion of the pronuclei is followed by a reorganization in which the synkaryon divides one or more times. Some or all of the resulting nuclei may differentiate into macronuclei and micronuclei. Only one nuclear division precedes differentiation in *Nyctotherus cordiformis* (242), several species of *Chilodonella* (167), and a few other ciliates (143). Differentiation occurs after the second division in *Paramecium aurelia* (70), *Euplotes eurystomus* (234), and about twenty other species (143). Differentiation follows the third division in *Bursaria truncatella* (205), *Opisthonecta henneguyi* (211), *Parachaenia myae* (154), *Vorticella microstoma* (88), *Paramecium bursaria* (57), *P. trichium* (72), *P. caudatum,* and a number of other species (143). Differentiation after a fourth postzygotic division has been reported in *Kidderia mytili* (143) and *Paramecium multimicronucleatum* (159). Behavior of the nuclei in ciliates showing two or more postzygotic divisions differs from species to species. All of the nuclei may

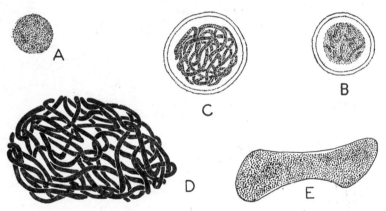

Fig. 2. 21. Development of a new macronucleus following conjugation in *Nyctotherus cordiformis;* A-D, x1150; E, x765 (after Wichterman).

remain functional, or some of them may degenerate. Variations may occur also in individual species, as in *P. caudatum* (71) and *P. trichium* (72).

Development of the micronucleus usually involves a decrease in size, whereas a differentiating macronucleus grows and often undergoes extensive changes in form as well as internal organization. The young macronucleus of *Nyctotherus cordiformis* (Fig. 2. 21) soon becomes finely granular and stains more intensely. Later, the granules give rise to threads during growth of the nucleus and then, as differentiation nears completion, the threads are replaced by the granules characteristic of the mature macronucleus. The early stages of differentiation are similar in *Euplotes eurystomus*. After the threads are replaced by granules the developing macronucleus elongates, extends posteriorly, and makes contact with a remnant of the old macronucleus. Fusion results in a complete macronucleus (234).

Depending upon the species, postconjugant fissions may or may not be necessary to restore the normal nuclear situation. Therefore, the final result of typical conjugation is the formation of 2-8 reorganized ciliates from a pair of exconjugants. In *Metopus sigmoides* (201), the pronucleus of one conjugant (the "donor") is accompanied by a large amount of cytoplasm during migration. After separation of the conjugants, the donor eventually dies. Conjugation in *Opisthonecta* (211), *Urceolaria* (67), and *Vorticella* (88) also produces only one functional exconjugant. One conjugant is a microconjugant, produced by budding, and the other is a macroconjugant. In *Vorticella microstoma* (Fig. 2. 22), a microconjugant

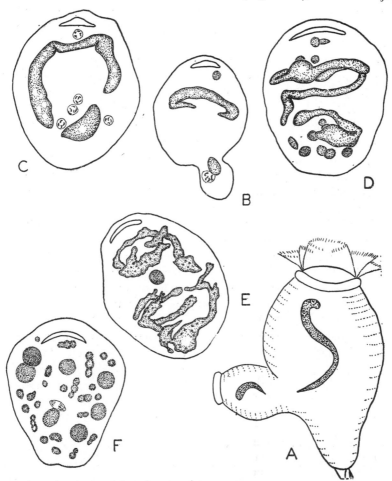

Fig. 2. 22. Conjugation in *Vorticella microstoma*. A. Formation of micro-conjugant by budding. B. Fusion of microconjugant and macroconjugant; micronucleus of former in the first pregamic division. C. Pregamic divisions of the microconjugant have produced four nuclei. D. Two spindle-shaped pronuclei are distinguishable. E. Synkaryon and remnants of degenerating macronuclei. F. One micronucleus in division; seven developing macronuclei. x1050 (after Finley).

becomes attached near the aboral end of a macroconjugant. Fusion then occurs and the endoplasm of the microconjugant gradually flows into the macroconjugant, leaving the pellicle behind. Pregamic divisions and formation of a synkaryon then occur much as in other ciliates.

Conjugation is often considered an orderly process which, once started, goes through a fixed series of nuclear activities. This is not always the case and variations are striking in several species. Furthermore, conjugation between particular strains of a species may be abnormal. For instance, in conjugation of certain Russian strains (variety IV) with several American strains of *P. bursaria,* the first pregamic division is usually not completed and all conjugants die before or after separation. The lethal effect is produced after cytoplasmic fusion, but before the exchange of pronuclei (57, 132). Mixtures of certain abnormal strains of *P. bursaria* with normal strains undergo typical pairing, but separation occurs after a few hours. The micronucleus enlarges slightly but does not start the first pregamic division (56). Polyploidy seems to have arisen frequently in *P. bursaria,* probably through the fusion of more than two pronuclei in conjugation (52). Chromosomal variations also are produced by matings between diploid and polypoid strains, as well as between micronucleate and amicronucleate races. In the latter case, each exconjugant contains a single haploid nucleus which undergoes three divisions and probably produces a new nuclear apparatus (53).

Nuclear behavior varies also in *Paramecium trichium* (72, 73). Micronuclei are sometimes transferred just after the second or even the first pregamic division. Occasionally only one of the migratory pronuclei actually migrates, so that conjugants sometimes contain one and three pronuclei. There also may be no exchange of pronuclei, with resulting autogamy in each conjugant. After the second pregamic division, three haploid nuclei sometimes degenerate and the fourth, without dividing again, migrates into the other conjugant. Each exconjugant thus contains a haploid nucleus which undergoes postzygotic divisions. Heteroploidy occurs frequently in *P. trichium* and has been noted also in *P. aurelia* and *P. caudatum* (71). The exchange of macronuclear fragments has been observed in *P. trichium* (72)—but not in other species of *Paramecium*—and also in several species of *Chilodonella* (166, 167).

Factors inducing conjugation

The possible causes of conjugation have been discussed for many years. Diverse ancestry was one of the prerequisites suggested by Maupas (176) and the more recent discovery of *mating types* has proven that apparently hereditary differentiation of potential conjugants does exist in certain species. However, conjugation has been observed within single clones, and also among the descendants of a single exconjugant after only a few fissions. Some of these matings between closely related conjugants

—as reported in *Paramecium* (4, 30, 94, 123), *Spathidium* (253), *Uroleptus* (34), and *Euplotes* (149)—have not yet been correlated with the basic concepts of mating types. Autogamy might bring about differentiation within clones of *Paramecium,* but such an explanation is of uncertain validity for other ciliates in which autogamy is unknown.

Sexual maturity as a requirement for conjugation also was suggested by Maupas, who believed that strains of ciliates are immature when first established in cultures and must complete a certain number of generations before they can conjugate. In contrast to this view, conjugation has occurred at intervals of only a few days in *Paramecium aurelia* (217) and *P. caudatum* (4). Jennings (130) has suggested that the duration of "immaturity" in *P. bursaria* varies inversely with the food supply.

Starvation is the third factor which Maupas considered essential. More recently, conjugation of *Paramecium multimicronucleatum* (93), *Spathidium spathula* (253) and *Uroleptus mobilis* (34), among others, has been found to follow exhaustion of the food supply. On the other hand, conjugation has occurred in *P. aurelia* (123) just as a rich food supply was beginning to decline, and also in *P. caudatum* (4), shortly before the populations reached the maximum. The nature of the significant changes which accompany or precede starvation is not yet known. However, the physiological condition of individual ciliates seems to be an important factor, since Boell and Woodruff (24) observed successful conjugation of *P. calkinsi* only between ciliates with subnormal respiratory rates. A mating reaction between a normal ciliate and one with a low respiratory rate sometimes occurred but conjugation was never completed. Ciliates with high respiratory rates failed to show any mating reactions.

Various environmental factors also have been correlated with conjugation. Darkness apparently favors and light suppresses conjugation in *P. aurelia* (219), although light shows no comparable effect on *P. caudatum* (97) or *Euplotes patella* (148). Temperature also influences conjugation, and different optima have been noted for different varieties of *P. aurelia* (223). In one variety the frequency of conjugation has ranged from zero at 24.5° to 68 per cent at 17.6° (219). Conjugation in *Conchophthirius lamellidens,* parasitic on the gills of a fresh-water mussel, has been observed most frequently on the day following the new moon (208). Dilution of the medium with weak solutions of aluminum and iron chlorides is said to have induced conjugation of *Paramecium caudatum* (258), but Ball (4) obtained negative results with several clones of *P. aurelia* and *P. caudatum.* One clone of *P. caudatum* did respond to such treatment but distilled water was just as effective as the salt solutions. Conjugation of *Glaucoma scintillans* has been stimulated by decreasing the salt content of the medium or increasing the concentration of glucose (43), and also by adding pyruvic acid to the medium (45).

The bacterial flora of cultures also may influence the incidence of conjugation. Chatton and Chatton (44) found that *Glaucoma scintillans* conjugated when fed on *Escherichia coli, Proteus vulgaris, Shigella dysenteriae,* or *Staphylococcus aureus,* but not on *Pseudomonas aeruginosa, P. fluorescens* or any one of several other bacterial species. Conjugation of *P. caudatum* was observed in cultures containing only a gram-negative bacillus, but not in other cultures containing at least three kinds of bacteria (46). Accordingly, it was suggested that so-called conjugating and non-conjugating races of ciliates may be determined by the bacterial flora. This conclusion was not supported by Sonneborn and Cohen (222) who induced conjugation invariably in a Johns Hopkins strain and never in Woodruff's strain of *P. aurelia* when both strains were maintained on the same bacterial types.

Mating types in ciliates[3]

Following the observations of Sonneborn (218, 219) on *Paramecium aurelia, P. calkinsi,* and *P. trichium* and those of Jennings (124, 125) on *P. bursaria,* mating types have been demonstrated also in *P. caudatum* (95, 96, 97, 98, 98a), *P. multimicronucleatum* (94, 95), and *Euplotes patella* (148, 149).

The situation in *P. bursaria* may be illustrated as follows. Two strains, A and B, have been established in pure lines. Conjugation does not occur among ciliates of strain A or among those of strain B, although mixtures of the two do show conjugation. Therefore strains A and B seem to belong to different sexes. A third strain, C, tested in the same way with strain A, behaves like strain B, and consequently might be expected to have the same sex. However, conjugation occurs also in mixtures with strains B and C. A fourth strain, D, is found to conjugate with any of the other three. At this point, conjugation in *P. bursaria* begins to strain basic concepts of bisexuality in animals, and confusion in terminology has been avoided by the substitution of "mating type" for "sex." Further investigation has demonstrated additional groups of mating types. A second group, or variety, contains eight mating types (E, F, G, H, J, K, L, M) which will not conjugate with the four types (A-D) in variety I. Mating types N, O, P, and Q have been assigned to a third variety, since they will not conjugate with types belonging to varieties I and II. Variety IV contains types R and S, which do not mate with members of varieties I, II or III. Variety V is represented by mating type T, composed of strains obtained from Russia, and will not mate with members of the other varieties (132). A more recently recognized variety VI, including strains from Czechoslovakia, England and Ireland, contains mating types U, V, W and X (55).

In *Paramecium aurelia* seven varieties have been recognized (224). Six of these contain two mating types, and one type has been assigned to

---

[3] This subject has been reviewed by Kimball (150).

variety 7. Normal conjugation occurs between the two mating types of each variety, but not between strains belonging to different varieties. Thirteen varieties, each with two mating types, have been identified in *P. caudatum* (98a).

At first, it was believed that conjugation never occurred between members of different varieties in *P. aurelia* and *P. bursaria*, but exceptions have been reported more recently. Type R of variety IV occasionally conjugates with four types of variety II in *P. bursaria*, although the participants die during or shortly after conjugation (132). Similar cases have been observed in *P. aurelia* (224). Mating type I will conjugate occasionally with type X, and mating type II with types V, IX, and XIII. Mating reactions in these intervarietal crosses of *P. aurelia* are always less intense than those within the same variety—only 1-40 per cent as many conjugant pairs in different combinations. In *P. caudatum* (98) intervarietal matings have occurred between variety 10 (type XX) and varieties 8 (type XV)

TABLE 2. 2. INDUCTION OF CONJUGATION IN *EUPLOTES PATELLA* BY FLUIDS FROM CULTURES

Culture fluids	Mating types of treated ciliates					
	I	II	III	IV	V	VI
I	−	+	+	+	+	+
II	+	+	+	+	+	+
III	+	−	−	+	−	+
IV	−	−	+	−	+	+
V	+	+	+	+	−	+
VI	−	+	+	+	−	−

and 9 (type XVII), and also between variety 2 (type IV) and variety 8 (type XV).

The situation in *Euplotes patella* (148, 149) resembles that in *P. bursaria*. Six mating types have been recognized in one variety, and there may be additional varieties. The mating reactions of *E. patella* are especially interesting because specific mating-type substances are released into the culture medium. Fluid from cultures of one mating type will induce conjugation among the ciliates of a single mating type in certain cases (Table 2. 2). The nature of this effect is uncertain. Kimball apparently favors the view that conjugation is induced in animals which are all of the same mating type, rather than that the mating type is changed in some of the treated ciliates and not in others. A particular mating-type substance induces conjugation only in a type which does not produce that substance, and these effects have been correlated with the inheritance of mating types in *E. patella* (Chapter IX).

Certain analogous effects of culture fluid have been observed in *Para-*

mecium bursaria (54). Fluid from cultures of several Russian strains (type T) induces conjugation within individual mating types of varieties II, III, IV and VI, although the effect is usually limited to a small percentage of the ciliates in a culture.

The recognition of mating types in certain ciliates has shown that conjugating pairs, in these species at least, are composed of physiologically different organisms. However, the relation of mating types to the concept of bisexuality in animals remains uncertain in *Paramecium bursaria* and *Euplotes patella*. On the other hand, *P. aurelia* and *P. caudatum* might possibly be interpreted as species composed of "bisexual" varieties which interbreed with difficulty or not at all.

Nuclear phenomena of uncertain significance

Endomixis (250) was originally described in *Paramecium aurelia* as a complete nuclear reorganization occurring in individual ciliates (251). Macronuclear disintegration and two micronuclear divisions occur without the usual third pregamic division of conjugation. Only two of these eight micronuclear derivatives persist, so that the first fission leaves each ciliate with one functional nucleus. Two nuclear divisions occur. Two of the products then differentiate into macronuclei, while the others divide to form four micronuclei. A second fission completes the reorganization.

The significance of endomixis in the life-cycle is still unknown. Woodruff believed that meiosis does not occur—although the second pregamic division is reductional in conjugation of *P. aurelia*—and he suggested that endomixis might be analogous to diploid parthenogenesis. The discovery of autogamy in *P. aurelia* (70) and the accumulation of genetic data have thrown doubt upon the occurrence of endomixis in *P. aurelia*.

Hemixis involves unusual behavior of the macronucleus only. The process has been observed in *Paramecium aurelia, P. caudatum*, and *P. multimicronucleatum* (70). In one type of hemixis there is a precocious division of the macronucleus and the normal nuclear situation is restored in the next fission. In another type, the macronucleus extrudes one or more densely staining masses and then behaves normally in subsequent fissions. A third type of hemixis combines the elimination of chromatic material with precocious division of the macronucleus.

THE PHYSIOLOGICAL LIFE-CYCLE

The description of conjugation by O. F. Müller in 1786 stimulated much interest in the sexual activities of Protozoa. For many years, it was believed that the "ovary" (macronucleus) of ciliates gave rise to "ova" (products of macronuclear disintegration), while the "testis" (micronucleus) produced "spermatozoa" (chromosomes). In conjugation, two hermaphroditic ciliates were supposed to exchange spermatozoa. In certain cases, small organisms (probably parasites) within the conjugants were interpreted as "embryos" developing within viviparous parents. These interpretations were overthrown by Bütschlii (26, 27) and Engelmann (80), who showed that the supposed ovary and testis are nuclei and suggested that products of the micronuclei might be exchanged in conjugation. The fusion of pronuclei in conjugation was reported a few years later (133).

Once conjugation was found to involve nuclear reorganization, and occasionally the reorganization of locomotor structures, the process was interpreted as a sort of rejuvenation. Engelmann (80) suggested that it was unnecessary to suspect any other effect. Bütschli (27) supported a physiological interpretation—ciliates become senescent during continued fission and as a result reproduce less and less frequently until conjugation rejuvenates them and restores the normal reproductive rate.

This question was first considered experimentally by Maupas, whose isolation-culture technique (175, 176) involved tracing single ciliates from one generation to the next in order to detect possible senescence. Since all his strains died eventually, Maupas suggested that ciliates, like higher animals, pass through a cycle of youth, maturity, and old age, ending in death. The characteristic feature of maturity was assumed to be an ability to conjugate normally. Conjugation was believed to rejuvenate ciliates only during the phase of maturity, and therefore was a prophylactic rather than a therapeutic measure.

Bütschli (28) maintained that conjugation increased fission-rate after a gradual decline. Hertwig's (113) observations on split-pairs—conjugants separated at the beginning of conjugation and used for starting parallel clones—indicated that fission-rates were usually higher in non-conjugant than in exconjugant lines. As a result, he concluded that conjugation merely regulates metabolism so as to prevent physiological exhaustion. Later investigations were designed to test the theories of Bütschli, Hertwig, and Maupas.

Joukowsky (137), after studying exconjugant and non-conjugant lines of *Paramecium caudatum* and *Pleurotricha lanceolata,* concluded that the degenerative changes described by Maupas were the result of unsatisfactory conditions in cultures. There were no characteristic differences between exconjugant and non-conjugant lines, neither type showed a decreasing fission-rate, and there appeared to be no physiological cycle.

The next important papers were those of Calkins (30, 31, 38) who started isolation-cultures of *Paramecium caudatum* on February 1, 1901. Four lines were started from each of two ciliates and transfers were made daily or every other day. After a time, recurrent "depressions" developed. The early depressions, believed to represent the senescence reported by Maupas, were cured by measures other than conjugation. The depression of May, 1901, apparently was cured by jolting during a train ride to

Woods Hole; that of August, 1901, by extract of raw beef; that of December, 1901, by beef extract; that of March, 1902, by a slight rise in temperature; that of June, 1902, by brain extract. Since the lines were rejuvenated by artificial means, the results were considered analogous to artificial parthenogenesis (31).

In these early papers, Calkins suggested that ciliates have the "potential of endless existence" without conjugation. Later on, however, the depressions became more severe. The "B" lines became extinct after 16 months, the "A" lines in December, 1902. Attempts to rejuvenate the ciliates—treatments with beef extract, pancreas, brain, mutton broth, lecithin, pineapple extract, apple juice, several acids and salts, dried *Paramecium,* the electric current and nitroglycerin—were all unsuccessful. As a result, Calkins (33) was convinced that the final depressions arose from "germinal exhaustion" which could not be prevented by external stimulation. Therefore, strains of *P. caudatum* must pass through a cycle of youth, maturity, and old age unless vitality is renewed by conjugation. A gradual decrease in fission-rate accompanied senescence and the rejuvenation by conjugation was believed to include an increase in fission-rate.

The observations of Enriques soon questioned the inevitability of senescence. The first important demonstration (81) was that excessive bacterial growth may lead to effects simulating senescence. Later results (82, 83) included the maintenance of *Glaucoma scintillans* without conjugation for almost 700 generations. The ciliates remained healthy so long as fresh medium was supplied; the use of old medium induced depressions. At this point, Enriques suggested that exhaustion of the investigator's patience is a more important factor than senescence of the ciliates in such investigations.

On May 1, 1907, Woodruff started the line of *Paramecium aurelia* which was to deal a more serious blow to the physiological life-cycle. In May, 1908, the strain had passed 490 generations (246), and at the end of four years (247), had survived for 2,121 generations without conjugation. By this time, the evidence indicated that *P. aurelia* might reproduce indefinitely without conjugation, or else that the "cycle" must be longer than that of any ciliate investigated previously.

The conclusion suggested by Woodruff's strain of *P. aurelia* did not remain unchallenged. Calkins and Gregory (37) maintained that some strains of *Paramecium* are conjugating races while others are non-conjugating, and it was argued that Woodruff's strain was a non-conjugating race which should not be compared with the conjugating strain of Calkins. Woodruff (248) met this objection by reporting conjugation in mass-cultures started from his strain at the end of 4,102 generations. The completion of 25 years without conjugation was reported in 1932 (249).

Evidence against the physiological cycle gradually accumulated from other sources. *Glaucoma scintillans* showed no senescence after 2,700 generations (84). Lines of *Paramecium caudatum* lived for ten years without conjugation or decrease in vitality (178, 179). The colonial flagellate, *Eudorina elegans,* was maintained for eight years without syngamy or indications of senescence (110, 111). *Actinophrys sol* passed more than 1,200 generations without syngamy (19). *Spathidium spathula,* previously credited with a cycle, survived for a thousand generations without conjugation or endomixis (252). *Didinium nasutum* was maintained by Beers without conjugation or a decrease in vitality so long as the food supply was adequate (8). However, depressions were readily induced by an inadequate diet (9).

In contrast to various other ciliates, *Uroleptus mobilis* failed to follow the prevailing pattern. Instead, a physiological cycle was reported, with the strains living an average of 350 generations (34, 35). Attempts to prolong the cycle by varying the environmental conditions were unsuccessful (2), and this species remains one in which the cycle has not been eliminated. More recently, Jennings (127, 131) concluded that his experience with *Paramecium bursaria* also supports the concept of a physiological cycle, although some clones were maintained for eight years before their health began to decline.

In spite of the fact that strains of various ciliates could be grown in the laboratory for long periods without conjugation—and perhaps they could be maintained indefinitely—one question remained unanswered. Does conjugation really have any stimulatory or rejuvenating effect on ciliates?

The early investigations had produced little information. A few observations by Hertwig (114) on *Dileptus gigas* and some inconclusive data cited by Calkins (33) represented the available evidence. Some years later, the first convincing experiments were reported by Calkins (34). Several strains of *Uroleptus mobilis,* which were entering depressions, showed a higher fission-rate and greater longevity after conjugation than the nonconjugant parental stocks. Comparable effects of conjugation were reported subsequently in *Spathidium spathula* (253) and *Paramecium bursaria* (131).

At present it seems clear that conjugation, whether or not it is essential, can produce a physiological stimulation in at least certain strains. However, it is equally evident that conjugation is no universal remedy for senescent ciliates. In fact, the odds are slightly against survival after conjugation in *Paramecium bursaria*. Records kept for 20,478 exconjugants show that under conditions in which all non-conjugant lines remained vigorous, 29.7 per cent of the conjugating ciliates died before the first post-conjugant fission, and only 47.3 per cent survived for more than four fissions (127). Conjugation between inbred lines is even more dangerous, and mortality often reaches 90-100 per cent in such cases in *P. bursaria*

(129). Conjugation between old stocks which are not closely related also may be almost 100 per cent lethal, although unrelated young stocks may show little or no mortality after conjugation (148).

LITERATURE CITED

1. Arndt, A. 1924. *Arch. f. Protistenk.* **49:** 1.
2. Austin, M. L. 1927. *J. Exp. Zool.* **49:** 149.
3. Baker, W. B. 1926. *Biol. Bull.* **51:** 321.
4. Ball, G. H. 1925. *Univ. Calif. Publ. Zool.* **26:** 385.
5. Barker, H. A. and C. V. Taylor 1933. *Physiol. Zool.* **6:** 127.
6. Beers, C. D. 1926. *J. Morph.* **42:** 1.
7. ——— 1927. *J. Morph.* **44:** 21.
8. ——— 1929. *Amer. Nat.* **63:** 125.
9. ——— 1933. *Arch. f. Protistenk.* **79:** 101.
10. ——— 1937. *Amer. Nat.* **71:** 521.
11. ——— 1945. *Physiol. Zool.* **18:** 80.
12. ——— 1945. *J. Elisha Mitchell Sci. Soc.* **61:** 264.
13. ——— 1946. *J. Exp. Zool.* **103:** 201.
14. ——— 1946. *J. Morph.* **78:** 181.
15. ——— 1947. *J. Elisha Mitchell Sci. Soc.* **63:** 141.
16. ——— 1948. *Biol. Bull.* **94:** 86.
17. Bělař, K. 1921. *Arch. f. Protistenk.* **43:** 287.
18. ——— 1922. *Arch. f. Protistenk.* **46:** 1.
19. ——— 1924. *Arch. f. Protistenk.* **48:** 371.
20. ——— 1926. *Ergebn. Fortschr. Zool.* **6:** 235.
21. Biecheler, B. 1937. *C. R. Soc. Biol.* **124:** 1264.
22. Bishop, A. 1925. *Quart. J. Micr. Sci.* **69:** 661.
23. Bodine, J. H. 1923. *J. Exp. Zool.* **37:** 115.
24. Boell, E. J. and L. L. Woodruff 1941. *J. Exp. Zool.* **87:** 385.
25. Brown, M. G. 1939. *Biol. Bull.* **77:** 382.
26. Bütschli, O. 1875. *Ztschr. wiss. Zool.* **25:** 426.
27. ——— 1876. *Abh. Senckenb. Naturf. Ges.* **10:** 213.
28. ——— 1889. "Protozoa" in *Bronn's Klass. Ordn. d. Tierreichs,* Abt. III (Leipzig: Winter).
29. Calkins, G. N. 1899. *J. Morph.* **15:** 711.
30. ——— 1902. *Arch. Entwickl. Org.* **15:** 139.
31. ——— 1902. *Biol. Bull.* **3:** 192.
32. ——— 1904. *J. Exp. Zool.* **1:** 423.
33. ——— 1906. *Biol. Bull.* **11:** 229.
34. ——— 1919. *J. Exp. Zool.* **29:** 121.
35. ——— 1920. *J. Exp. Zool.* **31:** 287.
36. ——— and R. C. Bowling 1926. *Biol. Bull.* **51:** 385.
37. ——— and L. H. Gregory 1913. *J. Exp. Zool.* **15:** 467.
38. ——— and C. C. Lieb 1902. *Arch. f. Protistenk.* **1:** 355.
39. Chalkley, H. W. and G. E. Daniel 1933. *Physiol. Zool.* **6:** 592.
40. Chatton, E. 1927. *C. R. Ac. Sci.* **185:** 553.
41. ——— and B. Biecheler 1936. *C. R. Ac. Sci.* **203:** 573.
42. ——— and S. Brachon 1936. *C. R. Ac. Sci.* **202:** 713.
43. ——— and Mme. Chatton 1925. *C. R. Ac. Sci.* **180:** 1137.
44. ——— and ——— 1925. *C. R. Soc. Biol.* **93:** 675.
45. ——— and ——— 1929. *C. R. Ac. Sci.* **188:** 1315.
46. ——— and ——— 1931. *C. R. Ac. Sci.* **193:** 206.
47. ——— and A. Lwoff 1935. *Arch. Zool. Exp. Gén.* **77:** 1.
48. ———, ——— and M. Lwoff 1931. *C. R. Soc. Biol.* **107:** 536.
49. ———, ———, ——— and J. L. Monod 1931. *Bull. Soc. Zool. Fr.* **56:** 367.
50. ———, ———, ——— and ——— 1931. *C. R. Soc. Biol.* **108:** 540.
50a. ———, M. Lwoff, A. Lwoff and L. Tellier 1929. *C. R. Soc. Biol.* **100:** 1191.

51. —— and S. Villeneuve 1937. *C. R. Ac. Sci.* **204**: 538.
52. Chen, T.-T. 1940. *J. Hered.* **31**: 175.
53. —— 1940. *J. Hered.* **31**: 185.
54. —— 1945. *Proc. Nat. Ac. Sci.* **31**: 404.
55. —— 1946. *J. Morph.* **78**: 353.
56. —— 1946. *Biol. Bull.* **91**: 112.
57. —— 1946. *J. Morph.* **79**: 125.
58. —— 1948. *J. Morph.* **83**: 281.
59. Cleveland, L. R. 1935. *Science* **81**: 598.
60. —— 1935. *Biol. Bull.* **69**: 46.
61. —— 1938. *Biol. Bull.* **74**: 1.
62. —— 1949. *J. Morph.* **85**: 197.
63. —— 1949. *Trans. Amer. Philos. Soc.* (N.S.) **39**: 1.
64. —— 1950. *J. Morph.* **86**: 185.
65. —— 1950. *J. Morph.* **86**: 215.
65a. —— 1950. *J. Morph.* **87**: 317.
65b. —— 1950. *J. Morph.* **87**: 349.
66. ——, S. R. Hall, E. P. Sanders and J. Collier 1934. *Mem. Amer. Acad. Arts & Sci.* **17**: 185.
67. Colwin, L. H. 1944. *J. Morph.* **75**: 203.
68. Darby, H. 1929. *Arch. f. Protistenk.* **65**: 1.
69. Dawson, J. A. and D. C. Hewitt 1931. *Amer. Nat.* **65**: 181.
70. Diller, W. F. 1936. *J. Morph.* **59**: 11.
71. —— 1940. *J. Morph.* **66**: 605.
72. —— 1948. *J. Morph.* **82**: 1.
73. —— 1949. *Biol. Bull.* **97**: 331.
74. Diwald, K. 1938. *Flora* **32**: 174.
75. Dobell, C. 1908. *Quart. J. Micr. Sci.* **52**: 75.
76. —— 1925. *Parasitol.* **17**: 1.
77. —— and A. P. Jameson 1915. *Proc. Roy. Soc. London, B,* **89**: 83.
78. Dogiel, V. 1925. *Arch. f. Protistenk.* **50**: 283.
79. Ellis, J. M. 1937. *Univ. Calif. Publ. Zool.* **41**: 343.
80. Engelmann, T. W. 1876. *Morph. Jahrb.* **1**: 573.
81. Enriques, P. 1903. *Monit. Zool. Ital.* **14**: 349.
82. —— 1905. *Rend. Accad. Lincei* (5) **14**: 351.
83. —— 1905. *Rend. Accad. Lincei* (5) **14**: 390.
84. —— 1916. *Rend. Ses. R. Acad. Sci. Inst. Bologna.* Ser. 7, v. 3, 12 pp.
85. Entz, G., Jr. 1924. *Biol. Hungar.* 1, fasc. 3, 5 pp.
86. Fairbarn, H. and A. T. Culwick 1946. *Ann. Trop. Med. Parasitol.* **40**: 421.
87. Fiennes, R. N. T.-W. 1945. *Nature* **156**: 390.
88. Finley, H. E. 1943. *Trans. Amer. Micr. Soc.* **62**: 97.
89. Garnjobst, L. 1928. *Physiol. Zool.* **1**: 561.
90. —— 1937. *Arch. f. Protistenk.* **89**: 317.
91. —— 1947. *Physiol. Zool.* **20**: 5.
92. Georgevitch, J. 1936. *Arch. f. Protistenk.* **87**: 151.
93. Giese, A. C. 1935. *Physiol. Zool.* **8**: 116.
94. —— 1939. *Amer. Nat.* **73**: 432.
95. —— and M. A. Arkoosh 1939. *Physiol. Zool.* **12**: 70.
96. Gilman, L. C. 1939. *Amer. Nat.* **73**: 445.
97. —— 1941. *Biol. Bull.* **80**: 384.
98. —— 1949. *Biol. Bull.* **97**: 239.
98a. —— 1950. *Biol. Bull.* **99**: 348.
99. Gimesi, N. 1930. *Arch. f. Protistenk.* **27**: 190.
100. Goodey, T. 1913. *Proc. Roy. Soc. London, B,* **86**: 427.
101. Gregory, L. H. 1923. *J. Morph.* **37**: 555.
102. Greiner, J. 1921. *Zool. Jahrb., Anat.,* **42**: 327.
103. Grell, K. G. 1940. *Arch. f. Protistenk.* **94**: 161.
104. Gross, F. 1934. *Arch. f. Protistenk.* **83**: 178.
105. Haagen-Smit, A. J. and K. V. Thimann 1938. *J. Cell. Comp. Physiol.* **11**: 389.

106. Hall, R. P. 1925. *Univ. Calif. Publ. Zool.* **20**: 29.
107. Hammond, D. M. 1937. *Quart. J. Micr. Sci.* **79**: 507.
108. ———, G. W. Bowman, L. R. Davis and B. T. Simms 1946. *J. Parasit.* **32**: 409.
109. Hartmann, M. 1909. *Arch. f. Protistenk.* **14**: 264.
110. ——— 1921. *Arch. f. Protistenk.* **43**: 223.
111. ——— 1924. *Arch. f. Protistenk.* **49**: 375.
112. Hauschka, T. S. 1943. *J. Morph.* **73**: 529.
113. Hertwig, R. 1889. *Abhandl. II Cl. königl. bayr. Akad. Wiss.* **17**: 151.
114. ——— 1905. *Sitzungsber. Ges. Morph. Physiol. München* **20**: 1.
115. Hollande, A. 1942. *Arch. Zool. Exp. Gén.* **83**: 1.
116. Horne, A. S. 1930. *Ann. Bot.* **44**: 199.
117. Hovasse, R. 1937. *Bull. Biol. Fr. Belg.* **71**: 220.
118. Ikeda, I. 1912. *Arch. f. Protistenk.* **26**: 241.
119. Ivanič, M. 1926. *Arch. f. Protistenk.* **56**: 63.
119a. ——— 1931. *Zool. Anz.* **93**: 81.
120. ——— 1934. *Arch. f. Protistenk.* **82**: 363.
121. Jameson, A. P. 1920. *Quart. J. Micr. Sci.* **64**: 207.
122. Janet, C. 1923. *Le* Volvox. *Troisième Mémoire. Ontogénèse de la blastéa volvocéene.* I. Part. (Macon: Protat Frères).
123. Jennings, H. S. 1910. *J. Exp. Zool.* **9**: 279.
124. ——— 1938. *Proc. Nat. Acad. Sci.* **24**: 112.
125. ——— 1938. *Proc. Nat. Acad. Sci.* **24**: 117.
126. ——— 1939. *Genetics* **24**: 202.
127. ——— 1944. *Biol. Bull.* **86**: 131.
128. ——— 1944. *J. Exp. Zool.* **96**: 17.
129. ——— 1944. *J. Exp. Zool.* **96**: 243.
130. ——— 1945. *Sociometry* **8**: 9.
131. ——— 1945. *J. Exp. Zool.* **99**: 15.
132. ——— and P. Opitz 1944. *Genetics* **29**: 576.
133. Jickeli, C. F. 1884. *Zool. Anz.* **7**: 468; 491.
134. Johnson, D. F. 1934. *Arch. f. Protistenk.* **83**: 241.
135. Johnson, P. L. 1930. *Arch. f. Protistenk.* **71**: 463.
136. Johnson, W. H. and F. R. Evans 1941. *Trans. Amer. Micr. Soc.* **60**: 7.
137. Joukowsky, D. 1898. *Verhandl. Nat.-Med. Ver. Heidelb.* **6**: 17.
138. Joyet-Lavergne, P. 1926. *C. R. Ac. Sci.* **182**: 1295.
139. ——— 1928. *Protoplasma* **3**: 357.
140. Kater, J. McA. 1929. *Univ. Calif. Publ. Zool.* **33**: 125.
141. Kidder, G. W. 1933. *Arch. f. Protistenk.* **79**: 25.
142. ——— 1933. *Biol. Bull.* **64**: 1.
143. ——— 1933. *Arch. f. Protistenk.* **81**: 1.
144. ——— 1934. *Biol. Bull.* **66**: 286.
145. ——— and C. L. Claff 1938. *Biol. Bull.* **74**: 178.
146. ——— and W. F. Diller 1934. *Biol. Bull.* **67**: 201.
147. ——— and C. A. Stuart 1939. *Physiol. Zool.* **12**: 329.
148. Kimball, R. F. 1939. *Amer. Nat.* **73**: 451.
149. ——— 1942. *Genetics* **27**: 269.
150. ——— 1943. *Quart. Rev. Biol.* **18**: 30.
151. Kirby, H. 1939. *Proc. Calif. Acad. Sci.* **22**: 207.
152. ——— 1944. *J. Morph.* **75**: 361.
153. ——— 1946. *Univ. Calif. Publ. Zool.* **53**: 163.
154. Kofoid, C. A. and M. Bush 1936. *Bull. Mus. Hist. Nat. Belg.* **12**: 1.
155. ———, E. McNeil and M. J. Kopac 1931. *Proc. Soc. Exp. Biol. Med.* **29**: 100.
156. ——— and O. Swezy 1915. *Proc. Amer. Acad. Arts & Sci.* **51**: 289.
157. Krichenbauer, H. 1937. *Arch. f. Protistenk.* **90**: 88.
158. Kudo, R. 1949. *J. Morph.* **85**: 163.
159. Landis, E. M. 1925. *J. Morph.* **40**: 111.
160. Lewert, R. M. 1950. *Amer. J. Hyg.* **51**: 155.
161. Lewin, R. 1949. *Biol. Bull.* **97**: 243.

162. Liesche, W. 1938. *Arch. f. Protistenk.* **91**: 243.
163. Loefer, J. B. 1931. *Arch. f. Protistenk.* **74**: 449.
164. Lucas, M. S. 1932. *Arch. f. Protistenk.* **77**: 407.
165. MacDougall, M. S. 1925. *Quart. J. Micr. Sci.* **69**: 361.
166. ——— 1935. *Arch. f. Protistenk.* **84**: 199.
167. ——— 1936. *Bull. Biol. Fr. Belg.* **70**: 308.
168. ——— 1947. *J. Nat. Malar. Soc.* **6**: 91.
169. Mackinnon, D. L. and D. I. Adam 1924. *Quart. J. Micr. Sci.* **68**: 187.
170. ——— and H. N. Ray 1937. *Parasitol.* **29**: 457.
171. MacLennan, R. F. 1935. *Arch. f. Protistenk.* **86**: 191.
172. ——— 1937. *J. Exp. Zool.* **76**: 423.
173. Manwell, R. D. 1928. *Biol. Bull.* **54**: 417.
174. Mast, S. O. 1917. *J. Exp. Zool.* **23**: 335.
175. Maupas, E. 1888. *Arch. Zool. Exp. Gén.* **6**: 165.
176. ——— 1889. *Arch. Zool. Exp. Gén.* **7**: 149.
177. Meglitsch, P. A. 1940. *Ill. Biol. Monogr.* **17**: 1.
178. Metalnikow, S. 1919. *Ann. Inst. Pasteur* **33**: 817.
179. ——— 1922. *C. R. Ac. Sci.* **175**: 776.
180. Moewus, F. 1938. *Jahrb. wiss. Bot.* **86**: 753.
181. ——— 1939. *Naturwiss.* **27**: 97.
182. ——— 1940. *Biol. Zentralbl.* **60**: 143.
183. Mühl, D. 1921. *Arch. f. Protistenk.* **43**: 406.
184. Mulsow, K. 1911. *Arch. f. Protistenk.* **22**: 20.
185. Myers, E. H. 1934. *Science* **79**: 436.
186. ——— 1936. *J. Roy. Micr. Soc.* **56**: 120.
187. ——— 1938. *Proc. Nat. Acad. Sci.* **24**: 10.
188. ——— 1940. *J. Mar. Biol. Assoc.* **24**: 201.
189. Naville, A. 1927. *Parasitol.* **19**: 100.
190. ——— 1927. *Ztschr. Zellforsch.* **6**: 257.
191. ——— 1927. *Arch. f. Protistenk.* **57**: 427.
192. ——— 1928. *Ztschf. Zellforsch.* **7**: 228.
193. ——— 1930. *Arch. f. Protistenk.* **69**: 327.
194. ——— 1930. *Quart. J. Micr. Sci.* **73**: 547.
195. Nigrelli, R. F. 1936. *Zoologica* **21**: 129.
196. Noble, A. E. 1932. *Univ. Calif. Publ. Zool.* **37**: 477.
197. Noble, E. R. 1938. *Univ. Calif. Publ. Zool.* **43**: 41.
198. ——— 1941. *J. Morph.* **69**: 455.
199. ——— 1943. *J. Morph.* **73**: 281.
200. ——— 1947. *Univ. Calif. Publ. Zool.* **53**: 263.
201. Noland, L. E. 1927. *J. Morph.* **44**: 341.
202. Pascher, A. 1916. *Ber. deutsch. bot. Gesellsch.* **34**: 228.
203. Pateff, P. 1926. *Arch. f. Protistenk.* **55**: 516.
204. Phillips, N. E. and D. L. Mackinnon 1946. *Parasitol.* **37**: 65.
205. Poljansky, G. 1934. *Arch. f. Protistenk.* **81**: 420.
206. Prater, A. N. and A. J. Haagen-Smit 1940. *J. Cell. Comp. Physiol.* **15**: 95.
207. Rafalko, J. S. 1947. *J. Morph.* **81**: 1.
208. Ray, H. and M. Chakravarty 1934. *Nature* **134**: 663.
209. Reichenow, E. 1921. *Arch. f. Protistenk.* **42**: 179.
210. Reynolds, B. D. 1934. *Arch. f. Protistenk.* **81**: 399.
211. Rosenberg, L. E. 1940. *Proc. Amer. Philos. Soc.* **82**: 437.
212. Schmähl, O. 1926. *Arch. f. Protistenk.* **54**: 359.
213. Schreiber, E. 1925. *Ztschr. f. Bot.* **17**: 337.
213a. Schulze, B. 1927. *Arch. f. Protistenk.* **58**: 508.
214. Smith, G. M. 1946. *Amer. J. Bot.* **33**: 625.
215. ——— 1948. *Science* **108**: 680.
216. Snyder, T. L. and H. E. Meleney 1941. *Amer. J. Trop. Med.* **21**: 63,
217. Sonneborn, T. M. 1936. *Genetics* **21**: 503.
218. ——— 1937. *Proc. Nat. Acad. Sci.* **23**: 378,

219. —— 1938. *Proc. Amer. Philos. Soc.* **79**: 411.
220. —— 1941. "Sexuality in Unicellular Organisms" in *Protozoa in Biological Research* (New York: Columbia Univ. Press).
221. —— 1942. *Cold Spr. Harb. Symp. Quant. Biol.* **10**: 111.
222. —— and B. M. Cohen 1936. *Genetics* **21**: 515.
223. —— and R. Dippell 1943. *Biol. Bull.* **85**: 36.
224. —— and —— 1946. *Physiol. Zool.* **19**: 1.
225. Sprague, V. 1941. *Ill. Biol. Monogr.* **18**: 1.
226. Strickland, A. G. R. and A. J. Haagen-Smit 1947. *J. Cell. Comp. Physiol.* **30**: 381.
227. Summers, F. M. 1935. *Arch. f. Protistenk.* **85**: 173.
228. Taft, C. E. 1940. *Trans. Amer. Micr. Soc.* **59**: 1.
229. Taylor, C. V. 1928. *Physiol. Zool.* **1**: 1.
230. —— and A. G. R. Strickland 1935. *Physiol. Zool.* **9**: 15.
231. —— and —— 1939. *Physiol. Zool.* **12**: 219.
232. Thimann, K. V. and H. A. Barker 1934. *J. Exp. Zool.* **69**: 37.
233. Thompson, S., D. Kirkegaard and T. L. Jahn 1947. *Trans. Amer. Micr. Soc.* **66**: 315.
234. Turner, J. P. 1930. *Univ. Calif. Publ. Zool.* **33**: 193.
235. Visscher, J. P. 1927. *J. Morph.* **44**: 383.
236. Webb, P. C. R. 1935. *Ann. Bot.* **49**: 41.
237. Wechsenfelder, R. 1938. *Arch. f. Protistenk.* **91**: 1.
238. Weisz, P. B. 1948. *J. Morph.* **84**: 335.
239. —— 1949. *J. Morph.* **85**: 503.
240. Wenrich, D. H. 1941. *J. Parasit.* **27**: 1.
241. Weyer, G. 1930. *Arch. f. Protistenk.* **71**: 139.
242. Wichterman, R. 1937. *J. Morph.* **60**: 563.
243. —— 1940. *J. Morph.* **66**: 423.
244. —— 1946. *Science* **104**: 505.
245. Wight, T. and V. Wight 1932. *Amer. J. Trop. Med.* **12**: 381.
246. Woodruff, L. L. 1908. *Amer. Nat.* **42**: 520.
247. —— 1911. *Arch. f. Protistenk.* **21**: 263.
248. —— 1914. *J. Exp. Zool.* **16**: 237.
249. —— 1932. *Trans. Amer. Micr. Soc.* **51**: 196.
250. —— 1941. "Endomixis" in *Protozoa in Biological Research* (New York: Columbia Univ. Press).
251. —— and R. Erdmann 1914. *J. Exp. Zool.* **17**: 425.
252. —— and E. L. Moore 1924. *Proc. Nat. Acad. Sci.* **10**: 183.
253. —— and H. Spencer 1924. *J. Exp. Zool.* **39**: 133.
254. Yarwood, E. A. 1937. *Parasitol.* **29**: 370.
255. Young, D. 1939. *J. Morph.* **64**: 297.
256. Young, D. B. 1922. *J. Exp. Zool.* **36**: 353.
257. Zimmermann, W. 1921. *Jahrb. wiss. Bot.* **60**: 256.
258. Zweibaum, J. 1912. *Ach. f. Protistenk.* **26**: 275.

III

The Classification of Protozoa

THE CLASSIFICATION of Protozoa serves various useful purposes in addition to furnishing a system for filing species in appropriate catalogs. A sound taxonomy favors progress in comparative morphology and physiology since it facilitates correlation of the information bearing on related organisms. The projection of experimental and observational data on a taxonomic background also is helpful in planning investigations to extend or limit the application of preliminary findings. In fact, without some knowledge of taxonomic relationships, the choice of material for certain types of research would be analogous to "wildcat" drilling for oil. Although a certain amount of "wildcatting" is always needed, the orderly development of a field often depends extensively upon systematically directed efforts. As more is learned about the interrelationships of Protozoa, the benefits derived from the field of taxonomy will become increasingly important.

A major aim of taxonomy[1] is the assignment of organisms to species and larger groups on the basis of degree of kinship. If the available data are extensive enough and have been interpreted correctly, such a taxonomic system not only indicates degrees of relationship among existing species, but also furnishes sound clues to phylogenetic relationships. Unfortunately, this taxonomic ideal has not yet been realized for the Phylum Protozoa as a whole.

The limitations of current systems are numerous. In the first place, the boundaries of the phylum are subject to debate, particularly in the case of phytoflagellates. In studying the Phytomastigophorea and their

---

[1] General problems of zoological classification and conventional taxonomic procedures have been reviewed in a compact monograph by Calman (6).

relatives, the taxonomist encounters organisms which range from typical flagellates (of which many are apochlorotic and some are holozoic) to filamentous algae with temporary flagellate stages. In assigning algal flagellates to the Phylum Protozoa and leaving their close relatives with the botanists, protozoologists obviously have made arbitrary decisions which are more indicative of taxonomic convenience than of biological relationships. The dual taxonomic role of the slime-molds as Sarcodina and Fungi indicates another point at which the boundaries of the Phylum Protozoa are obscure. Comparable uncertainty exists at the lower levels of protozoan taxonomy, and there are instances in which orders apparently overlap to such a degree that the exact positions of certain genera are still uncertain. In modern taxonomic practice, it is no novelty for a particular genus or family to be moved from one subphylum, class, or order to another. Old orders have sometimes disappeared completely, in suppressions or amalgamations, and new orders have been carved out of older groups. The continued erection of new genera and species is paralleled to some extent by the suppression of old names. In other words, a certain amount of taxonomic confusion extends throughout much of the Phylum Protozoa. This confusion does not indicate chaos. Instead, it is the result of continued activity in a field still seriously handicapped by the lack of adequate information.

TAXONOMY PRIOR TO 1900

Although current classifications leave much room for improvement, there has been tremendous progress since Gesner described one of the Foraminiferida as a mollusc in 1565. Protozoa apparently were first separated from other animalcules in 1752, when John Hill placed some of them in his group of *Gymnia* (animalcules without external organs). In 1786, O. F. Müller (17) erected the *Infusoria* (including about 150 species of Protozoa) as a subdivision of the worms, and divided the group into species with, and those without, visible locomotor organelles.

Ehrenberg's (10) more extensive monograph included descriptions of about 350 species from original observations, but an important part of his taxonomic system was based upon a liberal interpretation of the Infusoria as complete organisms. On the basis of feeding experiments with pigments, Ehrenberg concluded that a digestive system is characteristic of ciliates. "Polygastric" types were believed to have a mouth, oesophagus, many stomachs, a spiral intestine, an anus, and possibly a pancreas. The *Infusoria* were separated into *Anentera* (without a digestive tract) and *Enterodela* (with a digestive tract). The Anentera were subdivided into *Gymnia* (no visible appendages), including about 30 genera of flagellates; *Pseudopoda* (with pseudopodia), including *Amoeba, Arcella,* and certain Suctorea; and *Epitricha* (with cilia), including a few ciliates and several dinoflagellates. Additional ciliates were placed in the Enterodela which were subdivided, on the basis of number and position of openings to the supposed digestive tract, into *Anopisthia* (with one terminal opening), *Enantiatreta* (with an opening at each end of the body), *Allotreta* (with a lateral opening), and *Catotreta* (with a ventral opening).

Ehrenberg's basic misinterpretation of protozoan morphology was soon corrected by Dujardin (9) who reached the conclusion that Infusoria are simple organisms composed of a fundamental living substance, *sarcode*. Repetition of Ehrenberg's feeding experiments indicated that the supposedly fixed stomachs of ciliates are merely food vacuoles. Dujardin divided the Infusoria into *Asymmetrica* and *Symmetrica*. The former included species without visible locomotor organelles (bacteria), those with pseudopodia (mostly Sarcodina, in the modern sense), those with flagella, and those with cilia (about 50 genera of ciliates). The *Symmetrica* included the ciliate genus *Coleps*.

In 1845, von Siebold (20) redefined the "Protozoa," in which Goldfuss (11) had included certain coelenterates with the "Infusoria," and characterized them as unicellular animals. Although such a characterization is inadequate by modern standards, von Siebold's definition served a useful purpose in stressing morphological differences between Protozoa and higher animals. The Protozoa now included the Class *Infusoria*—the *Astoma*, without a mouth (*Opalina* and the flagellates), and the *Stomatoda*, with a mouth (about 30 genera of ciliates)—and the Class *Rhizopoda* with (pseudopodia).

Further investigation brought more recruits to the Protozoa. In 1845, von Kölliker concluded that gregarines are Protozoa instead of trematodes, and this interpretation was supported by Stein in 1848. Increased interest in these organisms finally led to Leuckart's erection of the Sporozoa in 1879. Preliminary observations of Meyen, and the extensive work of Huxley on *Thalassicolla* led J. Müller, in 1858, to establish the *Radiolaria* as a subdivision of the Rhizopoda. The group *Ciliata* was set up by Perty in 1852; the *Flagellata*, by Cohn in 1853; and extensive investigations on both groups were reported by Claparède and Lachmann in 1858-1861. By the time Stein's (21) monograph was completed, the Flagellata were divided into 15 families, some of which are now considered orders; the Ciliata, into the orders *Holotricha, Heterotricha, Hypotricha*, and *Peritricha*. Stein's classification of ciliates on the basis of distribution of cilia has been carried on, with modifications, into later systems.

Contemporary contributions included Haeckel's separation of the Heliozoa from the Radiolaria, erection of the Mastigophora by Diesing, the Sporozoa by Leuckart, the Myxosporidia and the Dinoflagellata by Bütschli, and the Sarcosporidia by Balbiani. As a result, the classification of Protozoa began to resemble more modern systems.

Kent's monograph (14) covered the following groups:

Class 1. Rhizopoda
  Order 1. Amoebina
  Order 2. Gregarinida
  Order 3. Arcellinida
  Order 4. Foraminifera
  Order 5. Labyrinthulida
  Order 6. Radiolaria
Class 2. Flagellata
  Order 1. Mycetozoa
  Order 2. Trypanosomata
  Order 3. Rhizo-Flagellata
  Order 4. Radio-Flagellata
  Order 5. Flagellata-Pantostomata

Order 6. Choano-Flagellata
Order 7. Spongida
Order 8. Flagellata-Eustomata
Order 9. Cilio-Flagellata
Class 3. Ciliata
  Order 1. Holotricha
  Order 2. Heterotricha
  Order 3. Hypotricha
  Order 4. Peritricha
Class 4. Tentaculifera
  Order 1. Actinaria
  Order 2. Suctoria

Kent's system differed from more recent ones in several respects—assignment of the Mycetozoa and the Spongida (sponges) to the Flagellata; inclusion of the gregarines in the Rhizopoda; recognition of a Class Tentaculifera to include the Suctoria and Actinaria.

Bütschli (2) recognized the Class Sporozoa, although some of the modern Coccidia were grouped with gregarines. The Microsporidia were listed as an appendix to the Sporozoa, with exact relationships to be determined. Among the Mastigophora, the Euglenoidina included several of the modern Chloromonadida, while such types as *Bodo* (now in the Protomastigida) and *Entosiphon* (one of the Euglenida) were assigned to the Heteromastigoda. Bütschli's Isomastigoda included the Chrysomonadida, Cryptomonadida and Phytomonadida of current systems, as well as certain Polymastigida and the dinoflagellate *Oxyrrhis*. The Trichonymphidae (now in the Hypermastigida) were listed as an appendix to the ciliates.

Class 1. Sarkodina
  Subclass 1. Rhizopoda
    Order 1. Rhizopoda
      Suborder 1. Amoebaea
      Suborder 2. Testacea
      Suborder 3. Perforata
  Subclass 2. Heliozoa
  Subclass 3. Radiolaria
Class 2. Sporozoa
  Subclass 1. Gregarinida
    Order 1. Monocystidea
    Order 2. Polycystidea
  Subclass 2. Myxosporidia
  Subclass 3. Sarcosporidia
Class 3. Mastigophora
  Order 1. Flagellata
    Suborder 1. Monadina
    Suborder 2. Euglenoidina

    Suborder 3. Heteromastigoda
    Suborder 4. Isomastigoda
  Order 2. Choanoflagellata
  Order 3. Dinoflagellata
    Suborder 1. Adinida
    Suborder 2. Dinifera
  Order 4. Cystoflagellata
Class 4. Infusoria
  Subclass 1. Ciliata
    Order 1. Gymnostomata
    Order 2. Trichostomata
      Suborder 1. Aspirotricha
      Suborder 2. Spirotricha
        Section 1. Heterotricha
        Section 2. Oligotricha
        Section 3. Hypotricha
        Section 4. Peritricha
  Subclass 2. Suctoria

TAXONOMIC SYSTEMS OF THE TWENTIETH CENTURY

The system proposed by Calkins (3) showed several changes. The Suborder Perforata (Foraminifera) became the Order Reticulariida. The silicoflagellates, now considered a subdivision of the Chrysomonadida, appeared as a separate order. The Order Phytoflagellida included groups now separated as the Orders Phytomonadida and Chloromonadida. The gregarines, coccidians, and haemosporidians were assigned to separate orders in the Telosporidia.

Class 1. Sarcodina
  Subclass 1. Rhizopoda
    Order 1. Amoebida
      Suborder 1. Gymnamoebina
      Suborder 2. Thecamoebina
    Order 2. Reticulariida
      Suborder 1. Nuda
      Suborder 2. Imperforina
      Suborder 3. Perforina
      Suborder 4. Tinoporinae
  Subclass 2. Heliozoa
    Order 1. Aphrothoracida
    Order 2. Chlamydophorida
    Order 3. Chalarathoracida
    Order 4. Desmothoracida
  Subclass 3. Radiolaria
    (20 orders)
Class 2. Mastigophora
  Subclass 1. Flagellida
    Order 1. Monadida
    Order 2. Choanoflagellida
    Order 3. Heteromastigida
    Order 4. Polymastigida
    Order 5. Euglenida
    Order 6. Phytoflagellida
      Suborder 1. Chloromonadina
      Suborder 2. Chromonadina

      Suborder 3. Chlamydomonadina
      Suborder 4. Volvocina
    Order 7. Silicoflagellida
  Subclass 2. Dinoflagellida
    Order 1. Adinida
    Order 2. Dinoferida
    Order 3. Polydinida
  Subclass 3. Cystoflagellidia
Class 3. Sporozoa
  Subclass 1. Telosporidia
    Order 1. Gregarinida
    Order 2. Coccidia
    Order 3. Haemosporidiida
  Subclass 2. Neosporidia
    Order 1. Myxosporidiida
    Order 2. Sarcosporidiida
Class 4. Infusoria
  Subclass 1. Ciliata
    Order 1. Holotrichida
      Suborder 1. Gymnostomina
      Suborder 2. Trichostomina
    Order 2. Heterotrichida
      Suborder 1. Polytrichina
      Suborder 2. Oligotrichina
    Order 3. Hypotrichida
    Order 4. Peritrichida
  Subclass 2. Suctoria

The system of Doflein (7) differed in several respects from that of Calkins. The phylum was divided into two subphyla, Plasmodroma and Ciliophora. The "Infusoria" disappeared, the Ciliata and Suctoria being advanced to classes of Ciliophora. In addition, the Foraminifera and Mycetozoa were recognized as orders of the Rhizopoda, and the Trichonymphidae were listed as an appendix to the Mastigophora.

Subphylum 1. Plasmodroma
  Class 1. Rhizopoda
    Order 1. Amoebina
    Order 2. Heliozoa
    Order 3. Radiolaria
    Order 4. Foraminifera
    Order 5. Mycetozoa
  Class 2. Mastigophora
    Subclass 1. Flagellata
      Order 1. Protomonadina
      Order 2. Polymastigina
      Order 3. Euglenoidina
      Order 4. Chromomonadina

      Order 5. Phytomonadina
    Subclass 2. Dinoflagellata
      Order 1. Adinida
      Order 2. Dinifera
    Subclass 3. Cystoflagellata
  Class 3. Sporozoa
    Subclass 1. Telosporidia
      Order 1. Coccidiomorpha
      Order 2. Gregarinida
    Subclass 2. Neosporidia
      Order 1. Cnidosporidia
      Order 2. Sarcosporidia
Subphylum 2. Ciliophora

Class 1. Ciliata
　Order 1. Holotricha
　Order 2. Heterotricha
　Order 3. Oligotricha

Order 4. Hypotricha
Order 5. Peritricha
Class 2. Suctoria

Hartmann (12) recognized five orders of Neosporidia among the Sporozoa. To the Subclass Flagellata, was added the Order Binucleata to include some of the Trypanosomidae and Haemosporidia as supposedly binucleate organisms. Since the binucleate nature of these organisms has never been established (21), the Order Binucleata has not been accepted by later workers.

Subphylum 1. Plasmodroma
　Class 1. Rhizopoda
　　Order 1. Amoebina
　　Order 2. Mycetozoa
　　Order 3. Foraminifera
　　Order 4. Heliozoa
　　Order 5. Radiolaria
　Class 2. Mastigophora
　　Subclass 1. Flagellata
　　　Order 1. Protomonadina
　　　Order 2. Polymastigina
　　　Order 3. Binucleata
　　　Order 4. Euglenoidea
　　　Order 5. Chromomonadina
　　　Order 6. Phytomonadina
　　Subclass 2. Dinoflagellata
　　　Order 1. Adinida
　　　Order 2. Dinifera

Subclass 3. Cystoflagellata
Class 3. Telosporidia
　Order 1. Coccidia
　Order 2. Gregarinida
Class 4. Neosporidia
　Order 1. Myxosporidia
　Order 2. Microsporidia
　Order 3. Sarcosporidia
　Order 4. Actinomyxidia
　Order 5. Haplosporidia
Subphylum 2. Ciliophora
Class 1. Ciliata
　Order 1. Holotricha
　Order 2. Heterotricha
　Order 3. Oligotricha
　Order 4. Hypotricha
　Order 5. Peritricha
Class 2. Suctoria

In the system of Minchin (16) the subphyla Plasmodroma and Ciliophora were dropped and the Class Infusoria restored. The Heliozoa and Radiolaria were recognized as subdivisions of the Actinopoda. In the Ciliata, erection of the Sections Aspirigera and Spirigera stressed differences in adoral ciliation.

Class 1. Mastigophora
　Subclass 1. Flagellata
　　Order 1. Pantastomatina
　　Order 2. Protomonadina
　　Order 3. Polymastigina
　　Order 4. Euglenoidina
　　Order 5. Chromomonadina
　　　Suborder 1. Chrysomonadina
　　　Suborder 2. Cryptomonadina
　　Order 6. Phytomonadina
　Subclass 2. Dinoflagellata
　　Order 1. Adinidia
　　Order 2. Dinifera
　Subclass 3. Cystoflagellata
Class 2. Sarcodina
　Subclass 1. Rhizopoda
　　Order 1. Amoebaea

　　　Suborder 1. Reticulosa
　　　Suborder 2. Lobosa
　　Order 2. Foraminifera
　　Order 3. Xenophyophora
　　Order 4. Mycetozoa
　Subclass 2. Actinopoda
　　Order 1. Heliozoa
　　Order 2. Radiolaria
Class 3. Sporozoa
　Subclass 1. Telosporidia
　　Order 1. Gregarinoidea
　　　Suborder 1. Eugregarinae
　　　Suborder 2. Schizogregarinae
　　Order 2. Coccidia
　　Order 3. Haemosporidia
　Subclass 2. Neosporidia
　　Division 1. Cnidosporidia

Order 1. Myxosporidia
Order 2. Actinomyxidia
Order 3. Microsporidia
Order 4. Sarcosporidia
Division 2. Haplosporidia
Order 1. Haplosporidia
Class 4. Infusoria
Subclass 1. Ciliata
Section 1. Aspirigera
Order 1. Holotricha

Suborder 1. Astomata
Suborder 2. Gymnostomata
Suborder 3. Hymenostomata
Section 2. Spirigera
Order 1. Heterotricha
Suborder 1. Polytricha
Suborder 2. Oligotricha
Order 2. Hypotricha
Order 3. Peritricha
Subclass 2. Acinetaria (Suctoria)

In 1926 two new systems, proposed by Calkins (4) and Wenyon (23), reflected several differences of opinion in treatment of the Sarcodina, Mastigophora, and Sporozoa. Wenyon's separation of the Cnidosporidia from other Sporozoa as a group of equal rank apparently represents a more realistic appraisal than that reflected in most classifications. In both systems, the Chrysomonadida and Cryptomonadida appeared as separate orders, and the Chloromonadida also in that of Calkins. Wenyon's transfer of the Cystoflagellata to the Zoomastigina is not generally favored. In the Ciliata, Wenyon followed Minchin in stressing differences in ciliature of the Holotrichida and the other orders. Wenyon retained the subphyla Plasmodroma and Ciliophora, whereas Calkins advanced the Mastigophora, Sarcodina, Sporozoa, and Infusoria to subphyla.

The system of Calkins (4):

Subphylum 1. Mastigophora
Class 1. Phytomastigoda
Order 1. Chrysomonadida
Order 2. Cryptomonadida
Order 3. Dinoflagellida
Order 4. Phytomonadida
Order 5. Euglenida
Order 6. Chloromonadida
Class 2. Zoomastigoda
Order 1. Pantastomatida
Order 2. Protomastigida
Order 3. Polymastigida
Order 4. Hypermastigida
Subphylum 2. Sarcodina
Class 1. Actinopoda
Subclass 1. Heliozoa
Subclass 2. Radiolaria
Class 2. Rhizopoda
Subclass 1. Proteomyxa
Subclass 2. Mycetozoa

Subclass 3. Foraminifera
Subclass 4. Amoebaea
Subphylum 3. Infusoria
Class 1. Ciliata
Order 1. Holotrichida
Order 2. Heterotrichida
Order 3. Oligotrichida
Order 4. Hypotrichida
Order 5. Peritrichida
Class 2. Suctoria
Subphylum 4. Sporozoa
Class 1. Telosporidia
Subclass 1. Gregarinida
Subclass 2. Coccidiomorpha
Order 1. Coccidia
Order 2. Haemosporidia
Class 2. Neosporidia
Subclass 1. Cnidosporidia
Subclass 2. Sarcosporidia

The system of Wenyon (23):

Subphylum 1. Plasmodroma
Class 1. Rhizopoda
Order 1. Amoebida
Order 2. Heliozoa
Order 3. Radiolaria

Order 4. Foraminifera
Order 5. Mycetozoa
Class 2. Mastigophora
Subclass 1. Phytomastigina
Order 1. Chrysomonadina

Order 2. Chryptomonadina
Order 3. Dinoflagellata
Order 4. Euglenoidida
Order 5. Phytomonadida
Subclass 2. Zoomastigina
Order 1. Protomonadida
Order 2. Hypermastigida
Order 3. Cystoflagellata
Order 4. Diplomonadida
Order 5. Polymonadida
Class 3. Cnidosporidia
Order 1. Myxosporidiida
Order 2. Microsporidia
Class 4. Sporozoa
Subclass 1. Coccidiomorpha
Order 1. Coccidiida
Order 2. Adeleida

Subclass 2. Gregarinina
Order 1. Schizogregarinida
Order 2. Eugregarinida
Subphylum 2. Ciliophora
Group 1. Protociliata
Class 1. Opalinata
Group 2. Euciliata
Class 1. Ciliata
Subclass 1. Aspirigera
Order 1. Holotrichida
Subclass 2. Spirigera
Order 1. Heterotrichida
Order 2. Oligotrichida
Order 3. Hypotrichida
Order 4. Peritrichida
Class 2. Suctoria

In the later system of Doflein and Reichenow (8) the Heterochlorida were added to the orders of Mastigophora, although the Phytomastigoda (Phytomastigina) and Zoomastigoda (Zoomastigina) were not recognized as subclasses. Addition of the Testacea increased the orders of Rhizopoda to six. Several new groups of ciliates were recognized and the Order Spirotricha was rescued, with modifications, from Bütschli's (2) system.

Subphylum 1. Plasmodroma
Class 1. Mastigophora
Order 1. Chrysomonadina
Order 2. Heterochloridina
Order 3. Cryptomonadina
Order 4. Dinoflagellata
Order 5. Euglenoidina
Order 6. Chloromonadina
Order 7. Phytomonadina
Order 8. Polymastigina
Order 9. Rhizomastigina
Class 2. Rhizopoda
Order 1. Amoebina
Order 2. Testacea
Order 3. Foraminifera
Order 4. Heliozoa
Order 5. Radiolaria
Order 6. Mycetozoa
Class 3. Sporozoa
Subclass 1. Telosporidia
Order 1. Gregarinae

Order 2. Coccidia
Order 3. Haemosporidia
Subclass 2. Cnidosporidia
Order 1. Myxosporidia
Order 2. Microsporidia
Subclass 3. Sarcosporidia
Subclass 4. Haplosporidia
Subphylum 2. Ciliophora
Class 1. Ciliata
Subclass 1. Protociliata
Subclass 2. Euciliata
Order 1. Holotricha
Order 2. Spirotricha
Suborder 1. Heterotricha
Suborder 2. Oligotricha
Suborder 3. Entodiniomorpha
Suborder 4. Ctenostomata
Suborder 5. Hypotricha
Order 3. Peritricha
Order 4. Chonotricha
Class 2. Suctoria

The system of Kudo (15) suggested progressive changes in treatment of the Sporozoa.

Subphylum 1. Plasmodroma
Class 1. Mastigophora
Subclass 1. Phytomastigina
Order 1. Chrysomonadida

Order 2. Cryptomonadida
Order 3. Dinoflagellida
Order 4. Phytomonadida
Order 5. Euglenoidida

Order 6. Chloromonadida
Subclass 2. Zoomastigina
  Order 1. Pantastomatida
  Order 2. Protomonadida
  Order 3. Polymastigida
  Order 4. Hypermastigida
Class 2. Sarcodina
  Subclass 1. Rhizopoda
    Order 1. Proteomyxa
    Order 2. Mycetozoa
    Order 3. Foraminifera
    Order 4. Amoebaea
    Order 5. Testacea
  Subclass 2. Actinopoda
    Order 1. Heliozoa
    Order 2. Radiolaria
Class 3. Sporozoa
  Subclass 1. Telosporidia
    Order 1. Coccidia
    Order 2. Haemosporidia

    Order 3. Gregarinida
  Subclass 2. Cnidosporidia
    Order 1. Myxosporidia
    Order 2. Actinomyxidia
    Order 3. Microsporidia
    Order 4. Helicosporidia
  Subclass 3. Acnidosporidia
    Order 1. Sarcosporidia
    Order 2. Haplosporidia
Subphylum 2. Ciliophora
  Class 1. Ciliata
    Subclass 1. Protociliata
    Subclass 2. Euciliata
      Order 1. Holotrichida
      Order 2. Heterotrichida
      Order 3. Oligotrichida
      Order 4. Hypotrichida
      Order 5. Peritrichida
  Class 2. Suctoria

In a later classification Calkins (5) omitted the Phytomastigophora, as a group, from the Mastigophora. However, the Peranemidae, a family of Euglenida, was transferred to the Protomonadida to contain *Peranema* and several related genera. Other Peranemidae (such as *Heteronema, Anisonema, Dinema,* and *Entosiphon*) were placed in the family Bodonidae of the Protomonadida. The Mastigophora were divided into two classes, Protomastigota (the Order Protomonadida) and Metamastigota. The opalinid ciliates were reduced from a separate subclass (Protociliata) to a family in the Astomida.

Subphylum 1. Mastigophora
  Class 1. Protomastigota
    Order 1. Protomonadida
  Class 2. Metamastigota
    Order 1. Hypermastigida
    Order 2. Polymastigida
      Suborder 1. Monokaryomastigina
      Suborder 2. Diplokaryomastigina
      Suborder 3. Polykaryomastigina
Subphylum 2. Sarcodina
  Class 1. Actinopoda
    Subclass 1. Heliozoa
    Subclass 2. Radiolaria
  Class 2. Rhizopoda
    Subclass 1. Proteomyxa
    Subclass 2. Mycetozoa
    Subclass 3. Foraminifera
    Subclass 4. Amoebaea
      Order 1. Amoebida
      Order 2. Testacea
Subphylum 3. Infusoria
  Class 1. Ciliata
    Subclass 1. Holotricha
      Order 1. Astomida
      Order 2. Gymnostomida

    Subclass 2. Spirotricha
      Order 1. Heterotrichida
      Order 2. Oligotrichida
      Order 3. Ctenostomida
      Order 4. Hypotrichida
    Subclass 3. Peritricha
    Subclass 4. Chonotricha
  Class 2. Suctoria
Subphylum 4. Sporozoa
  Class 1. Telosporidia
    Subclass 1. Gregarinina
      Order 1. Eugregarinida
      Order 2. Schizogregarinida
    Subclass 2. Coccidiomorpha
      Order 1. Coccidiida
        Suborder 1. Eimeriina
        Suborder 2. Haemosporidiina
        Suborder 3. Babesiina
      Order 2. Adeleida
  Class 2. Cnidosporidia
    Order 1. Myxosporidia
    Order 2. Actinomyxidia
    Order 3. Microsporidia
  Class 3. Acnidosporidia

In 1936 a list of subdivisions of the Protozoa, as generally favored by a number of American protozoologists, was prepared for the American Association for the Advancement of Science (18). This list of names, with their authors, illustrates the multiple origins of current systems.

Phylum Protozoa Goldfuss 1820 em. von Siebold 1845
  Subphylum 1. Plasmodroma Doflein 1901
    Class 1. Mastigophora Diesing 1865.
      Subclass 1. Phytomastigophora Calkins 1909
        Order 1. Chrysomonadida Stein 1878
        Order 2. Heterochlorida Pascher 1912
        Order 3. Cryptomonadida Stein 1878
        Order 4. Dinoflagellida Bütschli 1885
        Order 5. Euglenida Blochmann 1895
        Order 6. Chloromonadida Klebs 1892
        Order 7. Phytomonadida Blochmann 1895
      Subclass 2. Zoomastigophora Calkins 1909
        Order 1. Pantastomatida Minchin 1912
        Order 2. Protomastigida Klebs 1893
        Order 3. Polymastigida Klebs 1893
        Order 4. Hypermastigida Grassi 1911
    Class 2. Sarcodina Hertwig and Lesser 1874 em. Bütschli 1880
      Subclass 1. Rhizopoda von Siebold 1845
        Order 1. Amoebida Claparède and Lachmann 1858
        Order 2. Proteomyxa Lankester 1885
        Order 3. Testacea Schultze 1854
        Order 4. Foraminifera d'Orbigny 1826
        Order 5. Mycetozoa de Bary 1859
      Subclass 2. Actinopoda Calkins 1909
        Order 1. Heliozoa Haeckel 1866
        Order 2. Radiolaria Haeckel 1866
    Class 3. Sporozoa Leuckart 1879
      Subclass 1. Telosporidia Schaudinn 1900
        Order 1. Gregarinida Lankester 1866
        Order 2. Coccidiomorpha Doflein 1901
          Suborder 1. Coccidia Leuckart 1879
          Suborder 2. Haemosporidia Danilewsky 1886
      Subclass 2. Cnidosporidia Doflein 1901
        Order 1. Myxosporidia Bütschli 1881
        Order 2. Actinomyxidia Stolc 1899
        Order 3. Microsporidia Balbiani 1883
      Subclass 3. Sarcosporidia Balbiani 1882
        Order 1. Sarcosporidia Balbiani 1882
        Order 2. Globidia Badudieri 1932
      Subclass 4. Haplosporidia Caullery and Mesnil 1899
  Subphylum 2. Ciliophora Doflein 1901
    Class 1. Ciliata Perty 1852
      Subclass 1. Protociliata Metcalf 1918
        Order 1. Opalinata Stein 1867
      Subclass 2. Euciliata Metcalf 1918
        Order 1. Holotrichida Stein 1859
          Suborder 1. Gymnostomina Bütschli 1889
          Suborder 2. Trichostomina Bütschli 1889
          Suborder 3. Astomina Minchin 1912
        Order 2. Spirotrichida Bütschli 1889
          Suborder 1. Heterotrichina Stein 1859

Suborder 2. Oligotrichina Bütschli 1887
Suborder 3. Tintinnoina Claparède and Lachmann 1858
Suborder 4. Entodiniomorphina Reichenow 1929
Suborder 5. Hypotrichina Stein 1859
Order 3. Peritrichida Stein 1859
Order 4. Chonotrichida Wallengren 1896
Class 2. Suctoria Claparède and Lachmann 1858

Pearse's report (18), in which the preceding names were listed, strongly advocated adoption of the following endings for names of taxonomic groups: phylum, -a; subphylum, -a; class, -ea; subclass, -ia; order, -ida; suborder, -ina. The obvious advantages of such uniformity, both to professional taxonomists and to students, far outweigh any potential restrictions on creative license in formulating new taxonomic names. This system of uniform spelling has been adopted in one recent classification (13), and will be adhered to in the following chapters on taxonomy of the Protozoa.

The writer will follow the system outlined below; this is similar to the classification adopted by Jahn and Jahn (13).

Subphylum 1. Mastigophora
Class 1. Phytomastigophorea
Order 1. Chrysomonadida
Order 2. Heterochlorida
Order 3. Cryptomonadida
Order 4. Dinoflagellida
Order 5. Phytomonadida
Order 6. Euglenida
Order 7. Chloromonadida
Class 2. Zoomastigophorea
Order 1. Rhizomastigida
Order 2. Protomastigida
Order 3. Polymastigida
Order 4. Trichomonadida
Order 5. Hypermastigida
Subphylum 2. Sarcodina
Class 1. Actinopodea
Order 1. Helioflagellida
Order 2. Heliozoida
Order 3. Radiolarida
Class 2. Rhizopodea
Order 1. Proteomyxida
Order 2. Mycetozoida
Order 3. Amoebida
Order 4. Testacida
Order 5. Foraminiferida
Subphylum 3. Sporozoa
Class 1. Telosporidea
Subclass 1. Gregarinidia
Order 1. Eugregarinida
Order 2. Schizogregarinida
Subclass 2. Coccidia

Subclass 3. Haemosporidia
Class 2. Cnidosporidea
Order 1. Myxosporida
Order 2. Actinomyxida
Order 3. Microsporida
Order 4. Helicosporida
Class 3. Acnidosporidea
Subclass 1. Sarcosporidia
Subclass 2. Haplosporidia
Subphylum 4. Ciliophora
Class 1. Ciliatea
Subclass 1. Protociliatia
Order 1. Opalinida
Subclass 2. Euciliatia
Order 1. Holotrichida
Suborder 1. Astomina
Suborder 2. Gymnostomina
Suborder 3. Trichostomina
Suborder 4. Hymenostomina
Suborder 5. Thigmotrichina
Suborder 6. Apostomina
Order 2. Spirotrichida
Suborder 1. Heterotrichina
Suborder 2. Tintinnina
Suborder 3. Oligotrichina
Suborder 4. Entodiniomorphina
Suborder 5. Hypotrichina
Suborder 6. Ctenostomina
Order 3. Peritrichida
Order 4. Chonotrichida
Class 2. Suctorea

PROSPECTIVE SOURCES OF TAXONOMIC DATA

As will be noted in Chapters 4-7, there are still many taxonomic areas in which inadequate information makes disagreements unavoidable. Since it becomes increasingly evident that superficial characteristics form an inadequate foundation for a natural classification of Protozoa, present differences of opinion cannot be reconciled completely until more is known about the morphology, biochemistry, physiology, and life-cycles of many species. Therefore, future progress will depend largely upon the contributions of specialists working in different fields. Such details as the finer structure of flagella, the organization of ciliary patterns and peristomial areas in ciliates, distribution of the various types of chlorophyll and other pigments in flagellates, the composition of stored foods, the structure of endoplasmic organelles, the organization of nuclei, and the basic details of mitosis should all contribute to the development of a less imperfect taxonomic system. The bearing of biochemical data on taxonomic questions may prove to be very important. The determination of minimal food requirements and the analysis of synthetic potentialities, which are possible for species established in chemically defined bacteria-free media, may yield clues to relationships now obscured by morphological specializations. Taxonomists may even become concerned with such matters as comparative data on digestive enzymes. For instance, the observation that *Amoeba proteus* (*Chaos diffluens*) and *Pelomyxa carolinensis* (*Chaos chaos*) are similar in their content of peptidase and catheptic proteinase and are both quite different from *Pelomyxa palustris* (1), is especially interesting in view of the disputes concerning their generic status. And finally, a more thorough analysis of life-cycles is probably essential for the satisfactory classification of various genera and families whose taxonomic status is uncertain at present.

THE IDENTIFICATION OF PROTOZOA

In beginning a study of the Protozoa, the student is often interested in identifying species as they are encountered in the laboratory. Unfortunately, such identifications are not always easy, and are occasionally impossible with the more readily available library facilities. There is no comprehensive determinative manual for the Protozoa as a whole. Nor is there available a complete manual for any of the four major groups of Protozoa. As a result, the identification of a particular species sometimes becomes a problem for the specialist with extensive knowledge of a certain taxonomic group. In some cases, as pointed out by Pringsheim (19), the establishment of pure-line cultures from single organisms may be a desirable, or even an essential step.

However, the existence of such difficulties does not mean that the student should consider the task of identification a hopeless one. Many of the better known species are described recognizably in general taxonomic works that are widely accessible. In addition, there are increasing numbers of monographs dealing with single genera or families. It is only in the areas not adequately covered by general monographs and not yet touched by special surveys, that the protozoologist encounters major difficulties. In such cases, identification of a species may involve a laborious search through isolated and sometimes numerous papers dealing with members of the genus in question.

For those who are beginning to cultivate an acquaintance with the Protozoa, an illustrated key written by Jahn and Jahn (13) will prove to be very helpful. The authors have explained the use of taxonomic keys and have included instructive discussions of the criteria to be considered in identifying members of the major groups. This key also will be useful to the advanced student who has not specialized in taxonomy of the Protozoa. For species not listed by Jahn and Jahn, more extensive taxonomic works must be consulted. A number of these special monographs are listed in Chapters IV-VII.

LITERATURE CITED

1. Andresen, N. and H. Holter 1949. *Science* **110:** 114.
2. Bütschli, O. 1880-1889. "Protozoa" in Bronn's *Klassen und Ordnungen des Thierreichs* (Leipzig).
3. Calkins, G. N. 1901. The Protozoa (New York: Columbia Press).
4. ——— 1926. *The Biology of the Protozoa* (Philadelphia: Lea & Febiger).
5. ——— 1933. *The Biology of the Protozoa,* 2d ed. (Philadelphia: Lea & Febiger).
6. Calman, W. T. 1949. *The Classification of Animals: an Introduction to Zoological Taxonomy* (New York: J. Wiley & Sons).
7. Doflein, F. 1902. *Arch. f. Protistenk.* **2:** 169.
8. ——— and E. Reichenow 1927-1929. *Lehrbuch der Protozoenkunde* (Jena: G. Fischer).
9. Dujardin, F. 1841. *Histoire naturelle des zoophytes* (Paris).
10. Ehrenberg, C. G. 1838. *Die Infusionsthierchen als volkommene Organismen* (Leipzig).
11. Goldfuss, G. A. 1820. *Handbuch der Zoologie* (Nürnberg).
12. Hartmann, M. 1907. *Arch. f. Protistenk.* **10:** 139.
13. Jahn, T. L. and F. F. Jahn 1949. *How to Know the Protozoa* (Dubuque: W. C. Brown Co.).
14. Kent, W. S. 1880-1882. *A Manual of the Infusoria;* including a description of all known flagellate, ciliate and tentaculiferous Protozoa, British and foreign, and an account of the organization and affinities of the sponges (London).
15. Kudo, R. R. 1931. *Handbook of Protozoology* (Springfield: Thomas).
16. Minchin, E. A. 1912. *An Introduction to the Study of the Protozoa* (London: Arnold).
17. Müller, O. F. 1786. *Animalcula infusoria fluviatilia et marina* (Havniae et Leipzig).
18. Pearse, A. S. 1936. *Zoological Names. A List of Phyla, Classes and Orders* (Durham: Duke University Press).
19. Pringsheim, E. G. 1949. *Pure Cultures of Algae. Their Preparation and Maintenance* (Cambridge).
20. Siebold, C. T. E. and H. Stannius v. 1845. *Lehrbuch der vergleichende Anatomie,* H. 1.
21. Stein, S. N. F. v. 1859-1883. *Der Organismus der Infusionsthiere* (Leipzig).
22. Swezy, O. 1916. *Univ. Calif. Publ. Zool.* **16:** 185.
23. Wenyon, C. M. 1926. *Protozoology* (London: Ballière, Tindall & Cox).

IV

The Mastigophora

Class 1. Phytomastigophorea
  Order 1. Chrysomonadida
    Suborder 1. Euchrysomonadina
      Family 1. Chromulinidae
      Family 2. Syncryptidae
      Family 3. Ochromonadidae
      Family 4. Prymnesiidae
    Suborder 2. Silicoflagellina
    Suborder 3. Coccolithina
    Suborder 4. Rhizochrysodina
      Family 1. Rhizochrysidae
      Family 2. Myxochrysidae
    Suborder 5. Chrysocapsina
      Family 1. Chrysocapsidae
      Family 2. Celloniellidae
      Family 3. Hydruridae
      Family 4. Nageliellidae
  Order 2. Heterochlorida
    Suborder 1. Euheterochlorina
    Suborder 2. Rhizochloridina
    Suborder 3. Heterocapsina
  Order 3. Cryptomonadida
    Family 1. Cryptochrysidae
    Family 2. Cryptomonadidae
    Family 3. Nephroselmidae
  Order 4. Dinoflagellida
    Suborder 1. Prorocentrina
    Suborder 2. Gymnodinina
      Family 1. Protonoctilucidae
      Family 2. Gymnodiniidae
      Family 3. Polykrikidae
      Family 4. Noctilucidae
    Suborder 3. Peridinina
      Family 1. Glenodiniidae
      Family 2. Gonyaulacidae
      Family 3. Peridiniidae
      Family 4. Ceratiidae
      Family 5. Dinophysidae
      Family 6. Heterodiniidae
    Suborder 4. Dinocapsina
    Suborder 5. Dinococcina
      Family 1. Phytodiniidae
      Family 2. Blastodiniidae
      Family 3. Ellobiopsidae
  Order 5. Phytomonadida
    Family 1. Polyblepharidae

Family 2. Chlamydomonadidae
Family 3. Haematococcidae
Family 4. Phacotidae
Family 5. Spondylomoridae
Family 6. Volvocidae
  Order 6. Euglenida
    Suborder 1. Euglenoidina
    Suborder 2. Peranemoidina
    Suborder 3. Petalomonadoidina
  Order 7. Chloromonadida

Class 2. Zoomastigophorea
  Order 1. Rhizomastigida
  Order 2. Protomastigida
    Family 1. Codosigidae
    Family 2. Phalansteriidae
    Family 3. Trypanosomidae
    Family 4. Cryptobiidae
    Family 5. Amphimonadidae
    Family 6. Bodonidae
  Order 3. Polymastigida
    Family 1. Trimastigidae
    Family 2. Tetramitidae
    Family 3. Streblomastigidae
    Family 4. Retortomonadidae
    Family 5. Callimastigidae
    Family 6. Polymastigidae
    Family 7. Pyrsonymphidae
    Family 8. Hexamitidae
  Order 4. Trichomonadida
    Family 1. Monocercomonadidae
    Family 2. Devescovinidae
    Family 3. Calonymphidae
    Family 4. Trichomonadidae
  Order 5. Hypermastigida
    Suborder 1. Lophomonadina
      Family 1. Lophomonadidae
      Family 2. Joeniidae
      Family 3. Kofoidiidae
    Suborder 2. Trichonymphina
      Family 1. Hoplonymphidae
      Family 2. Staurojoeninidae
      Family 3. Holomastigotidae
      Family 4. Trichonymphidae
      Family 5. Teratonymphidae

Literature cited

$\mathbf{T}$HE Mastigophora possess flagella at some stage of the life-cycle, although many develop pseudopodia and show amoeboid activity. The group may be divided into two classes, Phytomastigophorea and Zoomastigophorea.

CLASS 1. PHYTOMASTIGOPHOREA

The phytoflagellates range from typical plants to forms whose affinities with animals are more apparent, and some genera have even occupied positions in both the Phytomastigophorea and the Zoomastigophorea in different systematic treatises. The majority possess chromatophores which contain chlorophyll, although the green color may be masked to some extent by other pigments. The rest of the phytoflagellates are colorless. Some differ from their pigmented homologues mainly in the lack of chromatophores, and in certain instances, both colorless and pigmented species belong to the same genus. At the other extreme, certain predominantly holozoic species have developed new organelles which assist in feeding.

Life-cycles may involve dimorphism, sometimes with alternation of amoeboid and flagellate stages, or flagellate and palmella stages. Sexual phenomena are well known in Phytomonadida and have been reported occasionally in certain other orders (Chapter II).

The Phytomastigophorea[1] may be divided into the following orders:

(1) *Chrysomonadida:* usually one or two flagella, sometimes three; typically with one or two, but sometimes more chromatophores ranging from golden-yellow to greenish-yellow or brown; a few genera lack chromatophores; no cytopharynx or "reservoir" is present; the cyst wall is typically siliceous and contains a pore; encystment is endogenous; stored reserves include leucosin and lipids, but no starch; many species are naked, some secrete a lorica or test, others are enclosed in a membrane to which siliceous scales or calcareous elements (coccoliths) are added; the majority are solitary, but some genera develop arboroid or spheroid colonies.

(2) *Heterochlorida:* typically naked, with two unequal flagella; one to a dozen or more chromatophores, pale yellow-green, or sometimes pale yellow; no cytopharynx; reserves include leucosin and lipids, but no starch; the cyst wall, which may contain two layers, lacks a pore; encystment is endogenous, as in Chrysomonadida.

(3) *Cryptomonadida:* biflagellate; pellicle usually restricts changes in

---

[1] From the botanical standpoint, the Class Phytomastigophorea is a somewhat artificial arrangement of certain algal groups. As considered in the present chapter, the Chrysomonadida represent part of the algal Class Chrysophyceae, the Phytomonadida correspond to the Order Volvocales of the Class Chlorophyceae, and the Dinoflagellida to the Class Dinophyceae. A modern discussion of the phytoflagellates as algae has been published by Smith (260).

form of the body, which often shows dorso-ventral differentiation; some genera have an open ventral "pharyngeal" groove; in others the groove is closed, posteriorly or throughout its length, to form a pouch; refractile granules ("trichocysts") usually lie just beneath the wall of the groove or pouch; there may be a single bilobed chromatophore or two or more chromatophores which are usually brown, less commonly red, blue, blue-green, or green; starch and lipids are stored.

(4) *Dinoflagellida:* biflagellate forms, typically with two grooves, a transverse *girdle* and a longitudinal *sulcus* in the body wall or theca; one of the flagella typically lies in the girdle; chromatophores, when present, are usually golden-brown to dark-brown, sometimes green or bluish-green; starch and lipids are stored.

(5) *Phytomonadida:* except in one family, there is a distinct membrane of cellulose or pectins, or a test impregnated with calcium or iron salts; usually two or four, sometimes eight flagella; there is often a single cup-shaped chromatophore; one or more pyrenoids are usually present; chlorophyll typically is not masked by other pigments; starch and lipids are stored; red haematochrome accumulates in some species.

(6) *Euglenida:* relatively large forms, usually with one or two flagella arising from an anterior reservoir ("gullet"); pellicle may be flexible or relatively rigid; green chromatophores, usually numerous and equipped with pyrenoids; reserves include paramylum and lipids; some species accumulate red haematochrome.

(7) *Chloromonadida:* typically biflagellate, one flagellum trailing; the body is often flattened dorso-ventrally, with a shallow groove on the ventral surface; presence of a cytopharynx, reported for some species, has been denied (232); chromatophores, when present, are typically numerous and grass-green (or "meadow-green"); no stigma is reported; lipids are stored.

Order 1. Chrysomonadida

This group, represented by fossils from Upper Cretaceous to recent deposits, is widely distributed in salt, brackish and fresh water. Although chromatophores occur in the majority, colorless holozoic species are common and there is a marked trend toward holozoic nutrition in many pigmented types. Formation of pseudopodia is fairly common. Some species possess delicate pseudopodia which superficially resemble the myxopodia of Foraminiferida and capture food in comparable fashion. Others form lobopodia. Non-flagellated amoeboid and palmella stages are not unusual and have become the dominant phase in some life-cycles. Most species measure less than 50μ and the majority probably less than half as much, although some fossils exceed 100μ. One, two, or three flagella may be present; if two, they may be equal or unequal in length. Mastigonemes (pantonematic pattern) have been reported on the flagellum, or on one of two flagella (200).

In the simpler species a thin periplast permits moderate amoeboid activity. Cortical specialization has followed several trends: (1) the deposition of a secreted layer just outside the periplast; (2) development of a lorica (Fig. 4. 2, A, F) or a test (Fig. 4. 2, C, D); (3) development of

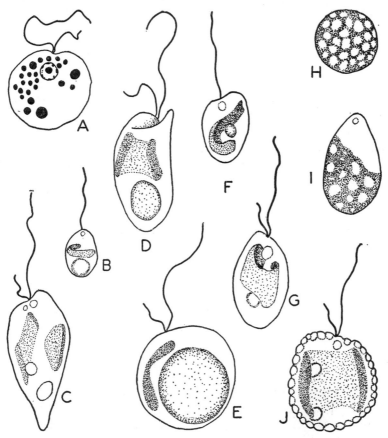

Fig. 4. 1. A. *Ochromonas granularis* Doflein, showing nucleus and stored lipids; chromatophore omitted; x2100 (after D.). B. *Chromulina annulata* Conrad; ribbon-like chromatophore, mass of leucosin; x3000 (after C.). C. *Ochromonas reptans* Conrad; two chromatophores, leucosin granules; x2250 (after C.). D. *O. granularis*, typical chromatophore, moderate leucosin; x2025 (after Doflein). E. *O. granularis*, chromatophore displaced by large mass of leucosin; x1875 (after Doflein). F. *Chromulina commutata* Pascher, narrow chromatophore, leucosin granules; x1400 (after P.). G. Unusually large chromatophore in *Ochromonas* sp.; schematic (after Pascher). H, I. *Chrysapsis fenestrata* Pascher, posterior and lateral views of net-like chromatophore; x2100 (after P.). J. *Ochromonas pinguis*, large chromatophore, peripheral zone of lipoid globules; x2500 (after Conrad).

a siliceous skeleton (Fig. 4. 9). The simplest type of secreted covering is represented by the layer of "mucus" in *Monas* (Fig. 4. 3, E, F). Secreted membranes may be thin, or they may be quite thick as in some of the Coccolithina (Fig. 4. 2, K). Siliceous scales (Fig. 4. 2, G) or calcareous coccoliths (Fig. 4. 10) are added to the membrane in various genera. In

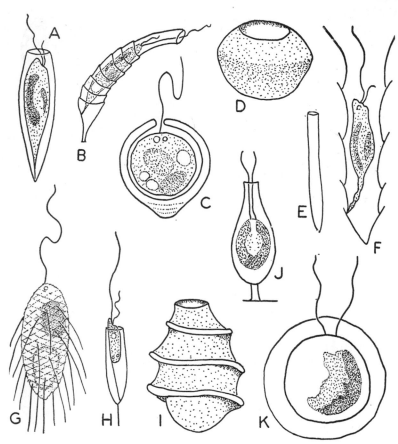

Fig. 4. 2. A. *Dinobryon utriculus* Stein, single loricate flagellate; x700 (after Pascher). B. *Hyalobryon voigtii* Lemmermann, a single flagellate (colony shown in Fig. 1. 2, C); x1300 (after Pascher). C. *Chrysococcus umbonatus* with test; x1845 (after Conrad). D. *Pseudokephyrion minutissimum* Conrad, test only; x3000 (after C.). E. *Dinobryon stokesii* Lemmermann, single lorica; x960 (after Pascher). F. Single lorica of *Hyalobryon lauterbornii* Lemmermann; x810 (after Pascher). G. *Mallomonas dentata* Conrad, chromatophore, covering of siliceous scales (some bearing spines); x2500 (after C.). H. *Stokesiella lepteca* (Stokes) Lemmermann; x1045 (after S.). I. *Kephyrion spirale* (Lackey) Conrad, test only; x4500 (after C.). J. *Derepyxis amphora* Stokes; x880 (after S.). K. *Syracosphaera mediterranea* Lohmann, shell membrane after dissolution of coccoliths in acid; single chromatophore; basal portions of the two equal flagella; x2100 (after L.).

some cases the inorganic elements apparently are adherent to the "shell-membrane"; in others, they are embedded in the membrane (46, 186).

Chromatophores (Fig. 4. 1, B-J) range from the network of *Chrysapsis fenestrata* to a broad plate or a narrow ribbon. In addition to the usual colors—golden-yellow to greenish-brown or brown—blue chromatophores have been reported (173). Pigments include chlorophyll *a*, lutein (a xanthophyll) and β-carotene. Supposed pyrenoids have been noted in some species but not in many others. A stigma may or may not be present in chlorophyll-bearing forms. Species within a genus, such as *Chromulina,*

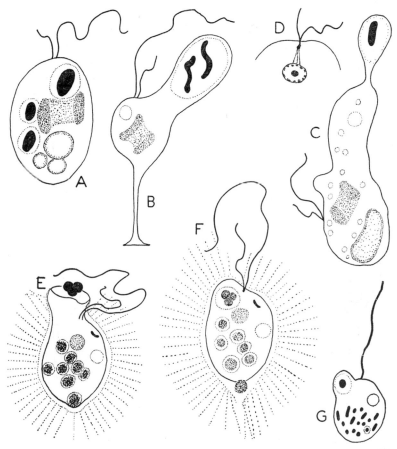

Fig. 4. 3. A-D. *Ochromonas granularis* (after Doflein). A. Specimen with three food vacuoles, chromatophore, leucosin; x1650. B. Temporarily attached form just after ingestion of food; x2100. C. An amoeboid form just after ingesting a bacillus; x2025. D. Nucleo-flagellar connections; x2100. E, F. *Monas vestita,* during and after ingestion of food; note stigma and outer layer of "mucus" with radiating strands; x1800 approx. (after Reynolds). G. *Oikomonas termo* (Ehrbg.) Kent, ingestion of a bacterium just completed; x1600 (after Lemmermann).

apparently may differ in this respect. Some colorless species (Fig. 4. 3, E) also have a stigma. Scattered granules, similar in color to the stigma, have been reported in *Dinobryon, Mallomonas,* and other genera (247).

Solid food is ingested by certain pigmented species as well as colorless types (Fig. 4. 3), and ingestion often involves formation of a food-cup in a particular region. Refractile granules of leucosin (Fig. 4. 1, B-F) and

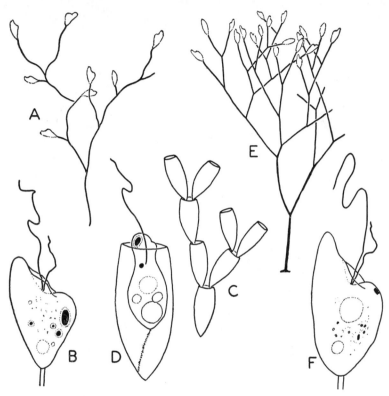

Fig. 4. 4. Apochlorotic colonial types. A, B. *Cladonema pauperum* Pascher; portion of colony and a single flagellate; schematic (after P.). C, D. *Codonodendron ocellatum* Pascher; portion of the *Dinobryon*-like colony, and a single flagellate showing stigma and ingested food; schematic (after P.). E, F. *Monadodendron distans* Pascher; portion of a colony and a single flagellate; schematic (after P.).

globules of oil or fat (Fig. 4. 1, A) are stored. Leucosin is sometimes considered a polysaccharide but its chemical nature has not been determined.

Colonial organization is fairly common. Arboroid types include *Hyalobryon* (Fig. 1. 2), *Dinobryon, Codonodendron* (Fig. 4. 4, C) and certain other loricate genera and also such naked forms as *Monadodendron* (Fig. 4. 4, E) and *Cladonema* (Fig. 4. 4, A). Spheroid colonies are developed in *Synura* (Fig. 4. 5, C), *Cyclonexis* (Fig. 4. 5, A, B), *Syncrypta* (Fig. 1. 2, F) and *Chrysosphaerella* (Fig. 4. 5, D), among others.

Life-cycles often include palmella or amoeboid stages. Species such as *Ochromonas granularis* (66) may become amoeboid (Fig. 4. 3, C) without losing the flagella. Amoeboid and flagellate phases occur in *Chrysamoeba radians* (66) and *Myxochrysis paradoxa* (203); in the latter (Fig. 4. 6, A-C), the amoeboid stage develops into a large plasmodium. A palmella is dominant in life-cycles of the Chrysocapsina; an amoeboid phase, in the Rhizochrysodina.

Endogenous formation of a siliceous cyst wall is characteristic (247). As

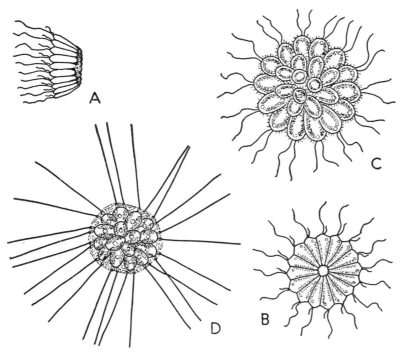

Fig. 4. 5. A, B. *Cyclonexis annularis* Stokes, lateral and surface views; x720 (after S.). C. *Synura uvella* Ehrbg.; x310 (after Stein). D. *Chrysosphaerella longispina* Lauterborn; x540 (after L.).

encystment begins in *Uroglena sonaica* (Fig. 4. 7, H-J) the flagella are resorbed and the organism, packed with fat globules, becomes approximately spherical. Within the cytoplasm, a thin membrane is laid down. This membrane gradually increases in thickness, a pore is differentiated, and surface decorations are added. The development of a plug finally closes the pore, separating the endocystic from the subsequently discarded ectocystic protoplasm (50). The plug may or may not be siliceous in different species. In either case, the plug is either dislodged or dissolved in excystment. Encystment in *Ochromonas granularis* (66) resembles that in *Uroglena*. In certain other types, such as *Chromulina* (67), part or all of the external cytoplasm is drawn into the cyst before the pore is plugged. Binucleate cysts, described in *Dinobryon divergens* (Fig. 4. 7, D-F), apparently are the result of nuclear division just before encystment (92). The mature cyst (Fig. 4. 7) is approximately spherical, but the external appear-

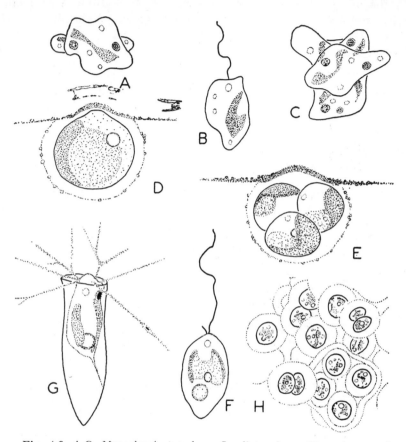

Fig. 4.6. A-C. *Myxochrysis paradoxa;* flagellate phase (B) and stages in development of the plasmodium; x1600 (after Pascher). D-F. *Kremastochrysis pendens* Pascher; non-flagellated forms suspended from the umbrella-like float, and a flagellate stage; schematic (after P.) G. Formation of slender pseudopodia in *Dinobryon sertularia;* diagrammatic (after Pascher). H. Gleocystis-stage in *D. sertularia;* diagrammatic (after Pascher).

ance varies with the presence or absence of surface decorations and a collar around the pore.

Following suggestions of Pascher (214), five suborders may be recognized: Euchrysomonadina, with a dominant flagellate stage; Silicoflagellina, with a siliceous skeleton; Coccolithina, with a peripheral zone of coccoliths; Rhizochrysodina, with a dominant amoeboid or plasmodial stage; Chrysocapsina, with a dominant palmella.

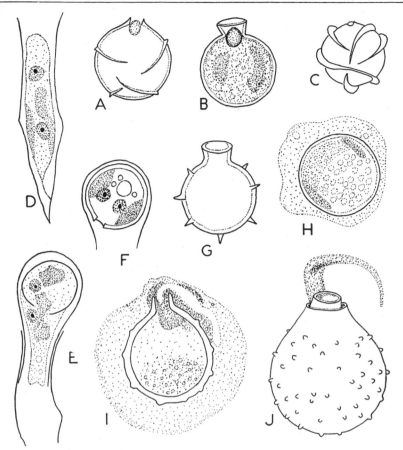

Fig. 4. 7. A. Cyst of *Cladonema pauperum;* diagrammatic (after Pascher). B. Cyst of *Ochromonas reptans;* x2250 (after Conrad). C. Cyst of *Cellionella palensis;* diagrammatic (after Pascher). D-F. *Dinobryon divergens;* completion of nuclear division (D) is sometimes followed by encystment (E) to produce a binucleate cyst (F); x1210 (after Geitler). G. Cyst of *Ochromonas ludibunda;* x1500 (after Conrad). H-J. Stages in development of the cyst wall in *Uroglena soniaca;* diagrammatic (after Conrad).

Suborder 1. Euchrysomonadina. On the basis of flagellar equipment four families have been erected: *Chromulinidae,* with one flagellum, *Syncryptidae,* with two equal flagella; *Ochromonadidae,* with one long and one short flagellum; and *Prymnesiidae,* with three flagella.

Family 1. Chromulinidae. This group includes solitary and colonial types. The type genus, *Chromulina* Cienkowski (67), contains small naked flagellates with one band-like chromatophore or two smaller ones (Fig. 4. 1, B, F). Amoeboid changes in form are observed in some species.

Solitary types without a lorica or test are assigned to *Chromulina* and several additional genera: *Amphichrysis* Korshikoff (165); *Chrysapsis* Pascher (202; Fig. 4. 1, H, I);

Chrysoglena Wislouch (207); and the colorless *Oikomonas* Kent (181; Fig. 4. 3, G). *Cyrtophora* Pascher and *Pedinella* Wysotzki contain stalked sessile forms (202). In *Epicystis* Pascher (211), there is an epiphytic non-flagellated phase and a *Chromulina*-like stage. In *Pyramidochrysis* Pascher, the firm membrane is decorated with three longitudinal flanges, while that of *Mikroglena* Ehrenberg contains numerous granules (202). These granules may be analogous to the cortical inclusions of *Ochromonas pinguis* (Fig. 4. 1, J), or possibly represent primitive coccoliths.

Solitary loricate forms include: *Bicoeca* Clark, without chromatophores (181); *Chrysococcocystis* Conrad (47); *Lepochromulina* Scherffel (202); *Histiona* Voigt, colorless forms with a stalked lorica (225); and *Palatinella* Lauterborn, with several slender pseudopodia ("tentacles") surrounding the flagellum (202).

A test (or "shell") is present in the following: *Chrysococcus* Klebs (174; Fig. 4. 2, C), swimming types with a spheroid to ovoid test; *Kephyrion* Pascher (Fig. 4. 2, I), tests with a recognizable neck (51).

Siliceous plates cover much or all of the body in *Mallomonas* Perty and *Chrysosphaerella* Lauterborn. *Mallomonas* (Fig. 4. 2, G) includes about sixty species (45, 48), differing in shape and arrangement of the scales, and in the presence or absence of spines. *Chrysosphaerella* (Fig. 4. 5, D) includes spheroid colonial forms. "*Pseudomallomonas* Chodat" apparently falls within the limits of the genus *Mallomonas* (48).

Loricate colonial types without chlorophyll are included in *Codonodendron* Pascher (Fig. 4. 4, C, D) and *Stephanocodon* Pascher (224). In the latter, the simple four- or eight-rayed colonies are formed by the adherence of loricae near their basal ends. Also, *Poteriodendron* Stein may belong in this group (93).

Family 2. Syncryptidae. Two flagella of equal length are characteristic. *Syncrypta* Ehrenberg (Fig. 1. 2, F) includes spherical colonies with the flagellates embedded in a granular matrix (202). In *Chlorodesmus* Phillips (202), pairs of flagellates, adherent basally, are aligned in simple band-like colonies. The cortex is decorated with spines, perhaps similar to the siliceous scales of *Synura*. *Derepyxis* Stokes (Fig. 4. 2, J) includes solitary loricate types (202, 207).

Family 3. Ochromonadidae. This group, like the Chromulinidae, includes both solitary and colonial forms. *Ochromonas* Wysotzki (Fig. 4. 1, A, C, D-F) contains flagellates with a flexible periplast permitting changes in shape and sometimes the formation of a temporary protoplasmic "stalk" (Fig. 4. 3, B). A detailed cytological description is available for *Ochromonas granularis* Doflein (66). The colorless homologue of *Ochromonas,* the genus *Monas* Müller (including *Sterromonas* Kent and *Physomonas* Kent) contains at least 13 species (243), some of which have a stigma. The periplast of *Monas vestita* (Stokes) Reynolds is enclosed in a mucous envelope from which radiate slender mucous threads (Fig. 4. 3, E, F).

Additional solitary non-loricate types are assigned to the following genera: *Ochryostylon* Pascher, usually sessile with, or sometimes without, a delicate stalk (222); *Stomatochone* Pascher, colorless, usually sessile with a short protoplasmic stalk (222); *Kremastochrysis* Pascher (Fig. 4. 6, D-F), with an *Ochromonas*-like flagellate stage and a dominant non-flagellated form attached to a float which suspends the organism from the surface of the water (223).

Solitary loricate types are included in several genera. The lorica of the sessile *Epipyxis* Ehrenberg resembles that in the colonial *Dinobryon* (Fig. 4. 2, A). A stalked *Dinobryon*-type lorica is characteristic of *Stylopyxis* Bolochonzew (202) and the colorless *Stokesiella* (210; Fig. 4. 2, H). A cup-shaped to spheroid lorica bears a slender stalk in *Arthrochrysis* Pascher (222) and the colorless *Arthropyxis* (222). The stalked lorica of *Poteriochromonas* Scherffel (202) is funnel-shaped; that of *Stenocodon* Pascher (222) is compressed laterally, with an oval mouth. The stalkless lorica of *Pseudokephyrion* Pascher (Fig. 4. 2, D)—including "*Kephyriopsis* Pascher and Ruttner"—is cup-shaped.

Arboroid colonies of loricate flagellates are included in *Dinobryon* Ehrenberg (1, 202; Fig. 4. 2, A) and its colorless homologue, *Hyalobryon* Lauterborn (202; Fig. 4. 2, B). In the apochlorotic *Codonobotrys* Pascher (222), a cluster of individually stalked loricate flagellates is attached to a heavy common stalk. *Stylobryon* Fromentel (181), another colorless type, probably belongs to the Ochromonadidae.

Non-loricate arboroid colonies are assigned to several genera. In *Anthophysis* Bory and *Cephalothamnion* Stein, both colorless genera, the flagellates are attached in clusters at the ends of branching stalks (181). In the colorless *Cladonema* Kent em. Pascher (Fig. 4. 4, A), *Monadodendron* Pascher (Fig. 4. 4, E, F), and *Dendromonas* Stein (181), as well as in the pigmented *Chrysodendron* Pascher (207) which often forms small colonies, the flagellates are attached singly to branches of the stalk.

More or less spherical colonies are characteristic of several genera. In *Uroglena* Ehrenberg, including *Uroglenopsis* (181), the flagellates are embedded in a gelatinous matrix (50). No matrix is evident in *Cyclonexis* Stokes (Fig. 4. 5, A, B), *Skadovskiella* Korshikoff (163, 165), *Synochromonas* Korshikoff (165), or *Synura* Ehrenberg (165; Fig. 4. 5, C).

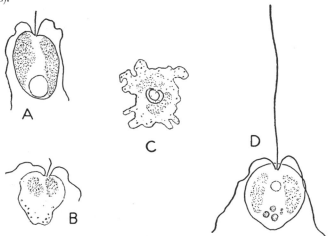

Fig. 4. 8. Prymnesiidae. A. *Prymnesium parvum* Carter; x2360 (after C.). B, C. *Platychrysis pigra* Geitler, flagellate and amoeboid stages; x1850 (after Carter). D. *Chrysochromulina parva* Lackey; x3200 approx. (after L.).

Family 4. Prymnesiidae. These flagellates have three flagella and a rather plastic body. *Prymnesium* Massart (Fig. 4. 8, A) has a short inactive median flagellum and two long ones, and usually two yellow-green to brown chromatophores. *Platychrysis* Geitler (Fig. 4. 8, B, C) shows both amoeboid and flagellate stages. The flagella of the latter resemble those of *Prymnesium,* but are coiled and apparently inactive in the amoeboid stage (31). In *Chrysochromulina* Lackey (174; Fig. 4. 8, D) the median flagellum is longer than the other two, which are usually trailed in swimming.

An interesting occurrence of *Prymnesium parvum* has been reported in brackish fish-ponds in Palestine. Populations of the flagellates reached 500,000/ml. or more, changing the color of the water to a yellowish-brown and resulting in death of many fish (241).

Suborder 2. Silicoflagellina. These widely distributed marine flagellates occur also as fossils from Upper Cretaceous to recent deposits. Their taxonomic position was in doubt until Borgert (124) discovered the flagellum and assigned them to a new group, the Silicoflagellata. Their

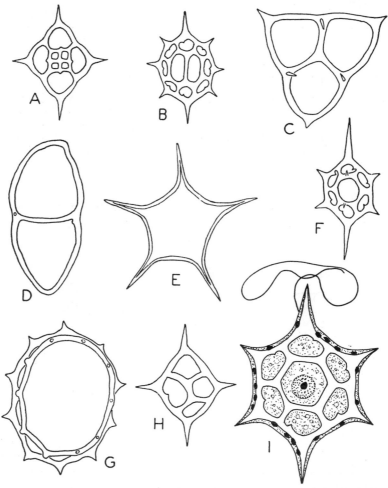

Fig. 4. 9. Silicoflagellina. A-H. Skeletons of various species (after Deflandre). A. *Dictyocha crux*, x560. B. *D. octonaria*, x560. C. *D. triacantha* Ehrbg. from Tertiary, x345. D. *D. navicula* Ehrbg. from Tertiary, x345. E. *Vallacerta hortoni* Hanna from Upper Cretaceous, x540. F. *Dictyocha speculum* Ehrbg. from Tertiary, x630. G. *D. polyactis* Ehrbg. from Tertiary, x630. H. *D. fibula* Ehrbg., x560. I. *D. speculum*, showing nucleus, chromatophores, and internal skeleton; x1320 (after Deflandre).

characteristic siliceous skeleton varies in complexity in different species and has been interpreted as an external structure and as an internal one (Fig. 4. 9, I) by different workers (63). A single flagellum, numerous greenish-brown chromatophores, and stored granules of leucosin appear to be typical.

Generic boundaries have been disputed to some extent. However,

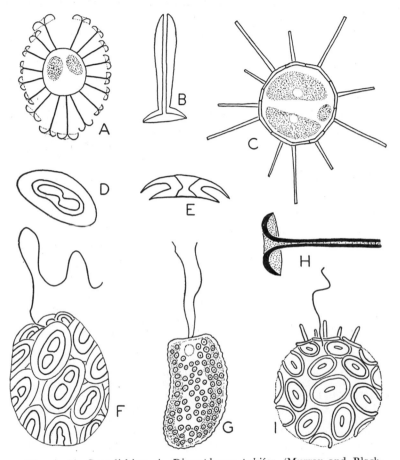

Fig. 4. 10. Coccolithina. A. *Discosphaera tubifer* (Murray and Black-man) Lohmann; schematic optical section showing rhabdoliths and two chromatophores; x2800 (after L.). B. Single rhabdolith from *Rhabdosphaera claviger* M. and B.; schematic (after Murray and Blackman). C. *Rhabdosphaera stylifer* Lohmann, showing nucleus and two chromatophores; x2100 (after L.). D. Surface view of placolith from *Coccolithus wallichi;* x2700 (after Lohmann). E. Optical section of coccolith from *Coccolithus pelagica;* schematic (after Murray and Blackman). F. *Coccolithus wallichi* showing arrangement of coccoliths; x1800 (after Lohmann). G. *Hymenomonas roseola* Stein; x750 (after Pascher). H. Longitudinal section of rhabdolith from *Discosphaera tubifer;* schematic (after Lohmann). I. *Syracosphaera pulchra,* anterior coccoliths with spines; x1900 (after Lohmann).

Lyramula Hanna and *Vallacerta* Hanna (Fig. 4. 9, E) seem to be limited to fossils from the Upper Cretaceous (101), while *Dictyocha* Ehrenberg (Fig. 4. 9, A-D, F-I) includes both living and fossil types. According to Deflandre (63), three generic names—*Cannophilus, Distephanus,* and *Mesocena*—have been applied to forms which fall within the genus *Dictyocha.*

Suborder 3. Coccolithina. These flagellates occur mostly in salt and brackish water; only a few are known from fresh water (46). Collections in the Mediterranean (186) have yielded specimens from depths of 400 meters, but the flagellates are most abundant in the zone above 100 meters. Two flagella of equal length have been observed most frequently. However, a few supposedly uniflagellate types have been reported; also flagella have not yet been seen in some described species. Either two or four chromatophores may be present (179). Little is known about the life-cycles. Schiller (250) has noted in two species of *Calyptrosphaera* stages which suggest fission within the theca, and he has pointed out the need for study of the Coccolithina in cultures.

The diagnostic feature of the group is the possession of calcareous *coccoliths* which may be deposited at the surface of, or embedded within, a secreted membrane (Fig. 4. 2, K). Several types of coccoliths (186, 250) are known. Solid platelets (*discoliths*), with or without spines, are found in *Syracosphaera* (Fig. 4. 10, I), *Pontosphaera,* and related genera. Perforated coccoliths (*tremaliths*) are of various kinds. Elongated tremaliths containing a long canal are known as *rhabdoliths* (Fig. 4. 10, A, B), while simple perforated plates or double discs joined by a short canal are called *placoliths* (Fig. 4. 10, D). Structure of the coccoliths has been used as a basis for differentiating several families (127).

Representative genera include *Acanthoica* Lohmann (46, 250), *Calyptrosphaera* Lohmann (250), *Coccolithus* Schwarz (Fig. 4. 10, F), *Deutschlandia* Lohmann (250), *Discosphaera* Haeckel (250; Fig. 4. 10, A), *Halopappus* Lohmann (250), *Hymenomonas* Stein (127, 174; Fig. 4. 10, G), *Pontosphaera* Lohmann (186, 260), *Rhabdosphaera* Haeckel (250; Fig. 4. 10, C), *Syracosphaera* Lohmann (31, 186, 250), and *Umbilicosphaera* Lohmann (186).

It is uncertain whether *Hymenomonas* actually belongs in this group. A pitted "shell" has been reported in *H. roseola* Stein (174), although discrete coccoliths have been described in *H. danubiensis* (127).

Suborder 4. Rhizochrysodina. The amoeboid phase is dominant. In the Rhizochrysidae, the amoeboid stages are solitary or else form loose aggregates with pseudopodial attachments. Genera which develop true plasmodia are placed in the Myxochrysidae.

Family 1. Rhizochrysidae. Net-like aggregates of naked organisms (221) are produced in *Rhizochrysis* Pascher (Fig. 4. 11, E) *Chrysarachnion* Pascher (Fig. 4. 11, G), and the apochlorotic *Leukapsis* Pascher. Similar aggregates of thecate organisms (221) are formed in *Heliapsis* Pascher

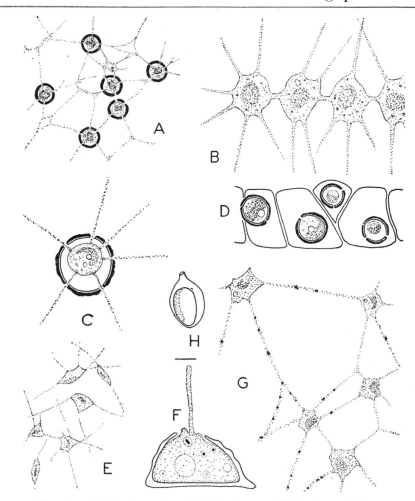

Fig. 4. 11. Rhizochrysodina. A. *Heliapsis mutabilis* Pascher, x550 approx. (after P.). B. *Chrysidiastrum catenatum* Lauterborn, x810 (after Pascher). C. *Heliochrysis erodians* Pascher, x1380 approx. (after P.). D. *H. sphagnicola* Pascher, parasitic stage; x610 approx. (after P.). E. *Rhizochrysis planktonica,* x1400 (after Pascher). F. *Heterolagynion oedogonii* Pascher, x3300 (after P.). G. *Chrysarachnion insidians* Pascher; diagrammatic (after P.). H. *Lagynion subovatum* Prescott and Croasdale; x665 (after P. & C.).

(Fig. 4. 11, A). *Chrysidiastrum* Lauterborn (Fig. 4. 11, B) shows a strong tendency to produce chains instead of definite nets.

The family also contains a number of **solitary types.** *Chrysamoeba* Klebs includes **naked amoeboid forms** with a *Chromulina*-like flagellate stage, as in *C. radians* (66). **Thecate species** are assigned to several genera. *Heterolagynion* Pascher (Fig. 4. 11, F) includes epiphytic forms, the lorica of which lacks a neck like that in *Lagynion* (201, 211; Fig. 4. 11, H). *Eleutheropyxis* Scherffel (248), *Plagiorhiza* Pascher, *Platytheca* Stein, *Kybotion* Pascher, and the colorless *Leukopyxis* Pascher resemble *Lagynion* and *Heterolagynion* in that pseudopodia emerge through a single opening in the lorica

(221). In *Diporidion* Pascher and *Porostylon* Pascher, there are two pores in the lorica, which bears a stalk in the latter genus (220). In *Heliochrysis* Pascher (Fig. 4. 11, C, D), intracellular parasites of *Sphagnum,* as well as in the similar *Heliaktis* Pascher, *Chrysocrinus* Pascher, and *Stephanoporos* Pascher, the spheroid to ovoid theca contains a number of pores through which slender pseudopodia extend (220).

Family 2. Myxochrysidae. In the life-cycle of *Myxochrysis* Pascher (203), a *Chromulina*-like flagellate becomes an amoeboid stage which

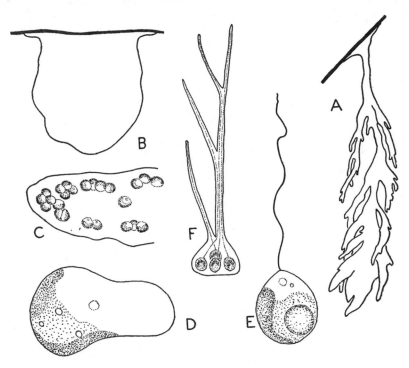

Fig. 4. 12. Chrysocapsina. A-E. *Celloniella palensis* (after Pascher). A. Branching palmella in flowing water, x10. B. Bladder-like stage attached to stones in dripping water. C. Tip of branch of palmella, highly magnified. D. Amoeboid stage. E. Flagellate stage (C-E, diagrammatic). F. *Nageliella natans* Scherffel, x400 approx. (after S.).

develops into a plasmodium (Fig. 4. 6, A-C). The mature plasmodium secretes a thick brownish membrane, within which many uninucleate naked stages or cysts are produced. Cysts hatch into the flagellate or amoeboid forms.

Suborder 5. Chrysocapsina. The dominant stage is a palmella which may grow to a fairly large size in some genera.

Family 1. Chrysocapsidae. The organisms are distributed throughout the matrix which is not highly differentiated, and fission may occur in any region of the palmella. The matrix of *Chrysocapsa* Pascher (202) is spheroid; that of *Phaeoplaca* Chodat (90), discoid; and the matrix of *Phaeosphaera* West and West (202) is cylindrical and sometimes branched.

Family 2. Celloniellidae. Fission does not occur throughout the palmella. Instead, growth of the palmella depends upon fission in particular groups of cells which produce new points of growth. In the sessile *Celloniella* Pascher (Fig. 4. 12, A-E), the form of the palmella varies with rate of flow of the water in which the mass is suspended (209).

Family 3. Hydruridae. Hydrurus Agardh (152, 202) resembles *Celloniella,* but the palmella is profusely branched and sometimes reaches a length of 25-30 cm. Furthermore, fission apparently is limited to the apical flagellates in each branch.

Family 4. Nageliellidae. Species of *Nageliella* Correns (202, 248), usually epiphytic on algae, develop a somewhat discoid palmella from the free surface of which extends a bundle of gelatinous filaments. In *N. natans* (Fig. 4. 12, F) each filament contains an axial fibril which arises from the apical end of each flagellate (248).

Order 2. Heterochlorida

These flagellates have a flexible periplast, typically two unequal flagella, and one or more pale yellow-green or pale yellow chromatophores. The occurrence of pyrenoids is doubtful. Leucosin and lipids are stored.

Endogenous encystment (Fig. 4. 13, A-D) is known in *Chloromeson* and *Myxochloris* (216). Unlike that in Chrysomonadida, the cyst wall is composed of two unequal valves and lacks a pore. In addition to the encystment of uninucleate stages, an entire plasmodium of *Myxochloris sphagnicola* may become enclosed in a membrane apparently containing pectins (213).

On the basis of life-histories, the Heterochlorida may be divided into three suborders: Euheterochlorina, with a dominant flagellate stage; Rhizochloridina, with a dominant non-flagellated or plasmodial stage; Heterocapsina, with a dominant palmella.

Suborder 1. Euheterochlorina. Representative types (Fig. 4. 13) include *Chloromeson* Pascher (31, 212, 216), *Nephrochloris* Geitler and Gemisi (31), and *Olithodiscus* Carter (31).

Suborder 2. Rhizochloridina. *Myxochloris* Pascher (Fig. 4. 14, D-G), *Rhizochloris* Pascher (Fig. 4. 14, A-C) and the loricate *Stipitococcus* West and West (Fig. 4. 14, H) are included. The dominant stage in *Rhizochloris arachnoides* is a small amoeba with slender pseudopodia and a number of chromatophores. An amoeboid plasmodium also has been observed. The flagellate stage apparently has only one flagellum. The vegetative stage of *Myxochloris sphagnicola* (213) is a plasmodium

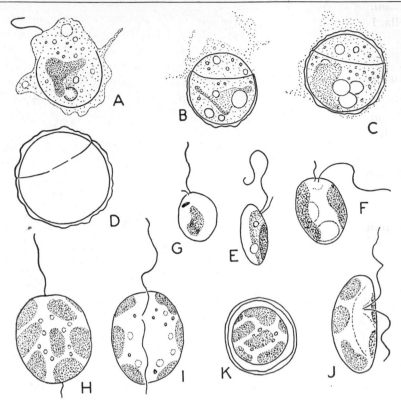

Fig. 4. 13. Euheterochlorina. A-D. *Chloromeson agile* Pascher; successive
stages in encystment; schematic (after P.). E, F. *Nephrochloris salina* Carter,
different aspects; E, x2430; F, x2250 (after C.). G. *Chloromeson parva* Carter;
stigma, one chromatophore; x2360 (after C.). H-J. *Olithodiscus luteus*
Carter; dorsal, ventral and ventro-lateral views; x1340 (after Carter). K.
Cyst of *O. luteus;* x1275 (after C.).

endoparasitic in *Sphagnum*. Encystment of the plasmodium is followed
by division into smaller plasmodia or into uninucleate flagellate or amoeboid stages.

Suborder 3. **Heterocapsina.** A palmella is the dominant stage (218)
in *Chlorosaccus* Luther, *Gleochloris* Pascher, and *Malleodendron* Pascher.

Order 3. Cryptomonadida

These typically biflagellate forms are widely distributed in fresh
water and fairly common in salt and brackish waters. Some marine types
have been reported as parasites (symbiotes?) in Radiolarida. A rather
constant body form, often with dorso-ventral differentiation, is characteristic. A ventral groove, or "pharynx," is commonly present. The
"pharynx" of *Chilomonas,* which may represent the primitive condition,
is an open groove extending almost to the middle of the body (Fig. 4.

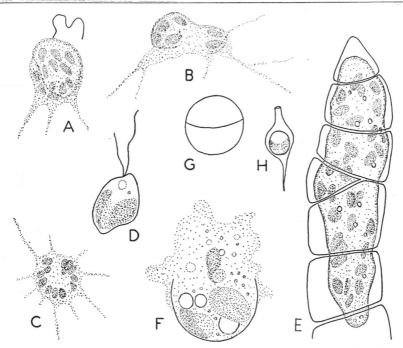

Fig. 4. 14. A-C. *Rhizochloris arachnoides* Carter (after C.). A. Flagellate stage, x2180. B. Amoeboid stage, x2080. C. Amoeboid stage, x1540. D-G. *Myxochloris sphagnicola,* diagrammatic (after Pascher): flagellate stage (D), plasmodium endoparasitic in *Sphagnum* (E), developing cyst (F) and mature cyst (G). H. *Stipitococcus capense* Prescott and Croasdale, x665 (after P. & C.).

15, L). In *Cryptomonas* (Fig. 4. 15, I-K) the posterior part of the pharynx is closed ventrally to form a pouch, leaving the anterior portion an open furrow. The wall of the pharynx and the groove is lined with refractile granules ("trichocysts"), usually visible in the living organism. These inclusions disappear in old cysts of *Cryptomonas* (110). The pharynx of the holozoic genus *Cyathomonas* is a pouch extending posteriorly and ventrally from the anterior end of the body, and partly encircled anteriorly by an incomplete ring of trichocysts.

One, two, or more chromatophores have been reported. The single chromatophore of *Cryptomonas* (Fig. 4. 15, I) and similar types is bilobed, a condition interpreted occasionally as two separate chromatophores. The chromatophore is usually brown, less commonly green, blue-green, or red. Storage of starch and lipids is characteristic. The colorless *Chilomonas paramecium* synthesizes amylopectin and β-amylose (117), and pectins have been reported in the endocyst in *Cryptomonas* (110).

Three families have been recognized: Cryptochrysidae, Cryptomonadidae, and Nephroselmidae.

Family 1. Cryptochrysidae. The pharyngeal groove, along which rows

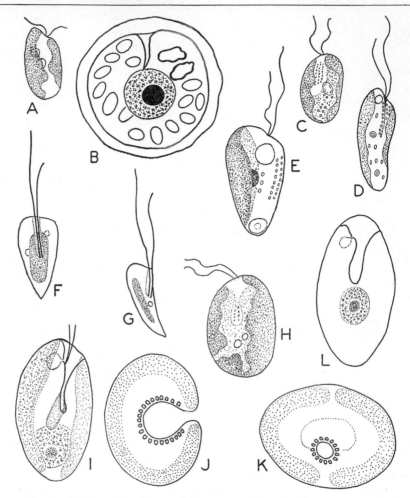

Fig. 4. 15. Cryptochrysidae and Cryptomonadidae. A. *Chroomonas vectinsis* Carter, x1845 (after C.). B. Cyst of *Cryptomonas ovata,* x1770 approx. (after Hollande). C. *Rhodomonas baltica* Karsten, x1440 (after Carter). D. *Cryptochrysis commutata* Pascher, x1250 (after P.). E. *Rhodomonas lacustris* Pascher and Ruttner, x2400 (after Pascher). F, G. *Cryptochrysis atlantica* Lackey, ventral and lateral views; x1450 approx. (after L.). H. *Chroomonas baltica* (Büttner) Carter, x1560 (after C.). I. *Cryptomonas similis* Hollande, showing gullet, contractile vacuole, chromatophore and nucleus; diagrammatic (after H.). J, K. *Cryptomonas ovata,* diagrammatic cross-sections anterior to, and at the level of the nucleus; note gullet, "trichocysts" and chromatophore (after Hollande.) L. *Chilomonas paramecium,* showing "pharyngeal" groove and contractile vacuole; diagrammatic (after Hollande).

of refractile granules are usually visible, is not closed ventrally. The flagella arise near the anterior end of the groove.

Chlorophyll-bearing types include: *Chroomonas* Hansgirg (31, 202; Fig. 4. 15, A, H), with one or two bluish chromatophores; *Cryptochrysis* Pascher (175, 202; Fig. 4. 15, D,

F, G); *Cyanomonas* Oltmanns (173, 202), with several blue-green chromatophores); *Rhodomonas* Karsten (31, 202; Fig. 4. 15, C, E), with reddish-brown chromatophores. **Chromatophores are lacking** in *Chilomonas* Ehrenberg (110; 202; Fig. 4. 15, L).

Family 2. Cryptomonadidae. In these flagellates, the pharyngeal groove is closed ventrally, through part or all of its length, to form a pouch. The genus *Cryptomonas* Ehrenberg (110, 202; Fig. 4. 15, I-K) includes chlorophyll-bearing forms; *Cyathomonas* Fromentel (110, 202), color-

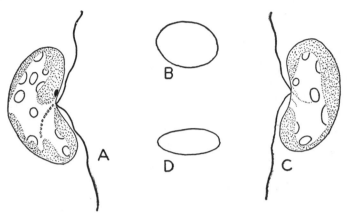

Fig. 4. 16. A. *Protochrysis phaeophycearum* Pascher, x1500 (after P.). B. Cross-section of same. C. *Nephroselmis olivacea* Stein, x1300 (after S.). D. Cross-section of *N. olivacea*.

less holozoic types in which the pharyngeal pouch is a functional gullet.

Family 3. Nephroselmidae. As compared with the other families, the Nephroselmidae show a modification of the primitive cryptomonad organization. If the origin of the flagella is considered anterior, these flagellates have become shortened along the anterior-posterior axis and correspondingly elongated along the transverse axis. The result is a more or less bean-shaped body, with the pharyngeal-groove and bases of the flagella lying near the equatorial plane. The two genera, *Nephroselmis* Stein (202; Fig. 4. 16, C, D) and *Protochrysis* Pascher (202; Fig. 4. 16, A, B) differ in shape of the body in cross-section.

Order 4. Dinoflagellida

This order includes many living species and a variety of fossil types (75). Most dinoflagellates are marine, forming an important part of the plankton. Under conditions not yet fully understood, the populations of certain dinoflagellates in localized areas may increase tremendously, sometimes to densities above 5,000,000 per liter. The result is discoloration of the water—"red water" or "red tide"—and luminescence at night, and occasionally the death of fish in large numbers (42).

The flagellate stages of many species fall within the range, 10-200µ. However, certain parasitic types grow to diameters of 600-700µ, while *Noctiluca scintillans* sometimes measures 1.0-1.5 mm. A *girdle* and a *sulcus* are characteristic of flagellate stages (Fig. 4. 17, A). The girdle (or annulus) is a groove which usually encircles the body in a descending, or sometimes in an ascending, left-hand spiral, although the two ends may meet in the same plane. In extreme cases, the girdle may trace more than one complete spiral, or it may be rudimentary as in *Protonoctiluca*

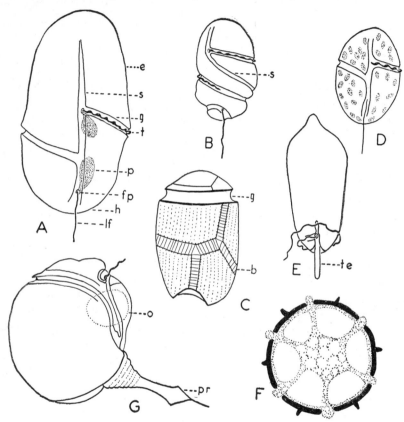

Fig. 4. 17. A. *Gymnodinium dorsum* Kofoid and Swezy; pusules opening into flagellar pores; x940 (after K. & S.). B. *Cochliodinium lebourae* Kofoid and Swezy, spirally twisted sulcus; x525 (after K. & S.). C. *Amphidiniopsis kofoidi* Woloszynska, dorsal view showing intercalary bands; x630 (after W.). D. *Gymnodinium racemosus* Kofoid and Swezy, showing chromatophores; x475 (after K. & S.). E. *Protonoctiluca (Protodinifer) tentaculatum* (K. & S.), showing tentacle arising from sulcus; x700 approx. (after Kofoid and Swezy). F. Cross-section of apical horn, *Ceratium hirundinella;* diagrammatic (after Entz). G. *Erythropsis extrudens* Kofoid and Swezy, showing prod and outline of ocellus; x450 (after K. & S.). Key: *b,* intercalary band; *e,* epicone; *fp,* flagellar pore; *g,* girdle; *h,* hypocone; *lf,* longitudinal flagellum; *o,* ocellus; *p,* pusule; *pr,* prod; *s,* sulcus; *t,* transverse flagellum; *te,* tentacle.

(Fig. 4. 17, E). The *epicone* and *hypocone,* the anterior and posterior regions of the body, are marked off by the girdle. The sulcus (longitudinal furrow) is usually a straight groove intersecting the girdle, although it may undergo spiral torsion (Fig. 4. 17, B), or may be expanded into a "ventral area." From the sulcus arise the tentacle of *Protodinifer* (Fig. 4. 17, E) and the prod of *Erythropsis* (Fig. 4. 17, G). The two flagella of typical species also emerge through one or two flagellar pores in the sulcus (Fig. 4. 17, A). The transverse flagellum is often ribbon-like (81, 159). Occasionally, as in *Peridinium,* species within a genus may differ in this respect (81).

A theca, composed of a cellulose-like substance and sometimes impregnated with calcium salts, is present in many dinoflagellates. The typical theca is composed of plates, the margins of which may be separated by intercalary bands (Fig. 4. 17, C) in some species and particularly in older specimens. The theca covering the epicone is known as the *epitheca;* the posterior portion, as the *hypotheca.* The two are joined by the *girdle band,* composed of one or more girdle plates. The theca may, as in *Ceratium hirundinella* (Fig. 4. 17, F), contain pores through which extend cytoplasmic papillae.

There are commonly two vacuoles, or *pusules* (Fig. 4. 17, A), usually containing a pink fluid. A slender canal extends directly from each pusule to a flagellar pore or else joins a common canal which opens externally. Intake of fluid has been observed in pusules of *Peridinium steini* (155), and it has been suggested that a pusule may function as a pharynx for intake of liquids and possibly solid particles (159).

The nucleus usually contains one or more nucleoli and many long chromosomes whose beaded structure may persist through mitosis. Chromatophores, present in many species, are often golden-brown to dark-brown, although sometimes yellow, orange, green, or bluish-green. In addition, various cytoplasmic pigments—either diffuse or forming granules or globules—occur in many species (159). The known pigments include chlorophyll *a,* chlorophyll *c,* peridinin, β-carotene, dinoxanthin, diadinoxanthin, and neodinoxanthin (Chapter I). Stored reserves include starch and lipids. A simple stigma, composed of red granules, occurs in various fresh-water species. At the other extreme, the Pouchetiidae possess a complex *ocellus* (Fig. 1. 17, H, M) composed of a lens and a mass of pigment.

The group shows a strong trend toward holozoic feeding, as indicated by inclusions which are obviously ingested food in many species and apparently such in others. In the chlorophyll-free *Cochliodinium rosaceum* (159), *Oxyrrhis marina* (Fig. 4. 18, C), *Noctiluca milaris,* and others, holozoic nutrition is undoubtedly important. Ingested food also appears in various chlorophyll-bearing species of *Gymnodinium, Gyrodinium,* and *Amphidinium* (159). Furthermore, such thecate types as

Ceratium (106) may capture and presumably digest microorganisms outside the theca by means of pseudopodial nets (Fig. 4. 18, A, B). These pseudopodia apparently arise from cytoplasmic papillae extending through pores in the theca (Fig. 4. 17, F).

The life-cycle may be apparently simple, or may show dimorphism or polymorphism (159). Sexual phenomena have been reported in several species (Chapter II). Fission is typically oblique (Fig. 2. 2, A-H) and, in armored species, involves regeneration of different portions of the theca by the daughter organisms. In contrast, as represented by certain species of *Glenodinium*, fission may occur within the theca and the

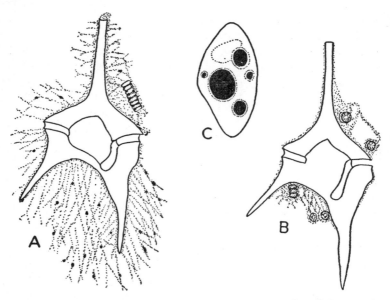

Fig. 4. 18. A, B. Capture of microorganisms by pseudopodial networks in *Ceratium hirundinella;* x425 (after Hofender). C. *Oxyrrhis marina,* four food vacuoles, nucleus in outline; x885 (after Hall).

daughter organisms are liberated as naked forms which later secrete a theca. In other cases, each daughter organism develops a new theca before it emerges from the parental one. Incomplete separation after fission may result in chains (Fig. 4. 19, I), which are characteristic of certain species but not of others. Reproductive cysts, known in a number of species, may be more or less spherical (*"pyrocystis"* type) or sometimes crescentic ("crescent-cysts"). In *Gymnodinium lunula* (159), crescent-cysts are developed within a pyrocystis-stage. Fresh-water species may produce a thick-walled protective cyst, as in *Ceratium hirundinella* (Fig. 2. 15, A). A palmella stage in which fission occurs is known in some species, and is the dominant phase in *Gleodinium* (Fig. 4. 24, C, D). In *Amyloodinium ocellatum* (Fig. 4. 19, A-C) the dominant phase

is a large ovoid stage, attached by means of a hold-fast to the gill-fila-
ments of a marine fish. At maturity, the parasite drops off the host,
the hold-fast is retracted, and the corresponding gap in the cellulose-
membrane is closed. Fission then results in many gymnodinioid flagellates which seek a new host (26, 199).

The Dinoflagellida may be divided into five suborders: *Prorocentrina*,
with a bivalve theca but no distinct girdle or sulcus; *Gymnodinina*,

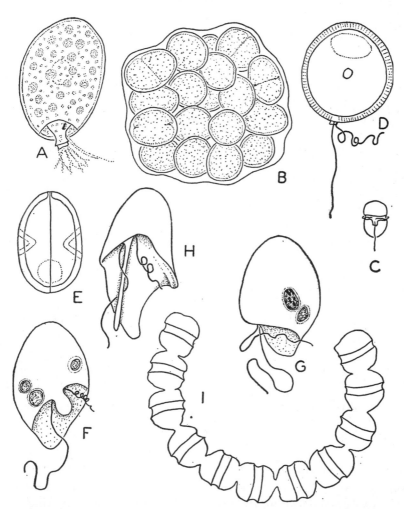

Fig. 4. 19. A-C. *Amyloodinium ocellatum,* x475 (after Nigrelli); parasitic stage (A), palmella stage after several fissions (B), and flagellate stage
(C). D, E. *Exuviella perforata* Gran, valve view and ventral view; x1230
approx. (after Lebour). F, G. *Oxyrrhis marina* Dujardin, ventral and dorsal
views; x875 (after Hall). H. *Oxyrrhis tentaculifera* Conrad, ventral view
showing long tentacle; x1890 (after C.). I. *Gymnodinium catenatum,* chain
formation; x350 (after Graham).

athecate types with a girdle and sulcus; *Peridinina,* with a theca composed of separate plates; *Dinocapsina,* with a dominant palmella and a gymnodinioid flagellate stage; *Dinococcina,* in which the life-cycle may include a dominant "pyrocystis" or crescent-cyst stage, a floating or attached palmella, and a gymnodinioid flagellate stage.

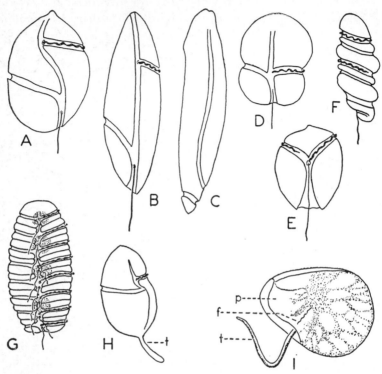

Fig. 4. 20. A. *Gyrodinium melo* Kofoid and Swezy, x475 (after K. & S.). B. *Gyrodinium submarinum* Kofoid and Swezy, x425 (after K. & S.). C. *Torodinium teredo* Kofoid and Swezy, x300 (after K. & S.). D. *Gymnodinium dissimile* Kofoid and Swezy, x475 (after K. & S.). E. *Amphidinium dentatum* Kofoid and Swezy, x575 (after K. & S.). F. *Cochliodinium pulchellum* Lebour, x720 (after K. & S.). G. *Polykrikos schwartzi* Bütschli, x250 (after K. & S.). H. *Pavillardia tentaculifera* Kofoid and Swezy, x475 (after K. & S.). I. *Noctiluca scintillans,* x60 approx. (after K. & S.). Key: *f,* longitudinal flagellum; *p,* oral pouch; *t,* tentacle.

Suborder 1. Prorocentrina. This group includes *Exuviella* Cienkowski (178, 249, 252), *Porella* Schiller (252) and *Prorocentrum* Ehrenberg (249, 252). *Exuviella perforata* (Fig. 4. 19, D, E) is a small marine flagellate with a thick bivalved theca. Each somewhat flattened valve is approximately circular in outline and shows a central conical invagination. The flagella, emerging anteriorly through pores in one valve, show a differentiation into longitudinal and transverse types. The two chromatophores are yellowish-brown to yellow.

Suborder 2. Gymnodinina. These are the unarmored dinoflagellates (159) which, except for some of the Gymnodiniidae, are limited to salt water.

Family 1. Protonoctilucidae. The girdle and sulcus are rudimentary and the transverse flagellum is not appreciably flattened. A tentacle is characteristic. There are no chromatophores and the organisms are holozoic. The family includes *Oxyrrhis* Dujardin (Fig. 4. 19, F-H) and *Protonoctiluca* Fabre-Domergue (*Protodinifer* Kofoid and Swezy). In the latter (Fig. 4. 17, E), the shallow girdle extends about one-fourth the circumference of the body, and the tentacle, arising from the sulcus, is more pronounced than in *Oxyrrhis*. Only one pusule is present. The longitudinal flagellum is vestigial in *Protonoctiluca* but is well developed in *Oxyrrhis*.

Family 2. Gymnodiniidae. Both girdle and sulcus are well developed and the transverse flagellum is typically flattened. Neither a tentacle nor an ocellus is present. Some species lack chromatophores and a number are holozoic. The family, represented in both fresh and salt water, includes the following genera: *Amphidinium* Claparède and Lachmann, *Cochliodinium* Schütt, *Gymnodinium* Stein em. Kofoid and Swezy, *Gyrodinium* Kofoid and Swezy (*Spirodinium* Schütt), *Massartia* Conrad (10, 31, 44), and *Torodinium* Kofoid and Swezy (159).

The genera may be distinguished largely on the basis of their girdles. The girdle forms one complete turn in *Amphidinium, Gymnodinium, Massartia,* and *Torodinium.* In *Amphidinium* (Fig. 4. 20, E) the girdle is anterior, so that the epicone is small. The girdle of *Gymnodinium* (Figs. 4. 17, D, 4. 20, D) lies nearer the equator and the ends are displaced less than one-fifth the body length. *Massartia* differs from *Gymnodinium* in having a larger and broader epicone. The girdle of *Torodinium* (Fig. 4. 20, C) is posterior and the epicone is several times as long as the hypocone. Posteriorly, the sulcus forms a half-turn around the body before intersecting the girdle. In *Gyrodinium* (Fig. 4. 20, A, B) the girdle makes 1.0 to less than 1.5 turns and the ends are displaced not less than one-fifth the body length. The girdle of *Cochliodinium* (Fig. 4. 20, F) makes 1.5 or more turns around the body.

Family 3. Polykrikidae. The single genus, *Polykrikos* Bütschli (Fig. 4. 20, G), contains permanent linear somatellae composed of two, four, or eight zooids as a rule, although chains of sixteen have been observed. Nematocysts are present. All species are marine.

Family 4. Noctilucidae. The diagnostic feature is a mobile tentacle which arises in the sulcal area and extends posteriorly. The known species are marine. Two genera, *Noctiluca* Suriray and *Pavillardia* Kofoid and Swezy, are assigned to the family. *Pavillardia* (Fig. 4. 20, H) shows a body and girdle of the *Gymnodinium*-type, but a longitudinal flagellum is absent and a tentacle arises from the posterior end of the sulcus. In *Noctiluca* (Fig. 4. 20, I), the mature organism is a highly vacuolated spheroidal stage ranging from 200 to 2,000µ in diameter. A short longitudinal flagellum is present. The girdle is vestigial, and the posterior portion of the sulcus is expanded into a deep pouch extending to the base of the tentacle.

Suborder 3. Peridinina. A theca composed of separate plates is characteristic. Such features as relative size of the epicone and hypocone, extent and torsion of the girdle and sulcus, and the number and arrangement of thecal plates are important in taxonomy. Three small families differ from the rest with respect to development of the girdle. In the Sinodiniidae, the girdle is an irregular belt, instead of a groove, and shows

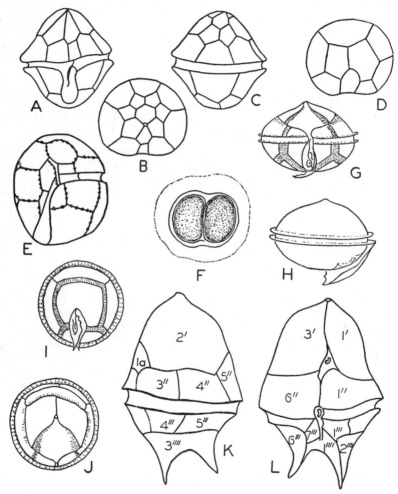

Fig. 4. 21. A-D. *Glenodinium cinctum* Ehrbg., x580 approx. (after Eddy); ventral, apical, dorsal, and antapical views. E. *Hemidinium nasutum* Stein, ventral view showing girdle, sulcus, and thecal plates; schematic (after Woloszynska). F. Palmella stage of *H. nasutum;* schematic (after Baumeister). G-J. *Diplopsalis lenticulata* Bergh; x700 (after Lebour); ventral, lateral, antapical, and apical views. K, L. *Heterodinium scrippsi* Kofoid, dorsal and ventral views; plates numbered; x350 (after K.).

no marginal ridges (*lists*), whereas the Lissodiniidae and Podolampidae have undergone apparently complete suppression of the girdle (197).

The thecal plates are usually differentiated into several circular series (Fig. 4. 21, K, L), and those in each series are conventionally numbered in order, beginning at the left of the sulcal plane or the mid-ventral suture (155). The *apical plates* (numbered 1′, 2′, 3′ . . .) extend to the apical pore, or sometimes to a closing plate if the pore is closed. *Anterior intercalary plates* (1a, 2a, . . .) lie between the apical and precingular plates. *Precingular plates* (1″, 2″, . . .) extend from the apical or intercalary plates to the girdle. The *girdle plates* (1, 2, 3 . . .) line the girdle. *Postcingular plates* (1′″, 2′″, . . .) lie in the hypotheca between the girdle and the antapical plates (or posterior intercalary plates, if present). *Posterior intercalary plates* (1p, 2p, . . .) lie between the postcingular and antapical plates. The *antapical plates* (1″″, 2″″, . . .) cover the posterior end. According to Kofoid's (155) system, the plate formula for *Diplopsalis lenticulata* (Fig. 4. 21, G-J) would be written as 3′1a6″5′″1″″ (omitting the girdle).

Family 1. Glenodiniidae. These flagellates have a thin theca, with plates which are not easily distinguished, and were at one time assigned to the Gymnodinina. Most species are known from fresh water (74, 254). *Glenodinium* (Ehrbg.) Stein (Fig. 4. 21, A-D) differs from *Glenodiniopsis* Woloszynska (Fig. 4. 22, M-O) in number of postcingular plates and in a sulcus limited mostly or entirely to the hypocone. In *Hemidinium* Stein (9, 11; Fig. 4. 21, E), the girdle extends only about a half turn. A palmella stage (Fig. 4. 21, F), resembling that of *Gleodinium,* has been reported for *H. nasutum* (11).

Family 2. Gonyaulacidae. The thecal plates are distinct and one antapical plate is characteristic. Several species are known from fresh water (74, 254), but most are marine. Species of *Gonyaulax* have attracted attention as the source of mussel poisoning on the Pacific Coast (Chapter X) and as a component of "red tide."

The family includes *Chalubinskia* Woloszynska (Fig. 4. 22, E-H), *Dinosphaera* Kofoid and Michener (157), *Diplopsalis* Bergh (178), *Entzia* Lebour (178), and *Gonyaulax* Diesing em. Kofoid (156). *Gonyaulax* (Fig. 1. 5, A, B) has a plate formula of 1-6′0-3a6″66′ ″1p1″ ″, while *Dinosphaera* (Fig. 4. 22, A-D) has 5 postcingulars and no posterior intercalary. *Diplopsalis* (Fig. 4. 21, G-J) has the plate formula, 3′1a6″5′ ″1″ ″; *Entzia,* 4′1-2a7″5′ ″1″ ″, but otherwise similar to *Diplopsalis. Chalubinskia* (Fig. 4. 22, E-H) has 3 postcingular and 1 antapical plates.

Family 3. Peridiniidae. The thecal plates are distinct as in the Gonyaulacidae, but there are two antapical plates. Many species occur in fresh water (74, 254); others are marine.

The family includes *Peridinium* Ehrenberg (64; Fig. 4. 22, I-K), *Amphidiniopsis* Woloszynska (Figs. 4. 17, C, 4. 22, L), *Glenodiniopsis* Woloszynska (Fig. 4. 22, M-O),

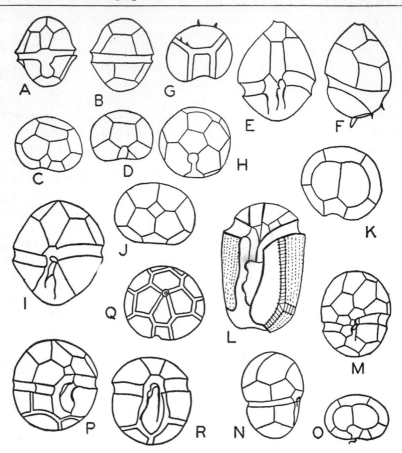

Fig. 4. 22. A-D. *Dinosphaera palustris*, ventral, dorsal, apical, and antapical views; x575 approx. (after Eddy). E-H. *Chalubinskia tatrica* Woloszynska, ventral, left lateral, apical, and antapical views; x675 (after W.).
I-K. *Peridinium kulczynskii* Woloszynska, ventral, apical, and antapical
views; x835 (after W.). L. *Amphidiniopsis kofoidi* Woloszynska, ventral view;
x630 (after W.). M-O. *Glenodiniopsis steinii* Woloszynska, ventral view;
x850 (after W.). P, Q. *Sphaerodinium limneticum* Woloszynska, x800 approx. (after W.). R. *Staszicella dinobryonis* Woloszynska, x720 (after W.).

Sphaerodinium Woloszynska (Fig. 4. 22, P, Q), and *Staszicella* Woloszynska (Fig. 4. 22,
R). The epitheca is distinctly smaller than the hypotheca in *Amphidiniopsis* and
Staszicella. The two genera are distinguished by the sulcus, which extends to the apex
in *Amphidiniopsis*, but only a short distance into the epitheca in *Staszicella*.

Family 4. Ceratiidae. The epitheca is prolonged into an apical horn,
the hypotheca into two or three posterior horns (Fig. 4. 23, A). The genus
Ceratium Schrank is represented by many marine and several fresh-water
species (74, 80). Species differ in number of posterior horns, in form and
length of the horns, and in the sculpturing and detailed pattern of the
thecal plates. Of the posterior horns, the *accessory* may be vestigial or

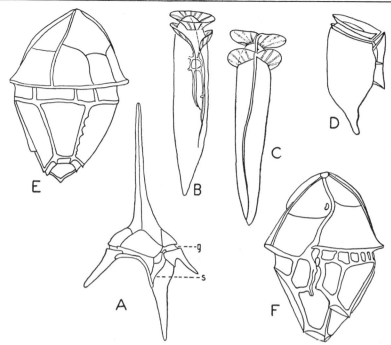

Fig. 4. 23. A. *Ceratium hirundinella* O. F. M., ventral view; diagrammatic (after Entz). B-D. *Dinophysis diegensis* Kofoid, ventral, dorsal, and right lateral views; B, C, x445; D, x505 (after K.). E, F. *Dolichodinium lineatum* (Kofoid and Michener) Kofoid and Adamson, dorsal and ventral views; x700 (after K. & A.). Key: *g*, gullet; *s*, sulcal area.

lacking, as in some strains of *C. furcoides* (Levander) Langhans; in addition, the *antapical* and *postequatorial* horns may be reduced in length, as in *C. brachyceros* Daday. The apical horn shows differences in length and is curved instead of straight in *C. cornutum* Schrank and *C. curvirostre* Kaas.

Family 5. Dinophysidae. The elongated body is laterally compressed, with a minute epitheca, and the girdle is bordered by prominent flanges ("collars"). The theca consists of right and left valves, joined in a median suture. Known species are marine. *Dinophysis* Ehrenberg (252; Fig. 4. 23, B-D), *Phalacroma* Schiller (252) and *Oxyphysis* Kofoid are included in the family.

Family 6. Heterodiniidae. The precingular ledge (or list) is well developed but the postcingular ledge is reduced or absent. A ventral pore lies between the apical pore and the single flagellar pore. The plate formula is 3-4′0-1a6″6 6-7′ ″3″ ″. The family includes *Heterodinium* Kofoid (Fig. 4. 21, K, L) and *Dolichodinium* Kofoid and Adamson (Fig. 4. 23, E, F).

Suborder 4. Dinocapsina. A dominant palmella and a gymnodinioid flagellate stage are the diagnostic features. In the palmella, a pectic sheath may enclose the usual cellulose membrane. The suborder includes only the family Gleodiniidae. The type genus is *Gleodinium* Klebs (132, 270; Fig. 4. 24, C, D). Structure and division of the nucleus in *G. montanum*, as noted in material from cultures (242), conform to the dinoflagellate

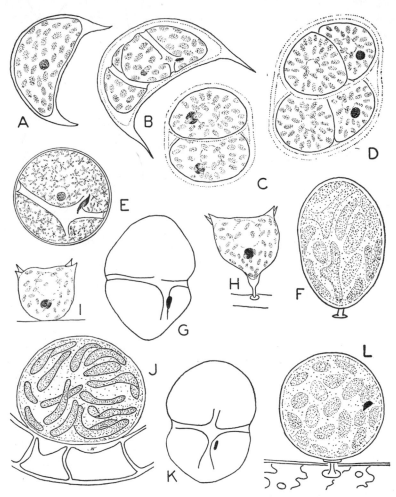

Fig. 4. 24. A, B. *Cystodinium iners* Geitler, crescent-cysts containing one and two organisms, the latter showing gymnodinioid features; x500 approx. (after Thompson). C, D. *Gleodinium montanum* Klebs, showing fission in palmella stage; x625 approx. (after Thompson). E. *Hypnodinium sphaericum* Klebs; stigma (beneath sulcus), chromatophores, large reddish oil globule; x195 approx. (after Thompson). F, G. *Dinopodiella phaseolus* Pascher, sessile and flagellate stages; x1250 approx. (after P.). H, I. *Tetradinium javanicum* Klebs, stalked and unstalked forms; schematic (after Thompson). J, K. *Phytodinedria procubans* Pascher, sessile and flagellate stages; x1250 approx. (after P.). L. *Stylodinium sphaera* Pascher, x940 approx. (after P.).

pattern. *Urococcus* Kützing, in which the palmella shows a very thick and stratified sheath, has been referred to the family (259).

Suborder 5. Dinococcina. The dominant phase is a "pyrocystis" or a "crescent-cyst" stage and the flagellate stages are typically gymnodinioid. The non-flagellated stage, which may be floating or sessile, has a cellulose membrane and is enclosed in a sheath composed of pectin.

Family 1. Phytodiniidae. This group, as the most typical family, shows the characteristics of the suborder. A number of American species have been described by Thompson (270).

The family includes: *Cystodinedria* Pascher (226); *Cystodinium* Klebs (11, 91, 205, 208, 225; Fig. 4. 24, A, B); *Dinastridium* Pascher (205); *Dinopodiella* Pascher (226; Fig. 4. 24, F, G); *Dissodinium* Klebs (205); *Hypnodinium* Klebs (205; Fig. 4. 24, E); *Phytodinedria* Pascher (226; Fig. 4. 24, J, K); *Phytodinium* Klebs (205); *Raciborskia* Woloszynska (219); *Stylodinium* Klebs (11, 205, 226; Fig. 4. 24, L); and *Tetradinium* Klebs (91, 205; Fig. 4. 24, H, I). According to Baumeister (11), the flagellate stage of "*Stylodinium tarnum*" has a theca composed of discrete plates.

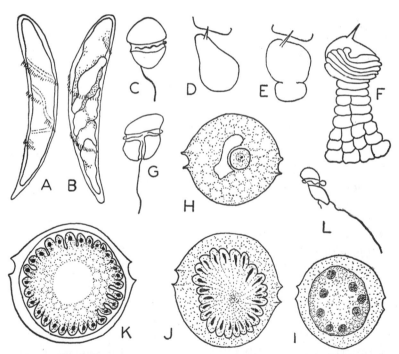

Fig. 4. 25. A-C. *Blastodinium spinulosum* Chatton; undivided parasitic stage (A), x210; trophocyte and four small sporocytes (B), x210; flagellate stage (C), x1840 (after C.). D-F. *Haplozoon dogieli*, x325 (after Shumway); young parasite (D), trophocyte and gonocyte (E), gonocytes and sporocytes (F). G. Flagellate stage of *Haplozoon clymenellae*, x1520 (after Shumway). H-L. *Coccodinium duboscqi* Chatton and Biecheler, parasitic in *Peridinium* sp.; growth and nuclear division preceding merogony (H-K); gymnodinioid stage (L); schematic (after C. & B.).

Family 2. Blastodiniidae. This group (36) includes intestinal parasites of copepods and sessile polychaetes; ectoparasites of copepods, annelids, and salpids; intracellular parasites of Siphonophora, tintinnioid ciliates, Radiolarida, and eggs of copepods; and parasites of the body cavity in copepods. *Amyloodinium* (Fig. 4. 19, A-C) parasitizes the gills of marine fish (26, 199), and *Oodinium limneticum* (118) has been described from the same location in fresh-water fish. Chromatophores are present in some Blastodiniidae and absent in others.

In a representative life-cycle (Fig. 4. 25, D-F), the young parasite divides into two cells, a "trophocyte" and a "gonocyte." The latter undergoes a number of divisions to produce "sporocytes" which develop into gymnodinioid flagellates. In the meantime, the trophocyte may divide into a second gonocyte and a trophocyte. The second gonocyte produces another generation of sporocytes, and the procedure may be repeated several times. This pattern is not followed in *Amyloodinium,* which apparently does not produce differentiated trophocytes and gonocytes.

The family includes *Amyloodinium* Hovasse and Brown (115; Fig. 4. 19, A-C), *Apodinium* Chatton (36), *Atelodinium* Chatton (36), *Blastodinium* Chatton (36; Fig. 4. 25, A-C), *Chytriodinium* Chatton (36), *Duboscquella* Chatton (36), *Endodinium* Hovasse (111), *Haplozoon* Dogiel (258; Fig. 4. 25, D-G), *Merodinium* Chatton (37) from Radiolarida, *Oodinium* Chatton (36, 112), *Paradinium* Chatton (37), *Protoodinium* Hovasse (112), *Syndinium* Chatton (36), and *Trypanodinium* Chatton (36). *Coccodinium* Chatton and Biecheler (Fig. 4. 25, H-L), parasitic in other dinoflagellates, possibly should be referred to this family.

Family 3. Ellobiopsidae. These ectoparasites of Crustacea resemble the Blastodiniidae in their parasitic stages, but the known free-living stages show no obvious relationships to dinoflagellates. Therefore, the taxonomic position of the group is uncertain. *Ellobiopsis* Caullery (32) is the type genus.

Order 5. Phytomonadida

These flagellates are mostly ovoid to spherical, but various spindle-shaped, hemispherical, flattened, and spirally twisted types are known. *Medusochloris phiale,* one of the more unusual forms, is a medusa-like flagellate which swims mainly by contractions of the body (204). Except in the Polyblepharidae, the body is enclosed in a distinct membrane, composed at least partly of cellulose. In the Phacotidae the membrane is impregnated with calcium salts to form a "shell." One to eight, but usually two or four flagella are present. The flagella of membrane-covered species may emerge through one opening or through individual flagellar pores (Fig. 4. 26, A-C). In the first case the flagella may or may not arise from a cytoplasmic papilla. Contractile vacuoles vary in number and position, but there are often two near the bases of the flagella. A single large green chromatophore is typical, although two or more smaller ones occur in some species. The usual single chromatophore is cup-shaped (Fig. 4. 26, B). However, lobed, "H-shaped," and other variations are known (Fig. 4. 26, D-J). The nucleus lies in the inner zone of cytoplasm. One or more pyrenoids, typically spherical or ellipsoidal, but sometimes U-shaped (Fig. 4. 26, K, L), are characteristic of green species. A single pyrenoid usually

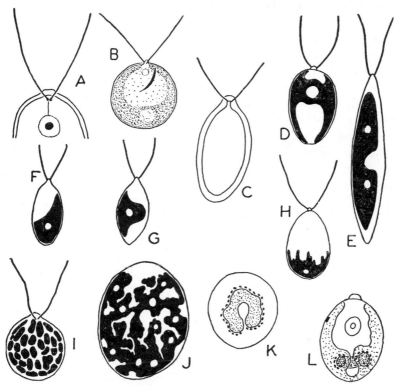

Fig. 4. 26. A-C. Flagellar insertions, schematic: A, *Chlamydomonas nasuta* (after Kater); B. *C. longirubra* (after Pascher); C. *C. ignova* (after Korshikoff). D-J. Various types of chromatophores; pyrenoids indicated as clear areas; schematic: D. *Chlamydomonas obversa* (after Pascher); E. *Chlorogonium elongatum* (after Dangeard); F, G. *Chlamydomonas ovata* (after Dangeard); H. *C. basistellata* (after Pascher); I. *C. korschikoffia* (after Pascher); J. *Gigantochloris permaxima* (after Pascher). K, L. Unusual U-shaped pyrenoid; optical cross-section and lateral view of flagellate; starch granules surround the pyrenoid; diagrammatic (after Vlk).

lies in the posterior portion of the cup-shaped chromatophore; if several pyrenoids are present, distribution is variable. A stigma, when present, is a rounded or discoid structure, usually anterior in position but sometimes near the equator. Starch, stored both in the cytoplasm and around the pyrenoid of chlorophyll-bearing species, occurs also in colorless types. Lipids, although usually not abundant, are stored by many phytomonads. A reddish pigment (red haematochrome) also may be accumulated in the cytoplasm. In the "haematocyst" of *Haematococcus pluvialis* (76), the pigment may completely mask the chromatophore.

The order may be divided into four families of solitary types and two of colonial genera. Among the solitary types, a typical cellulose membrane is lacking in the Polyblepharidae, present in the Chlamydomonadidae, and is replaced by a calcified bivalve "shell" in the Phacotidae. In the Haematococcidae cytoplasmic processes extend into the thick membrane. Colonial genera with a well developed matrix are assigned to the Volvocidae; those without a matrix, to the Spondylomoridae. The order has been surveyed by Pascher (206).

Family 1. Polyblepharidae. These are typically solitary types with somewhat flexible bodies. The genus *Raciborskiella* (Fig. 4. 27, C) is exceptional in that 4-8 flagellates may remain attached posteriorly to form simple aggregates (colonies?). Flagellar numbers of 1, 3, 4, 5, 6, and 8 have been reported, but there are usually two or four. Binary fission occurs in the flagellate stage, and the old flagella are usually inherited by the daughter organisms.

Chlorophyll-bearing species are included in the following genera: *Bipedinomonas* Carter (31), *Dunaliella* Teodoresco (227), *Heteromastix* Korshikov (31), *Korschikoffia* Pascher (206), *Mesostigma* Lauterborn (206; Fig. 4. 27, D), *Pedinomonas* Korshikov (206), *Phyllocardium* Korshikov (162), *Pocillomonas* Steinecke (206), *Polyblepharides* Dangeard (206), *Pyramimonas* Schmarda (*Pyramidomonas* Stein) (23, 31, 89, 217; Fig. 4. 27, J), *Raciborskiella* Wislouch (206; Fig. 4. 27, C), *Spermatozopsis* Korshikov (206), *Trichloris* Scherffel and Pascher (206; Fig. 4. 27, K), and *Tetrachloris* Pascher and Jahoda (227) with four flagella. **Chromatophores are lacking** in *Furcilla* Stokes (206) and *Polytomella* Aragão (128, 206; Fig. 4. 27, F-I). Cytological descriptions are available for *Pyramimonas* (25, 89) and *Polytomella* (128).

Collodictyon Carter (244; Fig. 4. 27, A, B) is sometimes included in this family. However, the plastic body, the longitudinal groove, the development of pseudopodia, and the lack of information on stored reserves cast doubt upon the validity of such an assignment.

Family 3. Chlamydomonadidae. There is a well-developed membrane, within which fission results in two or more daughter organisms (**Fig. 4. 28, A, B**). In *Chlamydomonas nasuta* (129), the plane of the first fission is perpendicular to the long axis of the body. Prior to fission, the organism either rotates within its membrane through an arc of 90°, or else the chromatophore and nucleus change their positions accordingly (Fig. 4. 28, C, D). The plane of the second fission is perpendicular to that of the first. In various species, adhesion of the membranes of adjacent organisms often produces large palmellar aggregates or sheets, especially during growth on a solid medium.

The following genera contain chlorophyll-bearing species: *Apiococcus* Korshikov (206), *Brachiomonas* Bohlin (206; Fig. 4. 28, F), *Carteria* Diesing (23, 206, 217; Fig. 4. 28, O), *Characiochloris* Pascher (206), *Chlamydomonas* Ehrenberg (94, 206, 217; Fig. 4. 28, C, D, G), *Chlorobrachis* Korshikov (206, 256), *Chloroceras* Schiller (207), *Chlorogonium* Ehrenberg (206; Fig. 4. 26, E), *Chlorophysema* Pascher (206), *Diplostauron*

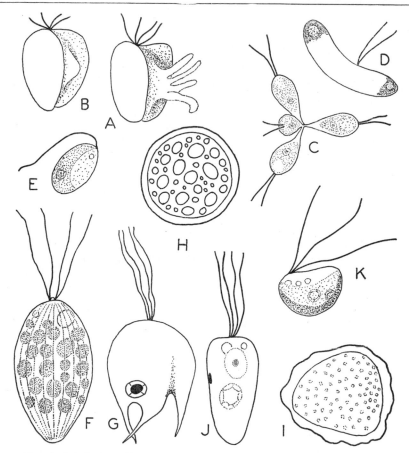

Fig. 4. 27. A, B. *Collodictyon triciliatum* Carter, basal portions of flagella, longitudinal groove, development of pseudopodia; x500 (after Rhodes). C. *Raciborskiella uroglenoides* Swirenko, cluster of four flagellates; x1000 approx. (after S.). D. *Mesostigma viride* Lauterborn; x2100 approx. (after Pascher). E. *Pedinomonas minor* Korshikoff, x3100 approx. (after K.). F-I. *Polytomella citri* Kater; living specimen showing stored food and contractile vacuoles (F); a variation in form, nucleus stained (G); young (H) and older (I) cysts; x2250 (after K.). J. *Pyramimonas tetrarhynchus* Schmarda; large chromatophore indicated as transparent to show positions of pyrenoid, anterior nucleus and contractile vacuoles; x1425 (after Geitler). K. *Trichloris paradoxa* Scherffel; x1100 approx. (after S.).

Korshikov (217), *Fortiella* Pascher (206), *Gigantochloris* Pascher (206; Fig. 4. 26, J), *Gleomonas* Klebs (206), *Hypnomonas* Korshikov (206), *Lobomonas* Dangeard (206; Fig. 4. 28, E), *Malleochloris* Pascher (206), *Nautococcus* Korshikov (161; Fig. 4. 28, I, J), *Phyllomonas* Korshikov (206), *Platychloris* Pascher (206), *Platymonas* West (31; Fig. 4. 28, N), *Scourfieldia* West (206; Fig. 4. 28, K, L), *Selenochloris* Pascher (207, 217), *Sphaerellopsis* Korshikov (206), *Sphenochloris* Pascher (206), *Spirogonium* Pascher (206), and *Stylosphaeridium* Geitler (206).

Colorless types are included in the following genera: *Chlamydoblepharis* Francé (206), *Hyalogonium* Pascher (206; Fig. 4. 28, M), *Parapolytoma* Jameson (121), *Polytoma* Ehrenberg (206), *Tetrablepharis* Senn (206), and *Tussetia* Pascher (206).

Four flagella are present in *Carteria, Chlorobrachis, Fortiella, Malleochloris, Platymonas, Spirogonium,* and *Tetrablepharis;* one flagellum in *Chloroceras* and *Selenochloris;* **two flagella** in other genera. In some cases, a knowledge of life-cycles is essential for assignments to genera. In *Nautococcus,* for example, there is a typical flagellate stage in addition to the floating stage without flagella (Fig. 4. 28, I, J); in *Stylosphaeridium,* the corresponding non-flagellated stage is epiphytic on filamentous algae. Cytological descriptions are available for *Chlamydomonas* (129), *Chlorogonium* (102), *Parapolytoma* (121), and *Polytoma* (78, 110).

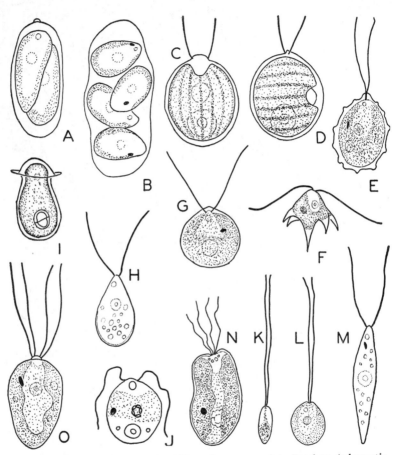

Fig. 4. 28. A, B. Fission in *Chlamydomonas seriata* Pascher (schematic, after P.). C, D. Rotation of the chromatophore at the beginning of fission in *Chlamydomonas nasuta;* schematic (after Kater). E. *Lobomonas rostrata* Hazen; x1750 approx. (after H.). F. *Brachiomonas westiana* Pascher; x690 approx. (after P.). G. *Chlamydomonas umbonata* Pascher, x1330 approx. (after P.). H. *Tussetia polytomoides* Pascher, x1400 approx. (after P.). I, J. *Nautococcus mammilatus* Korshikoff; stage with umbrella-like float, x1250; flagellate stage, x2500 (after K.). K, L. *Scourfieldia complanata* West, views of broad and narrow surfaces; x1725 approx. (after W.). M. *Hyalogonium klebsii* Pascher, x500 approx. (after P.). N. *Platymonas tetrathele* West, x1430 (after Carter). O. *Carteria coccifera* Pascher, x960 (after P.).

Family 3. Haematococcidae. The outer membrane is separated from the periplast by a thick layer of "gelatinous material" into which extend cytoplasmic processes. These features have been considered adequate grounds for separating the family from the Chlamydomonadidae (260). The Haematococcidae include *Haematococcus* Agardh (76; Fig. 4. 29, H) and *Stephanosphaera* Cohn (256; Fig. 4. 29, F, G).

Family 4. Phacotidae. The rather rigid membrane is often impregnated

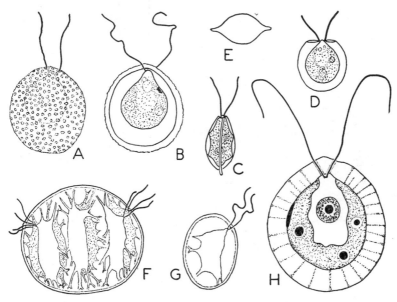

Fig. 4. 29. A, B. *Dysmorphococcus variabilis* Takeda, surface view and median optical section; x1200 (after Bold). C-E. *Pteromonas angulosa* Lemmermann, edge view, broad side, and outline in cross-section; x1000 approx. (after Pascher). F, G. *Stephanosphaera pluvialis* Cohn, colony and young stage; diameter of colony reaches 50-60μ; diagrammatic (after Pascher). H. *Haematococcus pluvialis* Flotow em. Wille, large flagellate stage; x1500 (after Elliott).

with calcium or iron compounds and possibly contains little or no cellulose. A bivalve membrane (or "shell"), which does not fit the enclosed organism very closely, is present in at least some genera. Fission occurs within the membrane.

The family includes the following genera: *Cephalomonas* Higinbotham (104), *Coccomonas* Stein (206), *Dysmorphococcus* (23; Fig. 4. 29, A, B), *Pedinopera* Pascher (206), *Phacotus* Perty (206, 207), *Pteromonas* Seligo (174, 206; Fig. 4. 29, C-E), *Thoracomonas* Skvortzow (206, 217), *Wislouchiella* (207).

Family 5. Spondylomoridae. The membranes of the individual flagellates are thin and the colony is not held together by a matrix. The larger colonies are composed of two or four circlets of flagellates so arranged that one organism does not lie directly above another. Individual flagellates have two or four flagella. Daughter colonies are produced by fission of any member of a colony within its original membrane. In contrast to the Volvocidae, a plakea stage is not formed in development.

The family includes the following genera: *Pascheriella* Korshikov (164; Fig. 4. 30, B), *Pyrobotrys* Arnoldi (*Chlamydobotrys* Korshikov) (256; Fig. 4. 30, A), *Spondylomorum* Ehrenberg (206, 207; Fig. 4. 30, D).

In *Corone* Fott (Fig. 4. 30, C), the widely separated flagellates are joined by tough strands. Since this type of organization differs from that of typical Spondylomoridae, perhaps a new family Coronidae should be recognized, as suggested by Fott (84).

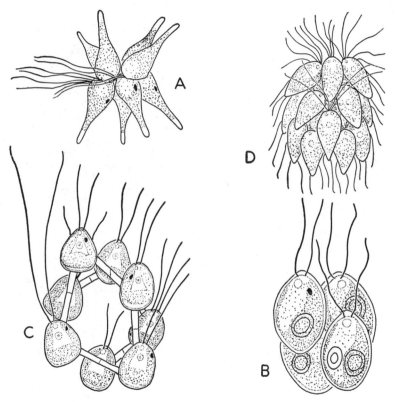

Fig. 4. 30. A. *Pyrobotrys (Chlamydobotrys) squarrosa* (Korshikoff), x1050 (after K.). B. *Pascheriella tetras* Korshikoff, x1575 (after K.). C. *Corone bohemica* Fott; length of colony (without flagella), 35-50µ; flagella (one pair shown full length) measure 35-40µ (after F.). D. *Spondylomorum quaternarium* Ehrbg. (after Stein); colonies reach lengths of 50-70µ.

Family 6. Volvocidae. This group differs from the Spondylomoridae in two major features: colonial organization is maintained by a matrix, and a plakea stage (Fig. 4. 32, C) appears in the development of a young colony.

The following genera are included: *Eudorina* Ehrenberg (103, 206); *Gonium* Müller (103, 206; Fig. 4. 31, D); *Pandorina* Bory (206; Fig. 4. 31, A); *Platydorina* Kofoid (154, 268; Fig. 4. 31, B, C); *Pleodorina* Shaw (206); *Stephanoon* Schewiakoff (206); *Volvox* Linnaeus (259); *Volvulina* Playfair (95).

Life-histories show basic similarities throughout the group, but certain genera are less specialized than others. In *Gonium, Pandorina,* and *Platydorina,* daughter colonies may be produced by any member of the parental colony. This is not the case in certain other genera. Reproduction is limited to flagellates of the posterior four rows in *Eudorina,* to

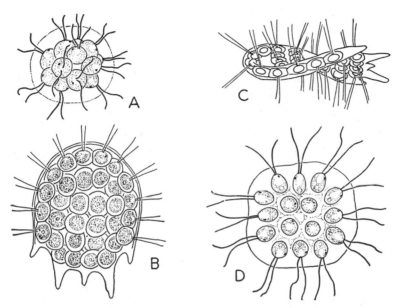

Fig. 4. 31. A. *Pandorina morum* (Müller) Bory (after Smith); colonies may reach 250μ in diameter. B, C. *Platydorina caudata* Kofoid; surface view, x225; lateral view, x260 (after K.). D. *Gonium pectorale* Müller; colonies reach diameters of 60-70μ; diagrammatic.

those in the posterior half of the colony in *Pleodorina,* and to a few flagellates ("gonidia") in the posterior half of the *Volvox* colony.

In development of a daughter colony, continued fission within the original membrane produces a hollow spherical or hemispherical stage, the *plakea* (Fig. 4. 32, C), in which the anterior ends of the flagellates are directed centrally. Later development in *Gonium pectorale* (103) involves a flattening of the plakea, and then further inversion, so that the young colony becomes slightly convex on the anterior, or flagellated, surface. In *Platydorina* (268) the plakea is a hollow sphere with a single opening (phialopore). After the 32-cell stage is reached, inversion occurs through the phialopore and the inverted daughter colony becomes a hollow sphere (Fig. 4. 32, Q). Further development involves collapse of the sphere, with intercalation of flagellates from opposite sides so that flagella are present on both surfaces (Fig. 4. 32, R). As secretion of the matrix begins, the young colony approaches the adult form at about the time dissolution of the parental matrix occurs.

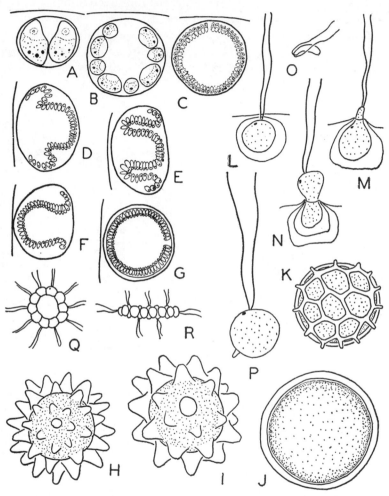

Fig. 4. 32. A-G. Development of a daughter colony in *Volvox aureus;* pyrenoids are indicated as black dots; diagrammatic (after Zimmermann). A-C. Fission results in a plakea, in which the anterior ends of the flagellates are directed centrally. D-G. The plakea undergoes inversion to produce the young colony. H-K. Mature zygotes, x615 (after Smith): *Volvox perglobator* (H), *V. globator* (I), *V. aureus* (J), *V. weismanni* (K), L-P. The mature macrogamete (L) of *Platydorina caudata* emerges from the parent colony (M, N); a microgamete (O) then penetrates the macrogamete (P); diagrammatic (after Taft). Q. *Platydorina caudata,* optical section of young colony after inversion and development of flagella; diagrammatic (after Taft). R. Young plate-like colony (lateral view) derived from the earlier spherical stage (Q); diagrammatic (after Taft).

Development of the *Volvox* colony (170, 234, 287) also involves the formation of a spherical plakea with a phialopore and the inversion ("extroversion") of the plakea through the phialopore to produce a young colony (Fig. 4. 32, A-G). This process of inversion in *Volvox* is of some general interest in its similarity to a process which the "stomatoblastula" undergoes in certain species of *Grantia* and *Sycon* (73). In general, the young colonies of *Volvox* escape separately after rupturing the surrounding membranes, but those of *V. aureus* may emerge through a common pore in the wall of the colony.

The details of sexual reproduction vary somewhat in different genera and species. The gametes are similar in *Gonium,* but anisogamy is obvious in *Eudorina, Pandorina, Platydorina, Pleodorina,* and *Volvox.* Some species of *Eudorina* and *Volvox* are heterothallic and others are homothallic, although the homothallic species of *Volvox* are protandrous. Some of the heterothallic species of *Volvox* show sexual dimorphism involving dwarf male colonies and large female colonies (259). *Pleodorina* is usually heterothallic, with occasional homothallic variants. Such variation is known also in the typically heterothallic *Volvox aureus. Pandorina, Platydorina,* and at least some species of *Gonium* (255) are heterothallic.

Sexual reproduction is preceded by differentiation of gametes. The developing macrogametes in *Platydorina caudata* (268) show no significant increase in volume but they become denser in appearance and acquire a yellowish tinge as they approach maturity. The flagella are retained and the mature macrogamete emerges from the colony as an active flagellate (Fig. 4. 32, L-N). The macrogametes escape from the female colony in *Pandorina* also, whereas those of *Eudorina, Pandorina,* and *Volvox* remain in place and are fertilized there. The development of microgametes in *Platydorina* is similar to that of a daughter colony. Fission, at the 32-cell stage, results in a curved plakea which soon undergoes inversion and develops into a sphere. Flagella are developed and the spheroid packets escape intact from the colonial matrix. Upon contact with macrogametes, the packet dissociates into its component gametes and fertilization occurs (Fig. 4. 32, O, P).

Microgametes of *Volvox* develop from enlarged cells resembling the "gonidia." Development of microgametes is precocious in *Volvox spermatosphaera, V. weismannia,* and several other species in that packets of gametes reach maturity while young male colonies are still within the parental colony. In other heterothallic species, mature packets develop only after the male colonies emerge from the parent and grow to about the size of female and asexual colonies. *Volvox spermatosphaera* differs from other species in that every flagellate in the male colony may develop into a packet of gametes. The mature packet is discoid in *Volvox aureus, V. spermatosphaera,* and *V. weismannia,* while spheroid packets are developed in *V. globator, V. perglobator,* and several others (259). The spheroid packet results when fission produces 256 or more cells; the inverted plakea remains plate-like when the number is only 16-128.

The developing macrogamete of *Volvox,* early in the life of the young colony, grows into a large spheroidal cell containing much stored food. Microgametes enter female colonies, sometimes before the ova are fully grown, and finally penetrate the ova as they approach or reach maturity. After fertilization, the zygote encysts. The ectocyst may show characteristic decorations (Fig. 4. 32, H-K). After disintegration of the female colony the cyst sinks to the bottom, where it remains dormant until the following spring. Under natural conditions, colonial forms may occur only during two or three months of the year, so that the encysted zygote is the predominant phase of the cycle (259). In laboratory cultures, however, repeated generations of asexual colonies have been obtained over a period of a year or more (275).

Order 6. Euglenida

The Euglenida[1] are rather large flagellates, mostly with one or two flagella. The body is generally elongated and often spindle-shaped, with some degree of spiral torsion, but modifications occur in such genera as *Phacus* (Fig. 4. 34, I-L). The reservoir (Fig. 4. 33, A-D), or "gullet," from which the flagella arise, is a characteristic feature. Flagellates assigned to two genera, *Chlorachne* and *Ottonia,* apparently lack reservoirs, but Schiller's (251) descriptions do not supply conclusive evidence that these are Euglenida. One or two contractile vacuoles empty into the reservoir, and each flagellum is inserted in the posterior or postero-dorsal wall of this cavity. The pellicle permits euglenoid movement (metaboly) in many species but it may be only slightly flexible, as in *Euglena acus,* or rather rigid in such genera as *Menoidium* and *Phacus.* As reported for *Euglena viridis* (228), this membrane gives negative tests for cellulose, but is completely digested by trypsin and presumably contains proteins. According to Chadefaud (34), the pellicle (Fig. 4. 33, E) consists of a thin epicuticle and a deeper and thicker cuticle. Only the epicuticle extends into the reservoir. The usually noticeable spiral striations seem to be cuticular ridges (34); presumably the rows of papillae in *Euglena spirogyra* are comparable decorations. The distribution of peripheral inclusions, and sometimes that of the chromatophores, may follow the spiral decorations of the pellicle. In addition to the pellicle, a lorica occurs in *Ascoglena* and *Klebsiella* (Fig. 4. 33, K, L); a shell, or test, in *Trachelomonas* (Fig. 4. 33, J).

Perhaps the majority of Euglenida are chlorophyll-bearing, although there are many colorless species. The chromatophores range from one to many and also vary in size and form (Fig. 4. 33, F-J) in different species. The green color of chlorophyll is not masked by other pigments. How-

---

[1] The literature on Euglenida has been reviewed by Jahn (119).

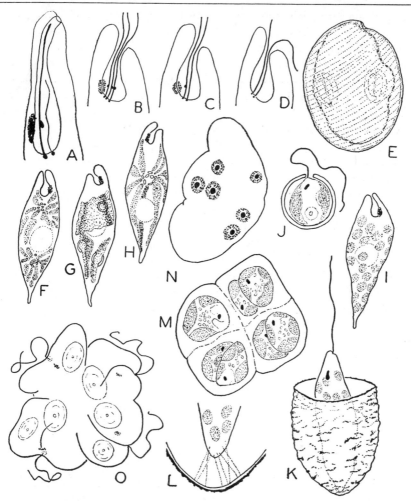

Fig. 4. 33. A-D. Flagella and reservoir: *Euglena mutabilis* (A), *Euglenamorpha,* green form (B), *Eutreptia* (C), *Distigma* (D); diagrammatic (after Hollande). E. Plasmolyzed specimen of *Euglena archaeoplastidiata,* pellicle separated from body, two pyrenoids shown; schematic (after Chadefaud). F-I. Various types of chromatophores in *Euglena: E. geniculata* (F), *E. anabaena* (G), *E. viridis* (H), *E. variabilis* (I); schematic (after Pringsheim). J. *Trachelomonas volvocina* Ehrbg., showing test, chromatophores, stigma, nucleus (outline); x720 (after Deflandre). K, L. *Klebsiella alligata,* external view of lorica and optical section through posterior end; x1000 approx. (after Pascher). M. *Euglena gracilis,* palmella; x455 (after Krichenbauer). N. *E. gracilis,* somatella with six nuclei; chromatophores not shown; x675 (after Krichenbauer). O. *Phacus caudata,* four daughter flagellates being produced from a somatella; x850 (after Krichenbauer).

ever, red haematochrome may accumulate in the cytoplasm in large amounts, as in *Euglena rubra* (125). Pyrenoids are usually attached to chromatophores or to non-pigmented "pyrenophores" (34). A typical pyrenoid consists of two pyrenosomes, each covered with a paramylum shell and applied to a surface of the chromatophore (Fig. 1. 17, L). The inner pyrenosome may be reduced in size, and is lacking in some cases (34). In such types as *Euglena gracilis* (Fig. 4. 34, A), there are many chromatophores, each of which probably bears a pyrenoid. At the other extreme, represented by *Euglena archaeoplastidiata* (Fig. 4. 33, E), there is one chromatophore equipped with two pyrenoids (34). Bleaching of the chromatophores in *Euglena gracilis* apparently is accompanied by resorption of the pyrenoids, which reappear if the flagellates are returned to the light and develop chlorophyll (240). A stigma, lying on the wall of the reservoir near the paraflagellar body (Fig. 4. 33, A-C), is characteristic of green species and also of certain colorless types (120, 237, 240). The stigma may divide in fission (8), or may undergo dispersal and re-aggregation of the pigment granules (96). Flagellar number and structure vary. The bifurcated flagellum of *Phacus* (Fig. 4. 34, H) and *Euglena* has been interpreted as a biflagellate condition (Fig. 4. 33, A) in which a rudimentary flagellum is often fused distally with a normal flagellum (110). The bifurcation apparently is absent in *Colacium* (123) and *Rhabdomonas* (99) but present in *Menoidium* (240). The situation in *Astasia* has been disputed, some workers reporting a non-bifurcated and others a bifurcated flagellum. More recent observations (240) indicate that the flagellum, in at least certain species of *Astasia,* is much like that of *Euglena* and that the rudimentary flagellum may or may not be independent of the normal flagellum. Such observations support the view that a biflagellate condition is the primitive one and indicate the desirability of reexamining those species in which a simple flagellum has been reported. No "bifurcation" has been reported in biflagellate or triflagellate species. A paraflagellar body (photoreceptor, or flagellar swelling) is characteristic of green species (Fig. 4. 33, A-C) but is absent in colorless forms.

Stored reserves include lipids and paramylum; the latter is an iodine-negative polysaccharide, insoluble in hot water and yielding glucose on hydrolysis. Paramylum is deposited as refractile bodies which may show concentric stratification in dilute solutions of KOH (62). Size and form may be fairly constant for a species, while the number ranges from typically one (*Phacus longicauda*) or two (*Euglena spirogyra*) large bodies to many small ones.

The life-cycle may include a flagellate stage, a palmella (Fig. 4. 33, M), and a cyst. Fission may occur in both palmella and flagellate stages. Palmella stages are unknown in many species and their distribution within the order remains uncertain, although they may be absent in colorless species (240). A palmella is dominant in the cycle of *Eugleno-capsa ochracea* (263), and a sessile non-flagellated stage plays a comparable role in *Colacium vesiculosum* (Fig. 4. 35, O, P). The sessile stage of the latter is derived from a flagellate which becomes attached at its flagellar end. The flagellum and reservoir disappear, a sheath and stalk are secreted, and mitosis may produce as many as eight nuclei. A naked

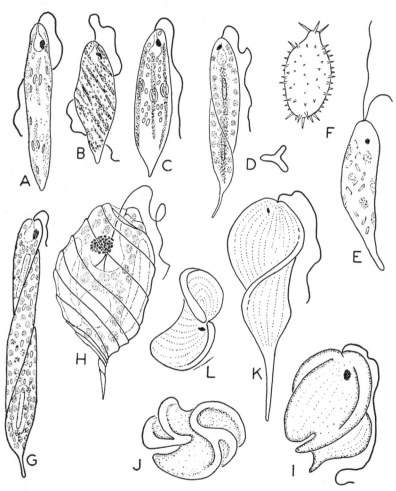

Fig. 4. 34. A-D. *Euglena: E. gracilis* Klebs (A), x1200; *E. sociabilis* Dangeard (B), x450; *E. pisciformis* Klebs (C), x1650; *E. tripteris* (D), x475 (after Johnson). E. *Eutreptiella marina* da Cunha, x1600 approx. (after da C.). F. *Trachelomonas hystrix*, test only; x600 (after Dangeard). G. *Euglena oxyuris* Schmarda, x350 (after Johnson). H. *Phacus pyrum*, showing two large lateral paramylum bodies, small discoid chromatophores, nucleus (in outline); x1750 (after Krichenbauer). I, J. *Phacus quinquemarginatus* Jahn and Shawhan, surface and anterior views; length, 35-52μ; schematic (after Allegre and Jahn). K, L. *Phacus torta* Lemmermann, broad surface and anterior end; length, 80-100μ; schematic (after Allegre and Jahn).

multinucleate form also has been observed in cultures (123). Either multinucleate stage may produce flagellate buds. A comparable plasmodium has been reported in *Euglena gracilis* (Fig. 4. 33, N) and *Phacus caudata* (Fig. 4. 33, O) by Krichenbauer (167); also, in *Astasia klebsii*. In *A. klebsii* no fission occurs in the plasmodial stage, which apparently originates as a result of increased osmotic pressure in old cultures. Even a return to a normal medium does not induce fission (57).

Although the Euglenida are mostly fresh-water flagellates, a number of genera are represented in salt-water and certain fresh-water species have become adapted to sea water under laboratory conditions (82). However, *Euglena gracilis* grows only in a salt concentration less than that of 40 per cent sea water (185).

Although it is not difficult to recognize Euglenida, in view of their characteristic features, subdivision of the group into taxonomically sound suborders and families apparently remains a problem for the future. The old three-family system—Euglenidae, Astasiidae, and Peranemidae—was convenient up to a certain point. Green flagellates could be placed in the Euglenidae, and holozoic types, often with a pharyngeal-rod apparatus, could be assigned to the Peranemidae. The residue of colorless flagellates could be dropped into the Astasiidae. Various observations have disturbed this taxonomic tranquillity. The discovery of colorless stigma-bearing flagellates (good species of *Euglena* except for the absence of chromatophores), the recognition of *Hyalocephalus* as a colorless homologue of *Phacus,* and recent observations on the loss of chlorophyll in *Euglena* make the presence or absence of chromatophores a feature of doubtful value in separating families. In fact, certain generally recognized species of *Astasia* are possibly nothing more than colorless strains of *Euglena* (239). Furthermore, Pringsheim and others have observed that growth of *Euglena gracilis* in darkness, following treatment with streptomycin, induces loss of the stigma after the chromatophores have disappeared. This new creation is a genetically stable strain which would be eliminated automatically from the old family Euglenidae. The old family Peranemidae also is not homogeneous in that a pharyngeal-rod apparatus is present in some genera and not in others, holozoic nutrition has not been demonstrated in certain cases, and differences in flagellar apparatus are well known.

Hollande (110) has divided the Euglenida into three groups which, in conformity with the present system, would be recognized as suborders— *Euglenoidina, Peranemoidina,* and *Petalomonadoidina.* These suborders would be divided into appropriate families as adequate information becomes available. Although separation of the Peranemoidina and Petalomonadoidina may not be clear cut, if the siphon of *Entosiphon* (Fig. 4. 37, B) is only a modified rod-apparatus as seen in *Peranema* (Fig. 4. 36,

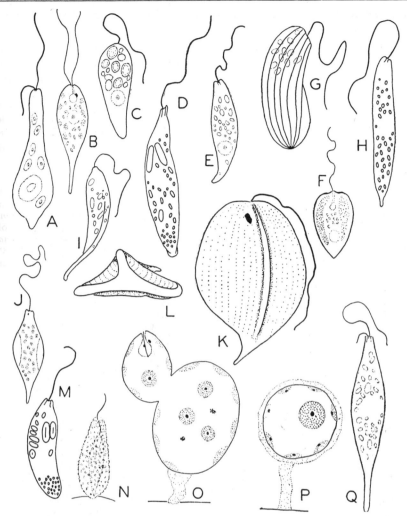

Fig. 4. 35. A. *Distigmopsis grassei* Hollande, x2430 approx. (after H.). B. *Eutreptia viridis* Perty, x240 (after Lemmermann). C. *Astasia comma* Pringsheim, x835 approx. (after P.). D. *Menoidium cultellus* Pringsheim, x500 approx. (after P.). E. *Astasia dangeardii* Lemmermann, x860 approx. (after Pringsheim). F. *Cryptoglena pigra* Ehrbg., x1300 (after Lemmermann). G. *Rhabdomonas incurva* Fresenius, x1470 (after Hall). H. *Astasia longa* Pringsheim, x720 approx. (after P.). I. *Astasia torta* Pringsheim, x835 approx. (after P.). J. *Lepocinclis marssoni* Lemm., showing two lateral paramylum bodies; x600 (after L.). K, L. *Phacus pleuronectes* (O. F. M.) Dujardin, dorsal surface and anterior end; chromatophores not shown; length, 40-100μ; schematic (after Allegre and Jahn). M. *Menoidium obtusum* Pringsheim, x500 approx. (after P.). N. *Ascoglena vaginicola* Stein, with lorica; x412 (after Lemmermann). O, P. *Colacium vesiculosum* Ehrbg., a budding multinucleate sessile stage and a uninucleate stage; x1955 (after Johnson). Q. *Distigma sennii* Pringsheim, x900 approx. (after P.).

C, D), Hollande's system seems to have certain advantages in the present stage of taxonomic progress.

Suborder 1. Euglenoidina. These flagellates have one or more flagella, may or may not contain chlorophyll, are not holozoic, may be metabolic, or may have a rigid pellicle. The flagellar sheath is not swollen at the base. On the basis of flagellar equipment, Hollande (110) recognized the families Euglenamorphidae, Eutreptiidae, Distigmidae, Euglenidae, and Menoidiidae, but the erection of definitive families may require more information than is now available.

The following genera may be assigned to the suborder: *Ascoglena* Stein (202; Fig. 4. 33, N); *Astasia* Dujardin (236, 238, 239, 240; Fig. 4. 35, C, E, H, I); *Colacium* Ehrenberg (123, 202; Fig. 4. 35, O, P); *Cryptoglena* Ehrenberg (202; Fig. 4. 35, F); *Distigma* Ehrenberg (108, 172, 236; Fig. 4. 35, Q), without chromatophores; *Distigmopsis* Hollande (110; Fig. 4. 35, A); *Euglena* Ehrenberg (124, 202; Fig. 4. 34, A-D, G); *Euglenamorpha* Wenrich (277; Fig. 4. 33, B), from tadpoles; *Eutreptia* Perty (202; Fig. 4. 35, B); *Eutreptiella* da Cunha (Fig. 4. 34, E); *Hyalocephalus* Pringsheim (236), a colorless

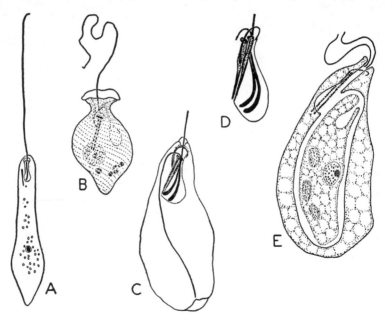

Fig. 4. 36. A. *Peranemopsis striata* Lackey; one long anterior flagellum; no second flagellum like that of *Peranema,* and only one pharyngeal-rod; length, 90-110μ (after L.). B. *Urceolus cyclostomus* (Stein) Mereschkowski, showing vestibule, reservoir, pharyngeal-rod apparatus, nucleus, ingested food; x933 (after Klebs). C. *Peranema trichophorum* (Ehrbg.) Stein, slightly contracted, ventral view showing pharyngeal-rod apparatus and trailing flagellum adherent to the body; in swimming, the anterior flagellum (shown in part) is extended as in *Peranemopsis* (A); schematic (after Chadefaud). D. Pharyngeal-rod apparatus of *P. trichophorum,* right lateral aspect; schematic (after Chadefaud). E. *Heteronema acus* (Ehrbg.) Stein; ingested *Euglena* in a food-vacuole not yet separated from the reservoir; flagella shown leaving cytostome; x2240 (after Loefer).

"Phacus"; Khawkinea Jahn and McKibben (120), similar to *Euglena* except for the absence of chromatophores; *Klebsiella* Pascher (215; Fig. 4. 33, K, L); *Lepocinclis* Perty (49, 202; Fig. 4. 35, J); *Menoidium* Perty (236, 238; Fig. 4. 35, M); *Phacus* Dujardin (3, 202, 230; Fig. 4. 34, H-L); *Rhabdomonas* Fresenius (99, 238; Fig. 4. 35, G); *Trachelomonas* Ehrenberg (60, 202; Figs. 4. 33, J, 4. 34, F). In addition, *Euglenocapsa* Steinecke (263), in which a palmella stage is dominant, may be a valid genus.

Suborder 2. Peranemoidina. These are colorless, metabolic types with two flagella, one of which is trailed. Each flagellum is said to be swollen

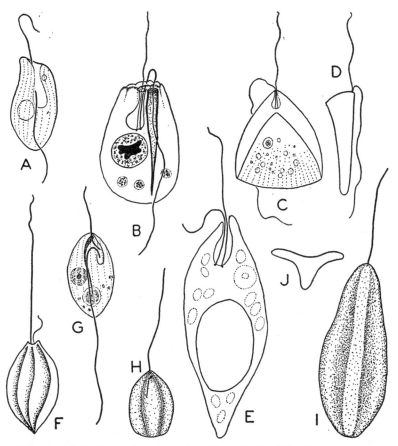

Fig. 4. 37. A. *Marsupiogaster striata* Schewiakoff, x835 (after S.). B. *Entosiphon sulcatum* (Duj.) Stein; length, 20-25μ; siphon, gullet, nucleus and food vacuoles; schematic (after Lackey). C, D. *Triangulomonas rigida* Lackey; 18x15μ; surface and lateral views (after L.). E. *Sphenomonas teres;* length, 20-40μ; large refractile inclusion of uncertain nature, smaller paramylum bodies (after Hollande). F. *Tropidoscyphus octocostatus* Stein, showing prominent ridges; x412 (after Lemmermann). G. *Anisonema acinus* Duj., showing one "pharyngeal-rod," nucleus, ingested food; x633 (after Lemmermann). H. *Notosolenus apocamptus* Stokes; length, 8-10μ; short trailing flagellum arises from convex ventral surfaces (after S.). I,J. *Petalomonas dorsalis* Stokes, 38-45μ; entire flagellate and optical cross-section (after Shawhan and Jahn).

at the base (110). Solid food is usually ingested. The characteristic pharyngeal-rod apparatus, which lies dorsal to the reservoir, is composed of two long rods and a shorter falcate rod which extends ventrally at its anterior end (Fig. 4. 36, C, D).

The conclusion of Tannreuther (268a), that the rod apparatus in *Peranema* is a "perforatorium" used for piercing the prey, has been confirmed by Chen (38). The identity of the cytostome and gullet in these holozoic Euglenida has been disputed. Chen (38) and Pitelka (229), among others, have been convinced that ingestion takes place through a cytostome and gullet independent of the reservoir and its external opening. Chadefaud (35), on the other hand, maintains that there is no separate gullet in at least certain members of the group. Previous observations on the continuity of food vacuoles with the cavity of the reservoir (Fig. 4. 36, E) in *Heteronema* (184) and *Peranema* (100) support the latter conclusion.

The following genera are included: *Heteronema* Stein (184, 202; Fig. 4. 36, E); *Peranema* Dujardin (35, 202, 229; Fig. 4. 36, C, D), trailing flagellum adherent to the pellicle; *Peranemopsis* Lackey (175; Fig. 4. 36, A); *Urceolus* Mereschkowsky (202; Fig. 4. 36, B). However, Pitelka (229) has considered *Heteronema* a synonym of *Peranema*.

Suborder 3. Petalomonadoidina. The body of these colorless flagellates is typically compressed and not plastic. There may be one or two flagella and each flagellum is swollen at the base (110). Some species are definitely holozoic. A pharyngeal-apparatus, described for several genera, may or may not be homologous with that of *Peranema*.

The suborder includes the following genera (110): *Anisonema* Dujardin (202; Fig. 4. 37, G); *Dinema* Perty (202); *Entosiphon* Stein (110, 171, 202; Fig. 4. 37, B); *Marsupiogaster* Schewiakoff (202; Fig. 4. 37, A); *Notosolenus* Stokes (202; Fig. 4. 37, H); *Petalomonas* Stein (251; Fig. 4. 37, I, J); *Scytomonas* Stein (202); *Sphenomonas* Stein (110, 202); *Triangulomonas* Lackey (175; Fig. 4. 37, C, D); *Tropidoscyphus* Stein (202; Fig. 4. 37, F).

Order 7. Chloromonadida

Little is known about these flagellates. The described species are fairly large (30-100µ) forms with somewhat plastic bodies which are usually dorso-ventrally flattened, and may show a ventral groove arising near the anterior end. The numerous bright green chromatophores are peripheral and radially arranged in *Chattonella* (Fig. 4. 38, B) and *Gonyostomum* (Fig. 4. 38, H). The pigments are said to include xanthophylls as well as chlorophyll; the mixture turns blue-green in dilute acid (69). No stigma has been reported. Oil droplets are usually stored. Glycogen also occurs in *Gonyostomum semen* (114), but starch apparently is not formed. There are typically two flagella, one of which is trailed.

A gullet (Fig. 4. 38, E, H, I) not unlike the reservoir of Euglenida

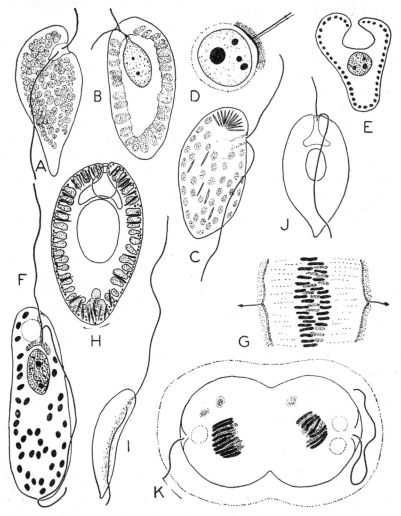

Fig. 4. 38. A, B. *Chattonella subsalsa* Biecheler; length, 30-50μ; surface
view showing chromatophores, ventral groove, and basal portions of flagella;
optical section showing chromatophores, nucleus, and flagellar connections
(after B.). C. *Merotrichia capitata* Skuja, showing ventral groove, chromatophores, and "trichocysts"; x550 (after S.). D. Nuclear cap and flagellar connections in *Vacuolaria virescens;* schematic (after Poisson and Hollande).
E. *Vacuolaria viridis* (Dangeard) Senn, longitudinal section of stained specimen showing nucleus, "gullet," and chromatophores; diagrammatic (after
Fott). F. *Vacuolaria virescens* Cienkowski; length, 50-150μ; stained specimen
showing chromatophores, contractile vacuole, nucleus and nuclear cap; schematic (after Poisson and Hollande). G. Dividing nucleus of *V. virescens;*
diagrammatic (after Poisson and Hollande). H-J. *Gonyostomum semen*
Diesing, length 40-65μ. H. Diagrammatic optical section showing chromatophores, trichocysts, nucleus (in outline), and contractile vacuole lateral to
"reservoir" (after Chadefaud). I. Ventral view, showing groove and flagella.
J. Optical section showing outline of nucleus and reservoir; diagrammatic
(after Drouet and Cohen). K. Fission in palmella stage, *Vacuolaria virescens;*
schematic (after Poisson and Hollande).

has been described in some species. However, it has been suggested that in *Vacuolaria* (Fig. 4. 38, F) at least, a large contractile vacuole has previously been misinterpreted as a gullet (232). The lack of such a gullet would suggest that the Chloromonadida are not closely related to the Euglenida. The dividing nucleus of *Vacuolaria* (Fig. 4. 38, G), strikingly different from the euglenoid type, points to the same conclusion, as does the insertion of the flagella (Fig. 4. 38, B, F). The flagella of *Gonyostomum semen*, on the other hand, apparently arise from the base of the triangular cavity, or "gullet" (70). A peculiar "supranuclear cap" (Fig. 4. 38, D), lying just anterior to the nucleus, occurs in *Vacuolaria* (232). Various globular, discoid, or spindle-shaped bodies, subpellicular in distribution (Fig. 4. 38, C, H), have been interpreted as mucous globules (15, 232) and as trichocysts (33). Upon discharge, such inclusions give rise to filaments in *Gonyostomum* (33). The cytoplasm of *Gonyostomum semen* (114) and *Chattonella subsala* (15) is differentiated into two zones, apparently separated by a delicate membrane ("central capsule"), perhaps merely an interface. The outer zone contains the chromatophores, vacuome, fat globules, and trichocysts. Fission occurs in flagellate stages of *Chattonella* (16) and *Gonyostomum* (69, 114), and in palmella stages of *Vacuolaria* (Fig. 4. 38, K). Cysts with a thick membrane have been reported in *Gonyostomum* (69).

The Chloromonadida are fresh water types whose ecological distribution may be somewhat restricted. *Gonyostomum semen*, for instance, seems to be limited to the rather acid waters of marshes (114).

The following genera have been referred to the order: *Chattonella* Biecheler (15, 16; Fig. 4. 38, A, B), *Coelomonas* Stein (231), *Gonyostomum* Diesing (33, 69, 70, 114; Fig. 4. 38, H-J), *Merotrichia* Mereschkowski (Fig. 4. 38, C), *Rhaphidomonas* Stein, *Rickertia* Conrad (43), *Thaumatomastix* Lauterborn, *Thaumatomonas* de Saedeleer (246), *Trentonia* Stokes (264), and *Vacuolaria* Cienkowski (83, 232). Three of these generic names are said to be invalid, since *Rhaphidomonas* is a synonym of *Gonyostomum*, and both *Coelomonas* and *Trentonia* appear to be synonyms of *Vacuolaria* (232). The relationships of *Thaumatomastix*, *Thaumatomonas*, and *Rickertia* to *Chattonella*, *Gonyostomum*, and *Vacuolaria* need further investigation.

CLASS 2. ZOOMASTIGOPHOREA

These flagellates have no chromatophores and they store lipids and glycogen but apparently no starch or paramylum. Some are saprozoic but there are many holozoic species. The body is generally rather plastic and no cellulose membrane or test is produced. Many are small and simple in structure, while others are perhaps as complex as any of the Protozoa. Zoomastigophorea occur as parasites in various groups of invertebrates, in all classes of vertebrates, and also in certain plants. As free-living flagellates, they are found in the soil and in both fresh and salt water. The life cycle is simple in the majority, but polymorphic cycles are known, as in the Trypanosmidae, and sexual phenomena have been reported in a few instances, most recently by Cleveland (Chapter II).

Present classifications are tentative at best and are based, to an important extent unfortunately, upon somewhat artificial criteria rather than upon detailed information which might suggest natural relationships. The recent erection of the order Trichomonadida (147), the result of a long series of intensive studies, has set a sound pattern for the possible establishment of additional coherent orders within certain areas of the class. In the meantime, the remnants of the "Polymastigida" may be retained, along with the other older orders, for taxonomic convenience. Accordingly, the Zoomastigophorea may be subdivided as follows:

Order 1. Rhizomastigida. This inadequately defined group of amoeboid flagellates has served occasionally as a repository for genera of uncertain taxonomic position, and has also been treated as a family of the Protomastigida.

Order 2. Protomastigida. These are solitary or colonial types with one or two flagella. The body is plastic but does not show the amoeboid activity of the Rhizomastigida.

Order 3. Polymastigida. The remnants of the old Order Polymastigida include mostly uninucleate and binucleate species, although there are a few with a number of nuclei. There are usually 3-8 flagella.

Order 4. Trichomonadida. These are uninucleate or multinucleate (but not binucleate) flagellates with an axostyle, a parabasal body, and a mastigont of 3-6 flagella. One of the flagella is typically a trailing flagellum which may or may not form part of an undulating membrane.

Order 5. Hypermastigida. These are uninucleate flagellates with many flagella. The known species are intestinal parasites of termites, wood roaches and cockroaches.

Order 1. Rhizomastigida

This order may be limited to flagellates with 1-4 flagella and amoeboid bodies which often show considerable pseudopodial activity. In at least some species, a cytoplasmic fibril ("rhizostyle") of uncertain significance extends posteriorly from one of the blepharoplasts.

The following genera may be assigned to the order: *Heliobodo* Valkanov (276; Fig. 4. 39, I); *Histomonas* Tyzzer (20, 273, 274, 280; Fig. 4. 39, A-F); *Mastigamoeba* Schulze (153); *Mastigella* Frenzel (88, 97, 153; Fig. 4. 39, L); *Mastigina* Frenzel (12, 13, 88; Fig. 4. 39, J, K); and *Rhizomastix* Alexeieff (191; Fig. 4. 39, G, H). *Tricholimax* Frenzel apparently is a synonym of *Mastigina* Frenzel (97). Certain other genera, sometimes included in the Rhizomastigina, probably do not belong here. *Pteridomonas* Penard possibly should be referred to the Chrysomonadida, while *Actinomonas* Kent and *Dimorpha* Gruber probably belong in the Helioflagellida (Chapter V). The relationships of *Multicilia* Cienkowski (177) are uncertain on the basis of available data. Although the body is amoeboid, the many flagella (or axopodia?) and the 1-4 nuclei are not very strong inducements for retaining this genus in the Rhizomastigida.

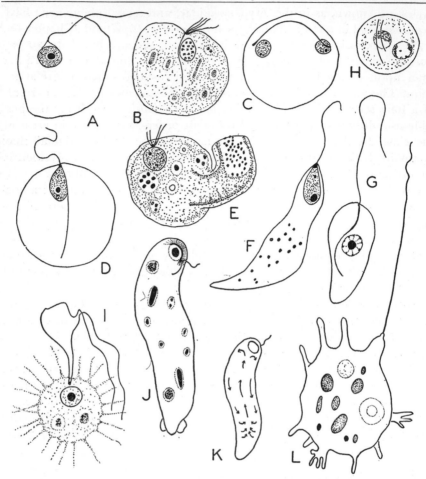

Fig. 4. 39. A-F. *Histomonas meleagridis* Tyzzer: A. Rounded stage showing nucleo-flagellar connections, x2310 (after Bishop). B. Specimen with four flagella and rhizostyle, x1866 (after Wenrich). C. Daughter nuclei joined by paradesmose, x2310 (after Bishop). D. Uniflagellate form with rhizostyle, x2310 (after Bishop). E. Ingestion of food by means of a "tube," x1866 (after Wenrich). F. Elongated uniflagellate form, x2310 (after Bishop). G. *Rhizomastix gracilis* Alexeieff, nucleus and rhizostyle stained; x2000 (after Mackinnon). H. Cyst of *R. gracilis,* two nuclei and two rhizostyles; x2000 (after Mackinnon). I. *Heliobodo radians* Valkanov; x2400 (after V.). J, K. *Mastigina hylae* (Frenzel) Goldschmidt (after Becker); specimen showing nucleus, flagellum, rhizostyle extending posteriorly, and cap-like "cape" fitting over nucleus anteriorly (J), x515; pattern of protoplasmic streaming (K), diagrammatic. L. *Mastigella polymastix* Frenzel, x400 (after F.).

Species of *Mastigamoeba* and *Mastigella* are similar with respect to the single flagellum and the development of slender pseudopodia. However, the nucleus is approximately central and not connected with the flagellum in *Mastigella,* while the nucleus in *Mastigamoeba* is anterior and apparently joined to the blepharoplast. In *Mastigina* the nucleus is anterior as in *Mastigamoeba* and is joined to the blepharoplast, but slender pseudopodia seem to be lacking. The nucleoflagellar relationships of *Mastigina hylae* (Frenzel) Goldschmidt have been described by Becker (12). In addition to the flagellum, two other structures are joined to the blepharoplast (Fig. 4. 39, J). A *rhizostyle* extends posteriorly, and a cap-shaped "cape" fits over the anterior surface of the nucleus. From the cape, filaments extend to the anterior end of the body.

Rhizomastix gracilis Alexeieff, recovered from an axolotl and from crane-fly grubs, shows a rhizostyle, extending almost to the posterior end of the body (Fig. 4. 39, G), but there is no "cape" as in *Mastigina hylae* and the nucleus is central (191). Nuclear division occurs within the cyst (Fig. 4. 39, H), and a second rhizostyle develops by outgrowth from a blepharoplast.

Heliobodo (Fig. 4. 39, I) includes spheroid uninucleate organisms with two flagella and many slender pseudopodia which apparently are not axopodia. Whether this genus actually belongs in the Rhizomastigida is uncertain.

Histomonas meleagridis Tyzzer (Fig. 4. 39, A-F) is associated with "blackhead" (enterohepatitis) in turkeys and chickens. An interesting feature of blackhead in turkeys is that young birds are readily infected by feeding them embryonated eggs of the cecal worm, *Heterakis gallinae*. The flagellates apparently remain viable in such eggs for more than a year when kept in a refrigerator (189). *H. meleagridis* is an amoeboid or slug-like organism which may produce slender pseudopodia and is capable of changing shape rapidly (20). Some of these slender pseudopodia may correspond to the tubular protrusions (Fig. 4. 39, E) noted by Wenrich (280) in stained preparations. The unusual variability in number of flagella raises questions concerning the validity of *Histomonas meleagridis* as a specific name for all the various strains described from birds. One flagellum is typical in cultures from chickens (20), although binucleate forms with two flagella, and tetranucleate forms with four, occur occasionally. In material from ring-neck pheasants (280), flagellate stages nearly always showed four flagella. Flagellar resorption occurs at an early stage of nuclear division so that non-flagellated uninucleate and binucleate forms are common and tetranucleate stages without flagella are sometimes seen (20). Whether the "rhizostyle" is a normal organelle, or merely an occasionally observed remnant of the paradesmose is still uncertain.

Order 2. Protomastigida

These are relatively small organisms with one or two flagella. The body is typically plastic, but not markedly amoeboid. Nutrition is saprozoic in some types and holozoic in many others. The order includes

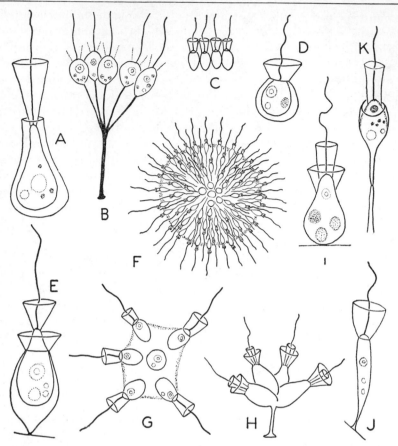

Fig. 4. 40. A. *Salpingoeca brunnea* Stokes, with theca; x660 (after Francé).
B. *Codonocladium umbellatum* (Tatem) Stein, x325 (after Lemmermann).
C. *Desmarella moniliformis* Kent, typical linear "colony"; x477 (after Lemmermann). D. *Lagenoeca globulosa* Francé, free-swimming loricate type; x530 (after Lemmermann). E. *Diplosigopsis entzii* Francé, sessile loricate type; x600 (after F.). F. *Sphaeroeca volvox* Lauterborn, x350 (after Lemmermann). G. *Protospongia haeckelii* Kent, x442 (after Lemmermann). H. *Codonosigopsis socialis* (Francé) Lemmermann, with double collar; x500 (after F.). I. *Diplosiga socialis* Frenzel, with double collar; x1350 (after F.). J. *Monosiga angustata* Kent, x2000 (after K.). K. *Codosiga botrytis* Ehrbg.; length of body (excluding collar), 7-16μ; body enclosed in a mucous envelope (outline emphasized); schematic (after Lapage).

free-living species and parasites of invertebrates, vertebrates, and certain plants. The life-cycle is often simple, but is dimorphic to polymorphic in Trypanosomidae. Interrelationships of the different families are not entirely clear and the limits of the order have been disputed to some extent. For example, *Trimastix* Kent and *Tricercomonas* Wenyon and O'Connor have been classified both with Protomastigida and the Polymastigida.

Six families may be assigned to the order: Codosigidae, Phalansteriidae, Trypanosomidae, Cryptobiidae, Amphimonadidae, and Bodonidae.

Family 1. Codosigidae. This group (30, 181) includes species with a "collar" (Fig. 4. 40). As described in *Codosiga* (Fig. 4. 40, K), this collar is a protoplasmic membrane which can be extended as a hollow cone surrounding the basal portion of the flagellum (176). The collar can be retracted completely. The body is enclosed in a thin "mucous envelope" apparently continuous with the stalk. During feeding, the anterior end of the body contracts away from the envelope and food particles, driven by flagellar currents, drop into this space. As the body surges back against the envelope, the food particles apparently are forced into the body. The expanded collar evidently directs food into the space between the body and the envelope. Many choanoflagellates resemble the choanocytes of sponges to such a degree that Kent (130) included them with the sponges in his order "Choano-flagellata." The similarity may involve not only the collar but also a parabasal body, or apical body (Fig. 1. 10, L, M). A single flagellum is characteristic. An interesting feature of the sessile *Codosiga botrytis* is that flagellates which become detached swim stalk-first (176). Both solitary and colonial forms are known. In addition, temporary clusters of several flagellates, failing to separate after fission, may remain attached to a stalk, as in *Codosiga* (176).

The family includes several genera of **naked flagellates**—*Codonosigopsis* Senn (Fig. 4. 40, H); *Codosiga* James-Clark (Fig. 4. 40, K); *Desmarella* Kent (174; Fig. 4. 40, C); *Diplosiga* Frenzel (Fig. 4. 40, I); and *Monosiga* Kent (245; Fig. 4. 40, J). **A lorica is present** in several others: *Diplosigopsis* Francé (Fig. 4. 40, E); *Lagenoeca* Kent (Fig. 4. 40, D); and *Salpingoeca* James-Clark (Fig. 4. 40, A). **Spheroid colonies** are developed in *Protospongia* Kent (Fig. 4. 40, G) and *Sphaeroeca* Lauterborn (Fig. 4. 40, F).

Poteriodendron Stein and *Histiona* Voigt, sometimes grouped with the choanoflagellates, probably are Chrysomonadida (93, 224). This is also the case for *Bicoeca* James-Clark (222).

Family 2. Phalansteriidae. Little is known about *Phalansterium* Cienkowski (181; Fig. 1. 3, A), although the presence of a simple collar closely fitting the flagellum suggests a relationship to the Codosigidae. The genus includes both branching and spheroid or discoid colonies with a granular matrix.

Family 3. Trypanosomidae. These parasites have a single flagellum ending in a blepharoplast, near which lies a spheroid or discoid kinetoplast (Fig. 1. 10, J, K). The flagellum may or may not form part of an undulating membrane. Life-cycles are dimorphic or polymorphic. Four different types (Fig. 4. 41) occur in the family—the leishmanial, leptomonad, crithidial, and trypanosomal forms. In invertebrate hosts, the flagellates are often attached to the lining of the digestive tract or to other surfaces. Such stages are sometimes referred to as *haptomonads;*

the unattached flagellates, as *nectomonads*. Attachment may involve loss of the distal portion of the flagellum, although the axoneme persists between the kinetoplast and the tip of the body (Fig. 4. 41, J).

On the basis of life-cycles, six genera have been recognized (285): *Crithidia, Herpetomonas, Leishmania, Leptomonas, Phytomonas,* and *Trypanosoma.* Only leptomonad and leishmanial forms are found in *Leptomonas, Leishmania,* and *Phytomonas.*

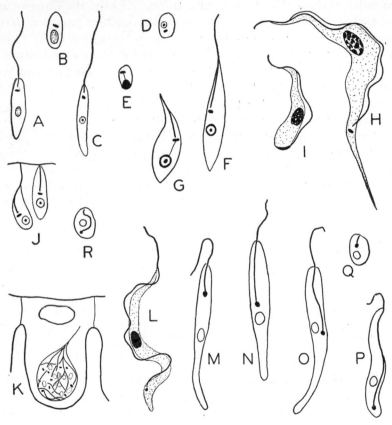

Fig. 4. 41. A, B. *Leptomonas patellae* Porter, leptomonad and leishmanial forms; x3120 (after P.). C, D. *Leishmania chamaelonis* Wenyon, leptomonad and leishmanial forms; from cloaca of *Chamaeleon vulgaris;* x2750 (after Wenyon). E-G. *Crithidia euryophthalmi* McCulloch, from *Euryophthalmus convivus;* leishmanial stage from hind-gut, crithidial stage (with narrow undulating membrane) from crop, and crithidial haptomonad from hind-gut; x1875 (after McC.). H-K. *Trypanosoma lewisi;* form from blood of the rat, small metacyclic trypanosome from hind-gut of flea, two crithidial haptomonads from the hind-gut, and a stage in intracellular reproduction (stomach of flea); H-J, x2400; K, x1350 (after Wenyon). L. *Trypanosoma brucei,* x1800 (after Wenyon). M-R. *Herpetomonas muscarum,* leptomonad form, two crithidial stages, trypanosomal form, and two leishmanial stages; x1600 approx. (after Wenyon).

Leptomonas Kent (Fig. 4. 41, A, B) includes parasites of invertebrates. However, the type species—*Leptomonas bütschlii* Kent from the gut of a nematode (*Trilobus gracilis*)—has not been studied in detail and it is not yet certain that more recently erected species actually belong in Kent's genus. According to current concepts of the genus, both haptomonad and nectomonad leptomonads may occur in the digestive tract and leishmanial stages are to be expected in the posterior intestine. The leishmanial forms of *L. ctenocephali,* which become resistant to desiccation (284), are voided in the feces and ingested by flea larvae. The infection persists through development of the flea (68).

Phytomonas Donovan. Members of this genus occur in invertebrates and plants. *Phytomonas davidi* (85) is found as leptomonad and leishmanial forms in the latex of *Euphorbia segetalis* and in the digestive tract of a bug, *Stenocephalus agilis,* which feeds on the plant. After a period of multiplication in the insect, leptomonad stages appear in the salivary glands. These are presumably the forms infective for plants. In addition, transfer of leishmanial stages from insect to insect has been reported.

Leishmania Ross (Fig. 4. 41, C, D). The life-cycle involves a vertebrate and an invertebrate host. In mammals, the leishmanial form is predominant, or else the only stage found, and occurs primarily in lymphoid-macrophage cells, and occasionally in mononuclear and polynuclear leucocytes of the peripheral blood. Leishmanial stages ingested by the invertebrate hosts (species of *Phlebotomus*) develop into leptomonad forms which multiply in the digestive tract. Infective stages are eventually inoculated into a vertebrate. *Leishmania donovani, L. tropica,* and *L. brasiliensis,* which are parasitic in man, are discussed in Chapter XII. *Leishmania chamaeleonis,* in contrast to the typical species of mammals, occurs both as leptomonad and leishmanial forms in the cloaca of a chameleon (285).

Crithidia Léger (Fig. 4. 41, E-G). Crithidial, leptomonad, and leishmanial forms occur in the invertebrate hosts. However, the leptomonad forms may be mere transitory stages in fission or in development of crithidial and leishmanial forms. The type species, *C. fasciculata,* was described from the intestine of *Anopheles maculipennis* (180). Leishmanial stages, produced in the hind-gut, apparently are eliminated and then ingested by new hosts. The occurrence of infections with *C. leptocoridis* in nymphs of the box-elder bug (188) indicates that insects may become infected before the adult stage is reached.

Herpetomonas Kent (Fig. 4. 41, M-R) is limited to invertebrates, but the life-cycle includes trypanosomal forms as well as the other types. Detailed studies of the type species, *H. muscarum* (Leidy) Kent—sometimes known as *H. muscae-domesticae* (Stein) Kent—have shown that trypanosomal stages occur in flies (283) and in cultures (68). Leishmanial stages may arise either from leptomonad or trypanosomal forms in the natural host, and the crithidial stage typically lacks an undulating membrane.

Trypanosoma Gruby (Fig. 4. 41, H-L). The life-cycle usually involves both vertebrates and invertebrates (arthropods, leeches). The trypanosomal stage occurs in the blood of vertebrates, while leptomonad and crithidial forms are rare, if they are found at all. Intracellular leishmanial stages may occur, as in *T. cruzi*. All four stages may occur in the invertebrate host. Haptomonads may be expected in insects infected with *T. lewisi* (hind-gut of fleas), *T. vivax* (proboscis of *Glossina morsitans*), or *T. gambiense* ("salivary glands" of *Glossina palpalis*), for example. The stage infective for vertebrates—the metacyclic trypanosome—is typically an active trypanosomal form often derived from crithidial haptomonads.

Methods of transfer from invertebrate to vertebrate vary with the species of *Trypanosoma*. In one group, which includes *T. cruzi* of man, *T. lewisi* of rats, and *T. melophagium* of sheep, metacyclic forms are voided from the hind-gut of the vector, and infection of the vertebrate follows contamination of wounds or mucous membranes. The metacyclic stages of *T. gambiense, T. rhodesiense, T. evansi,* and similar species develop anteriorly in the vector and are transferred to the vertebrate host by inoculation. A third type, represented by *T. equiperdum,* is transferred in vertebrates by coital contact and the vector has dropped out of the cycle.

Vertebrate hosts of trypanosomes include fishes, Amphibia, aquatic and terrestrial reptiles, birds, and various groups of mammals. Most species of *Trypanosoma,* if not all, are probably non-pathogenic in their natural hosts, or at least produce no serious damage. In man and domesticated ungulates, however, several species cause diseases of considerable medical and economic importance. This is particularly true in the tsetse fly areas of Africa, where sleeping sickness of man (Chapter XII) and trypanosomiasis in cattle, sheep, horses, and goats have been important hindrances to economic and social progress.

Family 4. Cryptobiidae. These are biflagellate parasites with a kinetoplast somewhat larger than that of the Trypanosomidae. One of the flagella extends anteriorly. The other, which is usually adherent to the body and may or may not form part of an undulating membrane, extends posteriorly as a free trailing portion.

The genera *Cryptobia* Leidy (Fig. 4. 42, A) and *Trypanoplasma* Laveran and Mesnil are usually included, although some workers believe that *Trypanoplasma* is a synonym of *Cryptobia*. However, this question needs further study, since an undulating membrane has been described in various species of *Trypanoplasma* but is absent in *Cryptobia helicis* (166). Furthermore, the aciculum of *C. helicis* may be lacking in *Trypano-*

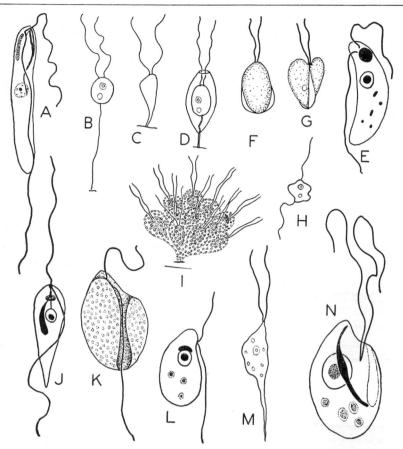

Fig. 4. 42. A. *Cryptobia helicis* Leidy, showing "parabasal body" (at left), trailing flagellum, aciculum, (at right) and nucleus; x2970 (after Kozloff). B. *Amphimonas globosa* Kent, x480 (after Lemmermann). C. *Amphimonas cyclopum* (Kent) Blochmann, x1500 (after K.). D. *Diplomita socialis* Kent, with lorica; x1000 (after Lemmermann). E. *Bodo caudatus* Hollande, x2250 (after H.). F, G. *Streptomonas cordata* (Perty) Klebs; different views showing keel; x1334 (after Lemmermann). H. *Pleuromonas jaculans* Perty, x767 (after Lemmermann). I. *Spongomonas uvella* Stein; gelatinous matrix contains many granules; x347 (after Lemmermann). J. *Proteromonas lacerti* (Grassi), showing "parabasal body" and a ring which encircles the flagellar axoneme and parabasal rhizoplast; x2550 approx. (after Grassé). K. *Colponema loxodes* Stein; trailing flagellum extends along prominent ventral groove; endoplasm is "granular"; x1200 (after Klebs). L. *Pseudobodo minima* Hollande; compact "parabasal body" anterior to the nucleus; x3600 (after H.). M. *Dinomonas tuberculata* Kent; x1710 (after K.). N. *Phyllomitus amylophagus* Klebs; ventral view showing pharyngeal groove and elongated "parabasal body"; x3375 (after Hollande).

plasma. Species of *Cryptobia* occur in the seminal vesicles and digestive tract of molluscs and certain other invertebrates, and in the digestive tract of marine fish. Species of *Trypanoplasma* occur in the blood of marine and fresh-water fishes.

Family 5. Amphimonadidae. These are naked or loricate types with two equal flagella (181). Naked types may be either free-swimming or sessile. Colonial forms are assigned to several genera. The group as a whole is much in need of investigation.

> **Solitary types** include *Amphimonas* Dujardin (245; Fig. 4. 42, B, D), *Diplomita* Kent (Fig. 4. 42, D), *Spiromonas* Perty (181), and *Streptomonas* Klebs (Fig. 4. 42, F, G). **Colonial types** are assigned to *Cladomonas* Stein (Fig. 1. 3, F), *Rhipidodendron* Stein (181) and *Spongomonas* Stein (Fig. 4. 42, I).

Family 6. Bodonidae. These are solitary naked flagellates reported from fresh and salt water, and from the digestive tract of certain reptiles and Amphibia. One of the two flagella is usually trailed in swimming. A parabasal apparatus is known in several genera. The Feulgen-positive parabasal body of *Bodo* divides in fission (110) and is thus similar to the kinetoplast of Trypanosomidae.

> The following genera are included: *Bodo* (Ehrbg.) Stein (*Prowazekia* Hartmann and Chagas) (110; Fig. 4. 42, E); *Cercobodo* Krassiltschick (109, 110; Fig. 1. 10, P); *Cercomonas* Dujardin (113, 282); *Colponema* Stein (151; Fig. 4. 42, K); *Dinomonas* Kent (130; Fig. 4. 42, M); *Phyllomitus* Stein (110; Fig. 4. 42, N); *Pleuromonas* Perty (181; Fig. 4. 42, H); *Proteromonas* Kunstler (*Prowazekella* Alexeieff) (98; Fig. 4. 42, J), from the intestine of lizards and salamanders; *Pseudobodo* Hollande (110; Fig. 4. 42, L).

Order 3. Polymastigida

Erection of the Order Trichomonadida by Kirby (147) has removed from the old Order Polymastigida several families of closely related uninucleate and multinucleate flagellates. As retained here, the Polymastigida include families which are excluded from the Trichomonadida but form an otherwise heterogeneous group. This arrangement will serve a practical purpose until accumulated data permit a more satisfactory classification. In this restricted sense, the Polymastigida usually have 3-8 flagella and one, two, or occasionally a number (*Microrhopalodina*) of nuclei. A parabasal apparatus is known in the Hexamitidae but its homology with that of the Trichomonadida is not yet certain. Seven families are retained in the order: Trimastigidae, Tetramitidae, Streblomastigidae, Retortomonadidae, Callimastigidae, Polymastigidae, and Pyrsonymphidae.

Family 1. Trimastigidae. There are three flagella, one anterior and two trailing (181). Almost nothing is known about the cytology of the group. One genus has been reported from salt water and two others from fresh water. The family includes *Dallingeria* Kent and *Trimastix*

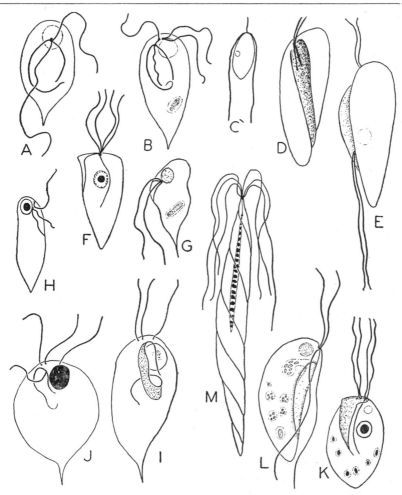

Fig. 4. 43. A. *Retortomonas gryllotalpae* (Grassi) Stiles, ventral view showing peristomial fibril, two flagella, nucleus (in outline); x2000 (after Wenrich). B. *Chilomastix intestinalis* Kuczynski, ventral view showing peristomial fibril, four flagella, food vacuole, nucleus (in outline); x2000 (after Wenrich). C. *Macromastix lapsa* Stokes, x2250 (after Lemmermann). D, E. *Costia necatrix* (Henneguy) Leclerq; ventral view showing groove and bases of flagella; lateral view; x3750 (after Tavolga and Nigrelli). F. *Copromastix prowazeki* Aragão, showing groove (at left), nucleus and rhizostyle; x1444 (after A.). G. *Retortomonas gryllotalpae*, lateral view (after Wenrich). H. *Retortomonas agilis* Mackinnon, x2880 (after Ludwig). I, J. *Chilomastix magna* Becker, showing nucleus, peristomial fibril, and intracytoplasmic band but not the cytostomal flagellum (I), x2160; protargol technique, showing peristomial fibril and flagella (J), x2850 (after Kirby and Honigberg). K. *Tetramitus rostratus* Perty, showing groove, rhizostyle, nucleus; x2250 (after Hollande). L. *Tetramitus salinus* (Entz) Kirby, showing groove, anterior nucleus, and food vacuole developing at base of gullet; x2320 (after K.). M. *Streblomastix strix* Kofoid and Swezy, showing flagella and long slender nucleus; x1400 (after K. & S.).

Kent, both with a long anterior flagellum, and *Macromastix* Stokes (Fig. 4. 43, C) with a short anterior flagellum. A lateral membrane (or keel?), which is not an undulating membrane, extends the length of the body in *Trimastix*. The flagellar equipment of *Macromastix* resembles that of the chrysomonad genus *Prymnesium* Massart (Fig. 4. 8, A). Similarly, *Chrysochromulina* (Fig. 4. 8, D) is similar to *Dallingeria* and *Trimastix*. Perhaps the Trimastigidae should be investigated for possible affinities with the Chrysomonadida.

Family 2. Tetramitidae. There are four unequal or equal flagella, one or two of which may be trailed. No parabasal body or axostyle has been reported, although a rhizostyle is present in *Tetramitus* (Fig. 4. 43, K) and *Copromastix* (Fig. 4. 43, F). A dimorphic cycle involving flagellate and amoeboid stages is known in *Tetramitus* (29, 110).

The following genera have been included in the family: *Costia* Leclerq (7, 59, 269; Fig. 4. 43, D, E), from the skin of fish; *Tetramitus* Perty (29, 110, 153, 245; Figs. 4. 43, K, L, 2. 14, C-E), in which the life-cycle includes amoeboid and flagellate stages; and *Tricercomonas* Wenyon and O'Connor (22, 65, 285; Fig. 11. 2, A-E), from the intestine of man. *Enteromonas* Fonseca may be an additional valid genus, although Dobell (65) has concluded that *Tricercomonas* is merely a synonym of *Enteromonas*. However, da Cunha and Muniz (53), as well as Fonseca, have described *Enteromonas intestinalis* with one long and two short flagella, and in contrast to *Tricercomonas,* without any trace of a fourth flagellum or caudal extension. The status of *Copromastix* Aragão is uncertain. *C. prowazeki* Aragão (Fig. 4. 43, F) is so similar to *Tetramitus rostratus* (29, 110) that the two flagellates probably should be referred to the same genus.

Family 3. Streblomastigidae. These parasites of termites (*Termopsis*), have an unusually slender body with a few spirally wound ridges and an anterior group of four flagella (131, 158). The flagella arise from the anterior tip of the body which can be extended as a slender holdfast organ. The only known genus is *Streblomastix* Kofoid and Swezy (Fig. 4. 43, M).

Family 4. Retortomonadidae. This family (278) includes *Retortomonas* Grassi (*Embadomonas* Mackinnon) (Fig. 4. 43, A, G, H) and *Chilomastix* Alexeieff (Fig. 4. 43, B, I, J). Both *Retortomonas* (18, 150, 187, 278) and *Chilomastix* (149, 198, 278) possess a cytostomal groove, in the margin of which a cytoplasmic fibril extends across the anterior end and posteriorly along each side. A true parabasal body is lacking. The significance of a differentiated intracytoplasmic "band," sometimes apparent just beneath the right limb of the peristomial fibril (149), is uncertain. In both genera, a single trailing flagellum emerges from the cytosomal groove. *Retortomonas* is distinguished from *Chilomastix* by the presence of one instead of three anterior flagella. The cytostomal flagellum in *Chilomastix* has been interpreted as part of an undulating membrane by Nie (198) and

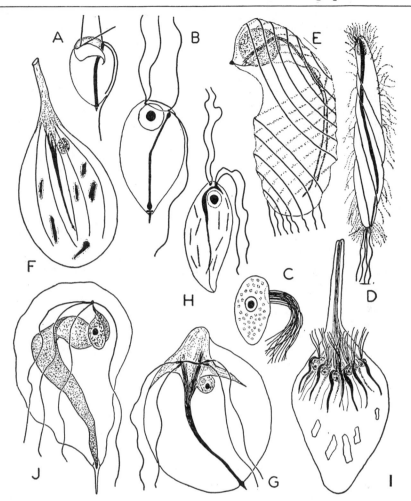

Fig. 4. 44. A, B. *Monocercomonoides pilleata* Kirby and Honigberg; protargol technique (A), showing pelta, "costa," axostyle, trailing flagellum,
bases of anterior flagella; specimen showing flagellar connections, nucleus,
and axostyle (B); x2880 (after K. & H.). C. *Callimastix equi* Hsiung, showing heavy tuft of flagella; x1166 (after H.). D. *Dinenympha fimbriata* Kirby;
nucleus, heavy axostyle, four adherent flagella which become free posteriorly, and bacteria attached to the body; x1000 (after K.). E. *Pyrsonympha
minor* Powell; nucleus, axostyle (split posteriorly); the adherent flagella
arise from the apical "centroblepharoplast" and extend posteriorly as eight
spiral cords; x900 (after P.). F. *Oxymonas dimorpha* Connell, non-flagellated attached form with extended rostellum; axostyle and subpellicular
supporting fibrils extend posteriorly from rostellum; nucelus and ingested
wood chips indicated; x425 (after C.). G. *O. dimorpha*, motile form, rostellum not extended; x1750 (after C.). H. *Polymastix phyllophagae* Travis and
Becker; nucleus, axostyle, adherent bacilli; x2400 (after T. & B.). I. *Microrhopalodina (Proboscidiella) multinucleata* (Kofoid and Swezy), showing
rostellum (which may be extended to several times body length), multiple
karyomastigonts (each with a heavy axostyle); bacteria are usually attached
to the body; x1150 (after K. & S.). J. *Saccinobaculus doroaxostylus* Cleveland; broad axostyle, nucleus, flagella; x600 (after C.).

several earlier workers. Such a relationship remains doubtful in certain species of *Chilomastix* (149).

Both *Retortomonas* and *Chilomastix* are represented by species in insects and vertebrates. *Chilomastix mesnili* and *Retortomonas intestinalis* of man are discussed in Chapter XI.

Family 5. Callimastigidae. This family includes *Callimastix* Weissenberg (Fig. 4. 44, C), represented by species from the stomachs of cattle, goats and sheep, from the cecum and colon of horses, and from the body cavity of *Cyclops*. The most striking feature is a compact antero-lateral group of flagella which beats as a unit.

Family 6. Polymastigidae. Four flagella arise as two pairs from the anterior end of the body. There is an axostyle but apparently no parabasal body. A pelta is present in *Monocercomonoides pilleata* (149), and a possibly homologous structure ("parabasal body") occurs in *Polymastix phyllophagae* (272). The family includes *Polymastix* Bütschli (98; Fig. 4. 44, H) from insects and *Monocercomonoides* Travis (149, 271; Fig. 4. 44, A, B) from rodents and insects.

Family 7. Pyrsonymphidae. These are uninucleate or multinucleate flagellates. Each karyomastigont usually contains four, but sometimes eight or twelve flagella, and one axostyle. An intranuclear spindle appears in mitosis (39). Some members of the family (e.g., *Kirbyella*, *Oxymonas*) are attached, by means of an extensible rostellum, to the gut wall of termites.

The family (139) includes **several uninucleate genera**—*Dinenympha* Leidy (133, 160; Fig. 4. 44, D), *Pyrsonympha* Leidy (160, 233; Fig. 4. 44, E), *Saccinobaculus* Cleveland (39; Fig. 4. 44, J) from the wood roach, *Metasaccinobaculus* de Freitas (87), and *Oxymonas* Janicki (*Opisthomitus* Duboscq and Grassé) (41, 52; Fig. 4. 44, F, G)—and the **multinucleate** *Microrhopalodina* Grassi and Foa (*Proboscidiella* Kofoid and Swezy) (159a; Fig. 4. 44, I) and *Baroella Kirbyella* Zeliff (286).

Oxymonas, Microrhopalodina, and *Baroella* seem to be restricted to the termite genus *Kalotermes; Saccinobaculus,* to the wood roach; the rest of the group, to *Reticulotermes.*

Family 8. Hexamitidae. These are binucleate organisms with six or eight flagella and, in at least certain genera, parabasal bodies and axostyles. Bilateral symmetry is typical of the family. The group includes free-living and parasitic types. Species of *Giardia* are widely distributed intestinal parasites of vertebrates. *Giardia lamblia* of man is discussed in Chapter XI. *Hexamita meleagridis* (105, 194) is associated with a catarrhal enteritis in young turkeys. Other species of *Hexamita* have been reported from monkeys (279), Amphibia (267), fishes (58), leeches (17), reptiles and rodents, and also as free-living flagellates. The genus *Trepomonas* also contains both free-living and parasitic species.

The family includes the following genera: *Giardia* Kunstler (Fig. 4. 45, H), *Gyromonas* Seligo (245; Fig. 4. 45, E, F), *Hexamita* Dujardin (*Octomitus* Prowazek) (Fig. 4.

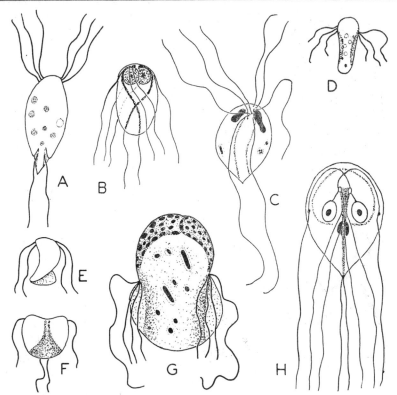

Fig. 4. 45. Hexamitidae. A. *Urophagus rostratus* (Stein) Klebs, x1200 (after K.). B. *Hexamita pitheci* (da Cunha and Muniz) Wenrich, from *Macacus rhesus;* paired nuclei, axostyles and flagella; x3465 (after W.). C. *Hexamita gigas* Bishop, from a leech (*Haemopsis sanguisugae*); elongated nuclei, two axostyles, food vacuoles; x2640 (after B.). D. *Trigonomonas compressa* Klebs, x833 (after K.). E, F. *Gyromonas ambulans* Seligo, narrow and broad surfaces; x945 (after S.). G. *Trepomonas agilis* Dujardin; two comma-shaped nuclei, paired flagella, ingested bacteria; x2500 (after Bishop). H. *Giardia muris* (Grassi), showing axostyle, paired nuclei, parabasal bodies, and flagella; concave ventral area indicated in outline; x2550, schematic (after Kofoid and Christiansen).

45, B, C), *Trepomonas* Dujardin (19; Fig. 4. 45, G), *Trigonomonas* Klebs (153; Fig. 4. 45, D), and *Urophagus* Klebs (Fig. 4. 45, A). It is possible that *Urophagus* should be considered a synonym of *Hexamita*.

Order 4. Trichomonadida

These flagellates have an axostyle, a parabasal body (not a kinetoplast), and a mastigont of 3-6 flagella (147). One flagellum is a trailing flagellum which may or may not form part of an undulating membrane. Each mastigont is typically associated with one nucleus, although a partial or complete dissociation has occurred in certain multinucleate species. A paradesmose appears in mitosis. Members of the order, as now known, are uninucleate or multinucleate, not binucleate.

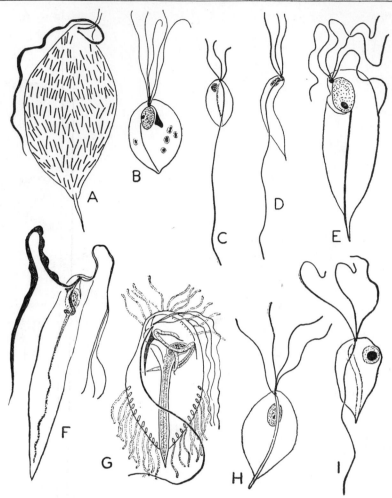

Fig. 4. 46. A. *Devescovina vestita* Kirby, showing adherent bacilli, trailing flagellum, projecting axostyle, basal portions of anterior flagella; x1165 (after K.). B. *Hexamastix termopsidis* Kirby; nucleus, axostyle, parabasal body, ingested bacteria; x2100 (after K.). C, D. *Tricercomitus termopsidis* Kirby; rounded form showing nucleus and axostyle (C), x1650; slender form (D) from recently molted nymph, x1600 (after K.). E. *Pseudotrichomonas keilini* Bishop, with short undulating membrane; x2970 (after B.). F. *Devescovina arta* Kirby; ribbon-like trailing flagellum, small cresta, parabasal body curled around axostyle; x1190 (after K.). G. *Parajoenia grassii* Janicki; stout axostyle with anterior expansion, branched parabasal body, pennant-like costa, four flagella, adherent spirochetes; subcuticular inclusions shown posteriorly; x875 (after Kirby). H. *Monocercomonas verrens* Honigberg, with projecting axostyle; x3420 (after H.). I. *Monocercomonas phyllophagae* (Travis and Becker); heavy axostyle, long trailing flagellum; x2700 (after T. & B.).

Family 1. Monocercomonadidae. There is either a free or an adherent trailing flagellum but no cresta and no undulating membrane with its underlying costa. The group includes parasites of the digestive tract in termites, certain other insects, and all classes of vertebrates. However, the distribution of particular genera ranges from that of *Tricercomitus,* in termites only, to that of *Monocercoconas,* reported from various groups of vertebrates and insects, including termites.

The family contains the following genera: *Hexamastix* Alexeieff (136; Fig. 4. 46, B), *Monocercomonas* Grassi (*Eutrichomastix* Kofoid and Swezy, *Trichomastix* Blochmann) (137; Fig. 4. 46, H, I), *Protrichomonas* Alexeieff (2), *Pseudotrichomonas* Bishop (21; Fig. 4. 46, E), *Tetratrichomastix* Mackinnon (190), and *Tricercomitus* Kirby (136; Fig. 4. 46, C, D).

Family 2. Devescovinidae. A group of three anterior flagella is characteristic and there is also a trailing flagellum which becomes a rather broad ribbon in some species. The trailing flagellum is often adherent to the body through part of its length but there is no undulating membrane. Bacteria are commonly attached to the surface of the body. The characteristic cresta varies from a small narrow structure to a wide band extending almost the length of the body. The parabasal body ranges from a short rod to a long structure coiled around the axostyle. The axostyle may curve forward along one side of the nucleus. More commonly, the anterior part of the axostyle is flattened into a capitulum. The Devescodinidae are known from termites, almost entirely from the Kalotermitidae. The occurrence of encystment is doubtful and flagellates probably are transferred by proctodeal feeding.

The following genera are included: *Bullanympha* Kirby (148; Fig. 1. 8, E), *Caduceia* França (142; Fig. 4. 47, B), *Devescovina* Foà (141; Fig. 4. 46, A, F), *Foaina* Janicki (143; Fig. 4. 47, C), *Gigantomonas* Dogiel (146; Fig. 2. 14, H-J), *Hyperdevescovina* Kirby (148; Fig. 4. 47, E), *Macrotrichomonas* Grassi (142; Fig. 4. 47, D), *Metadevescovina* Light (145; Fig. 4. 47, A), *Parajoenia* Janicki (143; Fig. 4. 46, G), and *Pseudodevescovina* Sutherland (145; Fig. 4. 47, F). *Gigantomonas* differs from the others in that the cycle includes an amoeboid stage, sometimes multinucleate, in which elements of the mastigont may be much reduced.

Family 3. Calonymphidae. These are multinucleate flagellates with eight (*Coronympha*) to hundreds of mastigonts (*Snyderella*), each usually containing four flagella. One of the four is typically a trailing flagellum. The cresta is well developed in some species but is small or else lacking in others. The axostyles range from fairly heavy separate structures to slender filaments which form a compact axial bundle. *Coronympha, Metacoronympha,* and *Stephanonympha* contain karyomastigonts exclusively. In *Calonympha* there are both karyomastigonts and mastigonts, while the mastigonts and nuclei are completely dissociated in *Snyderella.* The Calonymphidae have been reported mostly from the

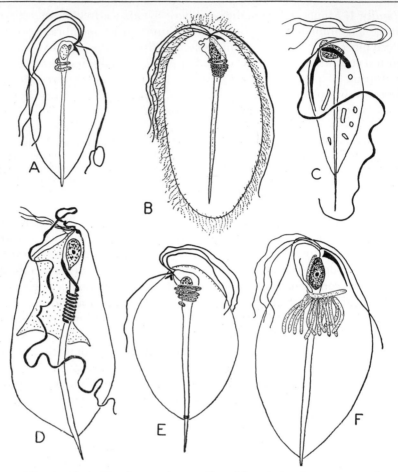

Fig. 4. 47. A. *Metadevescovina modica* Kirby, x750 (after K.). B. *Caduceia bugnioni* Kirby; adherent spirochetes indicated, bacilli not shown; axostyle expanded anteriorly; long parabasal body coiled around axostyle; x700 (after K.). C. *Foaina taeniola* Kirby, x1310 (after K.). D. *Macrotrichomonas lighti* (Connell) Kirby; large cresta (stippled), long coiled parabasal body; x700 (after K.). E. *Hyperdevescovina mitrata* Kirby, x750 (after K.). F. *Pseudodevescovina uniflagellata* Sutherland; axostyle expanded anteriorly, complex parabasal apparatus; x750 (after Kirby).

termite genus *Kalotermes; Snyderella* seems to be limited to a single species of that genus.

The family includes *Calonympha* Foà (122), *Coronympha* Kirby (135a, 140; Fig. 4. 48, F), *Metacoronympha* Kirby (140), *Snyderella* Kirby (135a; Figs. 1. 8, C; 1. 10, C), and *Stephanonympha* Janicki (134; Fig. 1. 10, D, E).

Family 4. Trichomonadidae. These are uninucleate types with an undulating membrane and an underlying costa. In addition, a pelta occurs

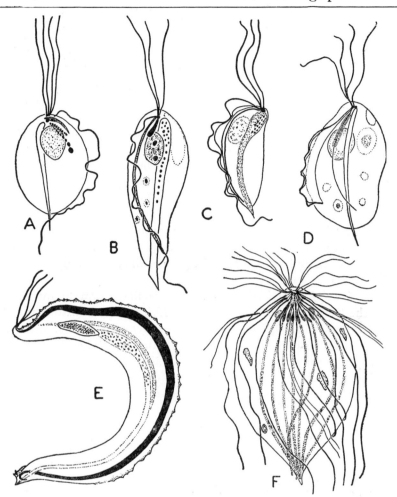

Fig. 4. 48. A. *Trichomonas limacis* Dujardin, showing pelta, beaded and bifurcated parabasal body, axostyle, and nucleus; x2415 (after Kozloff). B. *Tritrichomonas augusta* Alexeieff; axostyle, nucleus, parabasal body, heavy costa; x1680 approx. (after Samuels). C. *Tritrichomonas foetus*, parabasal body not shown; x2795 (after Wenrich and Emmerson). D. *Trichomonas gallinae* (Rivolta) Stabler, x3400 (after S.). E. *Pseudotrypanosoma gigantea* Grassi; heavy costa, long parabasal body parallel to axostyle, long undulating membrane; x575 (after Kirby). F. *Coronympha clevelandi* Kirby, showing anterior circle of karyomastigonts, axostyles extending posteriorly; x1400 (after K.).

in some species. The group is widely distributed in vertebrates and certain invertebrates. Several parasites of man are discussed in Chapter XI. *Trichomonas gallinae* is a pathogen in the anterior digestive tract of pigeons (261, 262); *Tritrichomonas foetus* is a parasite of the genital tract in cattle (196, 281); *Trichomonas gallinarum* occurs in the ceca of chickens and turkeys and the liver of turkeys. Like *Histomonas mele-*

agridis, T. gallinarum is associated with "blackhead" in poultry (4, 5).

The family includes the following genera: *Pentatrichomonas* Mesnil (Fig. 11. 3, A-C); *Pentatrichomonoides* Kirby (137); *Pseudotrypanosoma* Grassi (137; Fig. 4. 48, E); *Trichomonas* Donné (Fig. 4. 48, A, D), for which Morgan (195) has published a host-parasite catalog; and *Tritrichomonas* Kofoid (Fig. 4. 48, B, C).

Order 5. Hypermastigida

These are uninucleate organisms with many flagella. Multiple axostyles and parabasal bodies also are characteristic. All known species are intestinal parasites of termites, wood roaches or cockroaches. Feeding methods may be saprozoic or holozoic, and some species ingest wood chips swallowed by the host (77). Two suborders, Lophomonadina and Trichonymphina, have been recognized.

Suborder 1. Lophomonadina. In this group, the flagella and associated structures are arranged in one anterior group which is resorbed in fission. The suborder includes three families which differ in arrangement of the flagella.

Family 1. Lophomonadidae. The blepharoplasts form an anterior ring so that the flagella, if numerous (Fig. 4. 49, C), form a distinct tuft. The axostyle, at least in *Lophomonas* and *Torquenympha* (Fig. 4. 49, B), is a bundle of fibrils enclosing the nucleus anteriorly. The fibrillar bundle may be split posteriorly into several fibrils in *Torquenympha* (27). Members of the group are known from the digestive tract of cockroaches (*Lophomonas*), the wood roach (*Prolophomonas*), and certain termites (*Torquenympha*).

The family includes *Prolophomonas* Cleveland (39), *Lophomonas* Stein (168, 169), and *Torquenympha* Brown (27). The flagella number 24 or less in *Prolophomonas* (Fig. 4. 49, A) and *Torquenympha*, but are more numerous in *Lophomonas*.

Family 2. Joeniidae. Although limited to an anterior area, the blepharoplasts are arranged in longitudinal rows instead of a compact ring. As a result, there may be an anterior tuft of flagella, as in *Joenia* and *Joenopsis*, while the rest of the flagella are trailed. The flagellar rows may extend past the middle of the body in *Joenopsis* (55), but are shorter in *Microjoenia* (27, 55; Fig. 4. 49, D). A paired parabasal apparatus is quite simple in *Microjoenia*. In *Joenopsis* and *Joenia*, however, there are two filaments to which are attached numerous rod-like parabasal bodies (55).

The following genera have been reported from termites: *Joenia* Grassi, *Joenopsis* Cutler, *Joenina* Grassi (98a), *Mesojoenia* Grassi and Foà, and *Microjoenia* Grassi.

Family 3. Kofoidiidae. The flagella are arranged in a spiral series of permanent bundles. The nucleus lies within a "suspensorium" from which filaments radiate into the cytoplasm. These filaments may be

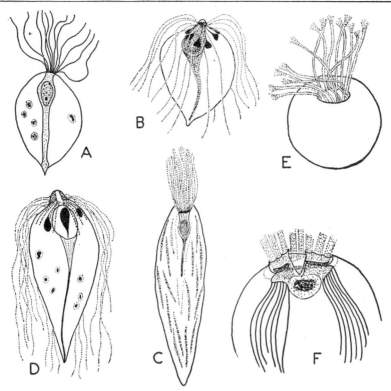

Fig. 4. 49. A. *Prolophomonas tocopola* Cleveland, showing axostyles, nucleus, food vacuoles; x1200 (after C.). B. *Torquenympha octoplus* Brown, showing parabasal bodies and fibrillar axostyle which surrounds the nucleus anteriorly; x1645 (after B.). C. *Lophomonas striata* Bütschli, showing axostylar filaments which form a "calyx" enclosing the nucleus; adherent bacteria (*Fusiformis lophomonadis* Grassé) indicated on body; x1475 approx. (after Kudo). D. *Microjoenia ratcliffei* Brown, showing two parabasal bodies, axostyle, nucleus, and anterior rows of blepharoplasts; x2380 (after B.). E. *Koifoidia loriculata* Light, showing bundles (loriculae) of flagella; x175. F. *K. loriculata*, anterior end of body showing nucleus suspended in membranous "suspensorium," bases of several loriculae, and body fibrils extending into cytoplasm; x750 (after L.).

analogous to the axostylar bundle in *Torquenympha* and *Lophomonas*. The general organization, although more complex, is similar to that in *Lophomonas*. The type genus is *Kofoidia* Light (183; Fig. 4. 49, E, F), reported from one species of *Kalotermes*.

Suborder 2. Trichonymphina. The retention of flagella and associated structures in fission is characteristic. Organization is basically bilateral, and there are either two or four sets of organelles which are separated equally in fission. Encystment is known for species of *Macrospironympha* and *Trichonympha* in the wood roach (39), but not for the Trichonymphina of termites.

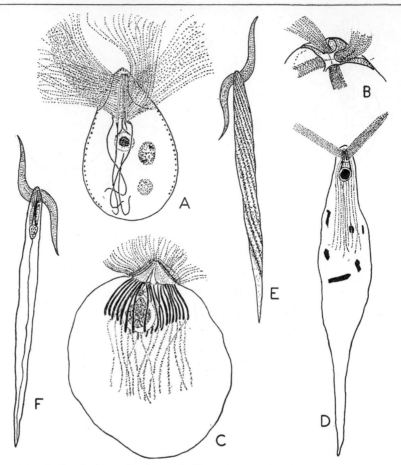

Fig. 4. 50. A. *Staurojoenina assimilis* Kirby, showing four flagellar groups, rhizoplast bands extending anteriorly from the nucleus, and the major body filaments extending posteriorly; cuticular striations indicated at lateral margins; x330 (after K.). B. Optical section, anterior end of *S. assimilis*, showing four flagellar groups; x330 (after Kirby). C. *Barbulanympha ufalula* Cleveland; two anterior flagellar groups, nucleus surrounded by parabasal bodies; axostylar filaments extend posteriorly; x200 (after C). D. *Urinympha talea* Cleveland; two flagellar groups, nucleus suspended by nuclear sleeve; axostylar filaments extending posteriorly; x350 (after C.). E, F. *Hoplonympha natator* Light; surface view showing two flagellar tufts and spiral pellicular grooves (E); optical section showing nucleus suspended by rhizoplast bands (enclosed in granular column); a delicate endoplasmic thread (primitive axostyle?) extends posteriorly; x855 (after L.).

Family 1. Hoplonymphidae. The flagella arise in two anterior groups. One group passes to each daughter organism in fission. *Hoplonympha* is represented in termites; three other genera, in the wood roach (*Cryptocercus*).

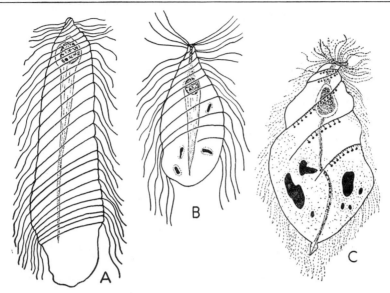

Fig. 4. 51. A. *Holomastigotoides hemigymnum* Grassi; nucleus, axostyle (expanded anteriorly), flagellar bands (flagella indicated only at sides of body); x320 approx. (after Mackinnon). B. *Spirotrichonympha elegans* (Mackinnon); rostellar tube, nucleus, axostyle (expanded anteriorly), flagellar bands (only the marginal flagella are shown); x1820 (after M.). C. *Spironympha porteri* Koidzumi; axostyle, nucleus, flagellar bands with attached parabasal bodies; marginal flagella indicated; adherent spirochetes posterior to the flagellar bands have sometimes been mistaken for flagella; x1600 approx. (after Brown).

The family includes *Barbulanympha* Cleveland (39; Fig. 4. 50, C), *Hoplonympha* Light (182; Fig. 4. 50, E, F), *Rhynchonympha* Cleveland (39), and *Urinympha* Cleveland (39; Fig. 4. 50, D).

Family 2. Staurojoeninidae. The flagella are arranged in four anterior groups. A number of slender fibrillar axostyles are attached to each flagellar group, and in *Idionympha* four groups of slender parabasal "cords" are associated with the flagellar groups.

The family includes *Staurojoenina* Grassi (133a; Fig. 4. 50, A, B) from termites and *Idionympha* Cleveland (39) from the wood roach.

Family 3. Holomastigotidae. The flagella arise from bands of basal granules which extend spirally around the body. Two, four, or more bands have been reported in different species. Apparent variations within a species possibly involve duplication in fission.

The family includes *Holomastigotes* Grassi (72, 160), *Holomastigotoides* Grassi and Foà (14, 160, 192; Fig. 4. 51, A), *Leptospironympha* Cleveland (39), *Macrospironympha* Cleveland (39), *Spironympha* Koidzumi (28; Fig. 4. 51, C), *Spirotrichonymphella* Grassi, *Spirotrichonympha* Grassi (54, 72, 160, 193; Fig. 4. 51, B) and *Spirotrichosoma* Sutherland (266). *Leptospironympha* and *Macrospironympha* have been reported from the wood roach; the other genera, from termites.

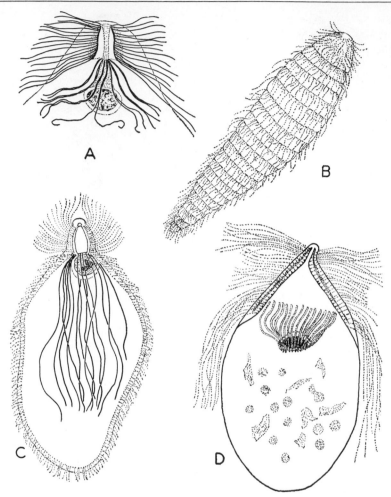

Fig. 4. 52. A. *Teratonympha* sp. from *Reticulotermes speratus;* anterior end of body showing rostral tube, rostral flagella, nuclear "sleeve" extending from nucleus into rostral tube, and supporting fibrils surround nuclear sleeve and nucleus; the fibrils end posteriorly in the first flagellar band; x840 (after Cleveland). B. Surface view of *Teratonympha* showing circular flagellar bands; flagella indicated diagrammatically; x280 (after Cleveland). C. *Eucomonympha inula* Cleveland, showing rostrum with anterior cap (operculum), nucleus, and fibrillar axostyles extending posteriorly; x350 (after C.). D. *Trichonympha corbula* Kirby, showing three flagellar zones and the parabasal bodies surrounding the nucleus; x475 (after K.).

Family 4. Trichonymphidae. Except for the tip of the rostrum, the surface of the body is flagellated in certain genera (*Deltotrichonympha, Eucomonympha, Mixotricha, Pseudotrichonympha*). In others, a small or a large posterior portion is bare. The flagella are arranged in longitudinal rows, and may form two or three transverse zones differing in length of the flagella. The parabasal apparatus consists of a number of parabasal cords, usually encircling the nucleus and attached by filaments to the parabasal lamella at the base of the rostrum (71, 144). Differences in form, size, and number of the cords are useful taxonomic features. In the rostrum, the conical anterior end of the body (Fig. 4. 52, C, D), the blepharoplasts and the parabasal lamella, internal to them, form a rostral "tube." This tube is sometimes widened posteriorly into a cone, as in *Eucomonympha* (Fig. 4. 52, C).

The family contains *Deltotrichonympha* Sutherland (72, 266), *Eucomonympha* Cleveland (39; Fig. 4. 52, C), *Mixotricha* Sutherland (266), *Pseudotrichonympha* Grassi (39, 160), and *Trichonympha* Leidy (39, 138, 144; Fig. 4. 52, D). *Trichonympha* is represented in termites (three families) and in the wood roach (39). *Eucomonympha* has been reported from the wood roach; the other genera, from single families of termites.

Family 5. Teratonymphidae. This family was erected for *Teratonympha* Koidzumi (*Cyclonympha* Dogiel) from termites. The rostrum is similar to that of Trichonymphidae, but the post-rostral flagella arise from circular bands underlying grooves which give the body a segmented appearance (40, 160; Fig. 4. 52, A, B).

LITERATURE CITED

1. Ahlstrom, E. H. 1937. *Trans. Amer. Micr. Soc.* **56:** 139.
2. Alexeieff, A. 1929. *Arch Zool. Exp. Gén.* **68:** 600.
3. Allegre, C. F. and T. L. Jahn 1943. *Trans. Amer. Micr. Soc.* **62:** 233.
4. Allen, E. A. 1936. *Trans. Amer. Micr. Soc.* **55:** 315.
5. ———— 1941. *Vet. Res.* **2:** 214.
6. Allen, W. E. 1945. *Trans. Amer. Micr. Soc.* **65:** 149.
7. Andai, G. 1933. *Arch. f. Protistenk.* **79:** 283.
8. Baker, C. L. 1933. *Arch. f. Protistenk.* **80:** 434.
9. Baumeister, W. 1938. *Arch. f. Protistenk.* **91:** 456.
10. ———— 1943. *Arch. f. Protistenk.* **96:** 325.
11. ———— 1943. *Arch. f. Protistenk.* **96:** 344.
12. Becker, E. R. 1925. *J. Parasit.* **11:** 213.
13. ———— 1928. *Biol. Bull.* **54:** 109.
14. Bernstein, T. 1928. *Arch. f. Protistenk.* **61:** 9.
15. Biecheler, B. 1936. *Arch. Zool. Exp. Gén.* **78** (N. et R.): 79.
16. ———— 1936. *C. R. Soc. Biol.* **123:** 1126.
17. Bishop, A. 1933. *Parasitol.* **25:** 163.
18. ———— 1934. *Parasitol.* **26:** 17.
19. ———— 1937. *Parasitol.* **29:** 413.
20. ———— 1938. *Parasitol.* **30:** 181.
21. ———— 1939. *Parasitol.* **31:** 469.
22. Boeck, W. C. 1924. *Amer. J. Trop. Med.* **4:** 519.
23. Bold, H. C. 1938. *Bull. Torrey Bot. Club* **65:** 293.
24. Borgert, A. 1891. *Ztschr. f. wiss. Zool.* **51:** 629.
25. Bretschneider, L. H. 1925. *Arch. f. Protistenk.* **53:** 124.
26. Brown, E. M. 1934. *Proc. Zool. Soc. London* **1934:** 583.
27. Brown, V. E. 1930. *Univ. Calif. Publ. Zool.* **36:** 67.
28. ———— 1931. *J. Morph.* **51:** 291.
29. Bunting, M. 1926. *J. Morph.* **42:** 23.
30. Burck, C. 1909. *Arch. f. Protistenk.* **16:** 169.

31. Carter, N. 1937. *Arch. f. Protistenk.* **90**: 1.
32. Caullery, M. 1910. *Bull. Sci. Fr. Belg.* (Ser. 7) **44**: 201.
33. Chadefaud, M. 1934. *Bull. Soc. Bot.* **81**: 106.
34. —— 1937. *Le Botaniste* **28**: 85.
35. —— 1938. *Rev. Algol.* **11**: 189.
36. Chatton, E. 1920. *Arch. Zool. Exp. Gén.* **59**: 1.
37. —— 1923. *C. R. Ac. Sci.* **177**: 1246.
38. Chen, Y. T. 1950. *Quart. J. Micr. Sci.* **91**: 279.
39. Cleveland, L. R. 1934. *Mem. Amer. Acad. Arts & Sci.* **17**: 185.
40. —— 1938. *Arch. f. Protistenk.* **91**: 442.
41. Connell, F. H. 1930. *Univ. Calif. Publ. Zool.* **36**: 51.
42. Connell, C. H. and J. B. Cross 1950. *Science* **112**: 359.
43. Conrad, W. 1920. *Bull. Acad. Roy. Belg.* (Sci.), No. **11**, p. 544.
44. —— 1926. *Arch. f. Protistenk.* **55**: 63.
45. —— 1927. *Arch. f. Protistenk.* **59**: 423.
46. —— 1928. *Arch. f. Protistenk.* **63**: 58.
47. —— 1930. *Arch. f. Protistenk.* **72**: 538.
48. —— 1933. "Revision du genre *Mallomonas* Perty (1851) incl. *Pseudomallomonas* Chodat (1920)." *Mem. Mus. Roy. Hist. Nat.*, No. **56**.
49. —— 1934. *Arch. f. Protistenk.* **82**: 203.
50. —— 1938. *Bull. Mus. Roy. Hist. Nat. Belg.* 14, No. **42**.
51. —— 1939. *Bull. Mus. Roy. Hist. Nat. Belg.* 15, No. **2**.
52. Cross, J. B. 1946. *Univ. Calif. Publ. Zool.* **53**: 67.
53. Cunha, A. M. da and J. Muniz 1927. *C. R. Soc. Biol.* **96**: 479.
54. Cupp, E. 1930. *Univ. Calif. Publ. Zool.* **33**: 351.
55. Cutler, D. W. 1920. *Quart. J. Micr. Sci.* **64**: 383.
56. —— 1921. *Quart. J. Micr. Sci.* **65**: 247.
57. Dach, H. von 1950. *J. Exp. Zool.* **115**: 1.
58. Davis, H. S. 1926. *Bull. U. S. Bur. Fish.* **42**: 9.
59. —— 1943. *J. Parasit.* **29**: 385.
60. Deflandre, G. 1926. *Monographie du genre Trachelomonas* (Nemours: A. Lesot).
61. —— 1930. *Arch. f. Protistenk.* **69**: 551.
62. —— 1934. *Bull. Biol.* **68**: 382.
63. —— 1936. *Les Flagellés Fossiles. Aperçu biologique et paléontologique. Role géologique* (Paris: Hermann & Cie.).
64. Diwald, K. 1939. *Arch. f. Protistenk.* **93**: 121.
65. Dobell, C. 1935. *Parasitol.* **27**: 564.
66. Doflein, F. 1922. *Arch. f. Protistenk.* **44**: 149.
67. —— 1923. *Arch. f. Protistenk.* **46**: 267.
68. Drbohlav, J. 1925. *Amer. J. Hyg.* **5**: 580.
69. Drouet, F. and A. Cohen 1935. *Biol. Bull.* **68**: 422.
70. —— and —— 1937. *Botan. Gaz.* **98**: 617.
71. Duboscq, O. and P. Grassé 1933. *Arch. Zool. Exp. Gén.* **73**: 381.
72. —— and —— 1943. *Arch. Zool. Exp. Gén.* **82**: 401.
73. —— and O. Tuzet 1937. *Arch. Zool. Exp. Gén.* **79**: 157.
74. Eddy, S. 1930. *Trans. Amer. Micr. Soc.* **49**: 277.
75. Eisenack, A. 1939. *Arch. f. Protistenk.* **93**: 81.
76. Elliott, A. M. 1934. *Arch. f. Protistenk.* **82**: 250.
77. Emik, L. O. 1941. *Trans. Amer. Micr. Soc.* **60**: 1.
78. Entz, G., Jr. 1918. *Arch. f. Protistenk.* **38**: 324.
79. —— 1925. *Arch. f. Protistenk.* **51**: 131.
80. —— 1927. *Arch. f. Protistenk.* **58**: 344.
81. —— 1928. *Ann. Protistol.* **1**: 1.
82. Finley, H. E. 1930. *Ecology* **11**: 337.
83. Fott, B. 1935. *Arch. f. Protistenk.* **84**: 242.
84. —— 1949. *Věst. Kráklouské c. spolecnost nauk—Trída math.-prirodovedecka.* Cislo **2**: 1.
85. França, C. 1920. *Ann. Inst. Pasteur* **34**: 432.
86. Franchini, G. 1923. *Ann. Inst. Pasteur* **37**: 879.

87. Freitas, G. de 1946. *Mem. Inst. Osw. Cruz* **43**: 349.
88. Frenzel, J. 1892. "Untersuchungen über die mikroskopische Fauna Argentiniens," Teil I: *Die Protozoen*, Abt. 1-2 (Cassel: Fischer).
89. Geitler, L. 1925. *Arch. f. Protistenk.* **52**: 356.
90. ———— 1926. *Arch. f. Protistenk.* **56**: 291.
91. ———— 1928. *Arch. f. Protistenk.* **61**: 1.
92. ———— 1935. *Österreich. bot. Ztschr.* **84**: 282.
93. ———— 1943. *Arch. f. Protistenk.* **96**: 119.
94. Gerloff, J. 1940. *Arch. f. Protistenk.* **94**: 311.
95. Gessner, F. 1931. *Arch. f. Protistenk.* **74**: 259.
96. Gojdics, M. 1934. *Trans. Amer. Micr. Soc.* **53**: 299.
97. Goldschmidt, R. 1907. *Arch. f. Protistenk.*, Suppl. **1**: 83.
98. Grassé, P. P. 1926. *Arch. Zool. Exp. Gén.* **65**: 345.
98a. Grassi, B. 1917. *Mem. R. Ac. Lincei* (5) **12**: 331.
99. Hall, R. P. 1923. *Univ. Calif. Publ. Zool.* **20**: 447.
100. ———— 1934. *Arch. f. Protistenk.* **81**: 308.
101. Hanna, G. D. 1928. *J. Paleontol.* **1**: 259.
102. Hartmann, M. 1919. *Arch. f. Protistenk.* **39**: 1.
103. ———— 1924. *Arch. f. Protistenk.* **59**: 375.
104. Higinbotham, N. 1942. *Bull. Torrey Bot. Club.* **69**: 66.
105. Hinshaw, W. R. and E. McNeil 1941. *Amer. J. Vet. Res.* **2**: 453.
106. Hofender, H. 1930. *Arch. f. Protistenk.* **71**: 1.
107. Hofker, J. 1930. *Arch. f. Protistenk.* **71**: 57.
108. Hollande, A. 1937. *Bull. Soc. Zool. France* **62**: 236.
109. ———— 1942. *Arch. Zool. Exp. Gén.* **82** (N. et R.): 119.
110. ———— 1942. *Arch. Zool. Exp. Gén.* **83**: 1.
111. Hovasse, R. 1922. *C. R. Soc. Biol.* **87**: 845.
112. ———— 1935. *Bull. Biol. Fr. Belg.* **69**: 59.
113. ———— 1937. *Arch. Zool. Exp. Gén.* **79** (N. et R.): 43.
114. ———— 1945. *Arch. Zool. Exp. Gén.* **84**: 239.
115. ———— and E. M. Brown 1946. *Proc. Zool. Soc. London* **116**: 33.
116. Hsiung, T.-S. 1930. *Iowa St. Coll. J. Sci.* **4**: 356.
117. Hutchens, J. O., B. Podolsky and M. F. Morales 1948. *J. Cell. Comp. Physiol.* **32**: 117.
118. Jacobs, D. L. 1946. *Trans. Amer. Micr. Soc.* **65**: 1.
119. Jahn, T. L. 1946. *Quart. Rev. Biol.* **21**: 246.
120. ———— and W. R. McKibben 1937. *Trans. Amer. Micr. Soc.* **56**: 48.
121. Jameson, A. P. 1914. *Arch. f. Protistenk.* **33**: 21.
122. Janicki, C. 1915. *Ztschr. f. wiss. Zool.* **112**: 573.
123. Johnson, D. F. 1934. *Arch. f. Protistenk.* **83**: 241.
124. Johnson, L. P. 1944. *Trans. Amer. Micr. Soc.* **63**: 97.
125. ———— and T. L. Jahn 1942. *Physiol. Zool.* **15**: 89.
126. Kamptner, E. 1928. *Arch. f. Protistenk.* **61**: 38.
127. ———— 1928. *Arch. f. Protistenk.* **64**: 19.
128. Kater, J. McA. 1925. *Biol. Bull.* **49**: 213.
129. ———— 1929. *Univ. Calif. Publ. Zool.* **33**: 125.
130. Kent, W. S. 1880-82. *A Manual of the Infusoria* (London).
131. Kidder, G. W. 1929. *Univ. Calif. Publ. Zool.* **33**: 109.
132. Killian, C. 1924. *Arch. f. Protistenk.* **50**: 50.
133. Kirby, H. 1924. *Univ. Calif. Publ. Zool.* **26**: 199.
133a. ———— 1926. *Univ. Calif. Publ. Zool.* **29**: 25.
134. ———— 1926. *Univ. Calif. Publ. Zool.* **29**: 103.
135. ———— 1928. *Quart. J. Micr. Sci.* **72**: 355.
135a. ———— 1929. *Univ. Calif. Publ. Zool.* **31**: 417.
136. ———— 1930. *Univ. Calif. Publ. Zool.* **33**: 393.
137. ———— 1931. *Univ. Calif. Publ. Zool.* **36**: 171.
138. ———— 1932. *Univ. Calif. Publ. Zool.* **37**: 349.
139. ———— 1937. *Univ. Calif. Publ. Zool.* **41**: 189.
140. ———— 1939. *Proc. Calif. Acad. Sci.* **22**: 207.

141. —— 1941. *Univ. Calif. Publ. Zool.* **45**: 1.
142. —— 1942. *Univ. Calif. Publ. Zool.* **45**: 93.
143. —— 1942. *Univ. Calif. Publ. Zool.* **45**: 167.
144. —— 1944. *Univ. Calif. Publ. Zool.* **49**: 185.
145. —— 1945. *Univ. Calif. Publ. Zool.* **45**: 247.
146. —— 1946. *Univ. Calif. Publ. Zool.* **53**: 163.
147. —— 1947. *J. Parasit.* **33**: 214.
148. —— 1949. *Univ. Calif. Publ. Zool.* **45**: 319.
149. —— and B. Honigberg 1949. *Univ. Calif. Publ. Zool.* **53**: 315.
150. —— and —— 1950. *Univ. Calif. Publ. Zool.* **55**: 35.
151. Klebs, G. 1892. *Ztschr. f. wiss. Zool.* **55**: 322.
152. —— 1892. *Ztschr. f. wiss. Zool.* **55**: 353.
153. Klug, G. 1936. *Arch. f. Protistenk.* **87**: 97.
154. Kofoid, C. A. 1899. *Bull. Ill. St. Lab. Nat. Hist.* **5**: 273.
155. —— 1909. *Arch. f. Protistenk.* **16**: 25.
156. —— 1911. *Univ. Calif. Publ. Zool.* **8**: 187.
157. —— and J. R. Michener 1912. *Univ. Calif. Publ. Zool.* **11**: 21.
158. —— and O. Swezy 1919. *Univ. Calif. Publ. Zool.* **20**: 1.
159. —— and —— 1921. "The Free-living Unarmored Dinoflagellates." *Univ. Calif. Mem.*, vol. **5**.
159a. —— and —— 1926. *Univ. Calif. Publ. Zool.* **28**: 301.
160. Koidzumi, M. 1921. *Parasitol.* **13**: 235.
161. Korshikov, A. A. 1926. *Arch. f. Protistenk.* **55**: 439.
162. —— 1927. *Arch. f. Protistenk.* **58**: 441.
163. —— 1927. *Arch. f. Protistenk.* **58**: 450.
164. —— 1928. *Arch. f. Protistenk.* **61**: 223.
165. —— 1929. *Arch. f. Protistenk.* **67**: 253.
166. Kozloff, E. 1948. *J. Morph.* **83**: 253.
167. Krichenbauer, H. 1937. *Arch. f. Protistenk.* **90**: 88.
168. Kudo, R. 1926. *Arch. f. Protistenk.* **53**: 191.
169. —— 1926. *Arch. f. Protistenk.* **55**: 504.
170. Kuschakewitsch, S. 1931. *Arch. f. Protistenk.* **73**: 323.
171. Lackey, J. B. 1929. *Arch. f. Protistenk.* **66**: 175.
172. —— 1934. *Biol. Bull.* **67**: 145.
173. —— 1936. *Biol. Bull.* **71**: 492.
174. —— 1939. *Lloydia* **2**: 128.
175. —— 1940. *Amer. Midl. Nat.* **23**: 463.
176. Lapage, G. 1925. *Quart. J. Micr. Sci.* **69**: 471.
177. Lauterborn, R. 1895. *Ztschr. f. wiss. Zool.* **60**: 236.
178. Lebour, M. V. 1922. *J. Mar. Biol. Assoc.* **12**: 795.
179. —— 1923. *J. Mar. Biol. Assoc.* **13**: 271.
180. Léger, L. 1902. *C. R. Soc. Biol.* **54**: 355.
181. Lemmermann, E. 1914. "Protomastiginae" in *Die Süsswasser-Flora Deutschlands, Österreichs und der Schweiz,* H. 1 (Jena: Fischer).
182. Light, S. F. 1926. *Univ. Calif. Publ. Zool.* **29**: 123.
183. —— 1927. *Univ. Calif. Publ. Zool.* **29**: 467.
184. Loefer, J. B. 1931. *Arch. f. Protistenk.* **74**: 449.
185. —— 1937. *Physiol. Zool.* **12**: 161.
186. Lohmann, H. 1902. *Arch. f. Protistenk.* **1**: 89.
187. Ludwig, F. W. 1946. *Trans. Amer. Micr. Soc.* **65**: 189.
188. McCulloch, I. 1915. *Univ. Calif. Publ. Zool.* **16**: 1.
189. McKay, F. and N. F. Morehouse 1948. *J. Parasit.* **34**: 137.
190. Mackinnon, D. L. 1913. *Quart. J. Micr. Sci.* **59**: 297.
191. —— 1913. *Quart. J. Micr. Sci.* **59**: 459.
192. —— 1926. *Quart. J. Micr. Sci.* **70**: 173.
193. —— 1927. *Quart. J. Micr. Sci.* **71**: 47.
194. McNeil, E., W. R. Hinshaw and C. A. Kofoid 1941. *Amer. J. Hyg.* **34, C**: 71.
195. Morgan, B. B. 1944. *Trans. Wisc. Acad. Sci. Arts & Lett.* **35**: 235,
196. —— 1947. *J. Parasit.* **33**: 201.

197. Nie, D. 1945. *Trans. Amer. Micr. Soc.* **64**: 196.
198. ———— 1948. *J. Morph.* **82**: 287.
199. Nigrelli, R. F. 1936. *Zoologica* **21**: 129.
200. Owen, H. M. 1949. *Trans. Amer. Micr. Soc.* **68**: 261.
201. Pascher, A. 1912. *Ber. deutsch. bot. Ges.* **30**: 152.
202. ———— 1913. "Chrysomonadinae, Cryptomonadinae, Eugleninae, Chloromonadinae" in *Die Süsswasser-Flora Deutschlands, Österreichs und der Schweiz*, H. 2 (Jena: Fischer).
203. ———— 1916. *Arch. f. Protistenk.* **37**: 31.
204. ———— 1917. *Biol. Zentralbl.* **37**: 241.
205. ———— 1927. *Arch. f. Protistenk.* **58**: 1.
206. ———— 1927. "Volvocales—Phytomonadinae" in *Die Süsswasser-Flora Deutschlands, Österreichs und der Schweiz*, H. 4 (Jena: Fischer).
207. ———— 1927. *Arch. f. Protistenk.* **58**: 577.
208. ———— 1928. *Arch. f. Protistenk.* **63**: 241.
209. ———— 1929. *Arch. f. Protistenk.* **68**: 637.
210. ———— 1929. *Ann. Protistol.* **2**: 157.
211. ———— 1930. *Beih. Bot. Centralbl.* **47**: 271.
212. ———— 1930. *Arch. f. Protistenk.* **69**: 401.
213. ———— 1930. *Arch. f. Protistenk.* **72**: 311.
214. ———— 1931. *Beih. Bot. Centralbl.* **48**: 317.
215. ———— 1931. *Arch. f. Protistenk.* **73**: 315.
216. ———— 1932. *Beih. Bot. Centralbl.* **49**: 293.
217. ———— 1932. *Arch. f. Protistenk.* **76**: 1.
218. ———— 1932. *Arch. f. Protistenk.* **77**: 305.
219. ———— 1932. *Beih. Bot. Centralbl.* **49**: 549.
220. ———— 1940. *Arch. f. Protistenk.* **93**: 331.
221. ———— 1940. *Arch. f. Protistenk.* **94**: 295.
222. ———— 1942. *Arch. f. Protistenk.* **96**: 75.
223. ———— 1942. *Beih. bot. Centralbl.* **61**: 462.
224. ———— 1943. *Intern. Rev. ges. Hydrobiol. Hydrogr.* **43**: 110.
225. ———— 1943. *Arch. f. Protistenk.* **96**: 288.
226. ———— 1944. *Beih. botan. Centralbl.* **62** (Abt. A): 376.
227. ———— and R. Jahoda 1928. *Arch. f. Protistenk.* **61**: 239.
228. Pigón, A. 1947. *Bull. Acad. Polon. Sci. Lett.*, Ser. B, **2**: 111.
229. Pitelka, D. R. 1945. *J. Morph.* **76**: 179.
230. Pochmann, A. 1942. *Arch. f. Protistenk.* **95**: 81.
231. Poisson, R. 1935. *Arch. Zool. Exp. Gén.* **77** (N. et R.): 36.
232. ———— and A. Hollande 1943. *Ann. Sci. Nat. Zool.* (Ser. 11) **5**: 147.
233. Powell, W. N. 1928. *Univ. Calif. Publ. Zool.* **31**: 179.
234. Powers, J. H. 1908. *Trans. Amer. Micr. Soc.* **28**: 141.
235. Prescott, G. W. and H. T. Croasdale 1937. *Trans. Amer. Micr. Soc.* **56**: 269.
236. Pringsheim, E. G. 1936. *Arch. f. Protistenk.* **87**: 43.
237. ———— 1937. Cytologia, *Fujii-Jubiläumsband*, p. 234.
238. ———— 1942. *New Phytol.* **41**: 171.
239. ———— 1948. *Biol. Rev.* **23**: 46.
240. ———— and R. Hovasse 1950. *Arch. Zool. Exp. Gén.* **86**: 499.
241. Reich, K. and M. Aschner 1947. *Palestine J. Bot.* **4**: 14.
242. Reichardt, A. 1927. *Arch. f. Protistenk.* **59**: 301.
243. Reynolds, B. D. 1934. *Arch. f. Protistenk.* **81**: 399.
244. Rhodes, R. C. 1919. *Univ. Calif. Publ. Zool.* **19**: 201.
245. Ruinen, J. 1938. *Arch. f. Protistenk.* **90**: 210.
246. Saedeleer, H. de 1931. *Rec. Inst. Torley-Rousseau* **3**: 89.
247. Scherffel, A. 1911. *Arch. f. Protistenk.* **22**: 299.
248. ———— 1927. *Arch. f. Protistenk.* **57**: 331.
249. Schiller, J. 1918. *Arch. f. Protistenk.* **38**: 250.
250. ———— 1925. *Arch. f. Protistenk.* **51**: 1.
251. ———— 1925. *Arch. f. Protistenk.* **53**: 59.
252. ———— 1928. *Arch. f. Protistenk.* **61**: 45.

253. ——— 1929. *Arch. f. Protistenk.* **66:** 436.
254. Schilling, A. J. 1913. "Dinoflagellatae" in *Die Süsswasser-Flora Deutschlands, Österreichs und der Schweiz*, H. 3 (Jena: Fischer).
255. Schreiber, E. 1925. *Ztschr. f. Bot.* **17:** 337.
256. Schulze, B. 1927. *Arch. f. Protistenk.* **58:** 508.
257. Shawhan, F. M. and T. L. Jahn 1947. *Trans. Amer. Micr. Soc.* **66:** 182.
258. Shumway, W. 1924. *J. Parasit.* **11:** 59.
259. Smith, G. M. 1944. *Trans. Amer. Micr. Soc.* **63:** 265.
260. ——— 1950. *The Fresh-water Algae of the United States*, 2d ed. (New York: McGraw-Hill).
261. Stabler, R. M. 1938. *J. Morph.* **69:** 501.
262. ——— 1947. *J. Parasit.* **33:** 207.
263. Steinecke, F. 1932. *Arch. f. Protistenk.* **76:** 589.
264. Stokes, A. C. 1888. *J. Trenton Nat. Hist. Soc.* **1:** 71.
265. Strong, R. P. 1924. *Amer. J. Trop. Med.* **4:** 345.
266. Sutherland, J. L. 1933. *Quart. J. Micr. Sci.* **76:** 145.
267. Swezy, O. 1915. *Univ. Calif. Publ. Zool.* **16:** 71.
268. Taft, C. E. 1940. *Trans. Amer. Micr. Soc.* **59:** 1.
268a. Tannreuther, G. W. 1923. *Arch. f. Entwickl. Orig.* **52:** 367.
269. Tavolga, W. M. and R. F. Nigrelli 1947. *Trans. Amer. Micr. Soc.* **66:** 366.
270. Thompson, R. H. 1949. *Amer. J. Bot.* **36:** 301.
271. Travis, B. V. 1932. *Iowa St. Coll. J. Sci.* **6:** 317.
272. ——— and E. R. Becker 1931. *Iowa St. Coll. J. Sci.* **5:** 223.
273. Tyzzer, E. E. 1920. *J. Parasit.* **6:** 124.
274. ——— 1934. *Proc. Amer. Acad. Arts & Sci.* **69:** 189.
275. Uspenski, E. E. and W. J. Uspenskaja 1925. *Ztschr. f. Bot.* **17:** 273.
276. Valkanov, A. 1928. *Arch. f. Protistenk.* **63:** 419.
277. Wenrich, D. H. 1924. *Biol. Bull.* **47:** 149.
278. ——— 1932. *Trans. Amer. Micr. Soc.* **51:** 225.
279. ——— 1933. *J. Parasit.* **19:** 225.
280. ——— 1943. *J. Morph.* **72:** 279.
281. ——— and M. A. Emmerson 1933. *J. Morph.* **55:** 193.
282. Wenyon, C. M. 1910. *Quart. J. Micr. Sci.* **55:** 241.
283. ——— 1913. *Arch. f. Protistenk.* **31:** 1.
284. ——— 1914. *Trans. Soc. Trop. Med. Hyg.* **7:** 97.
285. ——— 1926. *Protozoology* (London: Ballière, Tindall & Cox).
286. Zeliff, C. C. 1930. *Amer. J. Hyg.* **11:** 714.
287. Zimmermann, W. 1921. *Jahrb. wiss. Bot.* **60:** 256.

V

The Sarcodina

THE SARCODINA are mostly floating or creeping organisms, although a number are sessile. The thin periplast permits the formation of pseudopodia and the amoeboid movement of naked species. Locomotion may or may not involve the formation of definite pseudopodia. Certain amoebae, for instance, move by a protoplasmic flow which involves the body as a whole and does not depend upon pseudopodia. Some Sarcodina also develop flagella at certain stages in the life-cycle. Flagellate stages occur as gametes in various Foraminiferida; in certain other Sarcodina, a similar status of the flagellate stage is suspected but not proven. In addition, there are cases in which the flagellate stage seems to be merely a second active phase in a dimorphic life-cycle. The ability to develop a test is widely distributed. Such structures are found in Testacida and Foraminiferida and in the majority of Heliozoida. The lattice-work skeletons of many Radiolarida are analogous developments.

The Sarcodina as a group are widely distributed in fresh and salt water and in the soil. However, the Radiolarida have remained marine and the Foraminiferida which have invaded fresh water are primitive types sometimes considered Testacida. A number of the Sarcodina are parasitic. Various sessile forms may be epiphytic or epizooic, but endoparasitism is limited to the more primitive species or to possibly degenerate representatives of certain groups.

On the basis of pseudopodial equipment, the Sarcodina are often divided into two classes, Actinopodea and Rhizopodea. By definition, the Actinopodea possess axopodia. The Rhizopodea may have any other kind of pseudopodia but do not develop axopodia.

CLASS 1. ACTINOPODEA

These are mostly floating or sessile organisms, although flagellate stages are known in a few genera. Accessory lobopodia are developed occasionally, at least in certain species. The class may be divided into three orders: (1) Helioflagellida, with one or more flagella as either a permanent feature or a characteristic of the dominant phase in a dimorphic cycle; (2) Heliozoida, in which a flagellate stage apparently is rare and the inner cytoplasm is not separated from the outer zones by a *central capsule;* (3) Radiolarida, in which a central capsule is characteristic and skeletal structures are more highly developed than in Heliozoida.

Order 1. Helioflagellida

The relationships of this group are uncertain, and members of the order have been classified as Rhizomastigida (Mastigophora) and Proteomyxida, as well as Helioflagellida. The presence of axopodia, and also a "central granule" in certain genera, suggests closer affinities with the Heliozoida than with the Rhizomastigida or Proteomyxida. The Helioflagellida are of interest as possible sources of data bearing on phylogeny of the Actinopodea.

The following genera may be assigned to the order: *Acinetactis* Stokes (141, 143; Fig. 5. 1, A); *Actinomonas* Kent (45; Fig. 5. 1, K); *Ciliophrys* Gruber (45; Fig. 5. 1, D, E); *Dimorpha* Gruber (Fig. 5. 1, I-J); *Dimorphella* Valkanov (143; Fig. 5. 1, B, C); and *Tetradimorpha* Hsiung (61; Fig. 5. 1, F-H). A "central granule," from which the axonemes of the axopodia radiate, has been demonstrated in *Dimorpha, Dimorphella,* and *Tetradimorpha.* This central granule behaves as a centrosome during mitosis in *Dimorphella elegans* (Fig. 5. 1, C). With the possible exception of *Tetradimorpha,* the pseudopodia show the granules characteristic of axopodia; streaming of the granules has been described in *Acinetactis* and *Dimorphella.* More or less complete retraction of the pseudopodia occurs in swimming stages of *Acinetactis, Ciliophrys, Dimorpha,* and *Tetradimorpha.* Both marine and fresh-water species of *Ciliophrys* have been described; the other genera have been reported from fresh water.

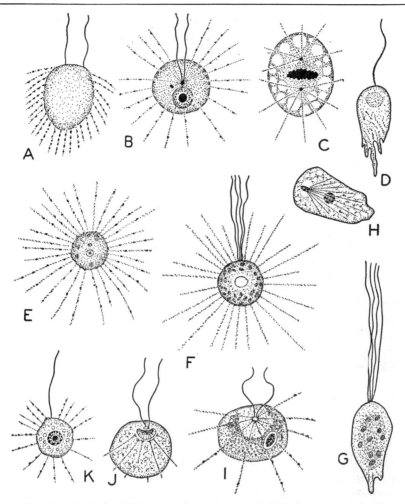

Fig. 5. 1. Helioflagellida. A. *Acinetactis arnaudoffi* Valkanov; two flagella, granular axopodia; x800 (after V.). B, C. *Dimorphella elegans* Valkanov; flagella and axopodia arising from a central granule (B); stage in division (C); x2400 (after V.). D, E. *Ciliophrys marina* Caullery; axopodia retracted in flagellate stage (D); granular axopodia extended (E); x960 (after Griessmann). F-H *Tetradimorpha radiata* Hsiung; axopodia extended, nucleus central, x325 (F); typical swimming stage, x480 (G); stained preparation showing nucleus, blepharoplast, axonemes of retracted axopodia (H), x490 (after H.). I-J. *Dimorpha mutans* Gruber; axopodia and flagella arising from a central granule (I); axopodia retracted (J); x1060 approx. (after Blochmann). K. *Actinomonas mirabilis* Kent, one flagellum, axopodia extended; x1360 (after Griessmann).

Order 2. Heliozoida

The Heliozoida possess radially arranged axopodia which rarely anastomose, and typically contain globules or granules. A flow of granules along the axopodia is characteristic. The finer structure of the pseudopodia has been discussed by Roskin (126). The inner and peripheral zones of cytoplasm are not separated by a central capsule. Most Heliozoida are approximately spherical floating types, and except for a few species of *Acanthocystis, Camptonema,* and certain other genera, occur in fresh water. The recognition of typical Heliozoida is easy enough. However, it is difficult to detect axonemes in the delicate pseudopodia of certain

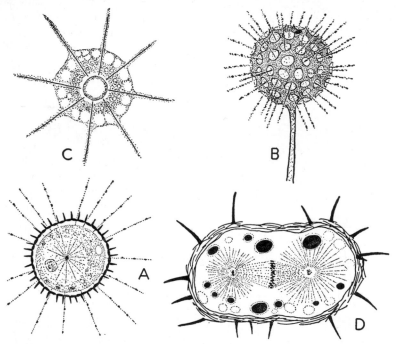

Fig. 5. 2. Basic morphological types in Heliozoida; diagrammatic. A. *Acanthocystis*-type: test composed of separate plates, spines sometimes present; nucleus not central; axopodia radiate from a central granule. B. *Clathrulina*-type, as in Desmothoracina: perforated test not composed of separate scales; stalk often present. C. *Actinophrys*-type: no test; nucleus approximately central in uninucleate forms. D. Nuclear division in *Acanthocystis aculeata,* showing supposed central granules at the poles of the spindle; x1010 (after Bělař).

forms and there are some species in which axonemes have not yet been reported.

With respect to the peripheral cytoplasm and its derivatives, Heliozoida may be divided into naked types and those which secrete some sort of a test. The test may contain discrete scales or spines (Fig. 5. 2, A), or it may be a continuous capsule containing many pores (Fig. 5. 2, B). In such naked types as *Actinophrys* (Fig. 5. 2, C), the outer cytoplasm contains many vacuoles, one or more of which may be contractile. The vacuolated layer encloses a thick granular zone of cytoplasm within which, in uninucleate species, a large nucleus is more or less centrally located.

Around the nucleus, there is a hyaline layer in which the axonemes end. In the *Acanthocystis*-type (Fig. 5. 2, A), the vacuolated zone is lacking and the body is covered with a test composed of skeletal elements embedded in a capsule. Some such covering is found in the majority of Heliozoa. Beneath the relatively thin ectoplasm there is a thick granular zone containing one or more contractile vacuoles, food vacuoles, and other inclusions. Within the granular layer, a zone of clear cytoplasm contains the "central granule" and a nucleus. The central granule, in which the axonemes converge, resembles a centrosome in its behavior during mitosis (Fig. 5. 2, D). However, Stern (139), on the basis of multinucleate and other abnormal stages seen in cultures, has argued that the central granule does not really function as a centrosome.

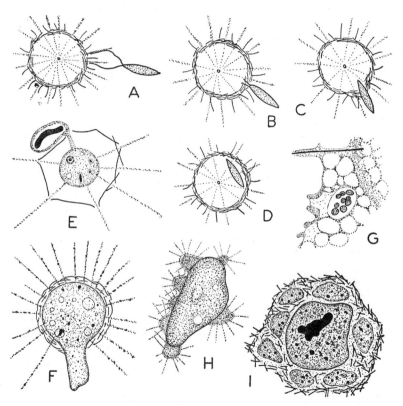

Fig. 5. 3. A-D. Ingestion of a flagellate by *Acanthocystis aculeata*, successive stages; x1215 (after Stern). E. Formation of a food vacuole outside the test in *Hedriocystis pellucida*; x1050 (after Hoogenraad). F. A large lobopodium, in addition to axopodia, in *Raphidocystis infestans*; x815 (after Wetzel). G. Cytostome-like structure, with food vacuole at the base of the "gullet," in *Actinosphaerium eichorni*; x34 (after Okada). H. A ciliate (*Paramecium*) attacked by a group of *Raphidocystis infestans*; x128 (after Wetzel). I. A ciliate completely surrounded by such a group; stained preparation; x238 (after Wetzel).

Feeding is predominantly holozoic, and food includes other Protozoa, algae, and occasionally rotifers or other small invertebrates. After capture of such organisms, axial filaments may disappear in the immediate region and a layer of cytoplasm surrounds the prey (Fig. 5. 3, E). Occasionally, captured microorganisms pass immediately into the deeper cytoplasm where digestion is completed (Fig. 5. 3, A-D). In addition to axopodia, lobopodia are sometimes formed (158) and the ingestion of food by means of gullet-like "food cups" also may occur (Fig. 5. 3, G). A protozoan version of the hunting pack has been described in *Raphidocystis infestans* (158). A ciliate, for example, may be attacked by a number of these Heliozoida, which adhere to the prey and may fuse to form a continuous layer of protoplasm enclosing the captured food (Fig. 5. 3, H, I). A simple life-cycle—including an active stage and a cyst—has been reported in a number of Heliozoida. Cysts with a siliceous ectocyst have been described in certain species (108). An alternation of generations, in one of which flagellate gametes are produced, has been reported in *Wagnerella borealis* (163), although this account has not been confirmed. The formation of a flagellate daughter organism (Fig. 5. 7, D, L), which leaves the parental test, has been described in *Monomastigocystis* (129) and *Hedriocystis* (54).

The work of Bělař and his predecessors has established the occurrence of pedogamy in certain Heliozoida, or at least the occurrence of syngamy following a gametic meiosis (Chapter II). The zygote so produced normally undergoes encystment.

Subdivision of the Heliozoida has been based largely upon the presence or absence of skeletal elements and their structure. On such a basis, the group may be divided into three suborders: (1) Actinophrydina, the naked types; (2) Acanthocystidina, with a gelatinous capsule in which separate skeletal elements are usually embedded; and (3) Desmothoracina, with a continuous test containing a number of pores.

Suborder 1. Actinophrydina. There is no capsule or test enclosing the outer zone of vacuolated cytoplasm. Since there is no central granule, the axopodia may end near the nuclear membrane (Fig. 5. 4, E) in uninucleate species, or near a nucleus or inner margin of the vacuolated layer in multinucleate types. Just beneath the vacuolated zone of *Actinosphaerium eichorni,* there is a finely granular layer (Fig. 5. 4, B) which may serve as a support for the bases of the axopodia (83, 108). Inside the granular layer lies the finely vacuolated endoplasm. The boundary between endoplasm and ectoplasm is not so sharply defined in the smaller Actinophrydina.

The suborder includes the following genera: *Actinophrys* Ehrenberg (5, 6, 83, 108; Fig. 5. 4, C-F), uninucleate fresh-water types; *Actinosphaerium* Stein (83, 108; Fig. 5. 4, A, B), multinucleate fresh-water types; *Camptonema* Schaudinn (133), multinucleate marine forms. *Actinosphaerium eichornii,* which often measures more than 300μ and

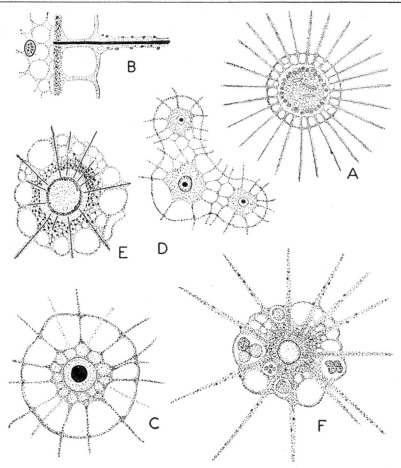

Fig. 5. 4. Actinophrydina: A. *Actinosphaerium eichorni* Ehrenberg (diameter may reach or exceed 300μ); axopodia, peripheral zone of vacuoles; ingested food (after Penard). B. Portion of peripheral cytoplasm, *A. eichorni,* showing an axoneme ending in a granular layer just beneath the vacuolated zone; diagrammatic (after Penard). C, D. *Actinophrys pontica* Valkanov; stained specimen (C), x1200; fused aggregate of three organisms (D), x800 (after V.). E, F. *Actinophrys sol* Ehrenberg; stained section of small specimen showing axonemes extending to nucleus, x975; living specimen from culture, x325 (after Bělař).

may exceed 1000μ in diameter, is the largest of the Actinophrydina. Other species fall within the range, 25-150μ.

Suborder 2. Acanthocystidina. There is typically a secreted capsule, sometimes "gelatinous" (Fig. 5. 5, A, G), in which skeletal elements are embedded. The ectoplasm is not extensively vacuolated. In some genera at least, the axonemes are known to end in a central granule. Data are lacking in other cases. In *Astrodisculus* (Fig. 5. 5, A), the capsule is thick but contains no skeletal elements. In other genera, the capsule varies in thickness and may be reduced to a thin membrane which binds the skeletal structures together. With the apparent exception of *Heterophrys,* the skeletal elements are siliceous. Aside from a few species such as *Lithocolla globosa* (108), in which foreign particles are cemented to a thin capsule, the skeletal scales and spicules are products of the organism.

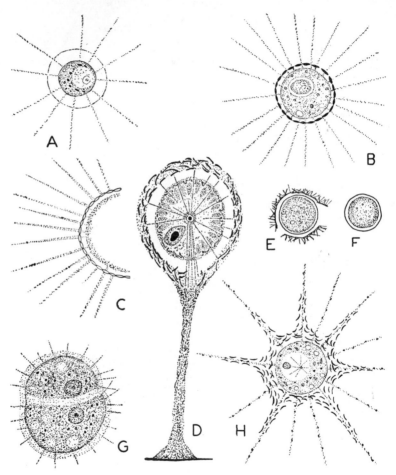

Fig. 5. 5. Acanthocystidina: A. *Astrodisculus radians* Greef, "gelatinous" covering without scales; x575 approx. (after Penard). B. *Pinaciophora fluviatilis* Greef (diameter, 45-50μ), test composed of scales (after Penard). C. *Acanthocystis rubella* Penard (diameter, 23-27μ); portion of body showing tangential scales; radially arranged spines are enclosed within the axopodia (after P.). D. *Cienkowskya mereschkowskyi* (diameter about 60μ), a sessile form; scales embedded in gelatinous mantle; distal portions of axopodia not shown (after Villeneuve). E-G. *Raphidocystis infestans* Wetzel; cyst being released from ruptured test (E) and freed cyst (F), x570; dividing form, skeletal elements dissolved with HFl to show gelatinous envelope (G), x820 (after W.). H. *Raphidiophrys pallida* Schulze, x250 (after Penard).

The differentiation of genera is based to an important extent upon thickness of the capsule and the form and arrangement of the skeletal elements (Fig. 5. 6, A-H).

The following genera are included in the suborder: *Acanthocystis* Carter (83, 108, 154; Fig. 5. 5, C); *Actinolophus* Schulze (149; Fig. 5. 6, I); *Astrodisculus* Greef (108; Fig. 5. 5, A); *Cienkowskya* Schaudinn (149; Fig. 5. 5, D); *Elaeorhanis* Greef (108); *Heterophrys* Archer (108; Fig. 5. 6, J); *Lithocolla* Schulze (108); *Oxnerella* Dobell (34);

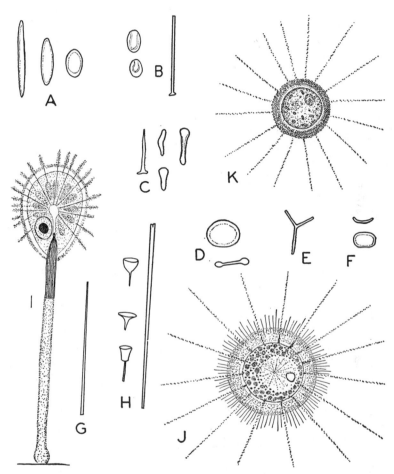

Fig. 5. 6. Acanthocystidina: A-H. Skeletal elements: A. *Raphidocystis ambigua;* B. *Acanthocystis mimetica,* spine and scales; C. *A. aculeata,* spine and scales; D. *Raphidiophrys elegans,* surface and edge views of scales; E. *Raphidocystis glutinosa;* F. *Raphidiophrys intermedia,* surface and edge views of scales; G. Spine of *Heterophrys myriopoda;* H. *Raphidocystis lemani;* schematic (after Penard). I. *Actinolophus pedunculatus* Schulze (body, 35 x 30μ), sessile on Bryozoa; radially arranged bodies within test believed to be ingested food (after Villeneuve). J. *Heterophrys myriopoda* Archer, x330 (after Penard). K. *Pompholyxophrys punicea* Archer, x400 approx. (after Penard).

Pinaciocystis Roskin (128); *Pinaciophora* Greef (108; Fig. 5. 5, B); *Pompholyxophrys* Archer (108; Fig. 5. 6, K); *Raphidiophrys* Archer (108, 158; Fig. 5. 5, H); *Raphidocystis* Penard (108, 158; Figs. 5. 3, F, H, I, 5. 5, E-G); and *Wagnerella* Mereschkowski (163).

The status of *Myriophrys* Penard (108) is uncertain. The secreted envelope with adherent scales, the slender granular pseudopodia, and the large eccentric nucleus would seem to qualify the genus for the Acanthocystidina. A coat of undulating "cilia or flagella" complicates matters. Perhaps these "flagella" should be investigated as possible bacteria adherent to the body. The genus *Chondropus* Greef (108) must remain unassigned until more is known about the organisms.

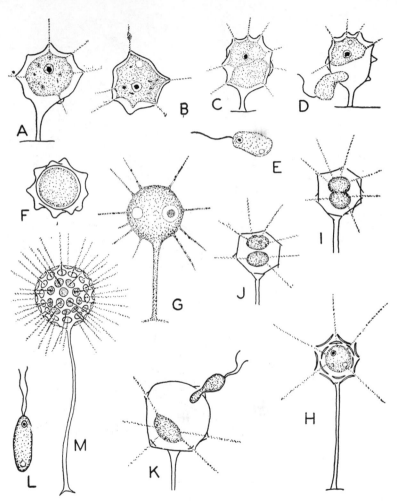

Fig. 5. 7. Desmothoracina: A-F. *Monomastigocystis brachypous* De Saedeleer (width, 9-15μ): specimen with short stalk (A); optical cross-section (B); in fission (C, D) one daughter organism develops into a flagellate (E); cyst (F) with double membrane (after De S.). G-L. *Hedriocystis pellucida:* young specimen without test (G), schematic (after Valkanov); mature form (H), x700; fission (I, J), x315; one daughter organism becomes a biflagellate stage which leaves the test (K, L), x525 (after Hoogenraad). M. *Clathrulina elegans* Cienkowski; diameter of test, 60-90μ (after Penard).

Suborder 3. Desmothoracina. In this group, there is a non-siliceous (108) one-piece test (Fig. 5. 2, B) containing pores through which pseudopodia are extended. Certain genera contain sessile types with stalks. The stalk in *Hedriocystis* (Fig. 5. 7, G, H) is said to be merely an extension of the body resembling a slender pseudopodium (144). In *Clathrulina* (Fig. 5. 8, E-H), the young organism first develops a protoplasmic stalk by outgrowth from the body. An outer covering is then secreted

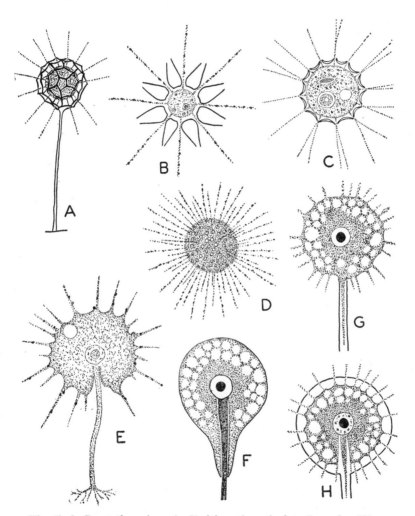

Fig. 5. 8. Desmothoracina: A. *Hedriocystis reticulata* Penard, x500 approx. (after P.). B. *Choanocystis lepidula* Penard, x730 approx. (after P.). C. *Clathrella foreli* Penard; diameter of test, 40-55μ (after P.). D. *Elaster greefi* Grimm, x700 (after Penard). E-H. *Clathrulina elegans* Cienkowski: cytoplasm grows down over the original stalk (F) and produces a hollow stalk (G), which becomes continuous with the test in older forms (H); schematic (after Valkanov).

and the protoplasmic core disappears, leaving a tubular mature stalk attached only to the test (144).

Although little is known about the life-cycles, fission within the test, the development of a flagellate stage from one of the daughter organisms, and encystment have been described (Fig. 5. 7) in *Monomastigocystis* (129) and *Hedriocystis* (54).

The taxonomic relationships of the Desmothoracina are still debatable. Superficially, they show striking resemblances to typical Heliozoida. Although the granular pseudopodia seem to be axopodia, they are sometimes so slender that the presence of axonemes is uncertain. The nucleus is central in some species and eccentric in others, but no central granule has been demonstrated. In view of the apparent absence of axonemes and a central granule, Valkanov (148) suggested transfer of the Desmothoracina to the Foraminiferida as another monothalamous group.

The following genera have been assigned to the suborder: *Choanocystis* Penard (108; Fig. 5. 8, B); *Clathrulina* Cienkowski (83, 108, 144; Fig. 5. 7, M); *Elaster* Grimm (108; Fig. 5. 8, D); *Hedriocystis* Hertwig and Lesser (54, 108, 144; Fig. 5. 7, G-L); *Monomastigocystis* de Saedeleer (129; Fig. 5. 7, A-F).

Order 3. Radiolarida

These marine organisms, with a geological history dating at least from Lower Silurian and probably from Cambrian time, are apparently the oldest known group of animals. Their most striking feature is their skeleton, which has undergone specialization to a remarkable degree. The general organization of the body and the possession of axopodia relate them to the Heliozoida, but the *central capsule,* separating inner and outer zones of protoplasm, is a differential feature.

The central capsule is nearly always a distinct layer, usually single but sometimes double (Fig. 5. 13, A), and can be detected without difficulty except in a few Actipylina (Acantharina). The capsule may be spherical, ovoid, or sometimes lobate or branched (Fig. 5. 11, C), and is composed of organic material designated variously as chitin, pseudochitin, or tectin. The capsule may be resorbed more or less completely in fission of the simpler species, it may increase in diameter with growth of the organism, and it may be somewhat changeable in form even in the mature organism. Perforations, either distributed uniformly or concentrated in one or more groups, permit cytoplasmic continuity and also serve as taxonomic features.

The skeleton of the Actipylina may be composed largely of strontium sulphate, usually with a radial arrangement of the skeletal elements. The basic components are spines which extend radially from the center of the body, passing through the central capsule (Fig. 5. 9, A). At the surface of the body there may also be a lattice-work test, or shell, which is fused with the radial spines (Fig. 5. 9, D). For the other groups of Radiolarida, siliceous skeletal elements are the rule. Rods and spines, if present, always lie outside the capsule. In addition to rod-like elements, or in their absence, one or more lattice-work layers may be deposited, peripheral to, and concentric with, the central capsule. The lattice framework may be spherical or non-spherical (bell-shaped, helmet-shaped, etc.), and in

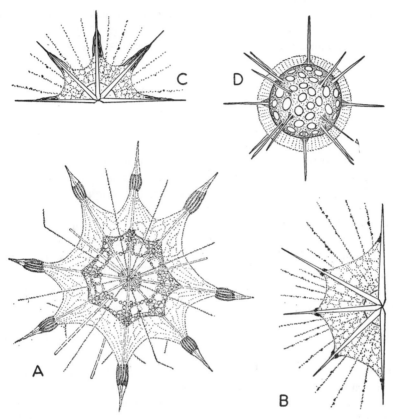

Fig. 5. 9. A. *Acanthometra pellucida,* showing central capsule, axial rods and "myonemes" (myophrisks) joining the superficial cytoplasm and the sheaths of the axial rods; x200 (after Moroff and Stiasny). B, C. Axial rods and myophrisks in Actipylina; ectoplasmic layer expanded and myophrisks contracted (B); ectoplasmic layer contracted and myonemes extended (C); schematic (after Schewiakoff). D. *Dorotaspis heteropora* Bernstein, showing lattice-work shell and axial rods; schematic (after B.).

the latter case may approach bilateral symmetry. Complicated skeletons already had been developed early in the known history of the Radiolarida (Fig. 5. 11, A, B).

The intracapsular cytoplasm contains the nucleus or nuclei, stored reserves, pigment granules in some species, and the so-called "yellow cells" in the Actipylina. The number of nuclei varies. The Actipylina are typically multinucleate, while the Monopylina and Tripylina are usually uninucleate. The extracapsular cytoplasm is concerned primarily with flotation, capture of food, and digestion. Several layers may be recognizable (Fig. 5. 11, D): the *sarcomatrix,* a so-called digestive layer next to the central capsule; the vacuolated *calymma,* which is a thick zone in some species; a thin layer outside the calymma; and the zone of axopodia whose axonemes often arise in the sarcomatrix. Food is captured much as in the Heliozoida. Since the size of solitary species ranges from about 50μ to several millimeters, the larger Radiolarida are able to feed on copepods and other small Crustacea, as well as on algae and Protozoa which come in contact with the pseudopodia.

The "yellow-cells" (zooxanthellae), present in many Radiolarida although not in the Tripylina, are more numerous in species with a well-developed calymma. They are typically intracapsular in the Actipylina, extracapsular in other groups. In the living host, these parasites are commonly spherical to ovoid. After death of the host, they may develop into palmella stages which give rise to flagellates. Certain of these flagellates have been referred to the Dinoflagellida (22, 58). Their reputed status as symbiotes remains somewhat uncertain.

Some of the Radiolarida, such as *Collozoum* and *Sphaerozoum,* are colonial forms (16, 140) in which a number of central capsules are embedded in an elongated or more or less spherical mass of extracapsular cytoplasm. In certain species at least, each central capsule contains a number of nuclei. Skeletal elements are often reduced to scattered spicules, although lattice-work shells occur in some species.

Life-cycles. As a result of the difficulties in obtaining adequate material for study, little is known about the life-cycles of Radiolarida. Various accounts in the older literature suggest that the life-cycles may be fairly complex, but more extensive observations are needed. Since some of the shallow-water species will survive in the laboratory for reasonable periods, perhaps the application of techniques which have already been so productive for Foraminiferida would yield valuable information on Radiolarida.

Although reproduction has been traced in relatively few species, fission occurs in species with simple skeletal elements. The central capsule is divided, and any skeletal elements are passed on to the two daughter organisms. Fission also has been reported within the helmet-shaped skeleton of certain Tripylina. One daughter organism retains the old shell; the other leaves and develops a new one. According to Brandt (14), certain Thallophysidae may undergo a complicated plasmotomy which follows dedifferentiation of the adult, and results in a number of small organisms, each with several nuclei. Budding possibly occurs in a few species (15), but the process needs further investigation.

Evidence for sexual phenomena in Radiolarida is still inconclusive, although the literature contains repeated descriptions of flagellate stages (flagellispores)—supposedly gametes. However, syngamy has not been observed, and Chatton (23) concluded that some of these supposed flagellate stages are probably parasites. This conclusion certainly seems justified for "flagellispores" which are similar to dinoflagellates. However, some of these flagellates (80) obviously are not dinoflagellates (Fig. 5. 10) and they show a marked resemblance to flagellate gametes of Foraminiferida (Fig. 5. 42).

Although the Radiolarida are not swimmers, at least some of them apparently can rise or sink in response to changing environmental conditions. A collapse of vacuoles in the calymma increases the specific gravity of the organism and thus induces sinking; regeneration of the vacuoles reverses this effect. Such a mechanism enables species living near the

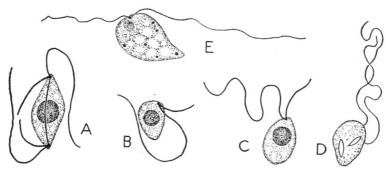

Fig. 5. 10. "Flagellispores" (gametes?) of Radiolarida: A, B. *Acantho-metra pellucida,* dividing gametocyte showing paradesmose (A) and biflagellate gamete (B); x4000 (after Le Calvez). C. *Xiphicantha alata,* x4000 (after Le Calvez). D, E. *Coelodendrum ramosissimum,* living (D) and stained (E); x2550 (after Le Calvez).

surface to sink when disturbed by rough wave action or when the temperature becomes unfavorable.

The majority of species probably live within the upper 1,500 feet, although a few forms have been dredged from depths of 2-3 miles. Within this vertical range, the fauna varies to a considerable extent with depth. The majority of the Peripylina are found within the upper 200 feet, while the Actipylina are most abundant below 150-200 feet. The Tripylina are to be found mainly within a range of 1,200 to 3,500 feet. The group as a whole is widely distributed over the oceans, although specific distribution varies considerably. Some species show essentially universal distribution while others may be limited to tropical or to polar waters. The greatest variety of species occurs within the equatorial zone. Radiolarian skeletons, sinking to the bottom, make up deposits of radiolarian ooze, and many fossil types are known.

Taxonomy.[1] The Radiolarida are subdivided, on the basis of skeletal structure and the distribution of pores in the capsule, into four suborders: (1) Actipylina ("Acantharia"), with a skeleton composed basically of radial spines which penetrate the central capsule to converge in the middle of the body; (2) Peripylina ("Spumellaria"), often with no skeleton or one limited to disconnected extracapsular rods and less commonly with a perforated shell; the spherical central capsule shows uniformly distributed pores; (3) Monopylina ("Nasselaria"), with a thick central capsule in which the pores are limited to one zone, or "porous plate" (Fig.

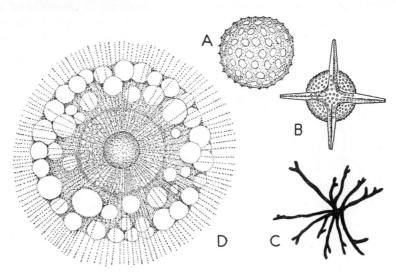

Fig. 5. 11. A. *Cenosphaera macropora* Rüst, from Ordovician (Lower Silurian) deposits; x120 approx. (after R.). B. *Staurolonche micropora* Rüst (Ordovician), x120 approx. (after R.). C. Branched central capsule of *Cytocladus spinosus*, x5 (after Schröder). D. *Thalassicolla nucleata,* from living; central capsule (surrounded by zone of small vacuoles), layer of hyaline cytoplasm, calymma, and axopodia (after Huth).

5. 12, F); and (4) Tripylina ("Phaeodaria"), in which the central capsule has one major and two accessory openings (Fig. 5. 13, A).

Suborder 1. Actipylina. The central capsule, sometimes irregular in shape, is rather uniformly perforated, although arrangement of the pores in rows or fields is often recognizable. The skeleton consists mainly of rods which converge inside the central capsule (Fig. 5. 9, A-C) and usually show an arrangement described by Müller's "law." There are often twenty

[1] More detailed information will be found in such special monographs as the following: *general:* Haeckel, E. 1887. Challenger Rep., Zool. 18; Hertwig, R. 1879. Der Organismus der Radiolarien (Jena); *Actipylina:* Popofsky, A. 1904. Ergebn. Planktonexped. 3, 1907. Nordisches Plankton 16; Schewiakoff, W. 1926. Fauna Flora G. Neapel 37; *Peripylina:* Schröder, O. 1914. Nord. Plankt. 17; *Monopylina:* Popofsky, A. 1913. Ergebn. Deutsch. Südpol.-exp. Bd. 14, Zool. 6; *Tripylina:* Borgert, A. 1903-1911. Ergebn. Planktonexp. 3.

(sometimes multiples of twenty) rods which form a characteristic pattern. An equatorial group emerges from the body in a plane essentially 90° from either pole, and two other groups emerge in planes about 45° above and below the equatorial plane. The basic skeleton is sometimes modified by lateral outgrowths from the rods which form a perforated shell, composed typically of twenty plates. Two such shells, concentric with the central capsule, are present in certain species. The outer layer of extra-capsular cytoplasm is joined to the skeletal rods, apparently by contractile fibrils ("myophrisks") which are said to bring about minor changes in form and volume of the body (Fig. 5. 9, B, C) and thus to aid in controlling flotation.

The suborder includes such genera as the following: *Acanthochiasma* Krohn, *Acan-thometra* Müller (*Acanthometron* Haeckel) (94; Fig. 5. 9, A), *Acanthonia* Haeckel, *Actinelius* Haeckel, *Amphilonche* Haeckel, *Diplocolpus* Haeckel, *Diploconus* Haeckel,

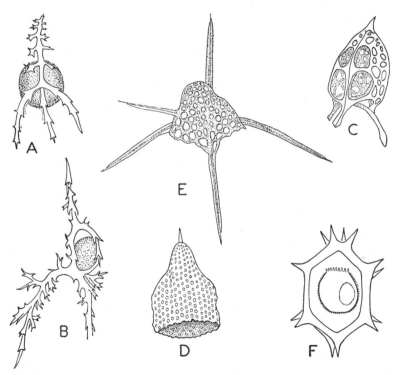

Fig. 5. 12. A-C. Skeletal features of Monopylina: tripod and central capsule (A); tripod and ring enclosing central capsule (B); helmet-like skeleton (cephalis, capitulum) derived from the more primitive tripod and ring (C); schematic (after Haeckel). D. Helmet-like skeleton of *Eucyrtidium cranioides* Haeckel, x110 approx. (after H.). E. Skeleton of *Dictyophimus gracilipes* Bailey, schematic (after Bernstein). F. *Lithocircus annularis* Hertwig, skeleton, central capsule with perforated plate, nucleus (in outline); schematic (after H.).

Dorotaspis Haeckel (Fig. 5. 9, D), *Hexaconus* Haeckel, *Litholopus* Haeckel, *Lithoptera* Müller, *Phractaspis* Haeckel, *Podactinelius* Schröder, *Sphaerocapsa* Haeckel, and *Thorocapsis* Haeckel.

Suborder 2. Peripylina. There is a fairly thick spherical central capsule in which numerous pores are uniformly distributed. There is no skeleton at all in some species. In others, a relatively simple skeleton consists of scattered extracapsular spicules, a perforated shell, or both. The latticework shells may be single, or in certain families, often multiple in a concentric series. In *Collosphaera, Collozoum,* and *Sphaerozoum* the central capsules, instead of separating after fission, remain embedded in a common extracapsular mass to form colonies which may measure several centimeters.

The following genera have been included in the Peripylina: *Acanthosphaera* Ehrenberg, *Archidiscus* Haeckel, *Cenolarcus* Haeckel, *Cenosphaera* Ehrenberg (Fig. 5. 11, A), *Chitoanastrum* Haeckel, *Collosphaera* Müller, *Collozoum* Haeckel (140), *Cromyodrymus* Haeckel, *Cytocladus* Schröder, *Druppula* Haeckel, *Euchitonia* Haeckel, *Lampoxanthium* Haeckel, *Orosphaera* Haeckel, *Physematicum* Haeckel, *Pipetta* Haeckel, *Sphaerozoum* Meyen, *Staurocyclia* Haeckel, *Staurosphaera* Haeckel, *Thalassicolla* Huxley (62; Fig. 5. 11, D), *Thalassolampe* Haeckel, *Thallasophysa* (14), *Thalassothamnus* Häcker.

Suborder 3. Monopylina. The thick-walled central capsule (Fig. 5. 12, F), which may be radially or bilaterally symmetrical, shows a single porous plate or, more often, a single field of small pores with thickened walls. The pseudopodia usually arise opposite this field. The siliceous skeleton, composed of solid elements, may show three distinct parts (tripod, capitulum, and ring). The basic form of the tripod (Fig. 5. 12, A) suggests the name applied to the structure. The ring, if present, is attached to the tripod (Fig. 5. 12, B). Outgrowths from the ring and tripod may result in a hemlet-shaped shell, the capitulum (Fig. 5. 12, C-E). Modification of these three basic elements, by suppressions or by the addition of appendages and decorations, gives rise to a variety of skeletons.

The suborder includes the following genera: *Cortiniscus* Haeckel, *Cystidium* Hertwig, *Dictyophimus* Ehrenberg (Fig. 5. 12, E), *Eucyrtidium* Haeckel (Fig. 5. 12, D), *Lithocircus* Müller (Fig. 5. 12, F), *Protympanium* Haeckel, *Stichoformis* Haeckel, *Theopera* Haeckel, *Theophormis* Haeckel, *Triplagia* Haeckel, *Zygostephanus* Haeckel.

Suborder 4. Tripylina. The central capsule has one major (the astropyle) and two accessory openings (parapyles), the latter usually lying opposite the first (Fig. 5. 13, A). The astropyle typically is covered with a striated plate, in which the central openings are often drawn out into tubes. A characteristic feature is an accumulation of greenish-brown material (perhaps the remnants of diatoms and other food) just outside the astropyle. This colored material ("phaeodium") is responsible for the name, "Phaeodaria," often applied to this suborder.

The siliceous skeletons show a wide range in complexity. The skeletons

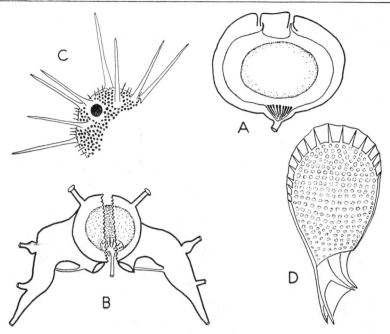

Fig. 5. 13. A Central capsule of Tripylina, showing inner and outer layers, astropyle, two parapyles, and large nucleus; diagrammatic (after Gamble). B. Bivalve shell and its appendages, galea with nasal process, or rhizocanna; astropyle drawn out into a tube; diagrammatic (after Gamble). C. *Castanidium sol* Häcker, portion of skeleton showing lattice-work shell and radial elements; diameter of shell, 400-500μ (after H.). D. Skeleton of *Challengeron armatum* Borgert, x170 (after B.).

of *Aulacantha* and related genera consist of separate elements, hollow radially arranged rods and smaller tangentially distributed spicules. The latter are often replaced by a lattice-work shell (Fig. 5. 13, C, D); or two shells may be present, one just outside the central capsule. In some genera, only the inner shell is developed. Several families show a bivalve inner shell (Fig. 5. 13, B), and each valve sometimes bears a hollow appendage, the galea.

The group includes the following genera: *Aulacantha* Haeckel (13), *Aulosphaera* Haeckel, *Cannosphaera* Haeckel, *Castanidium* Haeckel (Fig. 5. 13, C), *Challengeron* Haeckel (Fig. 5. 13, D), *Circoporus* Haeckel, *Coelacantha* Hertwig, *Coelodendrum* Haeckel, *Coementella* Borgert, *Conchoceras* Haeckel, *Euphysetta* Haeckel, *Medusetta* Haeckel, *Tuscarilla* Haeckel, *Tuscarora* Murray.

CLASS 2. RHIZOPODEA

These Sarcodina may have lobopodia, filopodia, or myxopodia but do not develop axopodia and do not show a foamy peripheral cytoplasm. Tests, well developed in certain groups, may be composed mainly of organic material, with or without added foreign particles, or largely of inorganic materials such as calcium salts. Binuclearity and multinuclearity are not uncommon.

The group is usually divided into five orders: (1) Proteomyxida, which often develop slender filopodia, sometimes delicate ones which superficially resemble axopodia; (2) Mycetozoida, plasmodial organisms, which move primarily by protoplasmic flow, and certain other types which develop a pseudoplasmodium; (3) Amoebida, naked forms which usually show lobopodia; (4) Testacida, which have a simple test and may form filopodia or lobopodia in different genera; (5) Foraminiferida, which have either a simple or a multi-chambered test and typically develop myxopodia.

Order 1. Proteomyxida

This order is not clearly defined and the interrelationships of the families usually assigned to it need investigation. The mature stage in certain genera is a large plasmodium; in others, an amoeboid uninucleate organism. Both flagellate and amoeboid stages occur in certain genera; in other cases, a flagellate stage is unknown. Three families are often included in this order: (1) Labyrinthulidae, uninucleate organisms which grow in "nets" and may form an aggregate (pseudoplasmodium) before encystment; (2) Pseudosporidae, uninucleate forms with amoeboid and flagellate stages; (3) Vampyrellidae, in which the mature stage is a plasmodium.

Family 1. Labyrinthulidae. These are little known Proteomyxida which parasitize eel grass and various algae. The organisms usually form a peculiar network (Fig. 5. 14, A, D), the organization of which has been disputed in *Labyrinthula*. According to one interpretation, the individual organisms are joined by cytoplasmic processes; according to another view (145), they are held together by a tubular membrane in *L. zopfi* (Fig. 5. 14, A, B). Neither interpretation is supported by the observations of Young (162) on *Labyrinthula macrocystis,* in which the "connections" are interpreted as filamentous "tracks" secreted by the individual organisms. At the advancing end of a net the organisms first form a clump (Fig. 5. 14, D). Then, hyaline filaments, one from each individual, "dart" forward to a length several times that of the organism. The filaments wave about until they meet and fuse to form a track. The organisms, by a method still undetermined, glide along such a track "like a drop of glycerin rolling down a taut silk thread" (162). One organism may overtake and pass another without either one leaving the track. Since the organisms may leave the track independently, they apparently do not lie within a tube. Growth of the net involves fission of the organisms.

The life-cycles need more investigation. A slowly moving pseudoplasmodium, composed of a mass of organisms embedded in a thin matrix, has been observed in *Labyrinthula macrocystis* (162). Encystment of 1-8

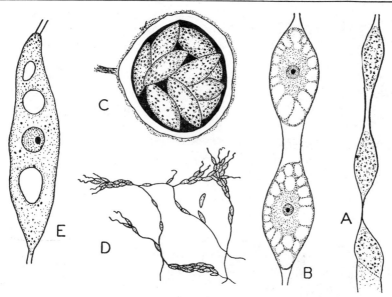

Fig. 5. 14. A-C. *Labyrinthula zopfi* Valkanov (individual organisms reach 8μ in length): portion of living network (A); two organisms stained (B); encysted stage, from living (C); schematic (after V.). D, E. *Labyrinthula macrocystis* Cienkowski: vegetative network (D), x380 approx.; single organism, stained, showing nucleus and vacuole (E), x2700 approx. (after Young).

organisms within one membrane has been described in *Labyrinthula zopfi* (Fig. 5. 14, C), and in *L. macrocystis,* a membrane may be formed around a pseudoplasmodium composed of 5-100 organisms (162).

The family includes *Labyrinthula* Cienkowski (145, 162), reported from eel grass and certain marine algae (*Cladophora, Chaetomorpha*); and *Labyrinthomyxa* Duboscq (35), reported from *Laminaria. Labyrinthula macrocystis* has been found associated with a fungal disease of eel grass (120, 162), and it is possible that the organisms, by attacking the plant cells, contribute to the spread of infection.

Family 2. Pseudosporidae. These organisms invade filamentous algae and Volvocidae. The parasitic stages are amoeboid. Either flagellate or amoeboid "swarm-cells" may be produced, depending apparently upon the species. The best known genus is *Pseudospora* Cienkowski (127, 134, 135; Fig. 5. 15). Several other genera—*Protomonas* Cienkowski, *Aphelidium* Scherffel, *Amoeboaphelidium* Scherffel, *Aphelidiopsis* Scherffel, *Pseudosporopsis* Scherffel, *Barbetia* Dangeard—appear to be related to *Pseudospora* and presumably belong to the same family (134).

A fairly complex life-cycle has been described for *Pseudospora parasitica* (135). Growth of the young amoeboid stage into a mature form may be followed by formation of a "zoocyst," or reproductive cyst (Fig. 5. 15, A-D). According to Schussnig (135), gametes eventually are produced

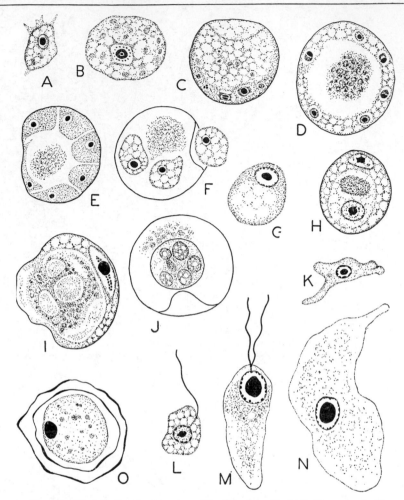

Fig. 5. 15. A-J. *Pseudospora parasitica* Cienkowski: A, B. Young and older amoeboid stages. C, D. Formation of "zoocyst." E, F. Production of uninucleate amoebae and their escape from the cyst. G. An amoeboid "gamete." H. Stage supposedly produced by fusion of two gametes. I. Nuclear fusion is said to have occurred in the "zygote." J. A "sporocyst" has developed from the encysted zygote; schematic (after Schussnig). K, L. *Pseudospora rovignensis* Schussnig, amoeboid and flagellate stages; schematic (after S.). M-O. *Pseudospora volvocis* Cienkowski, flagellate, amoeboid, and encysted stages; x1140 approx. (after Roskin).

and syngamy occurs (Fig. 5. 15, G-I). The supposed zygote promptly encysts. Within the "zoocyst," a second membrane ("sporocyst") is secreted to produce a resting cyst (Fig. 5. 15, J). Flagellate "swarm-cells" and small amoebae also have been reported in *P. rovignensis* (135), *P. eudorini,* and *P. volvocis* (127).

The taxonomic position of the family is still uncertain and it has been

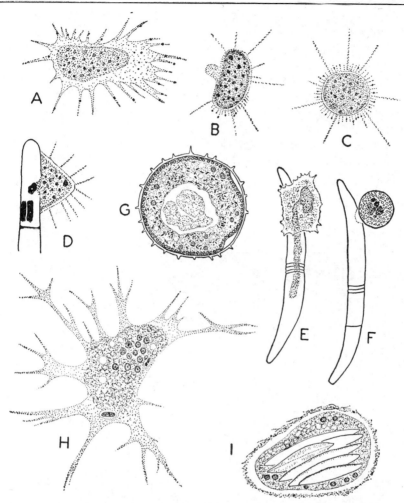

Fig. 5. 16. A-D. *Vampyrella lateritia* Leidy, schematic (after Hoogenraad): specimens showing different forms of pseudopodia (A-C); organism
ingesting contents of a *Spirogyra* cell. E-G. *Vampyrella closterii* Poisson and
Mangenot (after P. and M.): E. Specimen attached to *Closterium* and ingesting contents of the alga; x158. F. Cyst attached to empty cell wall of
Closterium; x158. G. Section of cyst showing central mass of ingested food,
nuclei, mitochondria, and a peripheral zone of neutral-red-stainable vacuoles; x563. H, I. *Arachnula impatiens* Cienkowski (after Dobell): small specimen with a number of nuclei and several contractile vacuoles, x200; cyst
with several nuclei and ingested diatoms, x500.

suggested that *Pseudospora* may belong in the Dimastigamoebidae (Order
Amoebida) rather than in the Proteomyxida (127).

 Family 3. Vampyrellidae. The mature stage, in the type genus, is a
fairly large plasmodium. Reproduction involves plasmotomy, and multinucleate cysts are formed by plasmodia. These general characteristics are

clearly represented in *Arachnula* Cienkowski (Fig. 5. 16, H, I), *Leptomyxa* Goodey (Fig. 5. 17), and *Vampyrella* Cienkowski (Fig. 5. 16, A-G). *Arachnula* may be a synonym of *Vampyrella* (33). *Chlamydomyxa* Archer, as represented by *C. montana* Lankester, closely resembles *Leptomyxa* Goodey and it is not certain that the two should be placed in separate genera. The mature stage of *C. montata* is a large plasmodium, the pseudopodia are similar to those of *Leptomyxa,* and several endocysts are produced within an ectocyst.

The life-cycles appear to be fairly simple. Excystment of a young plasmodium is followed normally by growth and nuclear division. In addi-

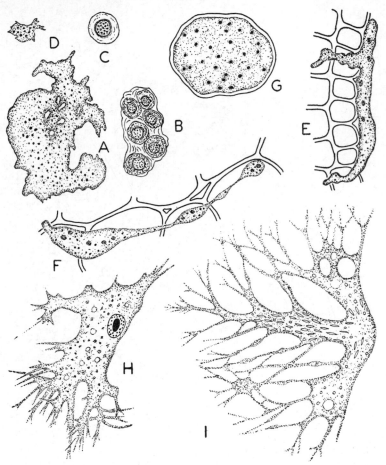

Fig. 5. 17. A-G. *Leptomyxa reticulata* Goodey: A. Multinucleate plasmodium, which may reach lengths of 2-3 mm.; x550. B. Ectocyst with six endocysts; x880. C. Single endocyst; x880. D. Small plasmodium after emergence from cyst. E. Plasmodium penetrating a root; x312. F. Plasmodium extending through several cells; x312. G. Stained cyst with many nuclei; x183. A-D, after Singh; E-G, after MacLennan. H. *Biomyxa merdaria* Hollande, x960 approx. (after H.). I. *Biomyxa vagans* Leidy, x125 (after L.).

tion, fusion of several plasmodia into a single large one measuring as much as 1500μ. has been described in *Vampyrella closterii* (112). Plasmotomy within the cyst has been reported in *Arachnula* (33) and *Vampyrella* (112). The details of encystment may vary slightly. In a strain of *Leptomyxa reticulata* recovered from hops (88), the cysts (Fig. 5. 17, G) were large (425-900μ) and contained only one endocyst. In other strains (43, 138) several multinucleate endocysts have been found within an ectocyst (Fig. 5. 17, B).

Leptomyxa reticulata occurs in the soil (138) and as a secondary invader of diseased hops (88). *Arachnula impatiens* has been described from fresh and brackish water (33), while species of *Vampyrella* attack *Spirogyra* (85) and *Closterium* (112) by digesting a portion of the cell wall and sucking out the contents.

Both large plasmodial forms (Fig. 5. 17, I) and smaller uninucleate organisms (52; Fig. 5. 17, H) have been assigned to *Biomyxa* Leidy but

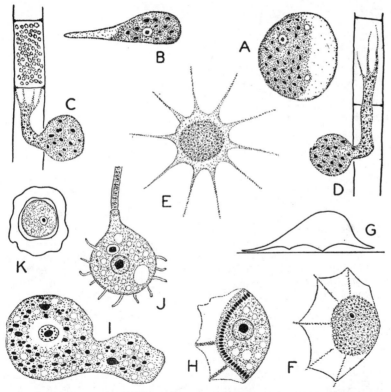

Fig. 5. 18. A-G. *Hyalodiscus rubicundus* Hertwig and Lesser: oval forms (35-70 x 20-50μ) seen from above (A) and from the side (B); invading cells of *Oedogonium* (C, D); resting form with radiating pseudopodia (E); specimens in locomotion, seen from above (F) and from the side (G); A-D, after Hoogenraad; E-G, after Penard. H-K. *Vampyrellidium vagans* Zopf: various amoeboid forms (H-J); resting cyst (K); schematic (after Ivanič).

the life-cycles are still unknown. *Hyalodiscus* Hertwig and Lesser (Fig. 5. 18, A-G) includes small organisms which may attack filamentous algae. Although several morphological varieties occur, the production of a large plasmodial stage has not been demonstrated for this genus. Schaeffer (132) concluded that *Hyalodiscus* belongs in the Amoebidae. *Vampyrellidium* Zopf (Fig. 5. 18, H-K) is similar to *Hyalodiscus*. The "axopodia" of *V. vagans* (63) resemble the ectoplasmic ridges of *Thecamoeba* (132).

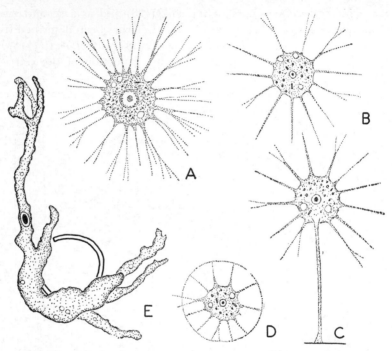

Fig. 5. 19. A. *Actinocoma ramosa* Penard (14-26μ); pseudopodia may show small granules in movement (after P.). B-D. *Nuclearia caulescens* Penard (16-20μ); free stage (B); form temporarily attached by pseudopodium (C); specimen with a gelatinous sheath (D); after P. E. *Gephyramoeba delicatula* Goodey, specimen clinging to cyst from which it has just emerged; x375 (after G.).

The status of *Gephyramoeba* Goodey (Fig. 5. 19, E) is somewhat uncertain. Although *Gephyramoeba delicatula* occasionally reaches lengths of 250μ, the organisms remain uninucleate and their cysts apparently have a single membrane (43). *Nuclearia* Cienkowski (Fig. 5. 19, B-D) includes uninucleate and multinucleate forms, either naked or with a capsule through which the pseudopodia extend. *Actinocoma* Penard, as represented by *A. ramosa* (Fig. 5. 19, A) is similar to noncapsulated uninucleate forms of *Nuclearia*. These organisms apparently have little in common with the plasmodia of *Vampyrella* and *Leptomyxa*.

Order 2. Mycetozoida

The mature stage of the Mycetozoida[2] is either a large plasmodium or a pseudoplasmodium. On the basis of differences in morphology and life-history, three suborders may be recognized: (1) Acrasina ("Acrasiales"), in which the structural unit is the uninucleate stage, although pseudoplasmodia may be formed by aggregation of myxamoebae without cytoplasmic fusion; (2) plasmodiophorina ("Plasmodiophorales"), parasites which are plasmodia at maturity but do not produce sporangia; (3) Eumycetozoina (Euplasmodida, "Myxogastres"), the typical free-

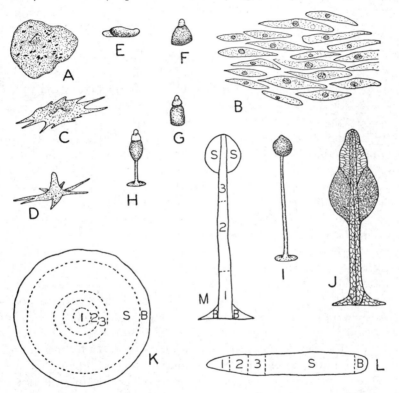

Fig. 5. 20. A, B. *Dictyostelium mucoroides* Brefeld (after Schuckmann): active amoeboid stage with ingested bacteria, x440 (A); portion of pseudoplasmodium showing spindle-shaped organisms, x440. C-M. *Dictyostelium discoideum* Raper (after Bonner): C-I. Successive stages in development of a pseudosporangium from a pseudoplasmodium; diagrammatic. J. Pseudosporangium, almost mature, showing basal disc, stalk, and spores; schematic, x140 approx. K-M. Diagrams illustrating changes in position of "cells" during development of a pseudosporangium (M) from a pseudoplasmodium (K). KEY: b, basal disc "cells"; s, spore "cells"; 1, 2, 3, stalk "cells" of three different regions.

[2] Detailed discussions of the Mycetozoida will be found in several monographs (46, 84, 86) and modern data have been reviewed by Martin (89).

living Mycetozoida in which the mature stage is a migratory plasmodium; more or less complex sporangia are produced in many genera.

Suborder 1. Acrasina. In this group, a small uninucleate "myxamoeba" is released from the cyst ("spore"). Sexual phenomena have not been demonstrated. These myxamoebae (Fig. 5. 20, A) lead an active life, feeding typically on bacteria and undergoing fission. Under certain conditions, which include a favorable humidity (137) and perhaps partial exhaustion of food (117), a pseudoplasmodium is developed by the adhesion of myxamoebae to one another (Fig. 5. 20, B). In spite of its organization, the pseudoplasmodium of *Dictyostelium discoideum* moves as a polarized unit (116) and may grow by fission of the component myxamoebae. The myxamoebae are said to cease feeding after formation of the pseudoplasmodium in *Dictyostelium* (137) and the aggregate apparently is a preliminary step toward sporulation.

Sporulation in some of the simpler Acrasina, such as *Guttulina*, involves merely a heaping up of the myxamoebae into a compact mass and then secretion of a cyst membrane (117). In such specialized types as *Dictyostelium discoideum* (11), a pseudoplasmodium, under favorable conditions, may first undergo a certain amount of migration. At sporulation, the pseudoplasmodium gradually assumes an upright position and becomes reorganized into a pseudosporangium (Fig. 5. 20, C-I). During the late migratory phase, the posterior components of the pseudoplasmodium are differentiated into intensely staining *pre-spore cells;* the anterior units become *stalk-cells;* those at the base of the pseudoplasmodium, *basal-disc cells.* Later on, the pre-spore cells are transformed into spores. Morphogenesis also involves changes in position of the units. The stalk-cells most anterior in the migratory stage are pushed up to and over the top of the stalk-sheath and down toward the basal disc during development of the pseudosporangium. As a result, the relative positions of various groups of cells are reversed (Fig. 5. 20, K-M). The pseudosporangia are quite specialized also in *Polysphondylium*. One interesting feature of this communal process is that sporulation follows a specific pattern. Even after being crushed and mixed together, pseudoplasmodia of two different species may reorganize and then produce their typical spore-bearing structures (118).

The best known genus is *Dictyostelium* Brefeld, species of which have been investigated in detail by several workers (11, 114, 116, 137). Certain species of *Dictyostelium* have been maintained in cultures (12, 25, 115, 116, 137). Other genera (102) include *Acrasis* Van Tieghem, *Coenonia* Van Tieghem, *Guttulina* Cienkowski, *Guttulinopsis* Olive, and *Polysphondylium* Brefeld. The status of *Sappinia* Dangeard, sometimes included in this group, is uncertain (117).

The Acrasina are free-living forms found commonly in soil and on decaying wood, leaves, and straw, and all of them apparently feed on bacteria.

Suborder 2. Plasmodiophorina. These organisms invade cells in the roots and underground stems of higher plants. Infections are often accompanied by the hypertrophy of tissues and formation of galls. A host index has been published by Karling (70). The mature stage is a plasmodium which may divide into small plasmodia or may give rise to uninucleate cysts ("spores"). Although chitin has been reported, cellulose apparently is not produced by the Plasmodiophorina.

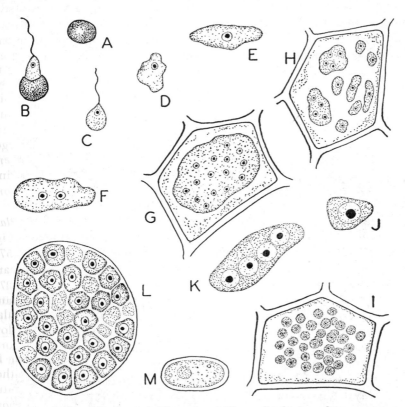

Fig. 5. 21. A-I. Typical life-cycle of Plasmodiophorina, diagrammatic (after Cook): A. Uninucleate cyst ("spore"). B. Excystment. C. Flagellate stage. D. Amoeboid stage, after loss of flagellum. E. Amoeboid stage supposedly formed by fusion of two flagellates. F. Binucleate amoeboid stage. G. Plasmodium in host cell. H. Products of plasmotomy. I. Developing spores. J-M. *Sporomyxa tenebrionis* Rietschel (from *Tenebrio molitor*), x1890 (after R.): uninucleate stage (J); amoeboid form with four nuclei (K); developing "spores" in sporocyst (L); uninucleate spore (M).

In a typical life-cycle (Fig. 5. 21, A-I) excystment releases a myxoflagellate in the soil. This flagellate ("swarm-cell") penetrates a cell in a root-hair of the plant host and becomes a myxamoeba. Or, according to some accounts (27), two myxoflagellates or two amoebae may fuse to produce a diploid myxamoeba. At any rate, the myxamoeba develops into a plasmodium which, at maturity, may undergo plasmotomy or produce uninucleate cysts (Fig. 5. 21, H, I).

Relationships to the Eumycetozoina are not yet clear and further investigation of the life-cycle is needed. In certain species, meiosis is supposed to precede formation of spores (28, 57, 155). For the group as a whole, however, data on gametogenesis and syngamy are inadequate from a cytological standpoint.

About a dozen genera have been erected, largely on the basis of the arrangement of spores in the spore-masses and the shape of the masses. However, Palm and Burk (105), in preparations of *Sorosphaera* from one host species, found so much variation in the spore-masses that they questioned the validity of the conventional generic criteria. On this basis, they suggested that six generic names (*Clathrosorus* Ferdinandsen and Winge, *Ligniera* Maire and Tison, *Membranosorus* Ostenfeld and Petersen, *Ostenfeldiella* Ferdinandsen, *Sorodiscus* Lagerheim and Winge, *Spongospora* Brunchorst) might be considered synonyms of *Sorosphaera* Schroeter. Furthermore, the authors suggested the advisability of placing all described Plasmodiophorina in only two genera, *Plasmodiophora* Woronin and *Cystospora* Elliott (37).

Cook (27), on the other hand, recognized the following genera: *Plasmodiophora* Woronin (29, 91), *Spongospora* Brunchorst (77, 104), *Ligniera* Maire and Tison (26), *Sorodiscus* Lagerheim and Winge (157), *Sorosphaera* Schroeter (10, 155) and *Tetramyxa* Goebel. These genera are differentiated partly by the arrangement and form of the spores (27). Spherical spores occur in groups of four without a common membrane in *Tetramyxa;* ellipsoidal or pyriform spores are grouped in irregular "spore-balls" within a common membrane in *Sorosphaera;* and in hollow spore-balls without a common membrane in *Spongospora.* A flat "spore-cake," composed of urn-shaped spores, is surrounded by a membrane in *Sorodiscus;* and in *Ligniera* and *Plasmodiophora* the spores are neither aggregated nor enclosed in a common membrane. The taxonomic status of *Sporomyxa* Léger (125; Fig. 5. 21, J-M), *Peltomyxa* Léger, *Cystospora* Elliott, and *Trematophlyctis* Patouillard has been disputed. According to Cook (27), these genera do not belong in the Plasmodiophorina.

Suborder 3. Eumycetozoina. The Eumycetozoina (Euplasmodia) include several hundred species of "slime-molds." The mature stage is a migratory plasmodium which reaches a length of several inches to a foot or more. Examined microscopically, the plasmodium in such types as *Physarum* shows many channels of various sizes. Through the channels flows a liquid containing many granules, the direction of flow being reversed at intervals (92). As the plasmodium moves, vessels may be resorbed in some areas and formed anew in others. The cytoplasm may be hyaline, or with inclusions and pigments, may be white or various shades of violet, blue, green, yellow, orange, red, and brown. Unfortunately, these colors vary so much, under both natural and experimental conditions, that they are not thoroughly reliable as taxonomic characteristics

(69). The diet may influence color of the plasmodium, since some species become pink in association with *Serratia marcescens* (69). The pigment of *Physarum polycephalum* is a pH-indicator, changing from yellow-green at pH 8.2 to a deep red-orange at pH 1.0 (136). Certain species with yellow pigment apparently require light for completion of the life-cycle, while several non-pigmented species develop sporangia equally well in light and in darkness (44).

The plasmodium is holozoic, feeding largely on bacteria and other microorganisms. A number of species have been grown in cultures with a variety of microorganisms as food (19, 44, 60, 100). In addition, *Fuligo septica, Badhamia foliicola,* and several others have been grown in pure cultures on autoclaved yeast (25), but the specific food requirements of these organisms are yet to be determined.

The Eumycetozoina occur on rotting leaves and logs, and the plasmodium usually grows in or beneath such decaying materials. The plasmodium penetrates decaying wood by extending slender processes through the interstices and, under experimental conditions, may pass through filters with pores measuring about 1.0µ (92). Shortly before sporulation, the plasmodium creeps to an exposed position, sometimes on trunks or stems of nearby plants, where conditions will facilitate desiccation and dispersal of spores. Subsequent behavior varies in different species. In the simpler cases a plasmodium merely gives rise to a compact flattened mass, or *aethalium* (Fig. 5. 23, A), or to an irregularly lobate body (*plasmodiocarp*) which retains to some extent the outline of the plasmodium (Fig. 5. 23, B). In either case, the entire mass becomes enclosed in a membrane and may be considered a single large spore-case (sporocarp). More often, the plasmodium produces individual *sporangia* (Fig. 5. 23, C-I), stalked in many species but not in others.

The sporangia usually begin development as dense areas which become segmented into knob-like masses. In many cases, the young sporangium undergoes vertical growth, followed by differentiation of a stalk and a spore case; in others, the sporangia remain sessile. The surface of the sporangium typically becomes enclosed in a resistant wall (peridium), which is commonly wrinkled at maturity. In stalked types, the peridium is usually continuous with the covering of the stalk, and the stalk extends to the substratum to end in a basal network, the hypothallus. Inside the peridium, a capillitium (a network of threads or bands) is often developed, although lacking in *Cribraria, Licea,* and related genera. The first indication of the capillitium in *Physarum polycephalum* (60) is the appearance of lacunae within the sporangium. These channels develop into hollow threads whose junctions (nodes) become filled with calcium salts as the sporangium approaches maturity. In other species, calcium may be deposited throughout the capillitium, may be limited to the peridium or its inner surface, or may not be deposited at all. The capillitial net, perhaps by contractions induced by desiccation, probably helps to distribute the spores after rupture of the peridium. During development of the capillitium, nuclear division may continue in the sporangial protoplasm for a time, but uninucleate pre-spores eventually are produced. These become enclosed in membranes to form the characteristic spores.

In addition to sporulation, another method of producing resistant stages is known in the Eumycetozoina. An entire plasmodium may be-

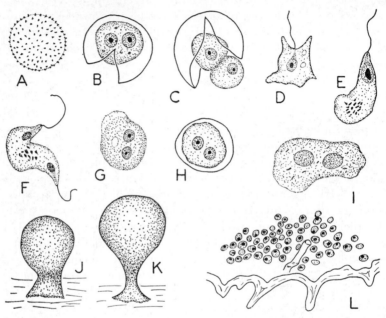

Fig. 5. 22. A-I. *Physarum polycephalum*, x1360 (after Howard): A. Spore. B. Completion of mitosis; spore membrane ruptured. C. Completion of fission at excystment. D. Amoeboid flagellate. E. Swimming flagellate. F. Flagellate zygote shortly after fusion of gametes. G. Amoeboid zygote after loss of flagella. H. Encysted zygote; gametic nuclei not yet fused. I. Zygote after first nuclear division in formation of young plasmodium. J-L. *Arcyria cinerea* (after Kränzlin): J-K. Stages in development of sporangium, x23. L. Portion of cross-section through a sporangium, showing spores, peridium, and part of a capillitial thread ("elater"), x375.

come sclerotized (17) upon subjection to desiccation. The plasmodium becomes partly dehydrated and is enclosed in a membrane, the *sclerotium,* said to consist mainly of cellulose. Once sclerotized, the organism can remain viable for several months and then become active again in the presence of adequate moisture and oxygen.

Development of the spores after liberation seems to be a complicated process. Prior to germination, each spore in *Ceratiomyxa* (41) develops four nuclei, so that a quadrinucleate amoeboid stage is released. The amoeboid stage is said to produce eight uninucleate myxoflagellates, supposedly gametes which fuse in pairs to produce amoeboid zygotes. In a number of other Eumycetozoina (40), one or two amoeboid "swarm-cells" are liberated and each amoeba then develops a flagellum. In *Physarum polycephalum,* for instance, the spore nucleus divides once at the beginning of germination and fission produces two amoeboid stages. One amoeba emerges, develops a flagellum, and then swims away. The second amoeba then repeats the process (59). Syngamy of the myxoflagellates produces amoeboid zygotes (60). Except perhaps for slight differences in

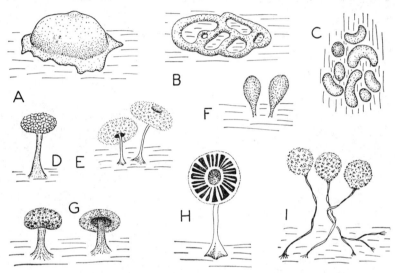

Fig. 5. 23. Sporangia in various Eumycetozoina (after MacBride): A. An aethallium of *Fuligo septica,* x0.75. B. A plasmodiocarp of *Hemitrichia serpula,* x2.2. C. Sessile sporangia of *Trichia inconspicua,* x11. D. *Physarum leucopus,* x11. E. *Didymium annulatum,* x13.5. F. *Trichia decipiens,* x6 approx. G. *Didymium melanospermum,* x7.5. H. Section showing capillitium in sporangium of *Physarella oblonga,* x24. I. *Badhamia magna,* x7.5.

vital staining, there is no evidence for two distinct types of "swarm-cells" (69), and this question remains open for the suborder. Although meiosis has been reported just before formation of the uninucleate "protospores" in *Ceratiomyxa* (41), there is much uncertainty as to the exact stage in which this process occurs in Eumycetozoina generally.

The following genera have been included in the suborder: *Arcyria* Wiggers (74), *Amaurochaete* Rostafinski, *Badhamia* Berkeley, *Ceratiomyxa* Schröter (41), *Cribraria* Persoon, *Didymium* Schräder, *Fuligo* Haller, *Licea* Schräder, *Lycogala* Adanson (153), *Margarita* Lister, *Orcadella* Wingate, *Physarum* Persoon (59, 60), *Reticularia* Bulliard, *Stemonitis* Gleditsch (7), *Trichia* Haller, *Tubulina* Persoon.

Order 3. Amoebida

The Amoebida normally form lobopodia in locomotion, or else move by a wave-like protoplasmic flow. Some species form slender accessory pseudopodia which may have little or no function in locomotion. A hyaline ectoplasm and a granular endoplasm are usually distinguishable. A flagellate stage has been reported in several species usually assigned to the order; in the rest, the cycle apparently is monomorphic. Many species occur in the digestive tract of invertebrates and vertebrates; others are free-living in fresh and salt water and in the soil.

The order is often divided into three families: Dimastigamoebidae, in which the life-cycle includes both a flagellate and an amoeboid phase; Amoebidae, free-living species without a flagellate stage; and Endamoebidae, the endoparasitic amoebae.

Family 1. Dimastigamoebidae. The dimorphic cycle includes a dominant amoeboid phase and a flagellate phase of relatively short duration. Members of the family have been reported from fresh water and from cultures inoculated with feces of certain insects and of various vertebrates (including man).

Naegleria gruberi is the best known representative (113, 156, 161). The small amoeboid stage (Fig. 5. 24, A, B, I) commonly forms one large lobopodium. The nucleus contains a large Feulgen-negative endosome which divides in mitosis. The flagellate stage (Fig. 5. 24, C, D, M), which has two equal flagella, is a temporary one under the conditions reported; ingestion of food has been described in only one instance (113). The transformation from amoeba to flagellate is induced by diluting the culture medium with water (113, 161). Cysts (Fig. 5. 24, E-H) are usually but not always uninucleate. The cyst membrane shows two well-defined layers and also several opercula, through one of which the organism emerges during excystment.

The generic composition of the family has been disputed. The type genus, *Dimastigamoeba* Blochmann (9), is based on *Dimastigamoeba* (*Dimorpha*) *radiata* (Klebs). The amoeboid phase (73) develops slender radially arranged pseudopodia; the flagellate stage has two unequal flagella, one of which is usually trailed. *Dimastigamoeba simplex* Moroff (Fig. 5. 24, Q) is similar to *D. radiata* (93). The genus *Naegleria* Alexeieff em. Calkins (2, 18) includes species with a flagellate stage showing two equal flagella, and an amoeboid stage which moves by means of a blunt lobopodium. There seems to be no sound reason for assuming that *Naegleria* is a synonym of *Dimastigamoeba*. The status of *Trimastigamoeba* Whitmore is uncertain, since stages with two, three, and four approximately equal flagella were figured for *T. philippinensis* (159). Such material might suggest a biflagellate organism in various stages of flagellar duplication prior to fission. Hollande (53) has suggested that *Naegleria* Alexeieff is a synonym of *Vahlkampfia* Chatton and Lalung-Bonnaire (Fig. 5. 26, A-F). However, a flagellate stage was not reported in *V. punctata* (24), and the structure of the dividing nucleus, although similar to it, is not identical with that described for *N. gruberi* (113).

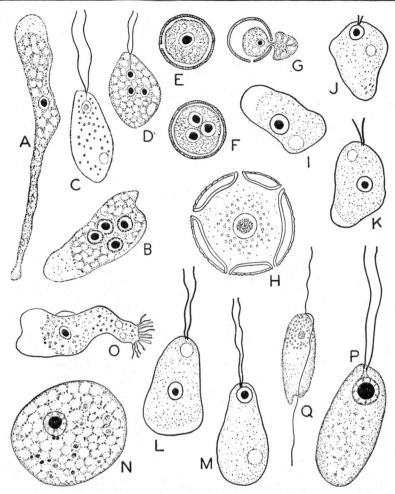

Fig. 5. 24. Dimastigamoebidae. A-M. *Naegleria gruberi:* A. Unusually elongated amoeba. B. Amoeba with four nuclei. C. Flagellate stage, from living. D. Flagellate with three nuclei. E, F. Cysts with one and three nuclei. G. Amoeba leaving cyst. H. Cyst showing several pores and unusual separation of inner and outer membranes. I-M. Stages in development of flagellate (M) from amoeboid stage (I). A-G, x1600 (after Wilson); H, x2400 (after Wenyon); I-M, x1215 (after Rafalko). N-P. *Naegleria (Vahlkampfia) tachypodia* (Gläser): rounded amoeba, two blepharoplasts on nuclear membrane (N), x2010; amoeba, from living (O), x1120; flagellate (P), x2010 (after Pietschmann). Q. *Dimastigamoeba simplex* Moroff (20-40 x 10-12μ), flagellate stage showing long trailing flagellum (after M.).

Until it is shown that the type species of *Vahlkampfia* has a flagellate phase, there is no justification for placing this genus in the family Dimastigamoebidae as now constituted. *"Vahlkampfia" tachypodia* Gläser does show a flagellate stage (111) closely resembling that of *N. gruberi*

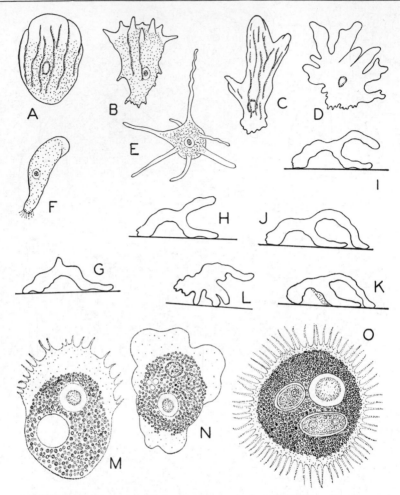

Fig. 5. 25. Various types of amoeboid activity in Amoebidae: A. Locomotion without formation of distinct pseudopodia, ectoplasmic ridges distinct, as in *Thecamoeba verrucosa*. B. Formation of conical pseudopodia along anterior margin and on free surface during locomotion, as in *Mayorella bigemma*. C. Formation of large pseudopodia which direct locomotion, as in *Amoeba proteus*. D. Formation of a number of large pseudopodia, including several which direct locomotion, as in *Amoeba dubia*. E. Floating form with slender and sometimes spiral pseudopodia, as in *Astramoeba flagellipodia*. F. Slug-like forms moving by protoplasmic flow, as in *Trichamoeba clava;* uroid (slender cytoplasmic projections at posterior end) present. G-L. Locomotion of "walking" type, as seen in thriving cultures of *Chaos* (*Pelomyxa*) *carolinensis*. M-O. *Acanthamoeba castellanii* (Douglas) Volkonsky (12-30μ), showing different forms of pseudopodia in one species. A-F, schematic (after Schaeffer); G-L, schematic (after Wilber); M-O, after Volkonsky.

(Fig. 5. 24, N-P) and therefore should be transferred to the genus *Naegleria*.

Family 2. Amoebidae. These are the free-living amoebae which lack a flagellate phase. Although complex cycles involving polymorphism and syngamy have been described, such interpretations apparently were based on cultures contaminated with other species of Amoebidae, Mycetozoa, and water-molds (67). At present, it appears that the life-cycle is limited to the amoeboid stage and a cyst.

Classification of the Amoebidae is not yet on a satisfactory basis and there remains a certain amount of disagreement concerning the genera which should be recognized. Furthermore, the concept of a single family for all the free-living amoebae is subject to the objection that habitat is not necessarily an accurate gauge of zoological relationships. Consequently, there is at least a reasonable basis for various suggestions that the group should be split into less heterogeneous families. In a sense, problems of taxonomy are complicated by the very simplicity of amoebae. Lack of the more obvious fixed characteristics typical of many other groups necessarily limits the taxonomist to consideration of range in size, form of the body, type of pseudopodia, methods of locomotion, structure of the nucleus, and the form and nature of cytoplasmic inclusions. Aside from the nuclear picture, which should show reasonable constancy, these characteristics vary within greater or lesser limits and presumably are subject to significant environmental influences. The effective utilization of such dynamic traits in taxonomy obviously demands extensive knowledge of amoebae, particularly as living organisms. Consequently, there is much need for the detailed study of many species which are not yet thoroughly characterized. In some cases, adequate characterization may depend upon pure-line cultures for determining the range in form and behavior to be expected of particular species. The systematic investigation of nuclear structure and division, on the order of some recent work with *Naegleria* (113), also should yield information of taxonomic value. For instance, a nucleus with a large endosome is characteristic of both *Vahlkampfia* (24) and *Acanthamoeba* (150), but the mitotic pictures are strikingly different, the endosome being resorbed in the latter.

It has been pointed out very clearly (132) that amoebae differ characteristically (Fig. 5. 25) with respect to types of pseudopodia, methods of locomotion, form of the body and the nature of its changes in form, presence or absence of a "uroid" (a group of thin cytoplasmic projections at the posterior end), form of the nucleus, and even the types of cytoplasmic crystals in certain large fresh-water species. Some amoebae, for example, form *determinate* pseudopodia which grow to a more or less definite size and are then withdrawn, never becoming large enough to include the entire amoeba and thus not directing locomotion. Others develop *indeterminate* pseudopodia which are not restricted in size and

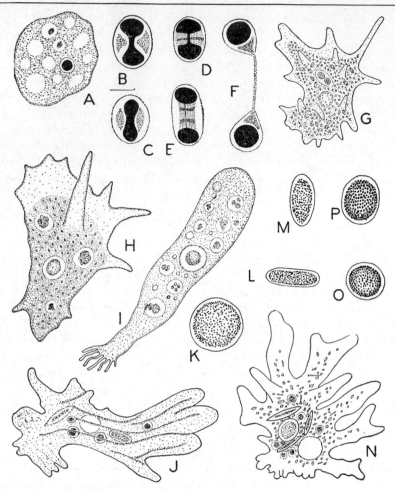

Fig. 5. 26. A-F. *Vahlkampfia punctata* (Dangeard) Chatton and Lalung-Bonnaire: amoeba stained to show nucleus (A), x1710; stages in mitosis, showing division of the endosome and other features (B-F), x3420 (after C. & L-B.). G. *Astramoeba stella* Schaeffer in active locomotion, x875 approx. (after S.); compare with floating stage of *A. flagellipodia* (Fig. 5. 25, E). H. *Mayorella conipes* Schaeffer, showing conical pseudopodia which do not direct locomotion; x1155 approx. (after S.). I. *Trichamoeba pallida* Schaeffer, a marine type showing typical uroid; x1100 approx. (after S.). J-M. *Amoeba proteus* (Pallas) Leidy, average length about 600μ: amoeba in locomotion, showing typical pseudopodia and ectoplasmic ridges (J); broad (K) and narrow (L, M) aspects of typical discoid nuclei (after Schaeffer). N-P. *Amoeba dubia* Schaeffer (average length usually about 400μ): typical amoeba (N), polar and lateral views (O, P) of the elongated nucleus (after S.).

may, as "main pseudopodia," become large enough to include the whole organism and thus direct locomotion. And there are also certain amoebae which develop no typical pseudopodia at all during locomotion. Such is the case in *Trichamoeba* and *Thecamoeba,* in which locomotion is best characterized as protoplasmic flow. The eventual correlation of such characteristics with adequate cytological data should furnish a much clearer picture of generic boundaries and relationships than is now available for the free-living amoebae.

Some of the genera which have been proposed for various types of Amoebidae are listed below; certain others have been characterized by Schaeffer (132).

Acanthamoeba Volkonsky (50, 150; Fig. 5. 25, M-O); *Amoeba* Ehrenberg (Fig. 5. 26,

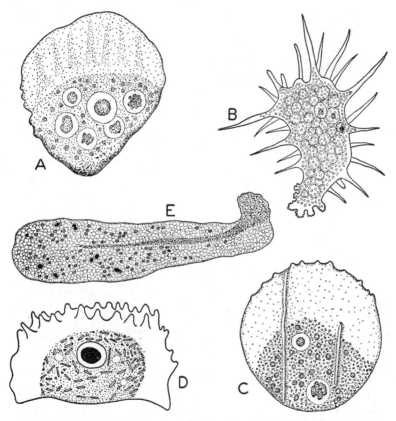

Fig. 5. 27. A. *Flabellula mira* Schaeffer (marine), in locomotion; x1740 approx. (after S.). B. *Dinamoeba mirabilis* Leidy, characteristic spine-like pseudopodia; some specimens show adherent rods, possibly bacteria; x125 (after L.). C. *Thecamoeba orbis* Schaeffer, in locomotion, showing typical ectoplasmic ridges; x1600 (after S.). D. *Hartmanella klitzkei* Arndt, many ingested bacteria, stained preparation; x1250 approx. (after A.). E. *Pelomyxa* ("gray type," *P. palustris*), longitudinal section of slug-like body showing many nuclei, several food vacuoles, central axis, and tail-piece ("telson") of hyaline cytoplasm; x53 approx. (after Okada).

J-P), represented by *Amoeba proteus* (Pallas) Leidy em. Schaeffer and *A. dubia* Schaeffer (131); *Astramoeba* Vejdowsky (132; Figs. 5. 25, E, 5. 26, G), erected for *A. radiosa* (Ehrenberg); *Chaos* Linnaeus, represented by *Chaos (Pelomyxa) carolinensis* (71, 75, 76, 160; Fig. 5. 25, G-L), multinucleate types which sometimes measure 4-5 mm. in length; *Dinamoeba* Leidy (83, 107, 132; Fig. 5. 27, B), erected for *D. mirabilis; Flabellula* Schaeffer (132; Fig. 5. 27, A); *Hartmanella* Alexeieff (150; Fig. 5. 27, D); *Mayorella* Schaeffer (132; Figs. 5. 25, B, 5. 26, H); *Pelomyxa* Greef (Fig. 5. 27, E), represented by *P. palustris* (83, 101, 107, 152), multinucleate types which move by protoplasmic flow and may reach a length of more than 2 mm; *Thecamoeba* Fromentel (132; Fig. 5. 27, C), established for *T. (Amoeba) verrucosa* (Ehrenberg); *Trichamoeba* Fromentel (132; Figs. 5. 25, F, 5. 26, I); *Vahlkampfia* Chatton and Lalung-Bonnaire (24; Fig. 5. 26, A-F). It is possible that *Hyalodiscus* Hertwig and Lesser (Fig. 5. 18, A-G) also should be included in this group.

Family 3. Endamoebidae. These are parasitic amoebae, found typically in the digestive tract of invertebrates and vertebrates. The range of hosts

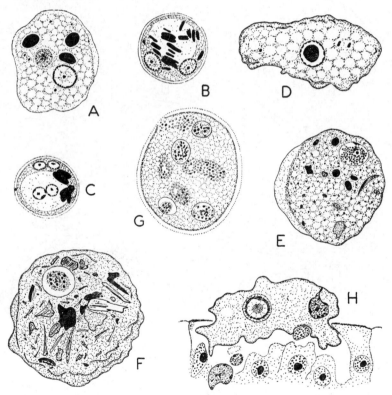

Fig. 5. 28. A-C. *Entamoeba invadens* Rodhain: amoeba in liver smear from *Coluber constrictor* (A); binucleate cyst with many chromatoid bodies (B); cyst with four nuclei (C); x1260 (after Geiman and Ratcliffe). D. *Endolimax termitis* Kirby, x1600 (after K.). E. *Endamoeba granosa* Henderson, from termites; x500 (after H.). F, G. *Endamoeba simulans* Kirby, from termites; amoeba with much ingested material (F); cyst with four nuclei (G); x530 (after K.). H. *Hydramoeba hydroxena* (Entz) Reynolds and Looper, section through the outer surface of *Hydra* showing destruction of the epithelium; x560 (after R. & L.).

may be wide even within a single genus, since different species of *Endolimax* have been reported from termites and from primates. Most Endamoebidae are probably endocommensals, or else approach such a status. However, there are notable exceptions, such as *Entamoeba histolytica* of man (Chapter XI), and *E. invadens* which may produce fatal infections in various reptiles (39, 119). As in the case of the Amoebidae, the assignment of genera to this family is based upon their sharing a common habitat rather than upon a consideration of more valid taxonomic criteria. It is not impossible that some of the Endamoebidae are more closely related to certain free-living amoebae than they are to other members of their own "ecological" family. The following genera have been included in the Endamoebidae:

Endamoeba Leidy (Fig. 5. 28, E-G), erected for Bütschli's *Amoeba blattae* (90, 95), contains parasites of cockroaches and termites (49).

Entamoeba Casagrandi and Barbagallo (Fig. 5. 28, A-C) includes species from the major groups of vertebrates. Although the validity of this generic name, as distinct from *Endamoeba* Leidy, has been disputed extensively, reasons for retaining *Entamoeba* as a generic name for *E. coli* and related amoebae are ably presented by Kirby (72). This usage emphasizes the fact that *E. blattae* and *E. coli* cannot logically be placed in the same genus. The three species parasitic in man are discussed in Chapter XI.

Endolimax Kuenen and Swellengrebel (Fig. 5. 28, D) is represented in termites and cockroaches as well as various vertebrates. *E. nana* of man is described in Chapter XI.

Dientamoeba Jepps and Dobell includes a parasite of the human colon, while *Iodamoeba* Dobell is represented in pigs and in man (Chapter XI).

Hydramoeba Reynolds and Looper (121, 122; Fig. 5. 28, H) includes a rather large amoeba which attacks the epithelial layers of *Hydra,* often with fatal results.

Order 4. Testacida

These are typically creeping organisms which develop lobopodia or filopodia and possess one-chambered tests. The primitive test is composed of an apparently single secreted layer. The material is said to be "pseudochitin" (1). The flexibility of the test in *Pamphagus* and *Cochliopodium,* for instance, indicates there is no significant addition of inorganic material. Mixtures of silica with the basic "chitinous" material are found in relatively firm tests which maintain a characteristic shape, as in *Hyalosphenia.*

The test of most Testacida apparently contains two layers (Fig. 5. 29, J). The inner layer is composed of "chitin," sometimes mixed with siliceous material. The structure of the outer layer varies in different genera. Although apparently bivalve in *Clypeolina marginata* (109), this layer seems to be continuous in other Testacida. In *Arcella* (Fig. 5. 29, C-F), more or less spherical elements are cemented together in a honeycomb pattern. In *Amphizonella* (Fig. 5. 29, L), the test is sometimes covered with a "gelatinous" layer. Difflugiidae ingest sand grains, and occasionally diatom shells, which are used with little or no modification in construction of the test. Such particles are embedded in a "chitinous" cement. The test of *Centropyxis* (Fig. 5. 29, K) apparently is constructed of a "chitinoid-siliceous" material which is usually, although not always, encrusted with sand grains. In *Lecquereusia* (Fig. 5. 29, A), sand grains or diatom shells are ingested and then modified in form before addition to the test (107). In the Euglyphidae (Fig. 5. 29, G-I), foreign particles are replaced by scales, which are formed and stored in the cytoplasm prior to fission. These scales are insoluble in hot sulfuric acid in *Nebela collaris* and seem to be completely siliceous (87). The Euglyphidae are thought to produce such scales from absorbed minerals, rather than by the modification of ingested particles. In *Euglypha* (47), it is possible to observe cytoplasmic inclusions showing similar optical properties and forming a graded series from small globules to typical scales. Such a "series" implies a gradual growth of the scale by addition of material from the cytoplasm.

The color of the test varies with the species and often to some extent with the individual specimen. Various shades of yellow and brown are the rule, and the color may become darker as the animal grows older. The yellow-brown tests presumably contain iron, while the occasionally observed violet tints (*Heleopera*) are attributed to manganese.

Pseudopodia. The pseudopodia of Testacida are of two general types, slender lobopodia (Fig. 5. 29, B, C) and typical filopodia (Fig. 5. 29, G). The former have rounded tips while the latter type tapers to a point. Extended filopodia may show some degree of rigidity, although they are flexible and may be swung about like sluggish flagella, as in *Trinema lineare* (36). In addition to these clearly defined types, pseudopodia somewhat intermediate in form have been described in *Cryptodifflugia* and *Cochliopodium*. The form of the pseudopodia seems to be a reliable taxonomic feature, and their relative number also may be fairly characteristic. Such species as *Hyalosphenia punctata* (107) normally move by means of one large pseudopodium. Other species typically extend several pseudopodia at once. In addition to the usual functions, filopodia in particular serve in attachment of Testacida to the substratum.

Contents of the test. Within the cytoplasm are found the nucleus or nuclei, ingested food, one or more contractile vacuoles, stored food, and often reserve shell-plates (Euglyphidae) or ingested sand grains to be used for construction of a new test. The majority of species have only one nucleus, which usually lies near the aboral pole of the test. However, *Arcella* (Fig. 5. 29, C) is binucleate, while such large species as *Difflugia urceolata* (107) are multinucleate. The perinuclear cytoplasm ("chromidium," "chromidial zone") of the Euglyphidae usually contains stored food which, in *Nebela collaris* (87), consists mainly of a glycogen-like carbohydrate. This chromidium has been implicated in various accounts of the chromidial origin of nuclei. Since the chromidium is sometimes stained so intensely that the nuclei are obscured, it was believed at one time that the nuclei periodically disintegrate into chromidia to form the chromidial zone. Since the nuclei could be seen in specimens without a

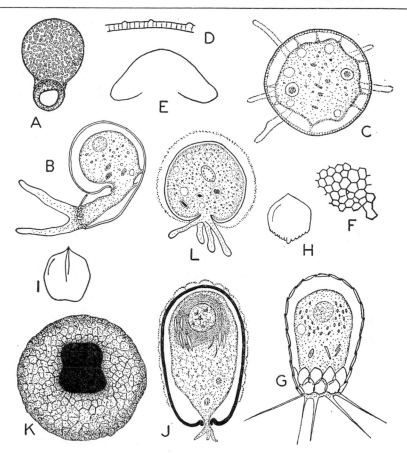

Fig. 5. 29. A, B. *Lecquereusia spiralis* (Ehrbg.) Penard (test, 125-140μ long); oral view, showing surface pattern (A); optical section (B), schematic (after P.). C-F. *Arcella vulgaris* Ehrenberg (test, 80-140μ in diameter); horizontal section (C), schematic (after Penard); optical section through wall of test (D), schematic (after Awerinzew); vertical section (E) through test (after Penard); surface pattern (F), schematic (after Awerinzew). G. *Euglypha aspera* Penard, plates shown at margin and around mouth; x206 (after P.). H, I. Plates from mouth region and from other parts of test (after P.). J. Stained section of *Heleopera rosea* (test 90-105μ long), showing test membrane with overlying plates; reserve plates in cytoplasm (after MacKinlay). K. Test of *Centropyxis aculeata* Stein, spineless variety (*C. ecornis*); x100 (after Leidy). L. *Amphizonella violacea* Greef (test 125-250μ long); chitinous test covered with a gelatinous layer which is often lacking (after Penard).

well-developed chromidium, it was assumed that the chromidia had been utilized for reconstitution of the normal nuclei.

In addition to the usual inclusions, non-contractile vacuoles supposedly filled with gas are frequently seen in species of *Arcella*. It has been suggested that these vacuoles function in flotation by increasing the buoyancy of the organism (8).

Life-histories. Fission in Testacida typically involves retention of the old test by one daughter organism. As traced in living *Nebela collaris* (87), stored sand grains are passed into the lower part of the cytoplasm which is protruded from the mouth of the test at the beginning of fission. This naked portion gradually assumes the form of an adult and then develops a new test. Nuclear division occurs next and is followed by fission and separation of the two organisms. In the Euglyphidae, reserve shell

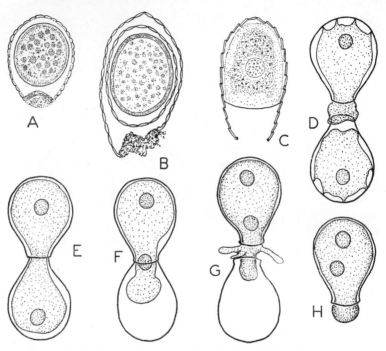

Fig. 5. 30. A. Cyst of *Heleopera picta* Leidy, test closed by operculum, organism within cyst membrane; x250 (after L.). B. Cyst of *Trinema enchelys*, cyst membrane, "cyst-shell," and original test (mouth plugged with debris); x1190 (after Volz). C. Encapsulated, or "drought-stage," in *Euglypha laevis*, as found on dry moss; shell closed by a secreted membrane (mouth of test sometimes plugged with debris); x800 (after Volz). D-H. "Association" in *Nebela collaris*, from living (after MacKinlay).

plates appear in the cytoplasm, are stored in the perinuclear region, and are used later for construction of the new test in fission.

Binary fission may not be the only method of reproduction. Occasional production of a number of small amoebulae has been reported in *Difflugia* (42), *Centropyxis* (20), and *Arcella* (21, 64). Perhaps this phenomenon is to be correlated with the reported occurrence of multinucleate stages in *Arcella* (107). These small amoebae may undergo fission, but they increase in size sooner or later and secrete a normal test. The observations of Cavallini (20, 21) were based on clone cultures. Although such reports have encountered scepticism, they suggest the desirability of further investigation under conditions which would eliminate possible contamination of cultures with other forms of Protozoa.

Phenomena suggesting syngamy also have been reported in Testacida. In the usual account, two mature organisms fuse with the mouths of their tests in contact and the binucleate mass is drawn into one test (36, 42, 106, 142). Unfortunately there is no real evidence that meiosis and the fusion of haploid nuclei occur. Until such data are available, interpretations must remain tentative. However, the actual occurrence of such cytoplasmic fusions (Fig. 5. 30, D-H) is attested not only by descriptions of stained material but also by continuous observations on living specimens (87). These findings, in conjunction with the occurrence of syngamy in Heliozoida and Foraminiferida, stress the need for more intensive study of life-cycles in Testacida.

Although Testacida are generally capable of surviving drought—remaining viable for some time on dried moss, for example—they often do not develop typical cysts. Instead, the pseudopodia are withdrawn, usually bringing into the mouth of the test a mass of debris which forms a plug. Inside the test, a chitinous membrane is secreted (Fig. 5. 30, C). The result is an effectively sealed "capsule-stage" (151), seemingly quite resistant to desiccation. Perhaps less commonly, true cysts (Fig. 5. 30, A, B) are produced. In such cases, the reserve shell-plates of Euglyphidae may be used for a "cyst-shell" within the test. A cyst membrane is then secreted inside the cyst-shell.

Ecological relationships. The Testacida as a group, and many of the individual species, are cosmopolitan inhabitants of fresh water. Ecologically, however, their distribution is more restricted. Some of the Testacida are commonly found in wooded areas or along streams on moss which is not constantly submerged. Others are typical of fauna reported for peat bogs, and a few species are commonly found in deep lake waters (depths of 60 feet or more). In general, the Testacida thrive best in acid waters and may be either rare or absent in neutral or alkaline waters. In surveys of various European bogs, species representing 18 genera and all three families have been found within the range, pH 5.0-6.4. Within these limits, differences in pH seemed to show little correlation with specific composition of the fauna, but relatively few organisms were found in an environment at pH 4.6 (103). The Testacida may prove interesting material for studying the relations of pH to the utilization of minerals.

Taxonomy. Subdivision of the order is usually based upon the structure of the test. Genera with a secreted test, either apparently homogeneous or containing minute structural elements, are assigned to the family Arcellidae. The family Difflugiidae is characterized by arenaceous tests, composed usually of sand grains although sometimes of other materials. The test of the Euglyphidae shows an outer layer of scales, or plates.

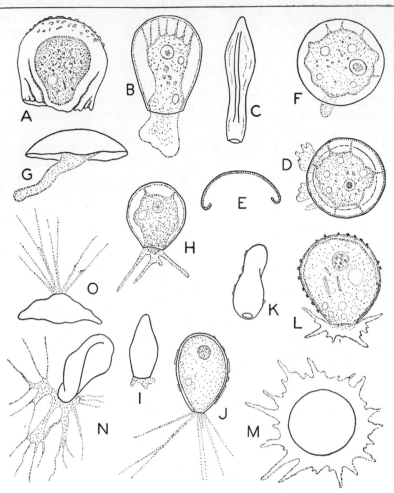

Fig. 5. 31. Arcellidae: A. *Corycia flava* (Greef) Penard (80-100μ), elastic membranous test, pseudopodia retracted (after P.). B, C. *Hyalosphenia cuneata* Stein (60-70μ), broad surface of specimen in locomotion, narrow surface of test (after Penard). D, E. *Pyxidicula operculata* Ehrenberg, view from above, vertical section of test (after Penard). F, G. *Pseudochlamys patella* Claparède and Lachmann (diameter about 40μ), specimens seen from above and from side (after Penard). H, I. *Cryptodifflugia compressa* Penard (16-18μ long), broad and narrow surfaces (after P.). J, K. *Plagiophrys parvipunctata* Penard (test averages 50μ long), broad and narrow surfaces (after P.). L, M. *Cochliopodium granulatum* Penard (test 70-90μ long), lateral and polar views (after P.). N, O. *Pamphagus mutabilis* Bailey (test usually 70-90μ long), test transparent, elastic, often twisted; in locomotion (N), and view from above (after Penard).

This system is convenient in that it is based upon fairly obvious characteristics, but it ignores such features as structure of the pseudopodia. The family Arcellidae, for instance, includes *Arcella* and *Pseudochlamys* with slender lobopodia and also *Pamphagus* and *Difflugiella* with typical

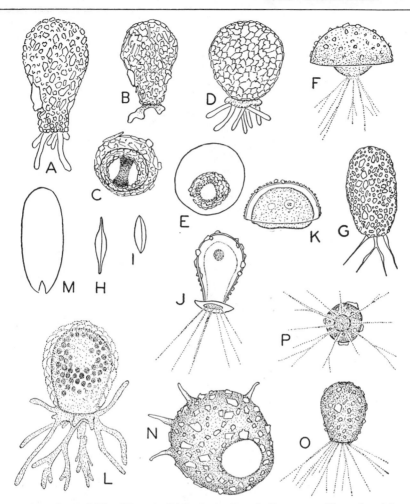

Fig. 5. 32. Difflugiidae. A. *Difflugia pyriformis* Perty; test 65 to (rarely) 400-500μ (after Penard). B, C. *Pontigulasia incisa* Rhumbler (test 85-150μ long), lateral view; oral view showing "bridge" inside test (after Penard). D, E. *Cucurbitella mespiliformis* Penard (test 125-140μ long), lateral view and oral view of test showing collar (after P.). F. *Frenzelina reniformis* Penard (test 26-30μ in diameter), hemispherical test, filopodia (after P.). G-I. *Clypeolina marginata* Penard (test 80-140μ long), view of broad surface, optical cross-sections of two tests (after P.). J. *Nadinella tenella* Penard, filopodia, collar, surface details shown at margin of test; schematic (after P.). K. *Parmulina cyathus* Penard (test usually 40-45μ long), surface detail shown at upper margin; schematic (after P.). L, M. *Heleopera picta* Leidy (x250), broad surface showing surface details, narrow surface in outline (after L.). N. *Centropyxis aculeata* Stein, x300 (after Hoogenraad). O, P. *Pseudo-difflugia fulva* (Archer) Penard (test 15-23μ long), lateral and oral views (after P.).

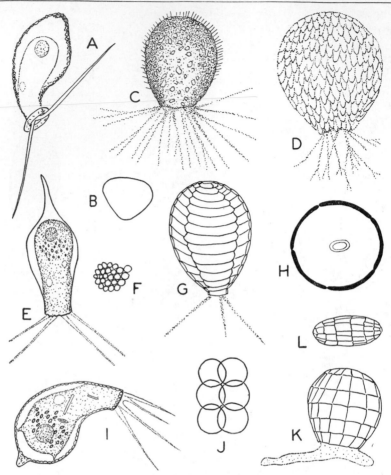

Fig. 5. 33. A-C. Difflugiidae; D-L. Euglyphidae. A, B. *Campascus trique-
ter* Penard (test 90-120μ long), lateral view (collar, surface detail at margin
of test); optical cross-section of test (after P.). C. *Diaphorodon mobile* Archer
(test 40-111μ long); test is somewhat plastic, with added foreign particles
(after Penard). D. *Assulina semilunum* Leidy, x375 (after Hoogenraad). E,
F. *Paraeuglypha reticulata* Penard (test 55-70μ long), organism showing shape
of test; surface pattern (after P.). G, H. *Paulinella chromatophora* Lauterborn (test usually 20-30μ long); surface view; optical cross-section of test,
position of mouth indicated (after Penard). I, J. *Cyphoderia trochus* Penard
(test usually 110-120μ long); schematic longitudinal section; surface pattern
of the hyaline scales (after P.). K, L. *Quadrula discoides* Penard (test 30-40μ
long), lateral and polar views (after P.).

filopodia. Objections to such disregard of pseudopodial structure have
been raised (130), and it is possible that division of the order into a
larger number of appropriate families would illustrate natural relationships somewhat more clearly than the present arrangement.

Genera included in the Arcellidae, Difflugiidae, and Euglphidae are listed below.

Family 1. Arcellidae. *Amphizonella* Greef (*Zonomyxa* Nüsslin) (107; Fig. 5. 29, L); *Arcella* Ehrenberg (31, 83, 107; Fig. 29, C-F); *Cochliopodium* Hertwig & Lesser (83, 107; Fig. 5. 31, L, M); *Corycia* Dujardin (107; Fig. 5. 31, A); *Cryptodifflugia* Penard (107; Fig. 5. 31, H, I); *Hyalosphenia* Stein (107; Fig. 5. 31, B, C); *Pamphagus* Bailey (*Chlamydophrys* Cienkowski) (4, 56, 83, 107; Fig. 5. 31, N. O); *Plagiophrys* Claparède & Lachmann (107; Fig. 5. 31, J, K); *Pseudochlamys* Claparède & Lachmann (83, 107; Fig. 5. 31, F, G); *Pyxidicula* Ehrenberg (107; Fig. 5. 31, D, E).

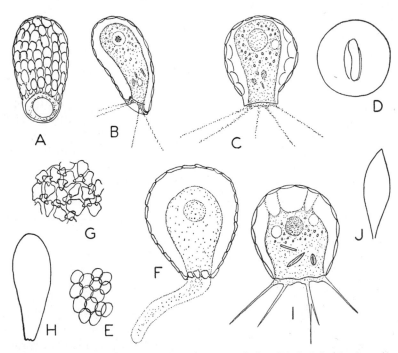

Fig. 5. 34. Euglyphidae. A, B. *Trinema enchelys* (Ehrbg.) Leidy (test 40-100μ long); oral view showing surface pattern; schematic longitudinal section (after Penard). C-E. *Sphenoderia lenta* Schlumberger (test averages 35μ long); lateral view, test in optical section; oral view (outline); surface pattern (after Penard). F-H. *Nebela vitraea* Penard (test 170-200μ long), broad and narrow aspects (in outline); surface pattern (after P.). I, J. *Placocista lens* Penard (test 65-67μ long); broad aspect, hyaline plates shown at margin; narrow aspect in outline (after P.).

Family 2. Difflugiidae. *Campascus* Leidy (83, 107; Fig. 5. 33, A, B); *Centropyxis* Stein (32, 68, 83, 107; Fig. 5. 32, N); *Clypeolina* Penard (107, 109; Fig. 5. 32, G-I); *Cucurbitella* Penard (107; Fig. 5. 32, D, E); *Cystidina* Volz (151); *Diaphorodon* Archer (107; Fig. 5. 33, C); *Difflugia* Leclerc (68, 83, 107; Fig. 5. 32, A); *Frenzelina* Penard (107); *Heleopera* Leidy (83, 107; Fig. 5. 32, L, M); *Lecquereusia* Schlumberger (107; Fig. 5. 29, A, B); *Nadinella* Penard (107; Fig. 5. 32, J); *Oopyxis* Jung (68); *Parmulina* Penard (107; Fig. 5. 32, K); *Phryngalella* Penard (107); *Pontigulasia* Rhumbler (107; Fig. 5. 32, B, D); *Pseudodifflugia* Schlumberger (83, 107; Fig. 5. 32, O, P).

Family 3. **Euglyphidae**. *Assulina* Ehrenberg (55, 83, 107; Fig. 5. 33, D); *Corythion* Taranek (107); *Cyphoderia* Schlumberger (83, 107; Fig. 5. 33, I, J); *Euglypha* Dujardin (83, 107; Fig. 5. 29, G-I); *Nebela* Leidy (68, 83, 107; Fig. 5. 34, F-H); *Pareuglypha* Penard (107; Fig. 5. 33, E, F); *Paulinella* Lauterborn (78, 107; Fig. 5. 33, G, H); *Placocista* Leidy (53, 107; Fig. 5. 34, I, J); *Quadrula* Schulze (83, 107; Fig. 5. 33, K, L); *Sphenoderia* Schlumberger (83, 107; Fig. 5. 34, C-E); *Trinema* Dujardin (36, 83, 107, 151; Fig. 5. 34, A, B).

Order 5. Foraminiferida

Two features are characteristic—myxopodia and a test surrounded by cytoplasm. The majority of living species measure less than 10 millimeters and are thus relatively small as compared with some of the extinct species. However, there are exceptions, such as *Bathysiphon filiformis* in which the test reaches a length of 50 mm (82). Most species are found in salt and brackish water, and the few reported from fresh water are relatively simple types. A small group contains specialized pelagic forms. More typically, however, the Foraminiferida are slowly creeping organisms, or else are migratory when young but sessile as adults. Various sessile species have been found attached to eel grass and seaweed. Attachment to seaweed or other floating objects presumably would be a significant factor in the distribution of such species.

The Foraminiferida as a group are distributed throughout the oceans, but there are characteristic local faunas restricted to particular areas. Vertical distribution is influenced by the type of shell, since calcareous tests go into solution at deeper levels. Geologically, Foraminiferida are represented from Silurian to Recent time, although they vary in abundance in different strata. The association of specific types with particular deposits has been applied to the determination of geological correlation, especially in drilling for oil. The most common type of modern deposit is *Globigerina*-ooze, formed from tests of pelagic Globigerinidae and Globorotaliidae at depths of 500-2500 fathoms.

Pseudopodia and their activities. Myxopodia are typical of Foraminiferida. These sticky pseudopodia form a meshwork when extended and show streaming of protoplasm, as indicated by the movement of granules which may reach a rate of 400-500µ per minute in *Iridia lucida* (81). As described in *Elphidium* (*Polystomella*) *crispum* (66), this circulation may be noted even in small branches of the network, granules moving up and down the pseudopodia and occasionally reversing directions. Granules flowing in opposite directions are often seen on opposite sides of a single pseudopodium. Length of the myxopodia may equal or may greatly exceed the diameter of the test. In some instances, an organism with a test measuring about 1.0 mm may form a myxopodial net covering an area 20-40 mm in diameter. Myxopodia may show considerable activity. In *Elphidium crispum* they are sometimes withdrawn at "lightning speed"; or they may be shot out "like little rockets" and then wave about in the water, "bending, undulating, quivering, and putting out side branches which meet and fuse and so establish the reticulum" (66). Myxopodia often appear to be covered with mucus which leaves a trail as the pseudopodia are retracted. The pseudopodia, in species with imperforate tests,

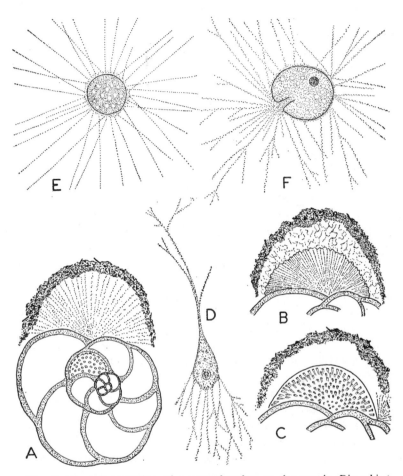

Fig. 5. 35. A-C. Addition of a new chamber to the test in *Discorbina bertheloti*, x45 (after Le Calvez): A. Pseudopodia have been retracted and an arenaceous cyst formed over the area of the future chamber; test shown schematically, pores indicated in one chamber. B. Pseudopodia have been retracted further and the form of the new chamber is evident. C. The first layer, a thin chitinous membrane, has been secreted; pores are formed. D-F. Changes in form of the pseudopodia during early development of *Iridia diaphana* (after Le Calvez): D. Creeping "embryo" as it emerges from the parental test, x100. E. Later pelagic stage with bristle-like pseudopodia, x150. F. At the beginning of fixation; typical pseudopodia are developing and the "bristles" of the pelagic stage are disappearing, x115. Compare with later stage of development (Fig. 5. 40, E) in which the myxopodia have increased in size.

arise mainly from an ectoplasmic stalk (raphe, peduncle) which extends through the aperture (Fig. 5. 43, G). In types with perforate tests, most of the pseudopodia may arise from the ectoplasm enclosing the test.

The pseudopodial pattern varies to some extent with environmental conditions, and in at least certain species (Fig. 5. 35, D-F), may undergo marked changes during development of the young organism. Although myxopodia are often characterized as pseudopodia showing a more fluid outer layer and a less fluid core, it is sometimes impossible to distinguish the two zones. However, even the more delicate myxopodia may show a certain degree of stiffness, in that they tend to follow a straight line and often extend unsupported for considerable distances through the water. The pseudopodia of certain species (Fig. 5. 44) sometimes assigned to the order apparently are filopodia.

The Foraminiferida are markedly holozoic. The pseudopodial net traps other Protozoa, algae (especially diatoms), and sometimes larval Crustacea and other small invertebrates. The captured food is promptly surrounded by cytoplasm. Food is usually drawn toward the test by a shortening of appropriate pseudopodia, and such particles may move at the rate of several millimeters an hour. Unless size is prohibitive, the prey may be drawn inside the test; diatoms, in particular, are often found in the endoplasm. However, the myxopodial net itself may have marked digestive abilities, although variation is noted from species to species. In general, the shorter myxopodia show greater digestive activity than the long delicate pseudopodia (82). Digestion often begins soon after the food is surrounded by cytoplasm and may be completed before the material reaches the test. In such types as *Elphidium crispum* this seems to be the normal method, to the exclusion of digestion within the endoplasm (66).

Other pseudopodial activities include the construction of tests and cyst walls. Such activities are especially noticeable in species which build arenaceous tests and cysts. In multilocular types, the addition of a new chamber to the test is often carried out within an arenaceous cyst wall laid down by the pseudopodia outside the area of the new chamber (Fig. 5. 35, A-C). Within the cyst, the pseudopodia form a reticulum outlining the cavity of the new chamber and the new wall is developed at the surface of the mass. If materials for a cover are excluded from cultures, formation of a new chamber proceeds without encystment in *Elphidium crispum* (66).

Many Foraminiferida are motile. Their characteristic creeping depends upon the contraction of distally attached pseudopodia, the body being dragged along the substratum as a result. Although creeping species may seem restless under laboratory conditions and can travel several millimeters in an hour, such locomotion is relatively slow in terms of size of the organism.

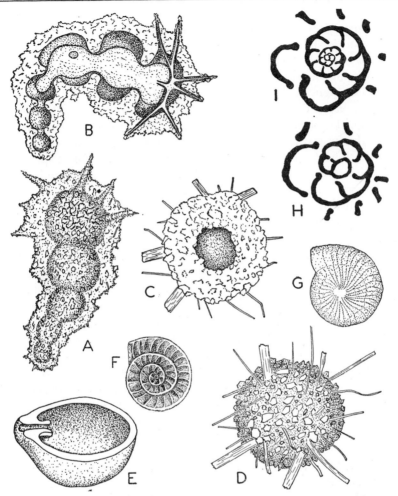

Fig. 5. 36. A, B. *Iridia serialis* Le Calvez, arenaceous test, upper and lower surfaces; x19 (after Le C.). **C, D.** *Webbinella crassa* Rhumbler, lower and upper surfaces of hemispherical test; pseudopodia are extended between base of test and substratum; x23 (after Le Calvez). **E.** *Allogromia laticollare* Arnold, half of approximately spherical test (diameter, 100-450μ), showing aperture (after A.). **F, G.** Test of *Camerina elegans*, dissection showing septa and foramina (F), external view showing sutures (G); x5 (after Jones). **H, I.** Central portions of test in *Planorbulina mediterranensis* d'Orbigny, megalospheric type (H) and microspheric type (I); x100 (after Le Calvez).

Colored granules or globules (xanthosomes)—brown, reddish, or yellow—are commonly seen in the myxopodia. Such inclusions often occur in the endoplasm, from which they apparently pass outside to be discarded in the trails left by retracted pseudopodia. The chemical nature of the xanthosomes is unknown, although they are often referred to as "excretory granules." It has been suggested that these inclusions are accumulated pigments derived from diatoms or other food.

Tests. On the basis of their construction, two varieties of tests may be recognized—tests composed entirely of secreted materials; and arenaceous tests consisting mainly of foreign materials held together by a secreted cement. Throughout the order there appears a primitive "chitinous" test which may become the definitive test of the adult, as in Allogromiidae (Fig. 5. 43, 44) and such types as *Iridia lucida* (81). It is uncertain whether this test is secreted by the myxopodia or is produced by actual transformation of an outer pseudopodial reticulum. In most species, the initial chitinous test is strengthened by the addition of inorganic salts or of foreign particles during development of the organism. In any case, the test is enclosed in a layer of cytoplasm continuous with the pseudopodia.

The basic structure of the arenaceous test is a thin "chitinous" layer. Onto this layer are cemented sand grains, sponge spicules, ambulacral plates of echinoderms, fragments of other tests, and the like (Fig. 5. 36, A-D). Such particles are picked up by the pseudopodia and pulled to the initial chitinous layer, where they are cemented into a wall. The more primitive species show no discrimination. Others tend to use a particular type of structural element, so that different species collected from the same area may show characteristic differences in construction of their tests. The nature of the cement varies with the species. In some of the primitive forms, the cement is chitinous, like the initial layer of the test. The most common is an orange to brownish material, supposedly containing iron and often known as "ferruginous" cement. A number of species produce a calcareous cement, and there are also a few in which the cement is siliceous. Arenaceous tests are found in about a third of the established families.

Calcareous tests, the predominant modern type, and the relatively rare siliceous tests differ from arenaceous tests in the absence of foreign particles. There are, however, interesting cases in which the first few chambers produced by the young organism are arenaceous while the later ones are strictly calcareous. Such ontogenetic evidence, and the existence of species forming graded series from typically arenaceous to completely calcareous tests, support the assumption (30) that the cement of primitive tests gradually became the predominant building material during evolution of the group.

Growth of the individual, in primitive types, may involve desertion of the old test and the construction of a new and larger one (30). The more specialized types merely add new chambers to the preceding ones as growth continues (Fig. 5. 35, A-C). In different species, the new chambers are added in characteristic series, and within reasonable limits, in relatively characteristic numbers to produce the test of the adult. The result is a wide variety of patterns (Fig. 5. 37).

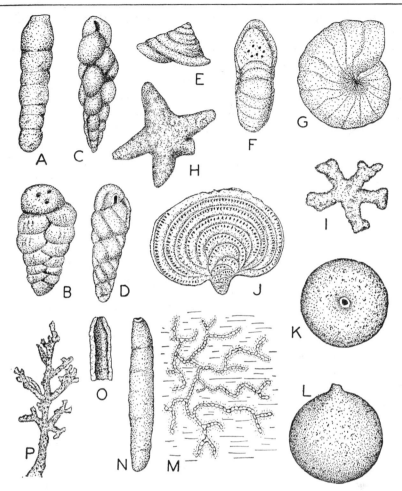

Fig. 5. 37. Various forms of tests: A. Rectilinear, uniserial, *Hyperam-minoides elegans* (Pennsylvanian deposits), x27 (after Cushman and Waters). B. Rectilinear, biserial, *Cribostomum bradyi* (Carboniferous), x19 (after Möller). C. Rectilinear, triserial, *Verneuilina schizea* (Lower Cretaceous), x38 (after Cushman and Alexander). D. Spiral, elongate, *Turrulina andreaei* (Oligocene), x49 (after Andreae). E. Spiral, conical, *Turrispirillina conoidea* (Jurassic), after Paalzow. F, G. Spiral, planispiral, *Cyclammina cancellata,* apertural and lateral views, x8 (after Brady). H, I. Stellate, *Pseudastrorhiza silurica* (Silurian), x45 (after Eisenack); *Astrorhiza arenaria,* x2.1 (after Le Calvez). J. Flabelliform (fan-shaped), *Pavonina flabelliformis,* x32 (after Parr). K, L. Spherical, *Saccammina fragilis,* apertural and lateral views, x27 (after Le Calvez). M. Unusual branching type, *Rhizonubecula adherens,* x3.5 (after Le Calvez). N, O. Simple tubular type, *Bathysiphon humilis,* surface view and section through apertural end, x23 (after Le Calvez). P. Arborescent, *Dendrophrya erecta,* x12 (after Brady).

The usual multilocular test opens to the outside through the *aperture* in the last chamber. This opening, which may be single or multiple (Fig. 5. 38), commonly lies at the base of the chamber wall but tends to become terminal in linear tests, shifting to the wall of the last chamber. The position, size, and shape of the aperture, and the number of openings are features of taxonomic importance. In addition to the aperture, the walls of perforate tests contain many small pores. In imperforate tests with a single aperture (Figs. 5. 42, 43), the ectoplasm extends to the outside as a condensed oral plug (buccal ectoplasm, peduncle, raphe).

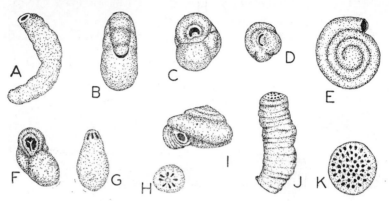

Fig. 5. 38. Various types of apertures: A. Simple terminal, *Psammonyx vulcanicus,* megalospheric type (after Rhumbler). B. Aperture at base of wall in last chamber, *Endothyra media* (Pennsylvanian), x32 (after Cushman and Waters). C. Terminal, with tooth, *Milliamina lata,* x28 (after Heron-Allen and Earland). D. Aperture with broad tooth, *Biloculinella globula,* x32 (after Cushman). E. Simple terminal, at end of coiled tube, *Cornuspira planorbis,* x52 (after Schultze). F. Aperture with bifid tooth, *Dentostomina bermudiana,* x16 (after Cushman). G, H. Multiple, radiate, *Nevillina coronata,* lateral and apertural views, x15 (after Sidebottom). I. Simple terminal, in coiled test, *Fischerina helix,* x52 (after Heron-Allen and Earland). J, K. Multiple, cribate, in wall of last chamber, *Polyphragma cribosum* (Cretaceous) (after Reuss).

In perforate tests the ectoplasm emerges through the many pores as well as through the aperture.

The initial chamber is known as the *proloculum*. In many multilocular (polythalamous) species, there are two varieties of tests differing in relative size of the proloculum (Fig. 5. 36, H, I). As discussed below, the *microspheric* type (with the smaller proloculum) is produced by an organism developing from a zygote. The *megalospheric* type (with the proportionately larger proloculum) is produced by individuals resulting from schizogony. As successive chambers are added, their limits are marked externally by sutures, and internally by septa (Fig. 5. 36, F, G). The sutures usually appear as grooves, but may be raised or else flush with the surface in some species. As each new chamber is formed, the anterior wall of the preceding chamber becomes a septum in the simpler cases and the old aperture now becomes a *foramen* joining the two chambers. These foramina were responsible for the name assigned to the group when the Foraminiferida were still considered Mollusca. The foramina in such multilocular species as *Planorbulina mediterranensis* (82) and *Elphidium crispum* (66) are gradually closed by "chitinous" deposits which first appear as rings and then spread across the openings to form "plugs." Periodically, the plugs break loose and are carried out of the test by cytoplasmic currents. The functional significance of such plugs is unknown. The septa are double in many specialized Foraminiferida, a posterior wall of each new chamber being deposited over the anterior wall of the preceding chamber. The structure may be further complicated by a canalicular system composed of tubules running through the wall of the test and within the double septa. The canals communicate with the chambers and also open to the outside, independently of the usual pores.

The endoplasm. The endoplasm contains the nucleus, or the multiple nuclei of mature agamonts, and various types of inclusions, including xanthosomes in many species. In some of the multilocular types, freshly ingested prey and undigested residues tend to be concentrated in the last or the last few chambers. In others, which complete digestion outside the test, the inner cytoplasm may be entirely free from such materials (66).

Life-cycles. A dimorphic life-cycle involving an alternation of generations was attributed to Foraminiferida in the early work of Lister and Schaudinn. Two adult forms were recognized, a *megalospheric* type (gamont) and a *microspheric* type (agamont), on the basis of a difference in size of the proloculum. Reproduction of the microspheric adult, by schizogony, results in uninucleate organisms which develop a proloculum larger than that of the parent. At maturity, each megalospheric organism produces gametes. After syngamy each zygote secretes a small proloculum and growth results in a microspheric adult.

Recent investigations have indicated that this concept is strictly applicable only to certain specialized Foraminiferida which produce flagellate gametes (82). In other cases, the two forms cannot be distinguished by size of the initial chamber, and occasionally the significance of microspheric and megalospheric forms in the life-cycle may appear to be reversed if only the absolute measurements of the initial chambers are considered. In some of these apparent contradictions, however, the microspheric chamber actually is smaller, *in proportion* to size of the test, than the megalospheric chamber. Life-cycles are now known to vary considerably in their details (Fig. 5. 39). Complications include the appearance, in certain species, of two varieties of agamonts, one with a larger proloculum than the other. In the terminology of Le Calvez (82), *apogamic* life-cycles, as observed in *Discorbis orbicularis,* involve only the sequence of stages 7-5-6-7 . . . (Fig. 5. 39). *Dimorphic* cycles, represented by *Patellina corrugata* (97), follow the sequence, 1-2-3-4-5-6-1. . . . *Holotrimorphic* cycles, represented by *Rotalia beccari* (51), involve both "microspheric" and "megalospheric" agamonts as well as a gamont and shows the sequence, 1-2-3-4-5-6-7-5-6-1 . . . *Paratrimorphic* cycles, as noted in *Planorbulina mediterranensis* (82), are complicated erratic modifications which may produce such sequences as 1-2-3-4-5-6-1 . . . 6-7-5-6-7. . . . In the typical cycle the microspheric agamont is multinucleate; the megalospheric gamont, uninucleate. However, both agamonts and gamonts of various primitive species remain uninucleate until the beginning of schizogony or gametogenesis (82), and the agamont of *Spirillina vivipara* contains only a few nuclei until time for schizogony (98). In the tri-

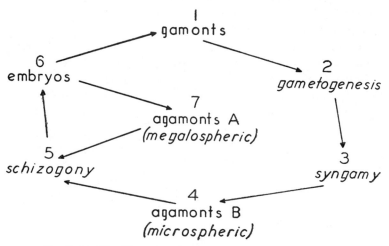

Fig. 5. 39. The life-cycles of Foraminiferida (after Le Calvez).

morphic cycles, both the "microspheric" and the "megalospheric" agamonts are multinucleate.

Reproduction of the agamont. Reproduction is typically a schizogonic process. Reproduction may occur within the parental test, as in *Iridia serialis* (Fig. 5. 40, D); or the multinucleate agamont may leave the test just before schizogony, as in *Spirillina vivipara* (Fig. 5. 40, A). The young stages of multilocular species, when set free, usually have 1-5 chambers formed by the "embryonic" ectoplasm at the expense of the parental cytoplasm. Reproduction may be simpler in some of the primitive species. *Microgromia elegantula,* for instance, undergoes fission and one of the resulting organisms leaves the parental test as an amoeboid stage which develops a new test after a few days (146). However, *Allogromia laticollare* undergoes schizogony to produce as many as forty young within the parental test (3).

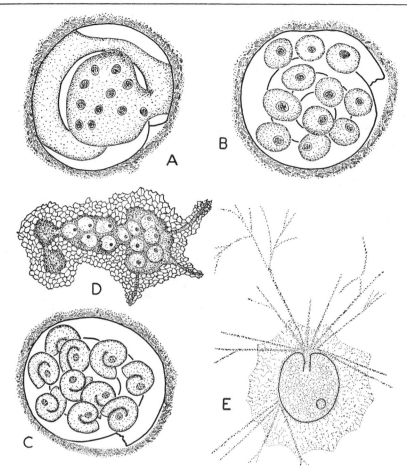

Fig. 5. 40. A-C. *Spirillina vivipara* (Ehrbg.), in reproductive test, x330 (after Myers): A. Multinucleate agamont leaving test in preparation for schizogony. B. Young organisms shortly after schizogony. C. Young gamonts with tests. D. Young organisms, products of schizogony, in parental test of *Iridia serialis,* x15 (after Le Calvez). E. Stage in development of *Iridia diaphana;* halo of tangled pseudopodia is about to produce the definitive chitinous test; compare with earlier stages in Fig. 5. 35, D-F; x115 (after Le Calvez).

Reproduction may be preceded by formation of a reproductive cyst, composed of foreign particles as well as solids expelled by the organism in preparation for reproduction. Reproductive cysts (Fig. 5. 40, A-C) are characteristic of *Patellina corrugata* (96) and *Spirillina vivipara* (82, 98), for example.

Gametogenesis and syngamy. The details of gametogenesis (gamogony) vary in different species. In some cases, represented by *Patellina corrugata* (96, 97) and *Spirillina vivipara,* two gamonts become associated in a process resembling syzygy in gregarines. In *S. vivipara*, each pair produces a common "fertilization-cyst" with an arenaceous wall (Fig. 5. 41, A-E). Nuclear division occurs in each gamont and the multinucleate gamonts then leave their tests and produce uninucleate gametocytes. Gametes are formed by division of the gametocytes, nuclear division being meiotic.

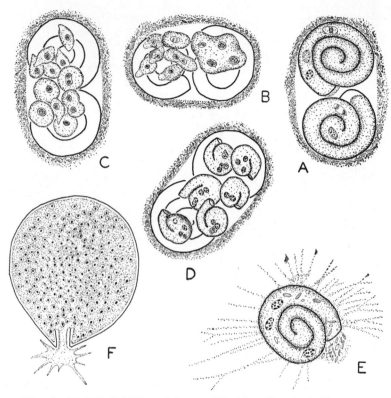

Fig. 5. 41. A-E. *Spirillina vivipara*, x330 (after Myers): A. Two gamonts in syzygy within a fertilization cyst, nuclei dividing. B. Production of amoeboid gametes. C. Gametes and zygotes in fertilization cyst. D. Zygotes have developed into agamonts with several nuclei; still within fertilization cyst. E. Immature agamont with three nuclei. F. Gamont of *Iridia lucida* prior to formation of gametocytes; schematic (after Le Calvez).

In these species, the gametes are amoeboid, are produced in small numbers, and are rather large—gametes of *S. vivipara* measure 50-60μ. The gamont of *Allogromia laticollare*, in contrast to *S. vivipara*, may produce as many as 400 small (4-6μ) amoeboid gametes. Self-fertilization has been reported, and the zygotes develop into multinucleate organisms before leaving the old test (3).

The production of flagellate gametes, usually biflagellate but sometimes uniflagellate (Fig. 5. 42), seems to be more common in Foraminiferida. Gametogenesis in *Iridia lucida* (82) is representative. Final stages in the process include a series of rapid nuclear divisions, resulting in many small nuclei (Fig. 5. 41, F), and then segmentation of the cytoplasm to produce uninucleate gametocytes (Fig. 5. 42). Each gametocyte develops

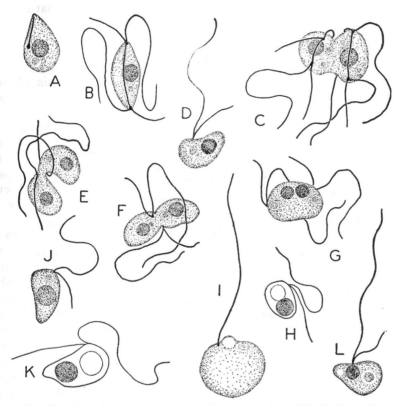

Fig. 5. 42. A-G. Gametogenesis and syngamy in *Iridia lucida*, x4000 (after Le Calvez): A. Gametocyte. B. Uninucleate gametocyte with para-desmose and two pairs of flagella. C. Stage with two nuclei, just before fission. D. Biflagellate gamete. E-G. Successive stages in syngamy. H. Gamete of *Iridia diaphana*, x4845 (after Le Calvez). I. Gamete of *Gromia oviformis*, x3400 (after Le Calvez). J. Gamete of *Planorbulina mediterranensis*, x4000 (after Le Calvez). K. Gamete of *Iridia serialis*, x4845 (after Le Calvez). L. Gamete of *Webbinella crassa*, x2400 (after Le Calvez).

a pair of flagella and then undergoes flagellar duplication and nuclear division. The paradesmose which appears in nuclear division is similar to that of many Mastigophora. Cytoplasmic division results in active flagellate gametes. The emergence of the mature gametes, which may number many millions, has been compared to a cloud of smoke rolling out of the test.

Flagellate gametes of Foraminiferida show such features as a densely staining nucleus and a large refractile body, or perhaps a few smaller inclusions, possibly representing stored food. It is interesting that similar gametes (Fig. 5. 10) have been reported for Radiolarida. The foraminiferan gamete usually has two flagella, but sometimes only one (*Gromia oviformis*), or rarely three (*Discorbis patelliformis*). In contrast to the more common type, amoeboid gametes are produced in *Patellina corrugata* and *Spirillina vivipara* (97, 98), and also in *Allogromia laticollare* (3).

The number of gametes produced by a gamont varies widely—millions in *Iridia lucida,* which does not undergo syzygy (82); only 250-300 flagellate gametes in the syzygous *Discorbis patelliformis* (99).

Syngamy is rapid in *Iridia lucida* (82). Two gametes make contact at their flagellar ends and fusion soon follows (Fig. 5. 42, E-G). From the general appearance of the gametes, syngamy in *I. lucida* appears to be isogamous, but there is no evidence for self-fertilization. In *Allogromia laticollare,* on the other hand, syngamy does involve fusion of gametes produced within a single test (3), and thus resembles pedogamy in Heliozoida (Chapter II).

Duration of the life cycle. Length of the cycle varies from species to species—three weeks or less in *Spirillina vivipara* (98), and about six weeks in *Patellina corrugata* (97), at laboratory temperatures; about a year in various dimorphic species of Mediterranean waters (82); probably about two years for a complete dimorphic cycle in *Elphidium crispum* (66). For the large species of deeper waters, no accurate data are available. In the Mediterranean and North Seas, where there are well differentiated summer and winter temperatures, correlation with seasons of the year is evident in some species. Agamonts are dominant in winter and early spring, while gamonts tend to replace the agamonts in early autumn. In regions with mild winters, seasonal correlation becomes almost insignificant and perhaps disappears completely in tropical seas (82).

The relatively slow pace of the cycles in large species is related to the amount of growth the young gamont or agamont must undergo before it reaches maturity. The gamont of *Elphidium crispum,* for example, develops a test with about 45-50, or occasionally more, chambers. In early development, at 55-60° F., the sixth chamber is completed after about 11 days; the fifteenth chamber, in about one month; the usual 40 or so, after almost four months (66). As compared with growth, schizogony and gamogony are comparatively rapid. Schizogony in *Iridia diaphana,* for instance, covers a period of about three days (82).

Taxonomy. Classification of the Foraminiferida is based upon form and composition of the test. The available information on other morphological features, especially in the living organisms, is not yet extensive

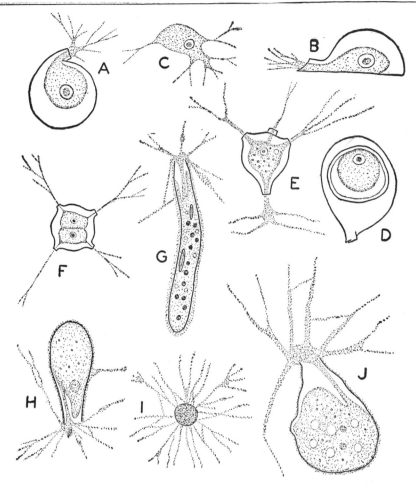

Fig. 5. 43. Allogromiidae: A-D. *Microgromia elegantula* Penard, upper and lateral views (A, B), organism outside test (C), and cyst (D); x920 approx. (after Valkanov). E. *Micrometes paludosa* Cienkowski, test 16-17μ long (after Penard). F. Completion of fission within test of *M. paludosa* (after Valkanov). G. *Rhynchogromia* (*Gromia*) *linearis* (Penard), a number of nuclei, ingested diatoms (after P.). H, I. *Diplogromia* (*Gromia*) *brunneri* (Blanc), test 60-250μ long, uninucleate organism, polar view showing pseudopodia (after Penard). J. *Lieberkühnia wagneri* Claparède and Lachmann, specimen with test 96μ long (after Penard).

enough to play a significant part in taxonomy. On the basis of structural features of the test, 50 families have now been recognized.[3]

The possession of arenaceous tests more or less completely separates a number of these families from others with a calcareous test. The absence

[3] For a detailed consideration of taxonomy, Cushman's (30) monograph may be consulted.

of perforations distinguishes a few families with calcareous tests from the majority which have perforate tests. Families with arenaceous tests are differentiated by the number of chambers—one, two, or many—and by the patterns in which the chambers are arranged in the multilocular types. The form of the test (Fig. 5. 37) and the type of aperture (Fig. 5.

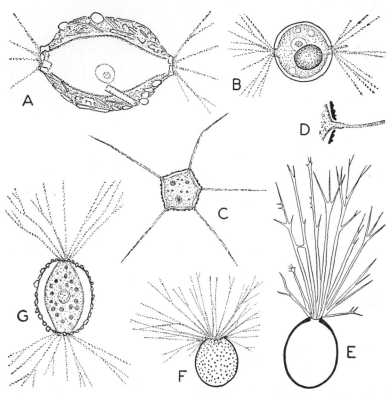

Fig. 5. 44. Allogromiidae: A. *Amphitrema wrightianum* Archer, schematic, x375 (after Cash). B. *Diplophrys archeri* Barker (diameter of test, 8-20μ), schematic optical section showing nucleus and large refractile inclusion; test thin, hyaline (after Penard). C, D. *Artodiscus saltans* Penard (body, 18-23μ); entire organism showing pseudopodia unlike those of typical Foraminiferida (C); single pseudopodium emerging through test (D); schematic (after P.). E. *Allogromia* (*Gromia*) *dujardini* Schulze, x29 (after S.) F. *Lecythium granulatum* (Schulze) Hopkinson, x360 (after S.). G. *Amphitrema stenostoma* Nüsslin, schematic optical section (after Penard).

38) also are bases for differentiating genera and species. In the most primitive family, the Allogromiidae, a chitinous test is characteristic of the adult organism.

Family Allogromiidae. The test is completely or mostly chitinous, usually with a single aperture, sometimes with an opening at each end. The wall may be a single chitinous layer, thin in some forms and relatively thick in others; or, foreign particles may be added to the outer surface. In *Diplogromia,* the wall of the test is double, the outer layer being arenaceous. The majority of species have been reported from fresh and brackish waters.

It is unfortunate that so little is known about these organisms since they appear to be favorable material for investigating basic characteristics of the Foraminiferida. Some of the Allogromiidae, at least, can be maintained in the laboratory and extensive investigation of their life-cycles should prove interesting. Reproduction by schizogony, much as in the more specialized marine types, and the production of amoeboid gametes have been observed in *Allogromia* under laboratory conditions (3). Perhaps further studies of this nature will answer various unsettled questions concerning the generic composition of the family.

The following genera have been referred to the Allogromiidae: *Allogromia* (3, 65, 124; Figs. 5. 36, E, 5. 44, E), test chitinous, ovoid to spherical; *Amphitrema* Archer (55, 107; Fig. 5. 44, A, G), foreign particles adherent to the chitinous test, one opening at each end; *Artodiscus* Penard (107; Fig. 5. 44, C, D), affinities with the Allogromiidae uncertain; *Boderia* Wright (124), peculiar marine types strikingly similar to a migratory stage which occurs in early development of certain less primitive marine species (Fig. 5. 35, D); *Diaphorodon* Archer (107; Fig. 5. 33, C), with filopodia, sometimes assigned to the Allogromiidae instead of the Testacida (Difflugiidae); *Dactylosaccus* Rhumbler (123, 124), thin chitinous test tubular and twisted; *Diplogromia* Rhumbler (124; Fig. 5. 43, H, I), double-walled test, outer layer of fine siliceous granules; *Diplophrys* Barker (107; Fig. 5. 44, B), spheroid chitinous test, opening at each end; *Lecythium* Hertwig and Lesser (Fig. 5. 44, F), filopodia, flexible chitinous test; *L. hyalinum* H. and L. referred to genus *Pamphagus* by Penard (107); *Lieberkühnia* Claparède and Lachmann (107, 110, 124; Fig. 5. 43, J), chitinous test, ectoplasmic stalk (peduncle) arises from the side of the body; *Microgromia* Hertwig and Lesser (146; Fig. 5. 43, A-D), small, chitinous test; *Micrometes* Cienkowski (107, 147; Fig. 5. 43, E, F), delicate chitinous test with several apertures; *Myxotheca* Schaudinn (38, 124), marine, test thin, approximately spherical, usually with adherent foreign particles; *Plagiophrys* Claparède and Lachmann (107; Fig. 5. 31, J, K), sometimes assigned to the Allogromiidae instead of the Testacida; *Rhynchogromia* Rhumbler (123; Fig. 5. 43, G), elongated chitinous test, terminal aperture; *Rhynchosaccus* Rhumbler (79, 123), thin tubular chitinous test, opening at each end; *Schultzella* Rhumbler (124), delicate spheroidal chitinous test, more than open aperture with variable positions.

LITERATURE CITED

1. Alexeieff, S. 1907. *Arch. f. Protistenk.* **8:** 95.
2. ———— 1912. *Bull. Soc. Zool. France* **37:** 55.
3. Arnold, Z. M. 1948. *Trans. Amer. Micr. Soc.* **67:** 231.
4. Bělař, K. v. 1921. *Arch. f. Protistenk.* **43:** 287.
5. ———— 1922. *Arch. f. Protistenk.* **46:** 1.
6. ———— 1924. *Arch. f. Protistenk.* **48:** 371.
7. Bisby, G. R. 1914. *Amer. J. Bot.* **1:** 274.
8. Bles, E. J. 1929. *Quart. J. Micr. Sci.* **72:** 527.
9. Blochmann, F. 1894. *Biol. Centralbl.* **14:** 197.
10. Bloomfield, J. E. and E. T. Schwartz 1910. *Ann. Bot.* **24:** 35.
11. Bonner, J. T. 1944. *Amer. J. Bot.* **31:** 175.
12. ———— and D. Eldredge, Jr. 1945. *Growth* **9:** 287.
13. Borgert, A. 1909. *Arch. f. Protistenk.* **14:** 134.
14. Brandt, K. 1902. *Arch. f. Protistenk.* **1:** 59.

15. ——— 1905. *Arch. f. Protistenk.* **6**: 245.
16. ——— 1905. *Zool. Jahrb.* (Suppl.) **8**: 311.
17. Brandza, M. 1928. *Le Botaniste* **20**: 117.
18. Calkins, G. N. 1913. *Trans. 15th Intern. Congr. Hydr. Demog.*, p. 1.
19. Camp, W. G. 1936. *Bull. Torrey Bot. Club* **53**: 205.
20. Cavallini, F. 1926. *J. Exp. Zool.* **43**: 225.
21. ——— 1926. *J. Exp. Zool.* **43**: 245.
22. Chatton, E. 1923. *C. R. Ac. Sci.* **177**: 1246.
23. ——— 1934. *C. R. Ac. Sci.* **198**: 309.
24. ——— and P. Lalung-Bonnaire 1912. *Bull. Soc. Path. Éxot.* **5**: 135.
25. Cohen, A. L. 1939. *Botan. Gaz.* **101**: 243.
26. Cook, W. R. I. 1926. *Trans. Brit. Mycol. Soc.* **11**: 196.
27. ——— 1933. *Arch. f. Protistenk.* **80**: 179.
28. ——— and B. Cleal 1943. *Ann. Bot.* (N.S.) **7**: 347.
29. ——— and E. J. Schwartz 1930. *Philos. Trans. Roy. Soc. London, B,* **218**: 283.
30. Cushman, J. A. 1948. *Foraminifera, Their Classification and Economic Use* (Cambridge: Harvard Univ. Press).
31. Deflandre, G. 1928. *Arch. f. Protistenk.* **64**: 152.
32. ——— 1929. *Arch. f. Protistenk.* **67**: 322.
33. Dobell, C. 1913. *Arch. f. Protistenk.* **31**: 317.
34. ——— 1917. *Quart. J. Micr. Sci.* **62**: 515.
35. Duboscq, O. 1921. *C. R. Soc. Biol.* **84**: 30.
36. Dunkerly, J. S. 1923. *Trans. Roy. Soc. Edinb.* **53**: 297.
37. Elliott, J. A. 1916. *Delaware Agr. Exp. St. Bull.* **114**: 1.
38. Föyn, B. 1936. *Arch. f. Protistenk.* **87**: 272.
39. Geiman, Q. M. and H. L. Ratcliffe 1936. *Parasitol.* **28**: 208.
40. Gilbert, F. A. 1928. *Amer. J. Bot.* **15**: 345.
41. Gilbert, H. C. 1935. *Amer. J. Bot.* **22**: 52.
42. Goette, A. 1916. *Arch. f. Protistenk.* **37**: 93.
43. Goodey, T. 1915. *Arch. f. Protistenk.* **35**: 80.
44. Gray, W. D. 1938. *Amer. J. Bot.* **25**: 511.
45. Griessmann, K. 1914. *Arch. f. Protistenk.* **32**: 1.
46. Hagelstein, R. 1944. *The Mycetozoa of North America* (Mineola, N. Y.: Author).
47. Hall, R. P. and J. B. Loefer 1930. *Arch. f. Protistenk.* **72**: 365.
48. Harper, R. A. 1900. *Botan. Gaz.* **30**: 217.
49. Henderson, J. C. 1941. *Univ. Calif. Publ. Zool.* **43**: 357.
50. Hewitt, R. 1937. *J. Parasit.* **23**: 491.
51. Hofker, J. 1930. *Ztschr. Zellforsch. Mikr. Anat.* **23**: 514.
52. Hollande, A. 1942. *Arch. Zool. Exp. Gén.* **82**: (N. & R.): 119.
53. ——— 1942. *Arch. Zool. Exp. Gén.* **83**: 1.
54. Hoogenraad, H. R. 1927. *Arch. f. Protistenk.* **58**: 321.
55. ——— 1935. *Arch. f. Protistenk.* **84**: 1.
56. ——— 1936. *Arch. f. Protistenk.* **87**: 417.
57. Horne, A. S. 1930. *Ann. Bot.* **44**: 199.
58. Hovasse, R. 1923. *Bull. Soc. Zool. France* **48**: 247.
59. Howard, F. L. 1931. *Amer. J. Bot.* **18**: 116.
60. ——— 1931. *Amer. J. Bot.* **18**: 624.
61. Hsiung, T. S. 1927. *Trans. Amer. Micr. Soc.* **46**: 208.
62. Huth, W. 1913. *Arch. f. Protistenk.* **30**: 1.
63. Ivanič, M. 1934. *La Cellule* **43**: 149.
64. ——— 1936. *Arch. f. Protistenk.* **86**: 471.
65. Jepps, M. 1926. *Quart. J. Micr. Sci.* **70**: 701.
66. ——— 1942. *J. Mar. Biol. Assoc.* **25**: 607.
67. Johnson, L. P. 1930. *Arch. f. Protistenk.* **71**: 463.
68. Jung, W. 1942. *Arch. f. Protistenk.* **95**: 253.
69. Kambly, P. E. 1939. *Amer. J. Bot.* **26**: 386.
70. Karling, J. S. 1942. *Plasmodiophorales* (New York).
71. King, R. L. and T. L. Jahn 1948. *Science* **107**: 293.
72. Kirby, H. 1945. *J. Parasit.* **31**: 177.

73. Klebs, G. 1892. *Ztschr. f. wiss. Zool.* **55**: 265.
74. Kränzlin, H. 1907. *Arch. f. Protistenk.* **9**: 170.
75. Kudo, R. 1946. *J. Morph.* **78**: 317.
76. ——— 1949. *J. Morph.* **85**: 163.
77. Kunkel, L. O. 1915. *J. Agr. Res.* **4**: 265.
78. Lackey, J. B. 1936. *Biol. Bull.* **71**: 492.
79. Le Calvez, J. 1935. *Arch. Zool. Exp. Gén.* **77** (N. et R.): 79.
80. ——— 1935. *Arch. Zool. Exp. Gén.* **77** (N. et R.): 99.
81. ——— 1936. *Arch. Zool. Exp. Gén.* **78**: 115.
82. ——— 1938. *Arch. Zool. Exp. Gén.* **80**: 163.
83. Leidy, J. 1879. "Fresh-water Rhizopods of North America." *U. S. Geol. Surv.* **12**.
84. Lister, A. and G. Lister 1925. *A Monograph of the Mycetozoa* (London: Wheldon and Wesley).
85. Lloyd, F. E. 1926. *Science* **63**: 364.
86. MacBride, T. H. and G. W. Martin 1934. *The Myxomycetes* (New York: Macmillan).
87. MacKinlay, R. B. 1936. *J. Roy. Micr. Soc.*, Ser. III, **56**: 307.
88. McLennan, E. I. 1930. *Austral. J. Exp. Biol. Med. Sci.* **8**: 9.
89. Martin, G. W. 1940. *Botan. Rev.* **6**: 356.
90. Meglitsch, P. A. 1940. *Ill. Biol. Monogr.* **17**: 1.
91. Milovidov, P. F. 1931. *Arch. f. Protistenk.* **73**: 1.
92. Moore, A. R. 1935. *J. Cell. Comp. Physiol.* **7**: 113.
93. Moroff, T. 1904. *Arch. f. Protistenk.* **3**: 69.
94. ——— and G. Stiasny 1909. *Arch. f. Protistenk.* **16**: 209.
95. Morris, S. 1936. *J. Morph.* **59**: 225.
96. Myers, E. H. 1934. *Science* **79**: 436.
97. ——— 1935. *Bull. Scripps Inst. Oceanogr.*, Tech. Ser. **3**: 355.
98. ——— 1936. *J. Roy. Micr. Soc.* **56**: 120.
99. ——— 1940. *J. Mar. Biol. Assoc.* **24**: 201.
100. Nauss, R. N. 1943. *Bull. Torrey Bot. Club* **70**: 152.
101. Okada, Y. K. 1930. *Arch. f. Protistenk.* **70**: 131.
102. Olive, E. W. 1902. *Proc. Bost. Soc. Nat. Hist.* **30**: 451.
103. Olivier, L. 1937. *Arch. Zool. Exp. Gén.* **78** (N. & R.): 169.
104. Osborn, T. G. B. 1911. *Ann. Bot.* **25**: 327.
105. Palm, B. T. and M. Burk 1933. *Arch. f. Protistenk.* **79**: 263.
106. Pateff, P. 1926. *Arch. f. Protistenk.* **55**: 516.
107. Penard, E. 1902. *Faune rhizopodique du bassin du Léman* (Genève: **Kündig**).
108. ——— 1904. *Les héliozoaires d'eau douce* (Genève: Kündig).
109. ——— 1907. *Arch. f. Protistenk.* **8**: 66.
110. ——— 1907. *Arch. f. Protistenk.* **8**: 225.
111. Pietschmann, K. 1929. *Arch. f. Protistenk.* **65**: 379.
112. Poisson, R. and G. Mangenot 1933. *C. R. Soc. Biol.* **113**: 1149.
113. Rafalko, J. S. 1947. *J. Morph.* **81**: 1.
114. Raper, K. B. 1935. *J. Agr. Res.* **50**: 135.
115. ——— 1937. *J. Agr. Res.* **55**: 289.
116. ——— 1940. *J. Elisha Mitchell Sci. Soc.* **56**: 241.
117. ——— 1940. *Amer. J. Bot.* **27**: 436.
118. ——— and C. Thom 1941. *Amer. J. Bot.* **28**: 69.
119. Ratcliffe, H. L. and Q. M. Geiman 1938. *Arch. Pathol.* **25**: 160.
120. Renn, C. E. 1936. *Biol. Bull.* **70**: 148.
121. Reynolds, B. D. and J. B. Looper 1928. *J. Parasit.* **15**: 23.
122. ——— and W. L. Threlkeld 1929. *Arch. f. Protistenk.* **68**: 305.
123. Rhumbler, L. 1894. *Ztschr. wiss. Zool.* **57**: 587.
124. ——— 1903. *Arch. f. Protistenk.* **3**: 181.
125. Rietschel, P. 1935. *Arch. f. Protistenk.* **86**: 349.
126. Roskin, G. 1925. *Arch. f. Protistenk.* **52**: 207.
127. ——— 1927. *Arch. f. Protistenk.* **59**: 350.
128. ——— 1929. *Arch. f. Protistenk.* **66**: 201.
129. Saedeleer, H. de 1930. *Ann. Protistol.* **3**: 1.
130. ——— 1933. *Arch. Zool. Exp. Gén.* **74**: 597.

131. Schaeffer, A. A. 1916. *Arch. f. Protistenk.* **37**: 204.
132. ——— 1926. *Taxonomy of the Amebas.* Carneg. Inst. Washington, Publ. No. 345.
133. Schaudinn, F. 1894. *Monatsber. Akad. Berlin* **10**: 621.
134. Scherffel, A. 1925. *Arch. f. Protistenk.* **52**: 1.
135. Schussnig, B. 1929. *Arch. f. Protistenk.* **68**: 555.
136. Seifriz, W. and M. Zetzman 1935. *Protoplasma* **23**: 175.
137. Singh, B. N. 1947. *J. Gen. Microbiol.* **1**: 361.
138. ——— 1948. *J. Gen. Microbiol.* **2**: 89.
139. Stern, C. 1924. *Arch. f. Protistenk.* **48**: 436.
140. Stiasny, G. 1910. *Arch. f. Protistenk.* **19**: 144.
141. Stokes, A. C. 1888. *J. Trenton Nat. Hist. Soc.* **1**: 71.
142. Swarczewsky, B. 1908. *Arch. f. Protistenk.* **12**: 173.
143. Valkanov, A. 1928. *Arch. f. Protistenk.* **63**: 419.
144. ——— 1928. *Arch. f. Protistenk.* **64**: 446.
145. ——— 1929. *Arch. f. Protistenk.* **67**: 110.
146. ——— 1930. *Arch. f. Protistenk.* **71**: 241.
147. ——— 1931. *Arch. f. Protistenk.* **73**: 367.
148. ——— 1940. *Arch. f. Protistenk.* **93**: 225.
149. Villeneuve, F. 1937. *Arch. Zool. Exp. Gén.* **78** (N. & R.): 243.
150. Volkonsky, M. 1931. *Arch. Zool. Exp. Gén.* **72**: 317.
151. Volz, P. 1929. *Arch. f. Protistenk.* **68**: 349.
152. Vonwiller, P. 1918. *Arch. f. Protistenk.* **38**: 279.
153. ——— 1919. *Arch. f. Protistenk.* **40**: 1.
154. Wailes, G. H. 1925. *Ann. Mag. Nat. Hist.*, Ser. 9, 16.
155. Webb, P. C. R. 1935. *Ann. Bot.* **49**: 41.
156. Wenyon, C. M. 1926. *Protozoology* (London: Ballière, Tindall & Cox).
157. Wernham, C. C. 1935. *Mycol.* **27**: 262.
158. Wetzel, A. 1925. *Arch. f. Protistenk.* **53**: 135.
159. Whitmore, E. R. 1911. *Arch. f. Protistenk.* **23**: 81.
160. Wilber, C. G. 1926. *Trans. Amer. Micr. Soc.* **65**: 318.
161. Wilson, C. W. 1916. *Univ. Calif. Publ. Zool.* **16**: 241.
162. Young, E. L. 1943. *Amer. J. Bot.* **30**: 586.
163. Zuelzer, M. 1909. *Arch. f. Protistenk.* **17**: 135.

VI

Sporozoa

ALL KNOWN SPOROZOA are parasitic. The usual infective stage is a sporozoite (Telosporidea), or an analogous sporoplasm (Cnidosporidea) which may be ingested by a new host or inoculated by some vector. Except in species transferred by inoculation, sporozoites are typically enclosed within a spore membrane, the origin of which varies in different groups. Sporozoa are not ciliated, and flagella are limited to the microgametes of certain species. Nutrition is predominantly saprozoic, although trophozoites of *Nosema mutabilis* apparently can ingest solid particles (76).

The group as usually defined shows a lack of homogeneity which led Wenyon (139) to restrict his Class Sporozoa to the Gregarinidia, Coccidia, and Haemosporidia—the Telosporidea as listed below—and to recognize the Cnidosporidea as a group of equal taxonomic rank. This arrangement expresses clearly the general belief that Sporozoa are not monophyletic in origin. However, the more common usage will be followed here, dividing the group into three classes, Telosporidea, Cnidosporidea, and Acnidosporidea.

CLASS 1. TELOSPORIDEA

The life-cycle typically shows asexual and sexual phases, both of which, except in the Eugregarinida, are characterized by reproduction. Reproduction in the sexual phase produces sporozoites, either directly from the zygote or from intermediate sporoblasts arising by division of the zygote. In such forms as malarial parasites sporozoites are clearly the result of schizogony (or *sporogony*, in this phase), but the appropriateness of this term is less obvious in certain Telosporidea which produce two sporozoites from each sporoblast. Sporozoites may be naked, or they may be produced within a spore membrane. The membrane, which often consists of more than one layer, may be secreted by the zygote, as in typical gregarines; or an encysted zygote may divide into two or more sporoblasts, each of which secretes a spore membrane. In the first case, the spore develops from an oocyst (encysted zygote); in the latter, from sporocysts (encysted sporoblasts). With a few possible exceptions, the membrane apparently is not divided into valves. Furthermore, there are no polar capsules in spores of the Telosporidea.

The asexual phase of the cycle is initiated by a sporozoite upon reaching a host. Growth of the sporozoite into a mature trophozoite (schizont) is followed by schizogony (or *merogony*, in this phase), except in the Eugregarinida. The trophozoite remains uninucleate throughout much of the growth period so that a plasmodium is usually developed shortly before merogony. Many Telosporidea are intracellular during this asexual phase. However, some of the gregarines are intracellular only in the early stages of growth, while certain others (coelozoic parasites) are found only in body cavities. The merozoites, produced in merogony, may repeat the cycle of growth and merogony but they eventually become differentiated into gamonts (gametocytes). The production of gametes generally involves schizogony (*gamogony*, in this stage), although in well defined anisogamy, the process is often limited to the production of microgametes.

The Telosporidea may be divided into three subclasses: Gregarinidia, Coccidia, and Haemosporidia. In their various hosts, development of most Gregarinidia is largely or completely extracellular; that of the other two groups, mainly intracellular. Sporocysts are usually developed within the oocyst of Coccidia but not in that of Gregarinidia. In the Haemosporidia, the sporozoites are not enclosed within spore membranes.

Subclass 1. Gregarinidia

The gregarines are typically parasites of the digestive tract and body cavities of invertebrates, although a few occur in tunicates and Enteropneusta. The early development of many species occurs within tissue cells, but the trophozoites usually emerge to complete the cycle in some body cavity of the host. In other gregarines young trophozoites may be attached to an epithelium but there is no intracellular stage. With the exception of such genera as *Merogregarina* and *Spirocystis*, in which intracellular merogony occurs, older trophozoites are typically free in the lumen of the digestive tract or in some other body cavity. In cephaline gregarines (Suborder Cephalina), the transition from the attached stage to the mature free trophozoite (*sporadin*, or *sporont*) often involves loss of the epimerite, an organelle of attachment. This is to be expected especially if the epimerite is firmly attached to the host's tissue or embedded in a tissue cell.

Gregarines vary widely in size, mature trophozoites ranging from about 10μ to 3-4 mm in different species. Form of the body also varies considerably (Fig. 6. 1). The fully grown gregarine is commonly an elongated, often spindle-shaped organism, but there are a number of exceptions. Among the elongated types, the body may be more or less cylindrical, or it may be distinctly flattened. The typical individual gregarine also is capable of undergoing contortions, which in some species, resemble euglenoid movement of certain Euglenida.

There is usually a well differentiated cortex which is sometimes rather thick—e.g., 5-6μ in *Rhynchocystis porrecta* (133)—and is composed of two layers, the sarcocyte and the myocyte (Fig. 6. 1, H). The outer surface is covered with a cuticle (*epicyte*), often marked with ridges or other decorations (Fig. 6. 1, G). In *Rhynchocystis pilosa* (133), cuticular "hairs" (Fig. 6. 11, G) are attached to the ridges. The sarcocyte, the layer underlying the cuticle, is usually homogeneous in appearance. The myocyte contains the myonemes characteristic of many gregarines. In some species

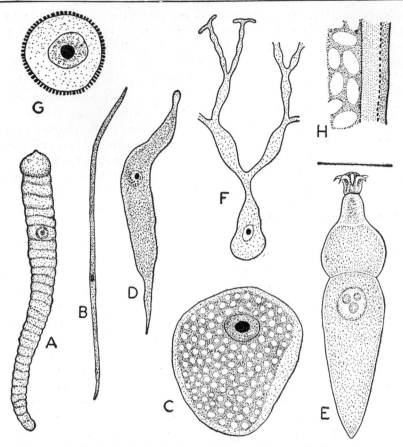

Fig. 6. 1. Variations in body form of Gregarinida. A. *Taeniocystis mira,* resembling a cestode strobila; mature form (length reaches 400-500μ) without epimerite; the anterior "segment" is the protomerite (after Léger). B. *Nematocystis anguillula,* slender species reaching a length of 500μ (after Berlin). C. *Apolocystis minuta,* approximately spherical mature form, x930 (after Troisi). D. *Schaudinnella henleae,* illustrating the spindle-shaped body common among gregarines; x975 (after Nusbaum). E. *Corycella armata,* a typical cephaline gregarine with barbed epimerite; mature forms reach 300μ in length (after Léger). F. *Aikinetocystis singularis,* in which the anterior part of the body is dichotomously branched, each tip ending in a "sucker"; tips of two branches shown; schematic, x400 approx. (after Gates). G. Cross-section of *Polyrhabdina spionis* at level of nucleus; note heavily ridged cuticle; x900 (after Mackinnon and Ray). H. Section through body wall of *Rhynchocystis porrecta* showing cuticle, sarcocyte, myocyte, and portion of the endoplasm with paraglycogen bodies; x1200 (after Troisi).

(Fig. 1. 13, D, E), both longitudinal and circular myonemes have been described, but only longitudinal ones have been seen in *R. pilosa* (133). The endoplasm, which contains the large nucleus, is rather homogeneous except for the frequent appearance of many paraglycogen granules (Fig. 6. 1, C) measuring 2-7μ in diameter in different species (34).

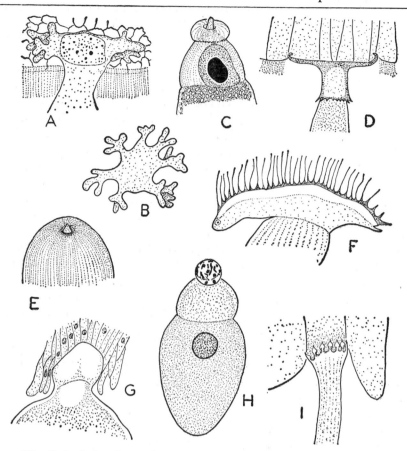

Fig. 6. 2. Epimerites and mucrons. A, B. Lobate epimerite of *Actino-cephalus parvus* (after Weschenfelder): longitudinal section (A), x2560; polar view (B), x1600. C. Anterior end of *Rhynchocystis pilosa*, an acephaline gregarine with an epimerite-like organelle; the large nucleus and a portion of the endoplasm are shown; x2800 (after Troisi). D. Epimerite of *Polyrhabdina spionis*, attached to epithelium; longitudinal section; x1750 (after Mackinnon and Ray). E. Anterior end of *Zygocystis wenrichi*, showing mucron; x334 (after Troisi). F. Attached trophozoite of *Nina gracilis*, expanded protomerite with multiple filamentous epimerites extending into intercellular spaces of an epithelium; tissue cells not shown; x600 (after Goodrich). G. Anterior end of *Zygosoma globosum*, globular epimerite attached to epithelium; x74 (after Noble). H. Trophozoite of *Gregarina rigida* with globular epimerite; x1315 (after Allegre). I. Epimerite of *Lecythion thalassemae* attached to epithelial cell; x1330 (after Mackinnon and Ray).

In one group (Cephalina) of the Eugregarinida, the body is differentiated into two regions, an anterior *protomerite* and a posterior *deutomerite*. The two regions are separated by an optically distinct transverse septum in most of the cephaline gregarines. The unusual protomerite of *Nina gracilis* (37) may undergo marked changes in form (Fig. 6. 8, B-D), and can be used as a sucker for attachment. The protomerite of the more typical cephaline gregarines is equipped with an epimerite, or hold-fast organelle, which varies in structure in different species (Fig. 6. 2). The multiple "epimerites" of *Nina gracilis* (Fig. 6. 2, F) are filaments secreted after the organism becomes attached by means of its expanded protomerite (37). The epimerites of certain species remain embedded in a tissue cell as the trophozoite emerges and the parasite may remain attached through much of the growth period. In other cases, the epimerite adheres to one or more epithelial cells. The epimerite is commonly, although not always, lost when the gregarine becomes detached from its anchorage. An analogous structure, the *mucron* (Fig. 6. 2, C, E), is present in certain acephaline gregarines, and a sucker-like depression lies at the anterior end of various others (Fig. 6. 12, A, B, F). The mucron serves for attachment in such species as *Rhynchocystis pilosa* (133), but may be rudimentary and apparently non-functional in other cases.

The trophozoite of the Schizogregarinida may either undergo merogony, or give rise to one or a few *gamonts* (gametocytes). Since merogony does not occur in Eugregarinida, surviving trophozoites develop into gamonts. The gamonts of typical Gregarinidia become associated in pairs or sometimes larger groups, a condition known as *syzygy* (Fig. 6. 3, A-C). In many species, syzygy occurs early so that the trophozoites, immature at first, are associated for some time before the differentiation of gamonts. In other cases, association occurs much later and gamonts are differentiated almost immediately afterward. In syzygy of cephaline gregarines the anterior end of one sporadin (the satellite) often adheres to the posterior end of another (the primite). Occasionally, two satellites may be attached to one primite, and in exceptional cases several individuals may form a chain. Such chains appear to be temporary associations.

Development of mature trophozoites into gamonts often involves noticeable changes. Autotomy of a posterior portion of the body precedes syzygy in *Rhynchocystis pilosa* (133), and elongated organisms tend to round up. The epimerite of cephaline gregarines, if not already lost, undergoes partial or complete resorption; likewise, cuticular decorations disappear. The associated gamonts—usually two, occasionally three—secrete an enclosing membrane to produce a *gametocyst*. In some genera—*Hentschelia, Lecythia* (85), and *Nina* (37, 79)—a gelatinous or mucous ectocyst encloses the usual membrane. Within the cyst each gamont undergoes gamogony (Fig. 6. 3, D). In such genera as *Hentschelia, Lecythion,* and *Nina*, gametocysts are voided from the gut at an early stage so that gamogony, and subsequent syngamy and sporogony, take place outside the host. In *Carcinoecetes* and *Cephaloidophora,* the gamonts apparently leave the intestine early in syzygy, often becoming attached to the exoskeleton of the crustacean host and developing a gametocyst as "ectoparasites" (5).

The original cuticle of each gamont persists within the gametocyst of

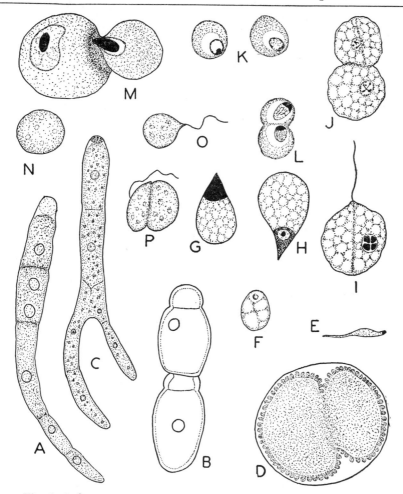

Fig. 6. 3. Syzygy, gamogony, gametes, and syngamy. A. Chain in *Nematopsis legeri*, from living (after Hatt). B. Simple syzygy in *Gregarina rigida;* x665 approx. (after Allegre). C. Multiple, branching syzygy in *Carcinoecetes hesperus*, penultimate satellites partially fused; x275 (after Ball). D. Gamogony within gametocyst (length, 185-223μ), *Monocystis ventrosa* (after Berlin). E, F. Microgamete (x4690) and macrogamete (x1875) of *Nina gracilis* (after Goodrich). G, H. Microgamete and macrogamete of *Urospora rhyacodrili;* x1710 (after Gabriel). I, J. Flagellated microgamete (showing axial filament) and syngamy, *Monocystis mrazeki;* microgamete, about 9.5μ; macrogamete, about 11μ (after Hahn). K, L. A pair of gametes and syngamy, *Gregarina blattarum;* x2830 (after Sprague). M. Syngamy in *Hyalosporina cambolopsisae*, microgamete with pointed nucleus; x4725 (after Chakravarty). N-P. Macrogamete, flagellated microgamete, and syngamy in *Hentschelia thalassemae;* x2430 (after Mackinnon and Ray).

Nina gracilis (37). The result is a partition separating the two groups of gametes except for a short time in which the microgametes are passing through to join the macrogametes. The cuticular sac of the microgameto-cyte, which contains a milky residue after completion of gamogony and migration of the microgametes into the other compartment, remains as a so-called "pseudocyst." As the spores approach maturity, the pseudocyst increases in volume, apparently through accumulation of gases, and serves as a float if the gametocyst has been deposited in sufficient water. The increasing internal pressure eventually ruptures the gametocyst.

In contrast to the Ophryocystidae, in which each gamont yields one functional gamete (Fig. 6. 5, B, C), most gregarines produce many gam-etes. In certain species, the gametes are obviously of two kinds (Fig. 6. 3, E-J, M-O), the microgamete being the smaller and sometimes bear-ing a flagellum. Even in apparent isogamy, it is sometimes possible to distinguish two types of gametes on the basis of cytoplasmic inclusions (Chapter II). Comparable differences in inclusions have been noted in the two gamonts within a gametocyst, as in *Cephaloidophora communis* (5).

As a rule, the gametes fuse completely in syngamy. *Hyaolsporina cambolopsisae* (14) is an exception in which only the nucleus of the micro-gamete enters the macrogamete (Fig. 6. 3, M). Soon after syngamy the zygote of most gregarines encysts. Within the oocyst membrane, the zy-gote divides into sporozoites and the oocyst thus becomes a spore. *Poro-spora* is an unusual genus in which no oocyst membrane is secreted, and sporozoites are thus not found in spores (42). The spores (Fig. 6. 4, A-Q) may be spindle-shaped, ovoid, cylindrical, or spherical in different species and are usually symmetrical, although asymmetrical or sometimes hetero-polar types are produced by certain gregarines. The membrane is com-monly smooth, although it may be equipped with long or short spines.

In most gregarines, the spores escape from the gametocyst by rupture of the membrane. In certain genera, however, one or more tubular *sporoducts* (Fig. 6. 4, R, S) are extruded from the wall of the mature gametocyst. The sporoducts in *Gregarina* develop as tubular structures extending inward from the gametocyst membrane and are everted shortly before sporulation (2). Spores extruded through such sporoducts are typically enclosed in mucous sheaths to form chains (Fig. 6. 4, P).

In parasites of the digestive tract, spores (or sometimes young game-tocysts, or even gamonts in syzygy, depending upon the species) are eliminated with the feces of the host. For species living in the coelom or analogous body cavities, the distribution of spores may be more com-plicated. The life-cycle of *Gonospora* is correlated with the breeding habits of its host (46). Gamogony and the production of spores coincide with spawning in the polychaete host, a circumstance which insures shed-ding of spores from the coelom along with spermatozoa or ova. As for Monocystidae in the seminal vesicles of earthworms, spores have been

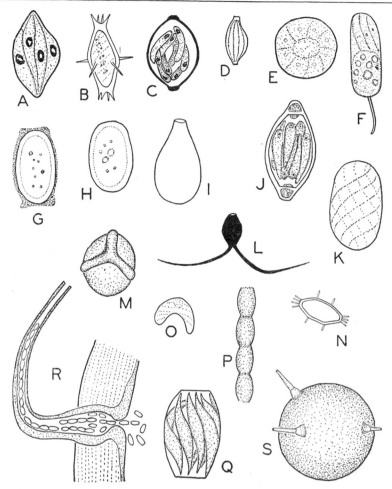

Fig. 6. 4. A-Q. Spores of different Gregarinida: A. *Metamera reynoldsi*, x2880 (after Jones). B. *Acanthospora repelini*, x2170 (after Léger). C. *Machadoella triatomae*, x2740 (after Reichenow). D. *Stomatophora simplex*, x1200 (after Bhatia). E. *Carcinoecetes hesperus*, x1580 (after Ball). F. *Urospora rhyacodrili*, about 23µ long (after Gabriel). G, H. *Gregarina blattarum*, with and without mucous sheath; x2770 (after Sprague). I. *Cystobia irregularis*, x885 (after Minchin). J. *Rhynchocystis porrecta*, x1000 (after Troisi). K. *Cephaloidophora communis*, x2900 (after Ball). L. *Ceratospora mirabilis*, schematic; 2770 approx. (after Léger). M. *Diplocystis schneideri*, x2600 (after Kunstler). N. *Cometoides capitatus*, x1730 (after Léger). O. *Menospora polyacantha*, 15x4µ (from Kamm, after Léger). P, Q. *Gregarinida rigida*, spores in sheath as extruded from sporoduct (P), and single spore (Q) about 8µ long (after Allegre). R. Everted sporoduct in gametocyst of *Gregarina blattarum*, from living; optical section showing expulsion of spores; x454 (after Sprague). S. Gametocyst (375µ) of *Gregarina rigida*, showing three everted sporoducts (after Allegre).

found in the sperm ducts and in cocoons (9). Therefore, transfer of the spores along with spermatozoa represents one method of dispersal. Death of the host would also liberate spores in the soil, and the ingestion of infected forms by birds and the elimination of spores in droppings has been suggested as a mechanism for wider dispersal.

The life-cycles of the Porosporidae (42) are interesting exceptions to the usual pattern in that both a crustacean and a molluscan host are

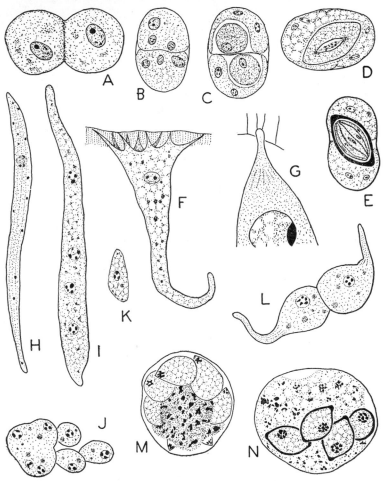

Fig. 6. 5. Schizogregarinida. A-E. *Ophryocystis mesnili:* syzygy (A); gametocytes in gametocyst (B); one gamete formed from each gametocyte (C); zygote after secreting oocyst membrane (D); sporozoites in oocyst (E); x1600 (after Léger). F. *Ophryocystis schneideri* attached to epithelium; x1600 (after Léger). G. *Merogregarina amaroucii,* anterior half of attached sporont; x1600 (after Porter). H-N. *Machadoella triatomae:* trophozoite (H); schizont, four nuclei (I); merogony (J); merozoite (K); syzygy (L); gametes formed within gametocyst (M); oocysts within gametocyst (N); L, x1012; other figures, x1995 (after Reichenow).

involved. Depending upon the species, trophozoites (Fig. 6. 10, F-H) grow to maturity in the intestine of a crab or a lobster. At the end of the growth period, each gregarine adheres to the lining of the rectum and undergoes encystment as an individual, not as a member of a syzygous pair. Encystment is followed by a series of rapid nuclear divisions and then the production of a number of small spherical *gymnospores* (Fig. 6. 10, A), each of which is composed of radially arranged "merozoites." When the cyst membrane finally ruptures, the gymnospores are released into the sea water. Later stages develop in a molluscan host. After reaching the mantle cavity of a lamellibranch, gymnospores may penetrate the epithelium of a gill-filament or of the foot. In addition, phagocytes may ingest gymnospores at the epithelial surface and take them into the tissues. After passing through the epithelium, the gymnospores develop to maturity in the tissue spaces. According to Hatt (42), the most plausible interpretation of his observations is that the "merozoites" of the gymnospores become differentiated into two types of gametes which undergo anisogamy. Each zygote apparently develops directly into a young sporozoite. The mature sporozoite of *Nematopsis* (Fig. 6. 10, D, E) is enclosed in a spore membrane surrounded by a gelatinous sheath, whereas the sporozoites of *Porospora* remain naked. In either case, a crustacean host apparently becomes infected by eating infected molluscan tissue.

In terms of the usual cycle, it might be assumed that transfer from the crustacean to the molluscan host interrupts the normal sequence of gamogony and syngamy. Such an interpretation would imply that gymnospores contain immature gametes which mature in the molluscan host. However, gymnospores are produced by single encysted gregarines, not by pairs in syzygy, and two types of gametes seem to develop within each gymnospore. Consequently, the mechanism of sexual differentiation in the Porosporidae remains an interesting problem.

Taxonomy

The Gregarinidia are divided into two orders on the basis of a major difference in life-cycles. In the Schizogregarinida merogony occurs in the asexual phase; in the Eugregarinida, there is no merogony.

Order 1. Schizogregarinida. The trophozoite undergoes nuclear division at maturity to produce a multinucleate schizont. Merogony then occurs and the surviving merozoites repeat the cycle of growth and merogony, perhaps several times before the merozoites develop into gamonts. Merogony may occur either inside a tissue cell, or in a body cavity. Extracellular types may be attached to an epithelium throughout much of the growth period. Gametocysts and spores are developed as in gregarines generally. The Schizogregarinida are parasites of various polychaetes, gephyrean worms, insects, and (rarely) tunicates and Enteropneusta.

The order has been divided into two families (80), Ophryocystidae and

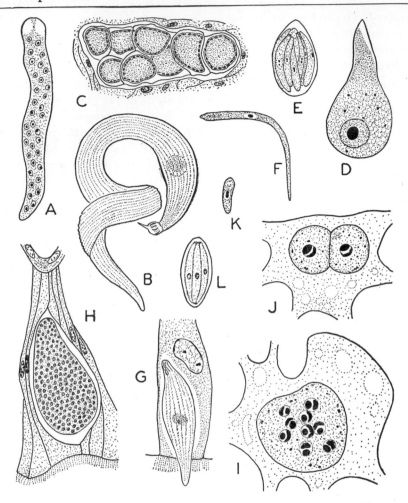

Fig. 6. 6. Schizogregarinida: A. *Schizocystis legeri,* elongated schizont; x1200 (after Léger). B, C. *Meroselenidium keilini,* mature form (B), merogony of cytomeres (meroblasts) formed by division of schizont (C); x500 (after Mackinnon and Ray). D, E. *Caulleryella pipientis,* trophozoite and spore; x900 (after Breslau and Bushkiel). F. *Lipotropha macrospora,* an unusually small gregarine with intracellular development in fat body of dipteran larvae; x1560 (after Keilin). G, H. *Selenidium caulleryi,* young trophozoite and schizont; x1680 (after Ray). I-L. *Lipocystis polyspora,* schizont in fat body of insect (I), syzygy in fat cell (J), merozoite (K), spore (L); x2000 approx. (after Grell).

Schizocystidae. In the former, a single spore is produced within each gametocyst (Fig. 6. 5, B, C); in the Schizocystidae, several to many spores are produced (Fig. 6. 5, M, N). Genera assigned to the two families are listed below:

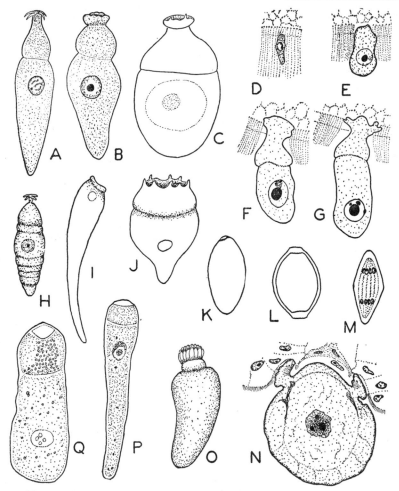

Fig. 6. 7. Cephalina: A. *Ancyrophora uncinata* (intestine of beetles), may reach length of 2 mm (after Léger). B. *Acanthospora repelini,* reaches length of 1 mm (after Léger). C. *Steinina rotundata* (gut of dog-flea), x540 (after Ashworth and Rettie). D-G. Development of protomerite and epimerite in *Actinocephalus parvus;* x2560 (after Weschenfelder); compare with Fig. 6. 2, A, B. H. *Taeniocystis mira,* young form (after Léger); compare with Fig. 6. 1, A. I. *Amphoroides calverti,* x117 (after Watson). J. *Prismatospora evansi,* x65 (after Ellis). K-M. Spores: *Actinocephalus parvus* (K), x2880 (after Weschenfelder); *Steinina rotundata* (L), 11-12μ long (after Ashworth and Rettie); *Coelorhynchus heros* (M), x330 (after Grell). N. *C. heros,* young trophozoite attached to gut wall; x225 (after Grell). O. *Anthorhynchus sophiae,* length up to 2 mm (after Schneider). P. *Carcinoecetes hesperus* (intestine of crabs), x306 (after Ball). Q. *Cephaloidophora communis* (intestine of barnacles), x546 (after Ball).

Family 1. Ophryocystidae. *Merogregarina* Porter (Fig. 6. 5, G) with intracellular merogony; *Ophryocystis* Schneider (78; Fig. 6. 5, A-F), with extracellular merogony; and *Spirocystis* Léger and Duboscq (80), with intracellular merogony.

Family 2. Schizocystidae. *Caulleryella* Keilin (Fig. 6. 6, D, E), *Lipocystis* Grell (40; Fig. 6. 6, I-L), *Lipotropha* Keilin (Fig. 6. 6, F), *Machadoella* Reichenow (117; Fig. 6. 5, H-N), *Meroselenidium* Mackinnon and Ray (87; Fig. 6. 6, B, C), *Schizocystis* Léger (69; Fig. 6. 6, A), *Selenidium* Giard (109, 114; Fig. 6. 6, G, H), *Selenocystis* Dibb (28), *Siedleckia* Caullery and Mesnil, and *Syncystis* Schneider.

Order 2. Eugregarinida. Each sporozoite which survives after reaching the host develops directly into a mature trophozoite which may eventually become a gamont. The Eugregarinida may be divided into two suborders, Acephalina and Cephalina. The body of Cephalina is differentiated into a protomerite and a deutomerite, and the typical protomerite is equipped with an epimerite, at least in attached stages. The body of the Acephalina is not differentiated into segments. The acephaline sporozoite commonly enters a tissue cell and grows for some time as an intracellular parasite. In cephaline gregarines, penetration of tissue cells is often incomplete and may not occur at all.

Suborder 1. Cephalina

Division into families is based on such features as structure of the epimerite, presence or absence of early syzygy, form of the trophozoites, structure of the spore membrane and shape of the spore, and methods by which the spores are released from the gametocyst.

Family 1. Acanthosporidae. The epimerite is usually knob-like or globular, with or without hooks, spines, or filaments in different genera. Early syzygy is unknown. The spores, usually equipped with polar and equatorial spines (Fig. 6. 4, B), are released by rupture of the gametocyst.

The family includes the following genera (66): *Acanthospora* Léger (Fig. 6. 7, B), *Ancyrophora* Léger (Fig. 6. 7, A), *Cometoides* Labbé (Fig. 6. 4, N), *Corycella* Léger (Fig. 6. 1, E), *Primatospora* Ellis (Fig. 6. 7, J).

Family 2. Actinocephalidae. The epimerite may be short and button-like, may lie at the end of a stalk, and may or may not be spiny. Early syzygy is unknown. The often biconical but sometimes asymmetrical spores (Fig. 6. 7, K-M) are released by rupture of the gametocyst.

The family contains the following genera (66): *Actinocephalus* Stein (140; Figs. 6. 2, A, B; 7, D-G), *Amphorocephalus* Ellis, *Amphoroides* Labbé (Fig. 6. 7, I), *Anthorhynchus* Labbé (Fig. 6. 7, O), *Asterophora* Léger, *Beloides* Labbé, *Bothriopsis* Schneider, *Coelorhynchus* Labbé (40; Fig. 6. 7, M, N), *Discorhynchus* Labbé, *Geneiorhynchus* Schneider, *Legeria* Labbé, *Phialoides* Labbé, *Pileocephalus* Schneider, *Pyxinia* Hammerschmidt, *Schneideria* Léger, *Sciadophora* Labbé, *Steinina* Léger and Duboscq (Fig. 6. 7, C, L), *Stictosopora* Léger, *Stylocystis* Léger, *Taeniocystis* Léger (77; Figs. 6. 1, A; 7, H).

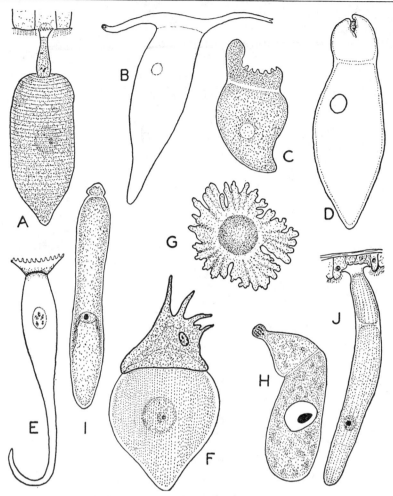

Fig. 6. 8. Cephalina: A. *Lecythion thalassemae,* trophozoite attached to epithelial cell; x380 (after Mackinnon and Ray). B-D. *Nina gracilis,* illustrating changes in form of the protomerite; arms extended (B), x60; partly contracted in young specimen (C), and closed during movement through intestinal debris (D), x400 (after Goodrich). E. *Dactylophorus robustus,* x120 approx. (after Léger). F, G. *Hentschelia thalassemae,* mature form with anterior end embedded in tissue cell (F), x400 approx., and view of anterior end (G), x1030 approx. (after Mackinnon and Ray). H. *Pyxinoides pugetensis* (from barnacles), x384 (after Henry). I. *Hyalosporina cambolopsisae* (from millipedes), mature form after losing small tongue-like epimerite; cuticular striations not shown; x90 (after Chakravarty). J. *Metamera reynoldsi,* attached to epithelium; x140 (after Jones).

Family 3. Cephaloidiphoridae. The epimerite is rudimentary. Early syzygy occurs and association is sometimes multiple. Ovoid spores (Fig. 6. 4, K) are released by rupture of the gametocyst.

Two genera are included: *Carcinoecetes* Ball (5; Fig. 6. 7, P) and *Cephaloidophora* (5, 45; Fig. 6. 7, Q).

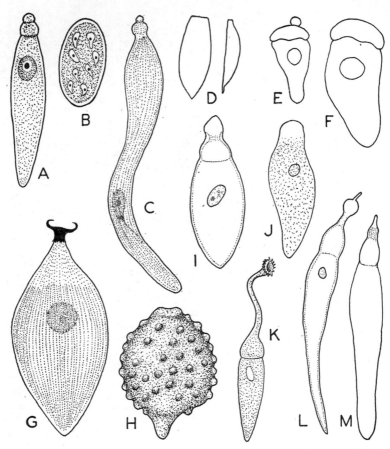

Fig. 6. 9. Cephalina: A, B. *Stenophora shyamaprasadi* (from centipede), sporont, x365; spore, x3150 (after Chakravarty). C, D. *Monoductus lunatus,* trophozoite, x216; broad and narrow aspects of spore, x3145 (after Ray and Chakravarty). E, F. *Colepismatophila watsonae,* young trophozoite with simple epimerite, x110; older form after loss of epimerite, x81 (after Adams and Travis). G. *Polyrhabdina spionis,* x298 (after Mackinnon and Ray); see also Fig. 6. 2, D. H. *Zygosoma globosum,* mature trophozoite, x74 (after Noble); see epimerite of younger stage in Fig. 6. 2, G. I. *Cystocephalus algerianus,* reaches length of 3-4 mm (after Schneider). J. *Lecudina pellucida* (from Kamm, after Kölliker). K. *Menospora polyacantha,* reaches length of 600-700μ (after Léger). L. *Bulbocephalus elongatus,* reaches length of about 1.5 mm (after Watson). M. *Stylocephalus giganteus,* reaches length of 1.8 mm (after Ellis).

Family 4. Dactylophoridae. The protomerite is typically metabolic and may serve as a sucker in attachment. In certain species, the "epimerites" are slender temporary structures, tapering to delicate filaments. The cuticle of the microgametocyte persists after gamogony as a "pseudocyst." The spores (Fig. 6. 4, A), ellipsoidal, or cylindrical with rounded ends, are released by rupture of the gametocyst. Members of the family have been reported from the intestine of Chilopoda.

The following genera are included (66): *Acutispora* Crawley, *Dactylophorus* Balbiani (Fig. 6. 8, E), *Dendrorhynchus* Keilin, *Echinomera* Labbé (37, 122), *Hentschelia* Mackinnon and Ray (85; Fig. 6. 8, F, G), *Lecythion* Mackinnon and Ray (85; Fig. 6. 8, F, G), *Metamera* Duke (65; Fig. 6. 8, J), *Nina* Grebnecki (37; Fig. 6. 8, B-D), *Rhopalonia* Léger, *Septicephalus* Kamm, *Trichorhynchus* Schneider.

Family 5. Didymophyidae. The epimerite is small, resembling the mucron of certain acephalines. Early syzygy occurs, in pairs or triplets, and a septum may not be apparent in the satellites. Ellipsoidal spores are released by rupture of the gametocyst.

The family includes the genus *Didymophyes* Stein (66).

Family 6. Gregarinidae. The epimerite is simple, knob-like, or somewhat elongated. Syzygy may occur early or late and is commonly multiple in some genera. Spores emerge through sporoducts, often in chains (Fig. 6. 4, P-S), or else by rupture of the gametocyst.

The following genera are included (66): *Anisolobus* Vincent, *Gamocystis* Schneider, *Gregarina* Dufour (2, 126; Fig. 6. 2, H), *Hirmocystis* Labbé, *Hyalospora* Schneider, *Hyalosporina* Chakravarty (14; Fig. 6. 8, E), *Leidyana* Watson, *Protomagalhaesia* Pinto, *Pyxinoides* Trégouboff (45; Fig. 6. 8, H), *Uradiophora* Mercier.

Family 7. Lecudinidae. The epimerite may be knob-like, with or without teeth and hooks, or an umbrella-like structure with lobate margin, or cylindrical with a lobate tip. A septum is not evident although the protomerite and deutomerite regions may differ in appearance. The spores are usually ovoid.

The following genera have been referred to the family, which includes the Polyrhabdinidae of Kamm (66): *Kofoidina* Henry, *Leucudina* Mingazzini (Fig. 6. 9, J), *Polyrhabdina* Mingazzini (85; Fig. 6. 9, G), *Scyia* Léger, *Ulivina* Mingazzini, *Zygosoma* Labbé (96; Fig. 6. 9, H).

Family 8. Menosporidae. The epimerite is cup-shaped, with marginal hooks, and is borne on a stalk. Early syzygy is unknown. Crescent-shaped spores (Fig. 6. 4, O) are released by rupture of the gametocyst.

A single genus is included: *Menospora* Léger (66; Fig. 6. 9, K).

Family 9. Monoductidae. The epimerite is usually a small knob, with or without prongs. Early syzygy is unknown. A single sporoduct is characteristic of *Monoductus* but not of other genera. The spores usually emerge in chains.

The following genera are included: *Colepismatophila* Adams and Travis (Fig. 6. 9, E, F), *Lepismatophila* Adams and Travis, *Monoductus* Ray and Chakravarty (111; Fig. 6. 9, C, D), and *Sphaerocystis* Léger.

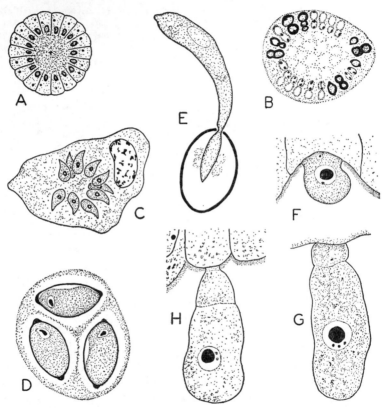

Fig. 6. 10. Porosporidae (after Hatt): A. Gymnospore of *Nematopsis legeri*, section, x3105. B. Later development of gymnospore (*Porospora gigantea*) in molluscan tissue, x3240. C. Sporozoites of *N. legeri* in phagocyte, molluscan gill, x2835. D. "Cyst" with spores, *N. legeri*, x1425. E. Sporozoite (*N. legeri*) escaping from spore in gut of crab; from living, x1425. F, G. Young and older trophozoites (*P. gigantea*) attached to intestinal epithelium in crustacean host; x1500. H. Young cephalin of *N. legeri* attached to epithelium of crustacean intestine; x1425.

Family 10. Porosporidae. The epimerite is a simple disc or rudimentary. Syzygy is often early and may be multiple, but a typical gametocyst is not produced. Instead, gymnospores (blastula-like clusters of "merozoites"), derived from individually encysted gregarines (42), leave the gut of the crustacean host. After gymnospores reach a suitable mollusc, development results in sporozoites (Fig. 6. 10, A-D), one from each zygote, as described above.

The family includes two genera (42): *Nematopsis* Schneider (Fig. 6. 10, H), with monozoic spores, from crabs; and *Porospora* Schneider (Fig. 6. 10, F, G), with naked sporozoites, from lobsters.

Family 11. Stenophoridae. The epimerite is rudimentary or absent. Early syzygy is unknown. Ovoid spores are released by rupture of the gametocyst.

Two genera are included (66): *Fonsecaia* Pinto and *Stephanophora* Labbé (15; Fig. 6. 9, A, B).

Family 12. Stylocephalidae. The epimerite ranges from globular or discoid to a complex elongated or conical organelle, sometimes lobate or equipped with bristles. Early syzygy is unknown. A pseudocyst is reported for some genera. Spores may be released in chains.

The following genera are included (66): *Bulbocephalus* Watson (Fig. 6. 9, L), *Cystocephalus* Schneider (Fig. 6. 9, I), *Lophocephalus* Labbé, *Oocephalus* Schneider, *Sphaerorhynchus* Labbé, *Stylocephalus* Ellis (Fig. 6. 9, M).

Suborder 2. *Acephalina*

These are non-septate, mostly coelomic parasites, many of which occur in the seminal vesicles of oligochaetes. Some of the exceptions are *Hyperidion* (86), a genus of uncertain taxonomic status, including intestinal parasites of echiuroid worms; and *Lankesteria* and *Allantocystis,* from the digestive tract of insects. A synoptic review of genera and families is available (10).

Family 1. Aikinetocystidae. The family contains *Aikinetocystis* Gates (Fig. 6. 1, F), in which the anterior end of the trophozoite is dichotomously branched, with sucker-like organelles at the tips. Trophozoites may reach lengths of 3-4 mm. Spores are similar to those of *Monocystis.*

Family 2. Allantocystidae. This family was established for *Allantocystis* Keilin (67), in which the elongated trophozoites undergo head-to-head syzygy. The gametocyst is much elongated (Fig. 6. 11, F). Spores are spindle-shaped, not quite symmetrical.

Family 3. Diplocystidae. Early syzygy may or may not occur. Spores (Fig. 6. 4, M) are ovoid to spherical. A small pseudopodial epimeritic organ may be present. Species are known from flatworms, insects and tunicates.

Two genera are included: *Diplocystis* Kunstler (62) and *Lankesteria* Mingazzini (112; Fig. 6. 11, A-D).

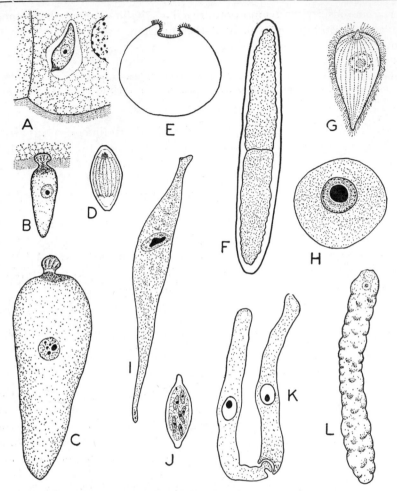

Fig. 6. 11. Acephalina: A-D. *Lankesteria culicis* Ross (after Ray), intra-cellular stage (A), young trophozoite attached to intestinal epithelium (B), x1332; mature trophozoite, cuticular striations omitted (C), x578; spore, from living (D), x2280. E. *Craterocystis papua,* schematic optical section show-ing anterior "sucker," x70 approx. (after Cognetti). F. Elongated gametocyst of *Allantocystis dasyhelei,* x425 approx. (after Keilin). G. *Rhynchocystis pilosa* Cuenot, young trophozoite, x1800 (after Troisi); see also Fig. 6. 2, C. H. *Apolocystis minuta,* young trophozoite, x1600 (after Troisi); compare with Fig. 6. 1, C. I. *Monocystis agilis* Stein, commonly 120-145μ (after Berlin). J. Spore of *Monocystis ventrosa* (after Berlin). K. *Ganymedes anapsides,* syzygy showing "ball-and-socket" junction, x515 approx. (after Huxley). L. *Beccaricystis loriai,* "sucker" at anterior end; x630 approx. (after Cognetti).

Family 4. Ganymedidae. Syzygy in primite-satellite fashion is charac-teristic. Gametocysts are spherical. Life-cycles are incompletely known for the only genus, *Ganymedes* Huxley (Fig. 6. 11, K).

Family 5. Monocystidae. Mature trophozoites range from spheroid (Fig.

6. 1, C) to much elongated types (Fig. 6. 1, B). A sucker-like epimeritic organ or a mucron may or may not be present. Spores are typically spindle-shaped. Various species of *Monocystis* and *Nematocystis* have been described in detail by Berlin (7). Many Monocystidae occur in the seminal vesicles of earthworms. The sporozoites of some species enter germinal cells and grow within the developing sperm-morulae. In other species parasitizing the seminal vesicles, development is extracellular. Species within a single genus, such as *Apolocystis* (133), may differ with respect to intracellular or extracellular development.

The following genera have been assigned to the family: *Apolocystis* Cognetti (106, 133; Figs. 6. 1, C; 11, H), *Echinocystis* Bhatia and Chatterjee (11), *Enterocystis* Zwetkow,

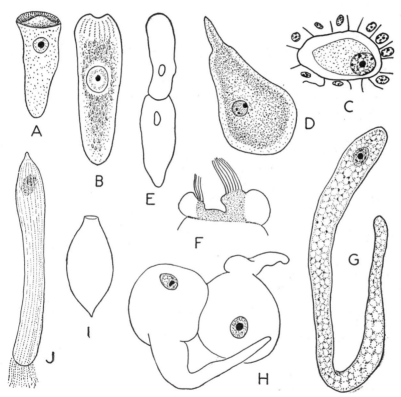

Fig. 6. 12. Acephalina. A, B. *Stomatophora simplex*, view of mobile anterior "sucker" with central mucron (A), x800; trophozoite, light anterior area representing region of sucker (B), x960 (after Bhatia). C-E. *Urospora rhyacodrili*, young trophozoite in gut wall (C), x1225; older trophozoite in seminal vesicle (D), x216; syzygy (E), x216 (after Gabriel). F. *Choanocystoides costaricensis*, anterior end of trophozoite showing "sucker," schematic, 730 approx. (after Cognetti). G, H. *Gonospora varia* Léger, mature stage and a pair in syzygy; x96 approx. (after Hentschel). I. Heteropolar spore of *Lithocystis brachycercus*, x1396 (after Goodrich). J. *Zygocystis wenrichi*, young trophozoite, x700 (after Troisi); compare with Fig. 6. 2, E.

Monocystis Stein (7, 41; Fig. 6. 11, I), *Nematocystis* Hesse (7; Fig. 6. 1, B), *Rhabdocystis* Boldt.

Family 6. Rhynchocystidae. The family contains only the genus *Rhynchocystis* Hesse (7, 133; Figs. 6. 2, C; 11, G). A mucron is more or less evident. The body is usually elongated, sometimes with an anterior conical or cylindrical "neck," and may be covered with cuticular "hairs." Early syzygy does not occur and autotomy may precede the association. Spores are typically spindle-shaped.

Family 7. Schaudinnelidae. The only genus is *Schaudinnella* Nusbaum (101; Fig. 6. 1, D), showing two types of gametocytes and well-marked anisogamy. Trophozoites may be free or attached, the latter stage with a primitive epimerite.

Family 8. Stomatophoridae. A discoid sucker-like epimerite is characteristic of the elongated to spheroid trophozoites. Early syzygy is unknown. Spores are usually truncate spindles.

The following genera are included: *Albertisella* Cognetti, *Astrocystella* Cognetti, *Beccaricystis* Cognetti (Fig. 6. 11, L), *Choanocystella* Cognetti, *Choanocystoides* Cognetti (Fig. 6. 12, F), *Craterocystis* Cognetti (Fig. 6. 11, E), *Stomatophora* Drzewecki (8; Fig. 6. 12, A, B).

Family 9. Urosporidae. Form of the trophozoite varies in different genera. Early syzygy is characteristic. The spore membrane may be drawn out into horns or flanges, and there is often a funnel-like depression at one end.

The family contains the following genera: *Ceratospora* Léger, *Cystobia* Mingazzini, *Gonospora* Schneider (46; Fig. 6. 12, G, H), *Lithocystis* Giard (36; Fig. 6. 12, I), *Pterospora* Racovitza and Labbé, *Urospora* Schneider (31, 92; Fig. 6. 12, C-E).

Family 10. Zygocystidae. The trophozoites are commonly pyriform. Early syzygy, sometimes with longitudinal pairing, is the rule. The spores are spindle-shaped, with thickened poles. Species are known from the seminal vesicles and coelom of oligochaetes.

The family contains the genera *Pleurocystis* Hesse and *Zygocystis* Stein (7, 133; Figs. 6 2, E; 12, J).

Subclass 2. Coccidia

The Coccidia are predominantly parasites of epithelial tissues in invertebrates (Annelida, Arthropoda, Mollusca) and vertebrates, and are typically intracellular throughout most of their life-cycles. Reproduction occurs in both asexual and sexual phases of the cycle, as in Schizogregarinida.

Life-cycles

An infection is initiated when the host ingests oocysts or sporocysts (spores), or in rare cases, when naked sporozoites are inoculated or ingested. Each surviving sporozoite enters a tissue cell and develops into a multinucleate schizont. Merogony then occurs. The resulting merozoites enter other cells and repeat the cycle. In typical Coccidia, merogony in-

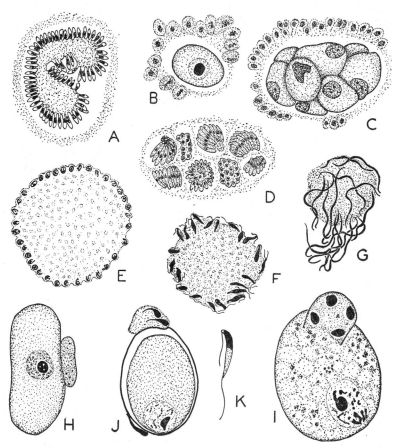

Fig. 6. 13. A. Merogony in *Ovivora thalassemae;* section of schizont, x500 (after Mackinnon and Ray). B-D. Merogony, involving formation of meroblasts, in *Caryotropha mesnili* (after Siedlecki): young trophozoite (B); meroblasts formed by division of a trophozoite (C); formation of merozoites from meroblasts (D); x535. E-G. Production of microgametes in *Ovivora thalassemae;* x850 (after Mackinnon and Ray). H. Syzygy in *Adelea ovata;* x1140 (after Shellack and Reichenow). I. Syzygy in *Adelina deronis*, microgametocyte with four nuclei; x1600 (after Hauschka). J. Zygote of *Adelea ovata,* oocyst membrane formed, three microgametes left outside; x1140 (after Shellack and Reichenow). K. Flagellate microgamete of *Caryotropha mesnili;* x1510 (after Siedlecki).

volves a preliminary arrangement of nuclei at the surface of the schizont and then a superficial budding (Fig. 6. 13, A). However, the trophozoite of *Caryotropha* (Fig. 6. 13, B-D) first divides into cytomeres (meroblasts) and each meroblast then produces merozoites.

There appears to be a limited number of merogonic cycles, the exact number varying with the species—usually two in *Adelina deronis* (43); three in *Eimeria separata* and *E. miyarii;* and four in *E. nieschulzi* of rats (118). The time required for completion of the first merogonic generation, as reported for different species, ranges from about 25 hours to 25 days.

The last generation of merozoites produces two types of gametocytes, which vary in relative numbers. In *Adelina deronis,* in which the gametocytes develop in syzygy and relatively few microgametes are produced, there are about twice as many microgametocytes as macrogametocytes (43). In *Eimeria nieschulzi,* which produces many microgametes, macrogametocytes outnumber microgametocytes about three to one (118). The mechanism underlying the differentiation of two kinds of gametocytes is not yet known. However, the development of a normal cycle in the host after experimental introduction of one oocyst (135) suggests that the basic sexual differentiation occurs early in development of the zygote, although its expression may be delayed until gametocytes appear.

The gametocytes may be similar in size (Eimeriida) or the macrogametocyte may be distinctly the larger (Adeleida). The macrogametocyte, during development, typically accumulates stored reserves such as the glycogen in *Eimeria tenella* (30), whereas the microgametocyte contains little stored food. The gametocytes of Eimeriida differentiate independently, and the microgametocyte typically produces many microgametes (Fig. 6. 13, E-G). In the Adeleida the two types of gametocytes, sometimes at an early stage of development, become associated in syzygy (Fig. 6. 13, H, I), which is correlated with the production of relatively few, often 2-4, microgametes (Fig. 6. 13, J). For the Coccidia as a group, the morphological differentiation of macrogametes and microgametes is marked and the production of small flagellate microgametes (Fig. 6. 13, K) is typical. Microgametogenesis in Eimeriida generally resembles the process described for *Ovivora thalassemae* (Fig. 6. 13, E-G). In *Merocystis* (105) and *Myriospora* (82), however, the microgametocyte divides into gametoblasts, each of which produces a number of microgametes. The details of syngamy seem to be similar throughout the group.

Either before or immediately after entrance of a microgamete the macrogamete usually secretes an oocyst membrane, although the zygote of the Haemogregarinina is at first a migratory ookinete which later secretes a thin flexible membrane. In the majority of Coccidia, the oocyst membrane is relatively thick and firm, and may be composed of two or

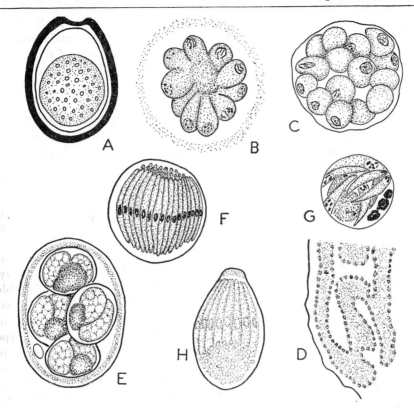

Fig. 6. 14. A. Oocyst of the *Eimeria*-type, with heavy ectocyst and thin endocyst; thin area in the ectocyst is the region of the micropyle; the zygote is undivided; diagrammatic (after Goodrich). B, C. *Ovivora thalassemae*, x500 (after Mackinnon and Ray): development of sporoblasts (B); oocyst containing sporoblasts (C). D. Oocyst of *Aggregata eberthi*, portion of a section; nuclei are arranged at the surfaces of folds in the plasmodial mass, shortly before the production of many sporoblasts; x305 (after Dobell). E. Sporozoites formed within sporocysts in oocyst of *Eimeria vison;* x1620 (after Levine). F-H. Oocysts containing sporozoites not enclosed in sporocysts: *Legerella parva* (F), x1440 (after Nöller); *Haemogregarina stepanowi* (G), x1890 (after Reichenow); *Pfeifferinella impudica* (H), x1560 (after Léger and Holland).

more layers (Fig. 6. 14, A). The mature macrogamete of *Eimeria stiedae* (Fig. 6. 18, E, F) contains a peripheral zone of globular inclusions which are extruded to form an ectocyst, continuous except for a *micropyle* (a minute opening through which the microgamete will enter). After syngamy the micropyle is closed by the secretion of more material but the closed area remains thinner than the rest of the ectocyst in certain species. Before the zygote rounds up, a relatively thin endocyst (Fig. 6. 14, A) is secreted within the ectocyst (38). Three layers have been described in *Eimeria intricata* (44)—a thin transparent outer layer, thickened as a polar cap over the micropyle; a thick brownish intermediate layer which becomes quite thin at the micropyle; and a thin colorless endocyst. Although there are a number of exceptions, size and structure of the oocyst are often rather characteristic of the species.

The zygote usually divides into sporoblasts, often leaving a residual mass, and each sporoblast usually secretes a sporocyst membrane (Fig. 6. 14, B-E). Less commonly, sporocysts are not produced, sporozoites being protected only by the oocyst membrane (Fig. 6. 14, F-H). The sporoblasts of *Karyolysus* are unusual in that they are released from the ruptured oocyst as motile elongated sporokinetes which invade the eggs of a mite. The sporoblast then rounds up and secretes a sporocyst membrane. By the time the egg has developed into a nymph, the sporoblast has produced sporozoites. In the more typical Coccidia, both the number of sporocysts and the number of sporozoites are features of taxonomic value.

Sporogony may or may not be completed within the host. The oocysts of avian and mammalian parasites are typically eliminated with the zygote undivided or in the process of forming sporoblasts. Under favorable conditions, sporozoites are developed within a few days, and the oocyst is then infective for a new host. At the other extreme, the production of sporozoites is completed within the host. Development of the latter type has led to an interesting modification of the coccidian life-cycle in *Shellackia* (Fig. 6. 19, A-F). Sporozoites are developed within an asporocystic oocyst, which eventually ruptures in the intestinal connective tissue of the reptilian host. The liberated sporozoites enter erythrocytes. Invaded blood corpuscles are swallowed by a mite, in which cells of the gut wall apparently ingest the sporozoites without destroying them. If such a mite is eaten by a vertebrate host the sporozoites are released and invade the intestinal epithelium. A comparable transfer by leeches occurs in *Lankesterella,* in which there is a similar invasion of erythrocytes by sporozoites.

In these cycles of *Shellackia* and *Lankesterella* the mite and the leech are mechanical vectors in which the parasites do not undergo development. A true intermediate host occurs in certain cases involving invasion of erythrocytes or leucocytes by gametocytes. After ingestion of gametocytes by a leech (*Haemogregarina*) or by a tick or mite (*Hepatozoon, Karyolysus*), gametogenesis and syngamy occur and sporozoites are produced in the invertebrate. Transfer of sporozoites may be effected by inoculation, as in the case of leeches feeding on a vertebrate, or by the ingestion of infected mites. *Aggregata eberthi* (29) shows an unusual cycle in which the "intermediate" host becomes infected by eating the "final" host. Merogony occurs in the intestinal connective tissue of a crab which has ingested sporocysts. If an infected crab is eaten by a squid, some of the merozoites develop into gametocytes, and syngamy and sporogony follow.

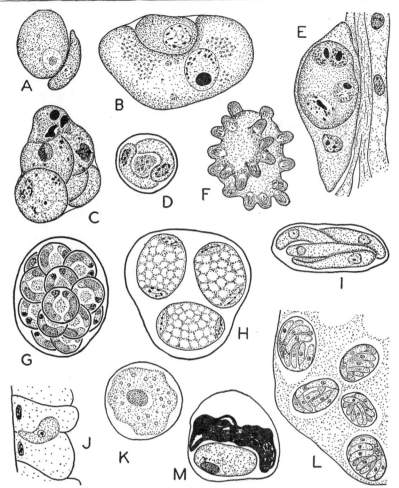

Fig. 6. 15. A-F. *Adelina deronis* Hauschka and Pennypacker (after Hauschka): Early (A) and later syzygy (B), x1700; sporoblasts in oocyst, remains of microgametocyte still attached (C), x1600; mature sporocyst (D), x1900; young schizont in a peritoneal cell (E), x1600; merogony (F), x1600. G. Oocyst of *Adelea ovata* Schneider, with sporocysts; x960 (after Shellack and Reichenow). H, I. *Chagasella hartmanni* (Chagas) Machado: oocyst with three developing sporocysts (H); sporocyst with four sporozoites (I); x750 (after C.). J, K. *Hepatozoon muris* (Balfour) Miller (after M.): ookinete penetrating intestinal epithelium (J): oocyst (K). L. *Hepatozoon canis* Léger, portion of oocyst containing sporocysts; x630 (after Wenyon). M. *Hepatozoon adiei,* gametocyte in leucocyte; x2100 (after Hoare).

Taxonomy

On the basis of life-histories, the Coccidia may be divided into two orders, the Adeleida and the Eimeriida. In the Adeleida, the gametocytes are associated in syzygy during differentiation and only a few microgametes are usually produced. In the Eimeriida, gametocytes develop independently and the microgametocyte typically produces many microgametes.

Order 1. Adeleida. On the basis of differences in the zygote and oocyst, the Adeleida may be divided into the suborders Adeleina and Haemogregarinina. The Adeleina form an inactive zygote which develops a typical oocyst. The ookinete of the Haemogregarinina secretes a flexible membrane which is stretched during development.

Suborder 1. Adeleina

Four families have been recognized. Sporocysts are developed in two families but not in the others.

Family 1. Adeleidae. Sporocysts are developed within an oocyst and the life-cycle is typical of the suborder.

The following genera have been assigned to the family: *Adelea* Schneider (Figs. 6. 13, H, J; 15, G), with a large oocyst and a variable but fairly large number of discoidal sporocysts, each containing two sporozoites; *Adelina* Hesse (43, 113; Fig. 6. 15, A-F), oocyst containing relatively few spherical sporocysts, each with two sporozoites; *Chagasella* Machado (Fig. 6. 15, H, I), oocyst containing three sporocysts, each with four sporozoites; *Klossia* Schneider (91, 93), oocyst containing many spherical sporocysts, each with four sporozoites.

Family 2. Dobelliidae. The only genus is *Dobellia* Ikeda (59), which is unusual in that the microgametocyte produces a fairly large number of microgametes in spite of the fact that syzygy occurs. Sporocysts are not produced. A single species has been reported from sipunculids.

Family 3. Klossiellidae. The oocyst contains a number of sporocysts, each with many sporozoites. Microgametogenesis yields two microgametes. The family contains the genus, *Klossiella* Smith and Johnson (128), represented in mice and guinea pigs.

Family 4. Legerellidae. The single genus, *Legerella* Mesnil (Fig. 6. 14, F), produces an oocyst with many sporozoites but no sporocysts. The known species occur in fleas and myriapods.

Suborder 2. Haemogregarinina

Members of this group differ from other Adeleida in that the life-cycle involves two hosts and the zygote is an ookinete. Three families, each with a single genus, are generally recognized.

Family 1. Haemogregarinidae. In *Haemogregarina* Danilewsky (Fig. 6. 16, A-E), the small oocyst contains no sporocysts. The sexual phase of the cycle occurs in leeches; asexual stages, in various turtles. Merozoites invade erythrocytes of the vertebrate and develop into gametocytes.

Family 2. Hepatozoidae. The large oocysts contain many sporocysts, each with a dozen or more sporozoites. The gametocytes appear in leucocytes of the vertebrate host. Sexual stages occur in tsetse flies (50), lice, mites, and ticks. The type genus is *Hepatozoon* Miller (50; Fig. 6. 15, J-M), represented by several species in birds and mammals.

Family 3. Karyolysidae. The sporoblasts become sporokinetes which invade the egg of a mite before secreting sporocyst membranes. Gametocytes appear in erythrocytes cf the vertebrate host. Several species of *Karyolysus* Labbé (115; Fig. 6. 16, F-K) have been described from lizards.

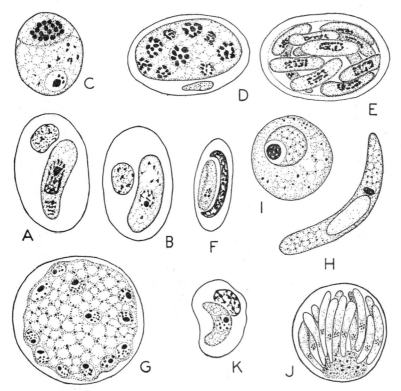

Fig. 6. 16. A-E. *Haemogregarina stepanowi* Danilewsky, x1890 (after Reichenow): microgametocyte (A); macrogametocyte (B); syzygy (C); schizont in erythrocyte (D); merozoites in erythrocyte (E). F-K. *Karyolysus lacertarum* (Danilewsky) Labbé (after Reichenow): gametocyte in erythrocyte (F), x1050; oocyst producing sporoblasts (G), x800; motile sporokinete (H) and sporokinete in egg of mite (I), x1050; sporocyst in larval mite (J), x800; merozoite in endothelial cell (K), x1050.

Order 2. Eimeriida. These Coccidia differ from the Adeleida in the absence of syzygy. Certain species are economically important as parasites of poultry, quail, pheasants, cattle, sheep, and such fur-bearing animals as the fox and mink (6, 12). Problems of control are aggravated by the survival of oocysts for prolonged periods on the soil. Six families of Eimeriida are often recognized. However, Hoare (51) has suggested a division of the group into only two families, the Selenococcidiidae and the Eimeriidae, the latter containing six subfamilies.

Family 1. Aggregatidae. Several to many sporocysts, in some species several hundred, are developed within the oocyst. In *Aggregata*, merogony occurs in crabs and syngamy and sporogony in cephalopods; in *Ovivora* both phases of the cycle are completed in one host. Life-cycles are incompletely known for various other members of the family.

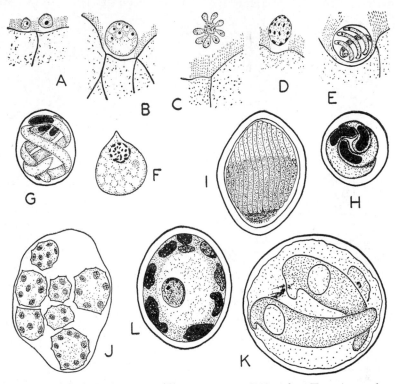

Fig. 6. 17. A-E. *Cryptosporidium parvum,* x3200 (after Tyzzer): trophozoites (A); schizont (B); merogony (C); microgametogenesis (D); oocyst with four sporozoites (E); all stages extracellular, on surface of intestinal epithelium (mice). F-H. *Aggergata eberthi* (Labbé): sporoblast before secretion of sporocyst membrane (F), x2000; lateral and polar views of sporocyst containing three sporozoites (G, H), x2200 (after Dobell). I. Sporocyst of *Myriospora trophoniae,* with sporozoites (after Lermantoff). J. Oocyst of *Caryotropha mesnili,* with several sporocysts; x535 (after Siedlecki). K, L. *Ovivora thalassemae* (after Mackinnon and Ray): egg of *Thalassema* containing two parasites (K), x240; sporocyst with 10 nuclei (L), x1440.

The following genera have been included: *Aggregata* Frenzel (29; Figs. 6. 14, D; 17, F-H), oocyst containing many sporocysts, each with 3-16 sporozoites in different species; *Angeiocystis* Brasil, oocyst with four sporocysts, each containing about thirty sporozoites; *Merocystis* Dakin (24, 105), two sporozoites in each of many sporocysts; *Myriospora* Lermantoff (82; Fig. 6. 17, I), oocyst with a few hundred sporocysts, each with 24-36 sporozoites; *Ovivora* Mackinnon and Ray (88; Figs. 6. 13, A, E-G; 14, B, C; 17, K, L), many sporocysts, each with about twelve sporozoites; *Pseudoklossia* Léger and Duboscq (81), oocyst with many dizoic sporocysts, sporogony in Pelecypoda, but merogonic cycle unknown.

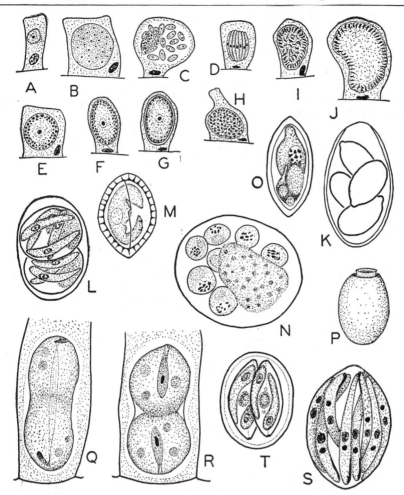

Fig. 6. 18. A-J. *Eimeria stiedae,* stages in epithelium of bile ducts (rabbits); x580-600; diagrammatic: growth stage (A); multinucleate schizont (B); merozoites (C, D); young and more mature macrogametocytes (E, F); oocyst membrane formed (G); stage in microgametogenesis (H); surface view and optical section, microgametes nearly mature (I, J). K. Oocyst with four sporocysts, *E. stiedae;* x860 (after Kessel and Jankiewicz). L. *Isospora bigemina,* oocyst with two sporocysts; x2400 (after Wenyon). M. Oocyst of *Echinospora labbei,* x1950 (after Léger). N, O. *Barrouxia schneideri* (after Shellack and Reichenow): oocyst with sporocysts (N), x1565; sporocyst with single sporozoite (O), x1895. P. Oocyst with collar, surface view, *Jarrina paludosa;* x1560 (after Léger and Hesse). Q-S. *Dorisiella scolelepidis* (after Ray): division of zygote into two sporoblasts (Q, R), x1340; sporocyst with eight sporozoites (S), x1650. T. Oocyst of *Cyclospora caryolytica,* two sporocysts; x1680 (after Schaudinn).

Family 2. Caryotrophidae. The oocyst contains many sporocysts, each with many sporozoites. The merogonic cycle involves division of the schizont into a number of meroblasts, each of which produces merozoites. Microgametogenesis involves a similar process. The only genus is *Caryotropha* Siedlecki (Figs. 6. 13, B-D; 17, J).

Family 3. Cryptosporidiidae. Development is extracellular, the parasites apparently being embedded in the mucus covering the epithelium of the gut. The small oocyst contains four sporozoites but no sporocysts. Certain parasites of mice have been assigned to the only genus, *Cryptosporidium* Tyzzer (134; Fig. 6. 17, A-E).

Family 4. Eimeriidae. The characteristics of the family are somewhat

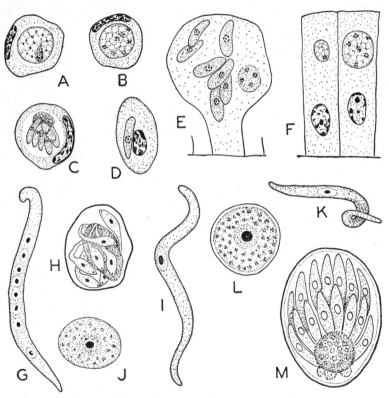

Fig. 6. 19. A-F. *Shellackia bolivari,* x900 (after Reichenow): zygote in subepithelial tissue, intestine of lizard (A); development of sporozoites from zygote (B, C); a sporozoite in an erythrocyte (D); sporozoites in cell of intestinal epithelium of mite (E); a young trophozoite and a schizont in intestinal epithelium of lizard after ingestion of infected mites (F). G-L. *Selenococcidium intermedium,* x765 (after Léger and Duboscq): schizont with eight nuclei, before invasion of an intestinal cell in lobster (G); completion of merogony (H); a macrogametocyte from the intestinal lumen (I); an intracellular macrogametocyte (J); a microgametocyte before invading a gut cell (K); oocyst (L). M. Oocyst of *Lankesterella minima,* with sporozoites (no sporocysts are formed); x1125 (after Nöller).

flexible. Sporocysts are lacking in a few cases; in others, the oocyst contains one, two, four, or many sporocysts. The number of sporozoites within each sporocyst also varies from one to many.

The following genera have been assigned to the family: *Barrouxia* Schneider (Fig. 6. 18, N, O), smooth oocyst containing many sporocysts, each with one sporozoite; *Caryospora* Léger (51), oocyst containing one sporocyst with eight sporozoites; *Cyclospora* Schneider (Fig. 6. 18, T), oocyst with two dizoic sporocysts; *Dorisiella* Ray (110; Fig. 6. 18, Q-S), zygotes (apparently with a very delicate oocyst membrane) producing two sporocysts, each with eight sporozoites; *Echinospora* Léger (Fig. 6. 18, M), spiny oocyst containing 4-8 bivalve sporocysts, each with one sporozoite; *Eimeria* Schneider (6; Fig. 6. 18, A-K), oocysts containing four dizoic sporocysts, many species known from mammals, birds, reptiles, Amphibia and fishes, and a few from Arthropoda; *Isospora* Schneider (6; Fig. 6. 18, L), oocyst with two tetrazoic sporocysts; *Jarrina* Léger and Hesse (Fig. 6. 18, P), oocyst with an elevated collar surrounding the micropyle, four dizoic sporocysts; *Pfeifferinella* Wasielewski (Fig. 6. 14, H), oocyst with eight sporozoites but no sporocysts; *Wenyonella* Hoare (51), oocyst with four tetrazoic sporocysts.

Family 5. Lankesterellidae. Sporozoites, developed within the asporocystic oocyst, are liberated in the vertebrate host and enter erythrocytes. Invaded corpuscles are ingested and transferred mechanically by an invertebrate vector (mite, leech). The merogonic cycle is then resumed in the new vertebrate host. In *Shellackia* Reichenow (Fig. 6. 19, A-F), development occurs in the intestinal epithelium of lizards. Sporozoites which have entered red corpuscles are transferred mechanically by a mite. In *Lankesterella* Labbé (100, 100a; Fig. 6. 19, M), development occurs in the endothelial cells of capillaries in frogs. Sporozoites, after entering erythrocytes, are transferred by a leech.

Family 6. Selenococcidiidae. The details of sporogony are unknown. The reported phases of the life-cycle are unusual in that growth stages of both schizonts and gametocytes are extracellular but enter tissue cells to complete their development. The only genus, *Selenococcidium* Léger and Duboscq (79a; Fig. 6. 19, G-L), contains a species reported from the intestine of lobsters.

Subclass 3. Haemosporidia

These are the typical blood parasites whose gametocytes, and also the merogonic cycle in some cases, occur in red blood cells. Syngamy and sporogony occur in an invertebrate host. The zygote becomes a migratory ookinete. Although an oocyst may be developed later, the membrane is never a thick, resistant covering. Sporozoites are never enclosed in a sporocyst membrane and inoculative transfer is the rule. In the Plasmodiida, the stages which invade red blood cells deposit pigment in their cytoplasm, but this apparently is not true for the Babesiida. Malarial parasites are known to split hemoglobin into globin and hematin, digest the protein, and retain the hematin in characteristic pigment granules (90).

The Haemosporidia may be divided into the Plasmodiida and the Babesiida. The life-cycle of the Plasmodiida resembles that of Coccidia, with well-marked merogony and sporogony. The life-cycles of many Babesiida are incompletely known. Some species apparently undergo fission in red corpuscles of the vertebrate host. Merogony in lymphocytes has been reported for certain others. The fusion of similar gametes has been described in *Babesia* (27).

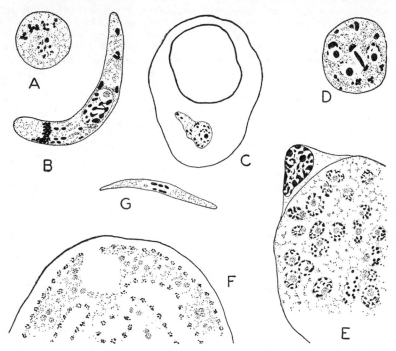

Fig. 6. 20. *Plasmodium circumflexum*, stages in mosquitoes (after Reichenow): macrogamete (A) and ookinete (B), x3640; ookinete in cell of gut wall (C), x1950; young oocyst with four nuclei (D), x3640; portion of a section through an older oocyst, remnant of gut cell shown (E), x1950; portion of a section through a mature oocyst, just before sporogony (F), x1850; a sporozoite (G), x3960.

Order 1. Plasmodiida. Throughout the order, merogony occurs in endothelial or related tissue cells of the vertebrate host. In one family, merogony is apparently restricted to parasites in such tissue cells. In the malarial parasites, however, merozoites from the basic merogonic cycle invade red blood cells and undergo a series of erythrocytic cycles of merogony. Gametocytes develop from some of these erythrocytic merozoites. In other Plasmodiida, only the gametocytes appear in blood cells. In either case, gametocytes are ingested by an invertebrate host in which syngamy and sporogony occur.

Gametogenesis and syngamy of Plasmodiida resemble these processes in Eimeriida. The gametocytes (Fig. 6. 21, F, G) are more or less similar in size, and are not associated during development. At maturity, the microgametocyte rounds up and produces a few slender microgametes which are rapidly separated from the residual protoplasm in a process of "exflagellation." Syngamy results in a migratory ookinete (Fig. 6. 20, A-C). This ookinete may pass through the gut wall of the vector and come to rest beneath the membrane covering the gut; or as in *Plasmodium circumflexum* of birds and mosquitoes (116), it may invade an epithelial cell of the gut and develop there. The zygote apparently secretes a thin oocyst membrane which is stretched as the parasite grows. Repeated nuclear division results in a multinucleate sporont, or "oocyst" (Fig. 6. 22, A), which produces many sporozoites. Sporoblasts are not formed, although the sporont in *Plasmodium* becomes extensively "vacuolated" before sporogony (Fig. 6. 20, F). Some workers have interpreted this apparent vacuolation as a series of infoldings from the surface. The liberated sporozoites (Fig. 6. 20, G) migrate through the tissues, and some of them reach the anterior part of the digestive tract from which they are inoculated into a vertebrate.

After inoculation into a vertebrate, the sporozoites typically invade, or are ingested by, phagocytic cells of the viscera within an hour or so. The sporozoite becomes a trophozoite which develops into a multinucleate schizont and undergoes merogony (Fig. 6. 21, A, B). The surviving merozoites may enter other tissue cells, so that exoerythrocytic merogonic cycles continue throughout the infection. In the Plasmodiidae, merozoites from the first or a later exoerythrocytic merogony may enter red blood cells and develop into schizonts, thus starting a series of cycles in the blood. Sooner or later, merozoites develop directly into gametocytes which, at maturity, are infective for the vector. In the Haemoproteidae, merogony does not occur in erythrocytes, although gametocytes (Fig. 6. 22, E-J) do invade blood cells after the infection has been in progress for some time.

For many years the erythrocytic stages of Plasmodiidae were the only stages known in vertebrates. As a result of investigations by Coulston, Garnham, Hawking, Huff, James, Porter, Raffaele, Shortt, and others (reviews: 32, 54, 55, 108), the occurrence of exoerythrocytic merogony in reptilian, avian, and mammalian parasites is now clearly established. In the typical infection, a *pre-erythrocytic phase* results from the development of sporozoites introduced by the vector and may include one (primates) or several merogonic cycles (birds). Products of the first pre-erythrocytic merogony have been referred to as *cryptozoites;* the merozoites formed in later exoerythrocytic cycles, as *metacryptozoites* (56). Exoerythrocytic stages in later stages of an infection are known also as *phanerozoites* (57). Merozoites from pre-erythrocytic merogony continue the exoerythrocytic cycle after invasion of blood cells occurs. Exo-erythrocytic schizonts, in such species as *Plasmodium gallinaceum* (56), may be of two kinds, macroschizonts and microschizonts. The latter produce many micromerozoites (100-1000 or so) which enter erythrocytes. The macroschizonts produce a smaller number (64 or less, in *P. relictum*) of macromerozoites which enter cells other than erythrocytes. In experi-

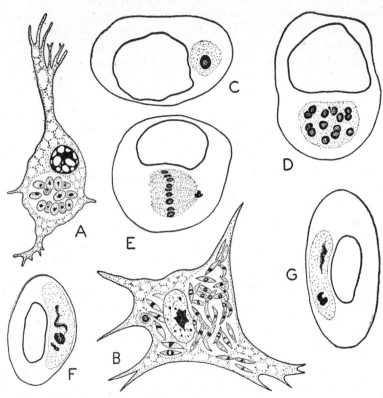

Fig. 6. 21. Malarial parasites in birds: A, B. Exoerythrocytic stages of *Plasmodium relictum* and *P. gallinaceum* in phagocytes (after Coulston and Huff). C-G. Erythrocytic stages of *Plasmodium elongatum*, Feulgen preparations (after Chen): trophozoite (C), schizont with 14 nuclei and a small pigment granule (D), and merozoites (E), x4050; microgametocyte with elongated nucleus and pigment (F), macrogametocyte (G), x3375.

mental avian infections, exoerythrocytic stages often appear after inoculation of erythrocytic forms.

Exoerythrocytic stages of Plasmodiida develop mainly in lymphoid-macrophage cells (cells of the "reticulo-endothelial system"), although their localization varies from species to species. In *Haemoproteus*, the parasites occur mostly in endothelial cells of visceral capillaries, especially in the kidney, liver, lungs, and spleen. *Plasmodium elongatum* has been found in a variety of blood-forming cells, while other avian parasites apparently prefer lymphoid-macrophage cells (55).

The erythrocytic cycle in Plasmodiidae is initiated by merozoites from an exoerythrocytic merogony. Growth into a schizont is followed by merogony (Fig. 6. 21, C-E), and the surviving merozoites enter other erythrocytes to repeat the process. The periodicity of erythrocytic merogony varies with the species, or even strains within a species, and the cycle covers a period of one to several days in different malarial parasites.

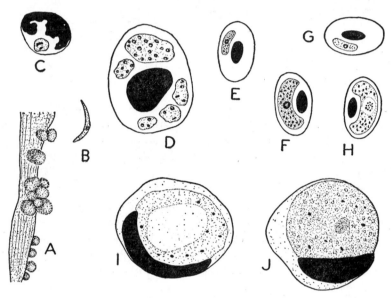

Fig. 6. 22. A-H. *Haemoproteus columbae:* oocysts on portion of gut in *Lynchia maura* (A), x105; and sporozoite (B), x1740 (after Adie); trophozoite in leucocyte (C); meroblasts, produced by division of a trophozoite, have undergone nuclear division in preparation for merogony (D); young and approximately mature macrogametocytes (E, F); young and mature microgametocytes (G, H); C-H, x1320 (after Aragão). I, J. Macro- and microgametocytes of *Leucocytozoon coccyzus*, x2136 (after Coatney and West).

Sooner or later, gametocytes (Fig. 6. 21, F, G) are developed, and the blood of the host is then infective for the vector.

The Order Plasmodiida may be divided into two families, the Haemoproteidae and the Plasmodiidae, differentiated by the absence of erythrocytic merogony in the former. Only the gametocytes of Haemoproteidae are to be expected in erythrocytes.

Family 1. Haemoproteidae. These are blood parasites of birds and reptiles. Merogony is exoerythrocytic, primarily in endothelial cells of visceral capillaries (*Haemoproteus*), or in lymphoid-macrophage cells of the viscera (e.g., spleen, liver) as in *Leucocytozoon simondi* (53). Schizonts of *Haemoproteus* often divide into meroblasts, each of which grows before producing merozoites. However, the formation of meroblasts may be skipped. Gametocytes of *Haemoproteus* develop in erythrocytes and deposit cytoplasmic pigment comparable to that of malarial parasites. Young gametocytes of *L. simondi* appear in lymphocytes, monocytes, myelocytes, and late polychromatophil erythroblasts (53); only those in the red cells deposit pigment in their cytoplasm. The Haemoproteidae of birds undergo syngamy and sporogony in blood-sucking flies (*Lynchia, Simulium,* and related genera) which ingest gametocytes from the blood (1, 48, 102, 103).

The family includes *Haemoproteus* Kruse (52, 102; Fig. 6. 22, A-H) and *Leucocytozoon* Danilewsky (53, 138; Fig. 6. 22, I, J). Checklists of species and host indices are available for *Leucocytozoon* (19), *Haemoproteus* (18), and for species of both genera found in North American birds (47).

Family 2. Plasmodiidae. This family includes one genus, *Plasmodium* Marchiafava and Celli (Figs. 6. 20, 21), which includes malarial parasites of reptiles (130, 131), birds (49), and mammals. Check-lists and host-indices are available for the genus (20) and for species parasitic in North American birds (47). Species causing malaria in man are discussed in Chapter XIII.

Order 2. Babesiida. The life-cycles are not yet completely known. Non-pigmented stages, in the red corpuscles of cattle and certain other mammals, are ingested by ticks and establish infections in these invertebrate hosts. With the demonstration by Smith and Kilbourne (123), that ticks transmit *Babesia bigemina,* arthropods were identified for the first time as vectors of protozoan parasites.

One of the most completely known life-cycles is that of *Theileria parva* (21, 22; Fig. 6. 23), which causes African Coast fever of cattle. Erythrocytic stages are ingested by a tick and liberated in the gut. Small parasites of two sizes are soon observed, usually in clumps, and syngamy is believed to occur. Larger parasites (Fig. 6. 23, A), believed to be zygotes, now replace the ones which first appeared in the tick. After preliminary growth, an elongated ookinete is developed within the zygote. Such ookinetes appear later in the body cavity near the salivary glands and some of them enter gland cells (Fig. 6. 23, B-D). The ookinete now rounds up and produces a number of sporoblasts, each of which divides into sporozoites (Fig. 6. 23, E, F). The sporozoites escape into the salivary ducts and are inoculated into the mammalian host when the tick begins to feed. Sporozoites pass by way of lymph vessels to a lymph gland, and the survivors invade lymphocytes where they develop into multinucleate schizonts (Fig. 6. 23, G), or "agamonts" (21). As the infection progresses, so-called gamonts appear. These stages stain less intensely and have smaller nuclei than those of the agamonts. Multinucleate gamonts (Fig.

6. 23, H) divide into uninucleate forms, some of which enter the blood stream and invade red corpuscles. The erythrocytic forms (Fig. 6. 23, I-S) are infective for ticks.

The life-cycle of *Babesia bigemina* (26, 27), the causative organism of Texas cattle fever, is similar to that of *Theileria parva*. Erythrocytic

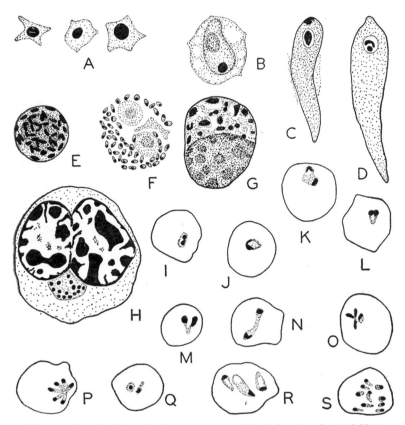

Fig. 6. 23. A-F. *Theileria parva*, stages in ticks (after Cowdry and Ham): A. Group of three "zygotes," x4550. B. Ookinete in gland cell. C, D. Growth of ookinete. E. Multinucleate sporoblast. F. Sporozoites surrounding a residual mass; B-F, x2925. G-S. *Theileria parva*, stages in cattle (after Cowdry and Danks): G. Multinucleate "agamonts" in a lymphocyte, x2925. H. A multinucleate "gamont" in a lymphocyte, x2600. I-P. Stages suggesting reproduction of *T. parva* in red corpuscles; x2925. Q-S. Corpuscles containing two, three and ten parasites; x2925.

stages are ingested by the tick and liberated from the corpuscles (Fig. 6. 24, K-M). Elongated "isogametes" later appear and undergo apparent isogamy (Fig. 6. 24, N-R). The zygotes become ookinetes which migrate through the gut wall. Those which invade ova continue their development in the resulting young ticks, producing sporoblasts (Fig. 6. 24, S-W) which become sporokinetes. Some of these sporokinetes invade cells of the developing salivary glands and give rise to sporozoites (Fig. 6. 24, X, Y). A variety of forms (Fig. 6. 24, A-J), similar to those for *Theileria*, finally appear in the red corpuscles of cattle after sporozoites are inoculated by a tick. These erythrocytic stages are infective for ticks.

The life-cycles of the two genera—*Babesia* Starcovici and *Theileria* Bettencourt, França and Borges—seem to differ primarily in the vertebrate phase. Multiplication in lymphocytes, as established for *Theileria*

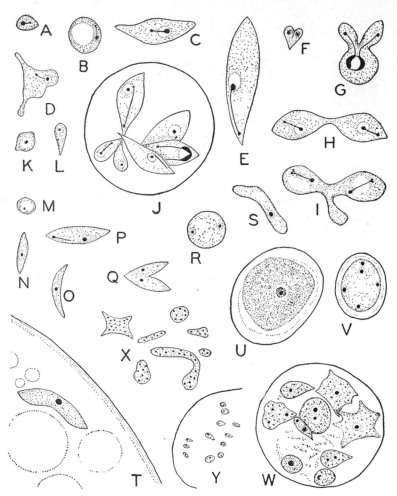

Fig. 6. 24. *Babesia bigemina* (after Dennis). A-J. Stages in red corpuscles of cattle; reproduction by fission is suggested by stages F-J; x4795. K-M. Parasites from the gut of ticks. N-P. Development of an "isogamete." Q, R. Supposed stages in isogamy. S. Ookinete from gut of a tick. T. Ookinete in ovum of tick; yolk globules outlined; portion of a section. U. Oocyst. V. Small oocyst with five nuclei; K-V, x2818. W. Developing sporoblasts, x3270. X. Sporokinetes, smear preparation from tick; x3270. Y. Group of sporozoites from embryonic salivary gland of tick; x1940,

parva (21), is not known to occur in *Babesia*. The supposed absence, in *Theileria*, of erythrocytic reproduction—a process generally accepted for *Babesia*—may not be a completely valid distinction. Erythrocytic stages of *Theileria parva* (21) may undergo a certain amount of growth and possibly reproduction as well (Fig. 6. 23, I-P). Such apparent differences in life-cycles form the basis for the usual recognition of two families, the Babesiidae and Theileriidae, with the general characteristics of their type genera.

Genera of uncertain status. Two additional genera, *Dactylosoma* Labbé and *Toxoplasma* Nicolle and Manceaux, may or may not belong in the

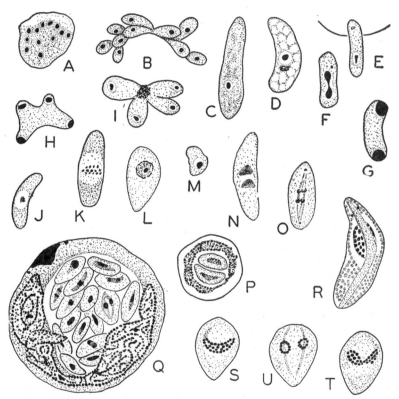

Fig. 6. 25. A-D. *Dactylosoma ranarum* (Kruse) Labbé, x2835 (after Mathis and Léger): multinucleate schizont (A), merogony (B), microgametocyte (C), macrogametocyte (D). E-K. *Dactylosoma jahni,* x1985 (after Nigrelli): parasite entering erythrocyte of a newt (E); stages in reproduction (F-I); microgametocyte (J); macrogametocyte (K). L-O. *Toxoplasma canis,* x2875 (after Ray): extracellular forms seen in smears from liver and spleen (L, M); binucleate form (N); stage in nuclear division (O). P-U. *Toxoplasma,* a strain of human origin maintained in mice (after Cross): P. Two parasites in a polymorphonuclear cell, x2500. Q. Group of parasites in a large mononuclear leucocyte, x2500. R. Extracellular stage showing nucleus, thick parastyle, and cytoplasmic granules. S, T. Nuclear division, Feulgen preparations. U. Binucleate stage with two parastyles; R-U, x4500.

Babesiida; the question cannot be decided without further knowledge of the life-cycles.

Dactylosoma Labbé. This genus (95, 100) includes little known non-pigmented forms occurring in erythrocytes of frogs, urodeles, and lizards. Merogony in red cells and the development of supposed gametocytes (Fig. 6. 25, A-K) have been described but the rest of the life-cycle is unknown.

Toxoplasma Nicolle and Manceaux. Organisms assigned to this genus have been found in various tissue cells of vertebrates—several types of leucocytes, lymphoid-macrophage (reticulo-endothelial) cells, cells of the central nervous system, and in erythrocytes of experimentally inoculated birds (144). In addition, extracellular stages have been observed by various workers. Several strains have been maintained in chick embryos by serial transfers (83). Life-cycles have not yet been worked out and the taxonomic status of the genus is uncertain. However, the protozoan nature of *Toxoplasma* has been affirmed in some of the more recent investigations (23, 89).

Individual parasites range from almost spherical to elongated forms (Fig. 6. 25, L-U). The larger stages are usually not more than 5-6μ long, while small forms may measure only 2-3μ in diameter. In addition to the nucleus and sometimes cytoplasmic globules, Cross (23) occasionally noted a longitudinal axostyle-like band ("cytostyle") just beneath the pellicle (Fig. 6. 25, R, U). Supposed flagella have been described by several workers, although more evidence is needed for any definite conclusion (23). Within invaded tissue cells the parasites occur singly or in groups (Fig. 6. 25, Q) in one or more vacuoles, or "pseudocysts." These pseudo-cysts have been interpreted in some instances as the results of schizogony, but most workers are agreed that reproduction by longitudinal binary fission is the rule.

The type species, *Toxoplasma gondii* Nicolle and Manceaux (16), was described from a North African rodent. Infections with *Toxoplasma* have been reported subsequently from a variety of birds (143) and mammals, including man, but there is much uncertainty in regard to the specific status of described types. The problem of differentiating species is complicated by the apparent lack of host-specificity (89). For instance, strains isolated from cases of human toxoplasmosis have been found infective for monkeys, rabbits, mice, guinea-pigs, hamsters, cotton rats, white rats, and chickens.

Infection with *Toxoplasma* seems to be responsible for several pathological conditions in man: (1) a type of congenital encephalomyelitis which appears in infants shortly after birth or even *in utero* (141, 142); (2) a type of acute encephalomyelitis in children (119); (3) a syndrome resembling spotted fever and associated with inflammation of the lungs (107); and (4) mild cases, in which the mothers of congenitally infected infants may show no history of previous toxoplasmosis. Human infections have been diagnosed microscopically and by inoculation of laboratory animals. A complement-fixation test also shows some promise for diagnosis of active toxoplasmosis (136).

CLASS 2. CNIDOSPORIDEA

A general characteristic of this group is the production of spores which differ distinctly from those of Telosporidea. Each spore (Fig. 6. 26, A) typically contains one or more polar capsules and also one or more sporoplasms analogous to the sporozoites of Telosporidea. Each polar capsule contains a coiled polar filament (Fig. 6. 26, C) which is extruded under certain conditions. This filament has been considered an organelle of attachment which prevents passage of the spore through the gut of the host before the sporoplasm can emerge. Another view is that the polar filament is a tube through which the sporoplasm travels from the spore directly into a tissue cell (104). The membrane of the spore may be apparently continuous, or it may consist of two or three sections, or valves (Fig. 6. 26, B, E). In many Cnidosporidea each spore appears to be multicellular in origin, in contrast to the sporocysts and oocysts of Telosporidea and the cysts of other Protozoa. Another distinction between the two classes is that the zygote of the Telosporidea undergoes sporogony, while that of the Cnidosporidea gives rise to one or more trophozoites. The young trophozoite is a small amoeboid organism which typically develops into a plasmodium (Fig. 6. 26, D, F). However, the trophozoites of Microsporida, which are almost exclusively intracellular parasites, are very small and the nuclei are few in number. The trophozoites of other Cnidosporidea typically invade body cavities of the host or else grow as tissue parasites (intercellular rather than intracellular). Reproduction of the trophozoite—by a so-called schizogony in certain Microsporida, or by fission, budding, or plasmotomy in other cases—has been reported. However, this phase of the cycle seems to have been eliminated completely in many Cnidosporidea.

The Cnidosporidea have been divided into four orders: Myxosporida, Microsporida, Actinomyxida, and Helicosporida. The spores of Myxosporida are bivalve, usually with two, but sometimes one or four polar capsules. The spore of the Actinomyxida contains three valves, three polar capsules, and one to many sporoplasms. The spores of Microsporida are small, usually with only one polar capsule, and the presence of separate valves is doubtful in most species. The spore of Helicosporida contains a single coiled filament but no polar capsules.

Order 1. Myxosporida. The Myxosporida are mostly parasites of fishes, less commonly of Amphibia and Reptilia. The supposedly more primitive types are coelozoic, invading the gall-bladder, kidney tubules, and urinary bladder. Others have been found in most tissues and organs of fishes, although a given species may be limited to a particular tissue. Some of these infections are frequently fatal to the hosts.

The life-cycles show certain general features, although details vary to some extent. The zygote is formed by the fusion of two haploid sporoplasmic nuclei, commonly during the dispersal of spores to new hosts (99).

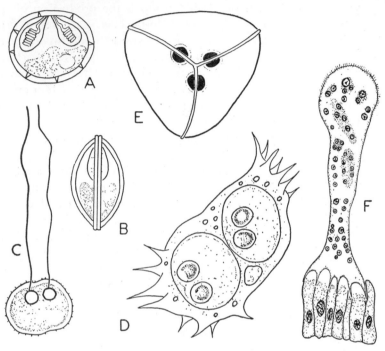

Fig. 6. 26. A. Spore of *Myxobolus osburni* Herrick, showing two polar filaments (coiled in capsules) and sporoplasm containing an iodinophilous vacuole; x2250 approx. (after Otto and Jahn). B. Spore of *M. osburni*, sutural view showing the two valves and the sutural ridges (after Otto and Jahn). C. Extruded polar filaments, spore of *Leptotheca ohlmacheri* (Gurley) Labbé; x1175 (after Kudo). D. Amoeboid trophozoite of *L. ohlmacheri* containing two spores; x1880 (after Kudo). E. Spore of *Sphaeractinomyxon gigas* Granata, polar view showing the three valves characteristic of spore membranes in the Actinomyxida; the three polar capsules are indicated in solid black; x850 (after G.). F. Trophozoite of *Myxobilatus asymmetricus* Davis, attached to epithelium of urinary bladder (fish); several developing sporoblasts are present; the free end of the trophozoite is covered with delicate bristles of uncertain significance; x800 (after D.).

After ingestion, the zygote escapes from the spore membrane and migrates to the tissue or body cavity in which development will occur. The growth phase includes both nuclear division and cytoplasmic growth. Depending upon the species, reproduction by plasmotomy (13), or by endogenous or exogenous budding may occur, particularly in monosporous and disporous species (99). If buds are produced, they may repeat the reproductive cycle or may develop directly into sporoblasts. The trophozoite of the large polysporous Myxosporida usually becomes a plasmodium (Fig. 6. 26, F) without intervening reproduction. The size of the mature trophozoite varies considerably in different species but lengths of 100-500μ are not uncommon.

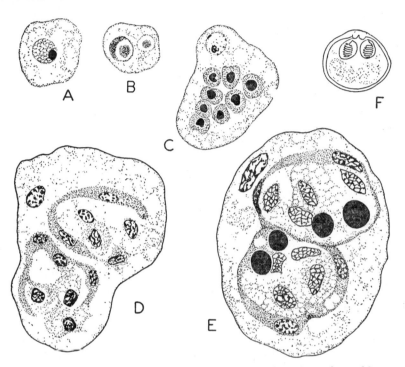

Fig. 6. 27. A. Young trophozoite with a single nucleus, *Leptotheca ohlmacheri*; x1880 (after Kudo). B. Binucleate trophozoite, *Ceratomyxa shasta* Noble; the more heavily stained nucleus will give rise to sporoblastic nuclei, the other will become the somatic residual nucleus; x2160 (after N.). C-F. *Leptotheca ohlmacheri* (after Kudo): C. Trophozoite with eight sporoblastic nuclei and a lightly stained somatic residual nucleus. D. Trophozoite with two sporoblasts; in each, two cystogenous "cells" lie at the periphery in a dense zone of cytoplasm; somatic residual nucleus lies outside the sporoblasts. E. Later stage in the development of spores; the development of polar capsules from each pair of capsulogenous "cells" is under way; nuclei of the cystogenous "cells" lie in the denser peripheral cytoplasm; the nuclei of the sporoplasms are surrounded by vacuolated cytoplasm; C-E, x1880. F. Mature spore with two polar filaments and two sporoplasms; x1200.

The growth phase often ends with the appearance of sporoblasts. However, growth continues during the production of spores in polysporous genera such as *Myxidium* (98). Although there are reports to the contrary, the most conclusive recent evidence (97, 98, 99) indicates that the sporoblast or pansporoblast is not the result of syngamy or plasmogamy. In typical sporulation, certain "cells" in the trophozoite become differentiated from the rest of the protoplasm. Each such "cell" is the initial stage of a sporoblast, or of a disporous pansporoblast if it is to produce two spores. In at least some species, the differentiation of a sporoblastic and a somatic nucleus is already apparent in the young binucleate trophozoite (Fig. 6. 27, B). Division of the sporoblastic nucleus during the growth phase results in a sporoblast with 6-8 nuclei, or a pansporoblast with a larger number of nuclei (Fig. 6. 27, C-E), the number varying with the number of polar capsules to be produced. If a pansporoblast is developed, it later divides into two sporoblasts.

Six nuclei appear in each developing spore of *Leptotheca ohlmacheri* (70; Fig. 6. 27, D, E). Two acquire differentiated zones of cytoplasm and become the cystogenous cells which gradually enclose the rest of the young spore and produce the valves of the spore membrane. Two other nuclei and their surrounding masses of cytoplasm become the capsulogenous cells which produce the polar capsules. The remaining two nuclei become the haploid nuclei of the sporoplasm. As a rule, however, young spores of species with two polar capsules contain eight nuclei (99). Two of these, the so-called residual nuclei, degenerate during later development. The development of the other six follows the course outlined for *Leptotheca*.

The spore membrane is composed of two valves united in a suture which may be either straight (Fig. 6. 26, B) or irregular (Fig. 6. 28, O), and is often marked by a sutural ridge formed by the thickened edges of the valves. The valves may be smooth or may be decorated with striations, ridges, or papillae. The spores of some species are ovoid, those of others may be spindle-shaped or somewhat asymmetrical, and the valves are sometimes drawn out into horns or spines (Fig. 6. 28). Each polar capsule lies near a pore which opens through the spore membrane in or near the sutural plane; or sometimes two adjacent capsules share a common pore. The mature spore usually contains a single sporoplasm, although two may be present as in *Lepthotheca ohlmacheri* (70). The single sporoplasm usually contains two nuclei, and in either case the sporoplasmic nuclei are haploid (74, 97, 99). A fairly large inclusion ("iodinophilous vacuole"), which is stained reddish-brown with iodine, is characteristic of the sporoplasm in certain genera (Family Myxobolidae), but not in the majority. The number of spores produced by each trophozoite varies in different cases, and a given species may be typically monosporous, disporous, or polysporous. However, this is not a rigidly fixed characteristic and all three types of sporulation are sometimes observed within a single species.

Although the occurrence of meiosis is well established, the stage at which this process apparently occurs varies in the descriptions of different species. In some cases (97, 98), meiosis occurs in one of the last nuclear divisions in development of the sporoblast, the products being the hap-

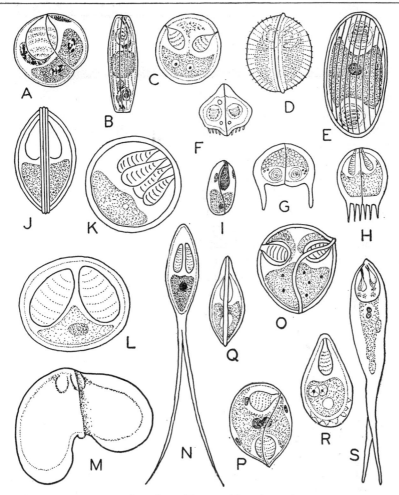

Fig. 6. 28. Spores of various Myxosporida: A. *Unicapsula muscularis* Davis, showing suture and the single polar capsule; x3125 (after D.). B. *Sphaeromyxa balbiani*, sutural view, one polar capsule at each pole; x1575 (after Kudo). C, D. *Sphaerospora polymorpha* Davis, optical section and sutural view; x2200 (after Kudo). E. *Myxidium melum* (11-12μ long), valve view (after Otto and Jahn). F. *Wardia ovinocua*, sutural view; x1575 (after Kudo). G. *Myxoproteus cornutus*, sutural view; x1200 (after Kudo). H. *Mitraspora cyprini*, sutural view; x1350 (after Kudo). I. *Coccomyxa morovi*, one polar capsule; x1065 (after Léger and Hesse). J, K. *Chloromyxum trijugum* Kudo, sutural and valve views; four polar capsules (after Otto and Jahn). L. *Myxosoma okobojiensis* (16.3x13.2μ), two large polar capsules (after Rice and Jahn). M. *Ceratomyxa shasta*, sutural view; x3040 (after Noble). N. *Henneguya magna*, overall length 87μ (after Rice and Jahn). O. *Sinuolinea capsularis*, sutural view; x1575 (after Kudo). P. *Zschokkella hildae*, sutural view; x630 (after Auerbach). Q, R. *Thelohanellus notatus*, sutural and valve views; x1605 (after Kudo). S. *Agarella gracilis*, four polar capsules; x1495 (after Dunkerly).

loid nuclei of the sporoplasm. According to certain other reports, meiosis occurs at an earlier stage so that all nuclei of the sporoblast are haploid, and a haploid cycle with the zygote as the only diploid stage also has been reported (99).

According to Kudo, who has published a check-list of species (72), the Myxosporida may be divided into three suborders on the basis of form and structure of the spores. In the Eurysporina the sutural plane is approximately perpendicular to the major axis of the spore, there are two polar capsules, one on each side of the sutural plane, and there is no iodinophilous vacuole. The Sphaerosporina have spherical spores with one, two, or four polar capsules and no iodinophilous vacuole. In the Platysporina, the sutural plane coincides with, or approximates, the major axis of the spore, there are one, two, or four polar capsules, and an iodinophilous vacuole may or may not be present. More recently, Tripathi (132) has suggested division of the Myxosporida into a "Suborder Unipolaria," with the polar capsules at or near one end of the spore, and a "Suborder Bipolaria" with one polar capsule at each end of the spore. The "Bipolaria" would include the Myxidiidae.

Suborder 1. Eurysporina

Family 1. Ceratomyxidae. Most known species are coelozoic parasites of marine fishes and are assigned to three genera: *Ceratomyxa* Thélohan (Fig. 6. 28, M), *Leptotheca* Thélohan (70; Fig. 6. 27, A, C-F), and *Myxoproteus* Doflein (Fig. 6. 28, G).

Family 2. Wardiidae. Histozoic or coelomic parasites of fresh-water fishes are included in this group, which contains two genera, *Mitraspora* Fujita (Fig. 6. 28, H) and *Wardia* Kudo (Fig. 6. 28, F).

Suborder 2. Sphaerosporina

Family 1. Chloromyxidae. In the only known genus, *Chloromyxum* Mingazzini (Fig. 6. 28, J, K), the spore contains four polar capsules.

Family 2. Sphaerosporidae. Spores with two polar capsules are found in *Sinuolinea* Davis (Fig. 6. 28, O) and *Sphaerospora* Thélohan (Fig. 6. 28, C, D).

Family 3. Unicapsulidae. A single polar capsule is characteristic of the only genus, *Unicapsula* Davis (Fig. 6. 28, A).

Suborder 3. Platysporina

Family 1. Coccomyxidae. In the only genus, *Coccomyxa* Léger and Hesse (Fig. 6. 28, I), the spore contains one polar capsule and no iodinophilous vacuole.

Family 2. Myxidiidae. The spores contain one polar capsule at each end.

Three genera are included: *Myxidium* Bütschli (Fig. 6. 28, E), *Sphaeromyxa* Thélohan (Fig. 6. 28, B), and *Zschokkella* Auerbach (Fig. 6. 28, P).

Family 3. Myxobolidae. The spores contain two polar capsules at one end and an iodinophilous vacuole.

The family includes the following genera: *Henneguya* Thélohan (Fig. 6. 28, N), *Myxobilatus* Davis (25; Fig. 6. 26, F), *Myxobolus* Thélohan (Fig. 6. 26, A, B), *Thelohanellus* Kudo (Fig. 6. 28, Q, R), and *Unicauda* Davis (25).

Family 4. Myxosomatidae. The spores contain two or four polar capsules and no iodinophilous vacuole. There are only two genera: *Agarella* Dunkerly (Fig. 6. 28, S) and *Myxosoma* Thélohan (Fig. 6. 28, L).

Order 2. Actinomyxida. This group includes organisms whose discoverer, Stolc, believed that they should be considered Mesozoa rather than Protozoa, in view of their complexity. The pansporoblast, or pansporocyst, typically develops eight spores, each with a membrane composed of three valves (Fig. 6. 26, E). In some species, each valve is drawn out into a horn, or spine, which may or may not be bifurcated. There are also three polar capsules, but the number of sporoplasms ranges from one to a hundred or more in different species. Species are known from sipunculids and tubificid annelids.

The life-cycle of *Triactinomyxon legeri* (84) is probably representative. The mature spore (Fig. 6. 30, D) contains a sporoplasmic mass in which lie 24 uninucleate sporoplasms and three or more residual somatic nuclei. The sporoplasms eventually fuse in pairs to produce 12 binucleate stages. Subsequently, the mass breaks up into several fragments which leave the spore membrane separately (Fig. 6. 29, A, B) and liberate the binucleate stages as small amoebae. Each amoebula (Fig. 6. 29, C) grows for a time and then undergoes nuclear division. Two of the nuclei, with associated cytoplasm, become peripheral in position and, as the cystogenous cells, produce a cyst around the remaining protoplasm (Fig. 6. 29, D). This stage is called a pansporoblast, or after the membrane is completed, a pansporocyst (84). The central binucleate mass next divides into two cells, one of which reproduces more rapidly than the other, so that a number of small cells and a few larger ones are produced (Fig. 6. 29, E, F). Anisogamy involves fusion of a large cell with a small one.

In development of sporoblasts within the pansporocyst, the nucleus of each zygote gives rise to seven nuclei (Fig. 6. 29, G). Three of these, with associated cytoplasm, migrate to one end of the developing spore as capsulogenous cells which later produce polar capsules (Fig. 6. 29, H). Three other cells, which are to produce the valves of the spore membrane, migrate to the opposite pole of the sporoblast (Fig. 6. 29, I, J). The seventh nucleus initiates a series of mitoses resulting in 27 nuclei. Three of these are residual somatic nuclei; the other 24 become sporoplasmic nuclei.

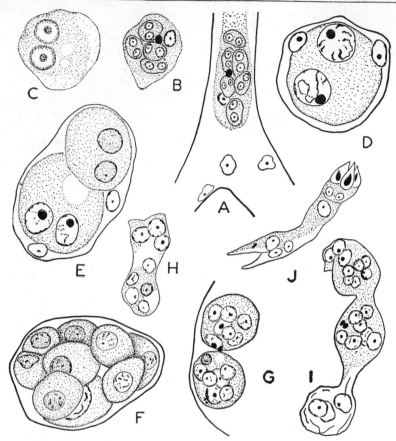

Fig. 6. 29. *Triactinomyxon legeri* Mackinnon and Adam (after M. & A.): A. Sporoplasmic fragment approaching point of exit from spore membrane; nuclei of valve cells shown below the sporoplasmic fragment. B. Sporoplasmic fragment after leaving the spore. C. Growing binucleate amoebula after release from a sporoplasmic fragment. D. Young pansporocyst, nuclei of cystogenous cells at the periphery. E. Pansporocyst containing two binucleate stages. F. Pansporocyst containing two large cells and a number of smaller ones; additional large and small cells are produced by division of each type. G. Two sporoblasts derived from two zygotes within a pansporocyst. H. A sporoblast in which the three capsulogenous cells have migrated to the upper pole. I. Developing spore; three cystogenous cells (valve-cells) have migrated to the lower pole; the seventh sporoblastic nucleus has produced a number of daughter nuclei in the sporoplasmic mass. J. Young spore with developing polar capsules and spore membrane; the seventh sporoblastic nucleus has not yet divided in this case. A, B, x1400; C-J, x1800.

Taxonomy

The taxonomy of the order has been discussed by Granata (39). Two families have been recognized. The spores of the Tetractinomyxidae have a continuous endocyst and an outer membrane composed of three valves. The endocyst is lacking in the Triactinomyxidae.

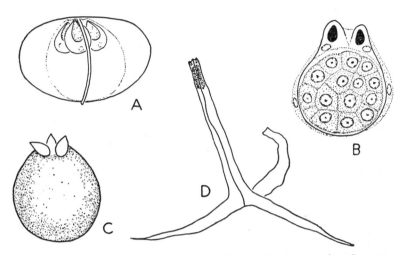

Fig. 6. 30. Spores of Actinomyxida: A. *Sphaeractinomyxon gigas* Granata, lateral view, x850 (after G.); compare with Fig. 6. 26, E. B, C. *Neoactinomyxum globosum* Granata, from stained (B) and living (C) material; x2470 (after G.). D. *Triactinomyxon legeri* Mackinnon and Adam, two horns expanded and the third partly expanded; sporoplasmic mass lies near the upper pole; x260 approx. (after M. & A.).

The following genera have been included in the two families:
Family 1. Tetractinomyxidae: *Tetractinomyxon* Ikeda (58).
Family 2. Triactinomyxidae: *Guyenotia* Naville (94), *Hexactinomyxon* Stolc (39), *Neoactinomyxon* Granata (39; Fig. 6. 30, B, C), *Sphaeractinomyxon* Caullery and Mesnil (39; Fig. 6. 30, A), *Synactinomyxon* Stolc (39), and *Triactinomyxon* Stolc (39, 84).

Order 3. Microsporida. These are small and generally intracellular parasites, mostly of arthropods and fishes, although a few have been reported from annelids and other hosts. As parasites of insects, Microsporida are commonly found in the epithelium of the gut and in the fat body or other tissues. Species invading fishes are commonly found in the skin and muscles.

The characteristic spores (Fig. 6. 31), the smallest of which may resemble yeasts or large bacteria, range from about 2.0 to more than 20μ in length in different species. It is doubtful that the spore membrane is composed of separate valves. A single polar filament is the rule, although two are present in *Telomyxa*. The polar filament, when extended, is strikingly long in proportion to size of the spore and may measure 25-500μ. The sporoplasm is binucleate in some Microsporida and uninucleate in others. As seen in invaded tissues, the spores often lie in groups within the sporont membrane, the number of spores being more or less characteristic of certain species.

After a spore is ingested by a new host the sporoplasm emerges as an amoeboid trophozoite (Fig. 6. 32, A), which may pass through the gut

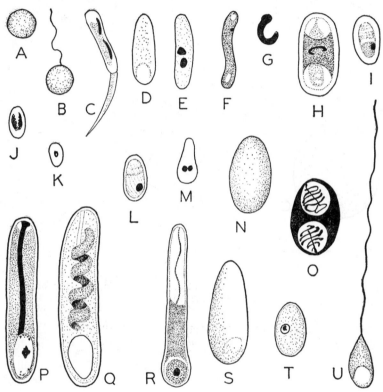

Fig. 6. 31. Spores of Microsporida: A, B. *Coccomyxa slavinae*, mature spore and one with extruded filament; x3700 (from Kudo, after Léger and Hesse). C. *Mrazekia lumbriculi*, binucleate sporoplasm; x1820 (after Jírovec). D, E. *Octosporca bayeri*, from living (D), and Feulgen preparation showing two nuclei (E); x2340 (after Jírovec). F. *Spiroglugea octospora*, x3900 (from Kudo, after Léger and Hesse). G. *Toxoglugea vibrio*, x3900 (from Kudo, after Léger and Hesse). H. *Nosema termitis*, x2990 (after Kudo). I. *Duboscqia legeri*, x3120 (after Kudo). J, K. *Plistophora intestinalis*, from Giemsa and Feulgen preparations; x2700 (after Jírovec). L. *Glugea acerinae*, Giemsa stain; x2700 (after Jírovec). M. *Thelohania cladocera*, two nuclei, Feulgen stain; x2700 (after Jírovec). N, O. *Telomyxa glugeiformis*, unstained and stained; x5400 (from Kudo, after Léger and Hesse). P, Q. *Bacillidium argoisi*, hematoxylin preparation (P); Feulgen preparation showing spiral nucleus (Q); x1950 (after Jírovec). R. *Cougourdella magna*, x2600 (after Hesse). S. *Stempellia magna*, x2070 (after Kudo). T. *Nosema elongatum*, Feulgen stain; x3300 (after Jírovec). U. *Gurleya richardi*, x3240 (from Kudo, after Cépède).

wall into the tissue spaces or blood stream, and thence into some particular type of tissue cell; or as in a number of species, the trophozoite remains in the epithelium of the gut. In any case the young trophozoite grows and reproduces by binary fission (Fig. 6. 32, B, C), as in *Nosema termitis,* or else by "schizogony" (Fig. 6. 32, F-H), as in *Duboscqia legeri*

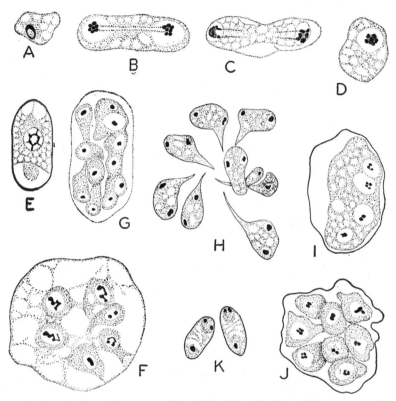

Fig. **6. 32.** A-E. *Nosema termitis,* x2990 (after Kudo): A. Young amoeboid trophozoite. B, C. Stages in fission of trophozoites. D. Young sporont. E. Immature spore; compare with Fig. 6. 31, H. F-K. *Duboscqia legeri,* x2760 (after Kudo): F-H. Stages in schizogony. I. Sporont with four nuclei. J. Sporoblasts have developed within the sporont membrane. K. Two immature spores which have developed from sporoblasts within the sporont membrane.

(73). The products of reproduction may repeat the reproductive cycle, or they may become sporonts which produce spores (Fig. 6. 32, D, I).

A sporont may develop directly into one sporoblast, as in *Nosema termitis* (75), or may undergo nuclear division and produce a number of sporoblasts within the original sporont membrane (Fig. 6. 32, J, K). Sporoblasts are either uninucleate or binucleate, depending upon the species. It has been impossible to determine with certainty the occurrence of nuclear division during development of the sporoblast. The best modern evidence indicates that, as in *Nosema* (75), *Duboscqia* (73), *Bacillidium*, and *Mrazekia* (63), the single nucleus or the two nuclei of the sporoblasts become the corresponding nuclei of uninucleate and binucleate spores. Accordingly, it appears that somatic differentiation and division of labor, as seen in the Myxosporida for example, are lacking in the Microsporida.

Taxonomy

Classification of the Microsporida is based primarily upon the form and structure of the spores and to a lesser degree upon differences in the details of sporogenesis. Four families have been recognized (71).

Family 1. Coccosporidae. The spores are spherical, or approximately so, and contain one polar filament. The family contains the genus *Coccospora* Kudo (71; Fig. 6. 31, A, B).

Family 2. Mrazekiidae. The spores have a single polar filament and are cylindrical, or tubular and curved. The ratio of length to thickness is greater than 5:1.

The family includes the following genera: *Bacillidium* Janda (64; Fig. 6. 31, P, Q), *Cougourdella* Hesse (71; Fig. 6. 31, R), *Mrazekia* Léger and Hesse (64; Fig. 6. 31, C), *Octosporea* Flu (64; Fig. 6. 31, D, E), *Spiroglugea* Léger and Hesse (71; Fig. 6. 31, F), and *Toxoglugea* Léger and Hesse (71; Fig. 6. 31, G).

Family 3. Nosematidae. The spores are usually ovoid or pyriform; if more elongated, the ratio of length to thickness is less than 4:1. There is only one polar filament.

The following genera have been assigned to the family. *Duboscqia* Pérez (73; Fig. 6. 31, I), *Glugea* Thélohan (137; Fig. 6. 31, L), *Gurleya* Doflein (71; Fig. 6. 31, U), *Nosema* Nägeli (75, 76; Fig. 6. 31, H, T), *Plistophora* Gurley (Fig. 6. 31, J, K), *Pyrotheca* Hesse (71), *Stempellia* Léger and Hesse (71; Fig. 6. 31, S), *Thelohania* Henneguy (Fig. 6. 31, M) and *Trichoduboscqia* Léger (71).

Family 4. Telomyxidae. The single genus, *Telomyxa* Léger and Hesse (71; Fig. 6. 31, N, O), is characterized by spores with two polar filaments.

Order 4. Helicosporida. This order was erected by Kudo for the genus *Helicosporidium* Keilin (68). The single known species, *H. parasiticum*, was found in larvae of a ceratopogonid dipteran, *Dasyhelea obscura*, from sap in wounds of elm and horse-chestnut trees. All stages of development occur in the body cavity of the host. Occasionally, however, parasites were found in fat bodies and in nerve ganglia, the invasions resulting in destruction of the fat bodies and reduction of the ganglia to neurilemma.

Young trophozoites grow and divide, frequently producing groups of eight (Fig. 6. 33, A-D). Sporulation is preceded by a period of rapid multiplication, and each spore apparently is developed from a group of

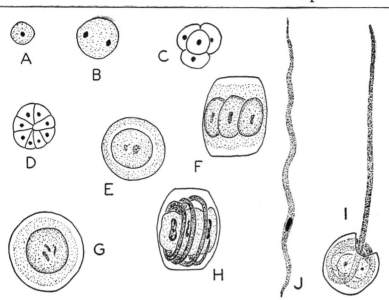

Fig. 6. 33. *Helicosporidium parasiticum;* A-H, x3720; I, x2325; J, x1400 (after Keilin): A. Young growth stage. B. Binucleate growth stage. C. Four-cell stage. D. Eight-cell stage. E-G. Stages in development of the spore; a young spore with a central mass surrounded by a protoplasmic rim (E); lateral and end views of a later stage with three central cells, spiral filament not yet differentiated (F, G). H. Mature spore showing peripheral spiral filament and the three central cells. I. Spore membrane ruptured and spiral filament protruding. J. Unravelled filament after rupture of the spore membrane; these filaments are 60-65μ long and contain one nucleus.

four cells. One of the four is believed to spread over the others to form a capsule (Fig. 6. 33, E-G). A spiral filament develops later but its exact origin is unknown. The mature spore (Fig. 6. 33, H) contains three cells ("sporozoites"), supposedly infective stages, and the spiral filament, be-lieved to play the role of an elater when the membrane is ruptured. When spores are placed in water the spore membrane is ruptured, the filament is extruded (Fig. 6. 33, I, J), and the three central cells are expelled.

CLASS 3. ACNIDOSPORIDEA

The organisms usually assigned to this class do not produce spores containing polar filaments and are thus unlike the Cnidosporidea. Their life-cycles fail to suggest any close relationship to the Telosporidea. Fur-thermore, the interrelationships of the groups included in the Acnido-sporidea are somewhat obscure, and as now constituted, the class may be largely a taxonomic convenience. As a result, the conventional division of the Acnidosporidea into the Subclasses Sarcosporidia and Haplospo-ridia indicates no firm belief that the two groups are as closely related as this arrangement might imply.

Subclass 1. Sarcoporidia

The characteristic "cysts" of these organisms[1] have been reported mainly from striated muscles of reptiles, birds, and mammals, while forms believed to be infective or developmental stages have been found in the blood, in the intestinal epithelium and submucosa, and in the feces of infected animals. Experimental infections have been produced by feeding infected muscle tissue and also by the intra-muscular injection of "spores."

Much of the evidence indicates that infective stages are ingested by a new host and that an intermediate host or mechanical vector is not necessary. There are some reports that infection may occur *in utero,* but the evidence is not entirely conclusive. The so-called "spores" of *Sarcocystis* have been found in feces of infected sheep (121), and after experimental feeding of laboratory animals, in the lumen of the intestine. In the intestine of mice fed infected muscle, "spores" penetrate the mucosa and appear in the blood stream after 5-6 hours (3). Circulatory distribution of the parasites is followed by invasion of muscle tissue and the eventual development of sarcocysts (Fig. 6. 34, E-I). The time required for development of typical sarcocysts has ranged from four to seven weeks after feeding infective stages.

Although this outline of the cycle seems to be based upon sound evidence, the details of development are incompletely known. One important gap is the scarcity of information concerning the "spores" after their production in the sarcocyst. There is some evidence that sarcocysts occasionally are ruptured and that the released parasites invade fresh tissue, but the route followed in reaching a new host is yet to be determined. The fact that "spores" have been recovered from the feces of various hosts (121) might suggest that after rupture of a sarcocyst, some of the parasites are transported through the circulatory system to the wall of the intestine and from there migrate into the lumen. This would involve retracing the route apparently followed in initial invasion. The obvious difficulties in tracing such parasites through the tissues account for the present lack of adequate information.

The parasites may be found in the oesophagus, heart, diaphragm, tongue muscles, and occasionally in other parts of the body. Invasion of smooth muscle apparently is rare, if it occurs at all. The earliest stages reported from muscles are single "sporoblasts" (Fig. 6. 34, E, F) and groups of several such forms. Development of the mature cyst from these stages has not been traced completely. The stage usually found in muscle is the sarcocyst (Fig. 6. 34, I-K), the size and shape of which vary. The larger sarcocysts are typically spindle-shaped in the diaphragm but are

---

[1] Literature on the Sarcosporidia has been reviewed by Badudieri (4) and Scott (120, 121).

more nearly ovoid in cardiac muscle. Mature cysts may reach a length of
25-50 mm and the larger ones contain several million "spores." The sarcocyst membrane (Fig. 6. 34, J, K) is composed of two or three layers, and
is enclosed in a zone of loose connective tissue and sometimes a layer

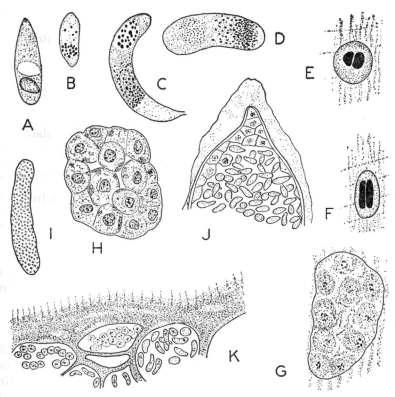

Fig. 6. 34. A-D. Spores of Sarcosporidia: A. *Sarcocystis platydactyli,* from
lizards; nucleus near blunt (posterior?) end, a central vacuole, and a granule
at the pointed end; x4750 (after Ball). B. *S. lacertae,* from lizards; x3120
(after Badudieri). C. *S. tenella,* x3120 (after Badudieri). D. *S. muris,* x3120
(after Badudieri). E-I. *Sarcocystis muris* in muscle of rat; E-H, x3120; I, x48
approx. (after Badudieri). E, F. Transverse and longitudinal sections, initial
stage of development. G, H. Successive stages in early development of a
sarcocyst. I. Mature sarcocyst. J. *Sarcocystis miescheriana,* from pig; section
showing outer striated "membrane" and portion of a sarcocyst containing
spores; x1440 (after Badudieri). K. *Sarcocystis tenella,* portion of a sarcocyst
membrane and adjacent developing spores; x1440 (after Badudieri).

of fibrous tissue. From the membrane, trabeculae extend inward to
form numerous compartments, many of which are filled with "spores"
(Rainey's corpuscles) in the mature sarcocyst. The striations of the so-
called striated membrane at the periphery of the sarcocyst seem to be
continuous with the connective tissue of the adjacent muscle fibres.

Therefore, the striated membrane may be a product of the host rather than of the parasite.

The term, "spore," is applied rather loosely to the elongated stages which develop in the sarcocyst, since there is no apparent spore membrane. The visible structures include a nucleus and more or less prominent granules (Fig. 6. 34, A-D). Several workers have noted that these "spores" can undergo twisting movements, rotation on the long axis, longitudinal contraction and elongation, or even locomotion (120).

Although the Sarcosporidia are commonly considered Protozoa and placed in the Acnidosporidea for lack of a more appropriate place, their protozoan nature has been questioned. One suggestion is that *Sarcocystis* from hogs is a fungus, identified as a species of *Aspergillus*. The reported evidence involves: (1) recovery of such a mold from cultures inoculated with sarcocysts removed from muscles of hogs; (2) recovery of sarcocysts from muscles of young pigs inoculated with conidia from such cultures; (3) recovery of a similar mold from experimentally infected animals (124). If this report can be confirmed, it should be possible to transfer to the mycologists the puzzling problems involved in taxonomy of the Sarcoporidia.

Aside from their interest as unusual parasites of uncertain relationships, the Sarcosporidia are of some importance in veterinary medicine as parasites of cattle, horses, sheep, and hogs. Sarcoporidiosis of man is apparently rare, although cases are reported occasionally (33).

Subclass 2. Haplosporidia

These organisms show certain similarities to the Cnidosporidea, although they produce cysts without polar filaments. Species have been reported from fishes, tunicates, insects, molluscs, annelids, nemertines, trematodes, and rotifers. They have been found in the coelom or other body cavities and also in tissues and individual cells in different cases.

The life-cycles are incompletely known. In some species, a small amoeboid stage emerges after a spore is ingested by the host. This uninucleate or binucleate trophozoite (Fig. 6. 35, A) may invade a tissue cell or some tissue of the host, or else make its way into a body cavity, where development is continued. Growth is usually accompanied by nuclear divisions (Fig. 6. 35, B), and the plasmodia of certain species contain many nuclei (Fig. 6. 35, C). In *Coelosporidium periplanetae*, however, occasional fission of binucleate trophozoites occurs, in addition to the development of plasmodia (60). Division of plasmodia into uninucleate stages (Fig. 6. 35, D, E) also occurs in *Coelosporidium* (60) but has not been reported in *Haplosporidium* (63).

The development of spores resembles that in certain Microsporidia. Uninucleate sporoblasts are formed within a mature plasmodium and each sporoblast apparently develops directly into a spore (Fig. 6. 35, F-H).

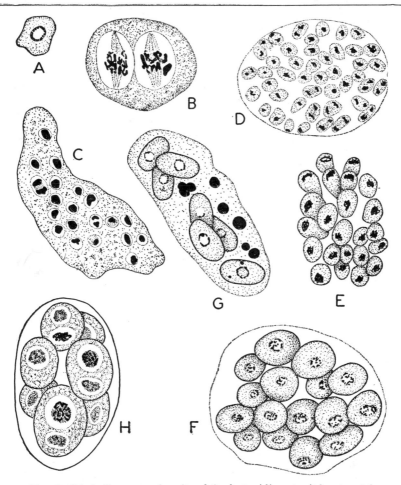

Fig. 6. 35. A. Young trophozoite of *Coelosporidium periplanetae* (after Ivanič). B. Nuclear division in binucleate trophozoite of *Haplosporidium cernosvitovi*, x2000 (after Jírovec). C. Plasmodium of *Coelosporidium periplanetae* (after Ivanič). D, E. Division of plasmodium (*C. periplanetae*) into uninucleate trophozoites (after Ivanič). F. Sporoblasts in *C. periplanetae* (after Ivanič). G. Young spores in plasmodium of *C. periplanetae*, x2290 (after Sprague). H. Spores within a pansporocyst in *Haplosporidium cernosvitovi*, x1375 (after Jírovec).

In *Haplosporidium cernosvitovi*, a histozoic species from oligochaetes, nearly mature spores generally lie within a distinct membrane (Fig. 6. 35, H).

Shape of the spore (Fig. 6. 36) and structure of the membrane vary in different species. The membrane apparently is bivalved in *Coelosporidium periplanetae* (Fig. 6. 36, B) and seems to be operculate in certain other species. In some cases, the membrane is extended into horns or may show adherent filaments, while the "tail" in *Urosporidium* possibly rep-

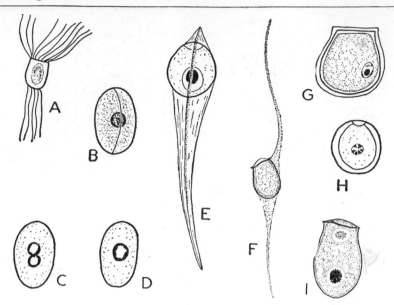

Fig. 6. 36. Spores of Haplosporidia: A. *Haplosporidium heterocirri,* x1540 (after Caullery and Mesnil). B-D. *Coelosporidium periplanetae,* from hematoxylin (B) and Feulgen preparations (C, D); x2910 (after Sprague). E. *Urosporidium fuliginosum,* x2800 (after Caullery and Mesnil). F. *Haplosporidium chitonis,* x3150 (after Goodrich). G. *Haplosporidium caulleryi,* x1540 (after Mercier and Poisson). H. *Anurosporidium pelseneeri,* x2660 (after Caullery and Chappellier). I. *Haplosporidium cernosvitovi,* x2000 (after Jírovec).

resents an outer membrane enclosing an operculate endocyst. Nuclear division within the spore, and spores with two nuclei, have been reported for *Coelosporidium periplanetae* (60, 125). The nuclei of a binucleate spore apparently fuse as the spore approaches maturity (125). In *Ichthyosporidium giganteum,* the two sporic nuclei are said to undergo meiosis. Two haploid nuclei then fuse to form a synkaryon while the other two degenerate (129). In addition, it has been reported that an encysted plasmodium of *I. hertwigi* may divide into amoeboid gametes which undergo syngamy within the cyst, the zygotes producing the pansporoblasts (129).

The following genera have been assigned to the Haplosporidia: *Anurosporidium* Caullery and Chappellier (Fig. 6. 36, H), *Bertramia* Caullery and Mesnil, *Coelosporidium* Mesnil and Marchoux (125), *Haplosporidium* Caullery and Mesnil (63), *Ichthyosporidium* Caullery and Mesnil (129), *Nephridiophaga* Ivanič (61), and *Urosporidium* Caullery and Mesnil (Fig. 6. 36, E).

LITERATURE CITED

1. Adie, H. 1924. *Bull. Soc. Path. Exot.* **17:** 605.
2. Allegre, C. F. 1948. *Trans. Amer. Micr. Soc.* **67:** 211.
3. Arai, K. 1925. *Arch. f. Protistenk.* **50:** 213.
4. Badudieri, B. 1932. *Arch. f. Protistenk.* **76:** 421.

5. Ball, G. H. 1938. *Arch. f. Protistenk.* **90**: 299.
6. Becker, E. R. 1934. *Coccidia and Coccidiosis* (Ames: Collegiate Press).
7. Berlin, H. 1924. *Arch. f. Protistenk.* **48**: 1.
8. Bhatia, B. L. 1924. *Quart. J. Micr. Sci.* **68**: 481.
9. ——— 1924. *J. Roy. Micr. Soc.* p. 187.
10. ——— 1930. *Parasitol.* **22**: 156.
11. ——— and G. B. Chatterjee 1925. *Arch. f. Protistenk.* **52**: 189.
12. Brackett, S., editor 1949. *Ann. N. Y. Acad. Sci.* **52**: 429.
13. Bremer, H. 1922. *Arch. f. Protistenk.* **45**: 273.
14. Chakravarty, M. 1935. *Arch. f. Protistenk.* **86**: 211.
15. ——— 1939. *Arch. f. Protistenk.* **92**: 67.
16. Chatton, E. and B. Blanc 1917. *Arch. Inst. Pasteur Tunis* **10**: 1.
17. Chen, T. T. 1944. *Amer. J. Hyg.* **40**: 26.
18. Coatney, G. R. 1936. *J. Parasit.* **22**: 88.
19. ——— 1937. *J. Parasit.* **23**: 202.
20. ——— and R. L. Roudabush 1936. *J. Parasit.* **22**: 338.
21. Cowdry, E. V. and W. B. C. Danks 1933. *Parasitol.* **25**: 1.
22. ——— and A. W. Ham 1932. *Parasitol.* **24**: 1.
23. Cross, J. B. 1947. *J. Inf. Dis.* **80**: 278.
24. Dakin, W. J. 1911. *Arch. f. Protistenk.* **23**: 145.
25. Davis, H. S. 1944. *Trans. Amer. Micr. Soc.* **63**: 311.
26. Dennis, E. W. 1930. *Univ. Calif. Publ. Zool.* **33**: 179.
27. ——— 1932. *Univ. Calif. Publ. Zool.* **36**: 263.
28. Dibb, M. J. 1938. *Parasitol.* **30**: 296.
29. Dobell, C. 1925. *Parasitol.* **17**: 1.
30. Edgar, S. A., C. A. Herrick and L. A. Fraser 1944. *Trans. Amer. Micr. Soc.* **63**: 199.
31. Gabriel, J. 1929. *Arch. f. Protistenk.* **67**: 46.
32. Garnham, P. C. G. 1948. *Trop. Dis. Bull.* **10**: 831.
33. Gilmore, H. R., B. H. Kean and F. M. Posey 1942. *Amer. J. Trop. Med.* **22**: 121.
34. Göhre, E. 1943. *Arch. f. Protistenk.* **96**: 295.
35. Goodrich, E. A. and H. L. M. P. Goodrich 1921. *Quart. J. Micr. Sci.* **65**: 157.
36. Goodrich, H. P. 1925. *Quart. J. Micr. Sci.* **69**: 619.
37. ——— 1938. *Quart. J. Micr. Sci.* **81**: 107.
38. ——— 1944. *Parasitol.* **36**: 72.
39. Granata, L. 1925. *Arch. f. Protistenk.* **50**: 139.
40. Grell, K. G. 1938. *Arch. f. Protistenk.* **91**: 526.
41. Hahn, J. 1928. *Arch. f. Protistenk.* **62**: 1.
42. Hatt, P. 1931. *Arch. Zool. Exp. Gén.* **72**: 341.
43. Hauschka, T. S. 1943. *J. Morph.* **73**: 529.
44. Henry, D. P. 1932. *Univ. Calif. Publ. Zool.* **37**: 269.
45. ——— 1938. *Arch. f. Protistenk.* **90**: 414.
46. Hentschel, C. C. 1926. *Parasitol.* **18**: 137.
47. Herman, C. M. 1944. *Bird Banding* **15**: 89.
48. Herms, W. B. and C. G. Kadner 1937. *J. Parasit.* **23**: 296.
49. Hewitt, R. I. 1940. *Bird Malaria* (Baltimore: Johns Hopkins Press).
50. Hoare, C. A. 1924. *Parasitol.* **32**: 210.
51. ——— 1933. *Parasitol.* **25**: 359.
52. Huff, C. G. 1932. *Amer. J. Hyg.* **16**: 618.
53. ——— 1942. *J. Inf. Dis.* **71**: 18.
54. ——— 1947. *Ann. Rev. Microbiol.* **1**: 43.
55. ——— 1948. *J. Parasit.* **34**: 261.
56. ——— and F. Coulston 1944. *J. Inf. Dis.* **75**: 231.
57. ——— and F. Coulston 1946. *J. Inf. Dis.* **78**: 99.
58. Ikeda, I. 1912. *Arch. f. Protistenk.* **25**: 240.
59. ——— 1914. *Arch. f. Protistenk.* **33**: 205.
60. Ivanič, M. 1926. *Arch. f. Protistenk.* **56**: 63.
61. ——— 1937. *La Cellule* **45**: 291.
62. Jameson, A. P. 1920. *Quart. J. Micr. Sci.* **64**: 207.
63. Jírovec, O. 1936. *Arch. f. Protistenk.* **86**: 500.

64. ——— 1936. *Arch. f. Protistenk.* **87**: 314.
65. Jones, A. W. 1943. *Trans. Amer. Micr. Soc.* **62**: 254.
66. Kamm, M. W. 1922. *Ill. Biol. Monogr.* **7**, No 1.
67. Keilin, D. 1920. *Parasitol.* **12**: 154.
68. ——— 1921. *Parasitol.* **13**: 97.
69. ——— 1923. *Parasitol.* **15**: 103.
70. Kudo, R. R. 1922. *Parasitol.* **14**: 221.
71. ——— 1924. *Ill. Biol. Monogr.* **9**, Nos. 2, 3.
72. ——— 1933. *Trans. Amer. Micr. Soc.* **52**: 195.
73. ——— 1942. *J. Morph.* **71**: 307.
74. ——— 1943. *J. Morph.* **72**: 263.
75. ——— 1943. *J. Morph.* **73**: 265.
76. ——— 1944. *Ill. Biol. Monogr.* **20**, No. 1.
77. Léger, L. 1906. *Arch. f. Protistenk.* **7**: 307.
78. ——— 1906. *Arch. f. Protistenk.* **8**: 159.
79. ——— and O. Duboscq 1909. *Arch. f. Protistenk.* **17**: 19.
79a. ——— and ——— 1910. *Arch. Zool. Exp. Gén.* **45**: 187.
80. ——— and ——— 1915. *Arch. f. Protistenk.* **35**: 199.
81. ——— and ——— 1915. *Arch. Zool. Exp. Gén.* **55** (N. & R.): 7.
82. Lermantoff, E. 1913. *Arch. f. Protistenk.* **32**: 205.
83. MacFarlane, J. O. and I. Ruchman 1948. *Proc. Soc. Exp. Biol. Med.* **67**: 1.
84. Mackinnon, D. L. and I. Adam 1924. *Quart. J. Micr. Sci.* **68**: 187.
85. ——— and H. N. Ray 1931. *Quart. J. Micr. Sci.* **74**: 439.
86. ——— and ——— 1931. *Quart. J. Micr. Sci.* **74**: 467.
87. ——— and ——— 1933. *Parasitol.* **25**: 143.
88. ——— and ——— 1937. *Parasitol.* **29**: 457.
89. Manwell, R. D., F. Coulston, E. C. Brinkley and V. P. Jones 1945. *J. Inf. Dis.* **76**: 1
90. Moulder, J. W. and E. A. Evans 1946. *J. Biol. Chem.* **164**: 145.
91. Nabih, A. 1938. *Arch. f. Protistenk.* **91**: 474.
92. Naville, A. 1927. *Parasitol.* **19**: 100.
93. ——— 1927. *Arch. f. Protistenk.* **57**: 427.
94. ——— 1930. *Quart. J. Micr. Sci.* **73**: 547.
95. Nigrelli, R. F. 1930. *Ann. Protistol.* **3**: 13.
96. Noble, E. R. 1938. *Univ. Calif. Publ. Zool.* **43**: 41.
97. ——— 1941. *J. Morph.* **69**: 455.
98. ——— 1943. *J. Morph.* **73**: 281.
99. ——— 1944. *Quart. Rev. Biol.* **19**: 213.
100. Nöller, W. 1913. *Arch. f. Protistenk.* **31**: 169.
100a. ——— 1920. *Arch. f. Protistenk.* **41**: 149.
101. Nusbaum, J. 1903. *Ztschr. wiss. Zool.* **75**: 281.
102. O'Roke, E. C. 1930. *Univ. Calif. Publ. Zool.* **36**: 1.
103. ——— 1934. *School. Forest. Conserv. Univ. Mich.*, Bull. No. 4.
104. Oshima, K. 1937. *Parasitol.* **29**: 220.
105. Patten, R. 1935. *Parasitol.* **27**: 399.
106. Phillips, N. E. and D. L. Mackinnon 1946. *Parasitol.* **37**: 65.
107. Pinkerton, H. and R. G. Henderson 1941. *J. Amer. Med. Assoc.* **116**: 807.
108. Porter, R. J. and C. G. Huff 1940. *Amer. J. Trop. Med.* **20**: 869.
109. Ray, H. 1930. *Parasitol.* **22**: 370.
110. ——— 1930. *Parasitol.* **22**: 471.
111. ——— 1933. *Arch. f. Protistenk.* **81**: 352.
112. ——— 1933. *Parasitol.* **25**: 392.
113. ——— and M. Das-Gupta 1940. *Parasitol.* **32**: 392.
114. Reed, N. 1933. *Parasitol.* **25**: 402.
115. Reichenow, E. 1921. *Arch. f. Protistenk.* **42**: 180.
116. ——— 1932. *Jen. Ztschr. Naturwiss.* **67**: 434.
117. ——— 1935. *Arch. f. Protistenk.* **84**: 431.
118. Roudabush, R. L. 1937. *Iowa St. Coll. J. Sci.* **11**: 135.
119. Sabin, A. B. 1941. *J. Amer. Med. Assoc.* **116**: 801.
120. Scott, J. W. 1930. *J. Parasit.* **16**: 111.

121. ——— 1943. *Bull. Wyoming Agr. Exp. Sta.,* No. 259.
122. Shellack, C. 1907. *Arch. f. Protistenk.* **9:** 297.
123. Smith, T. and F. H. Kilbourne 1893. *Bull. Bur. Anim. Ind.,* U. S. Dept. Agr. **1:** 177.
124. Spindler, L. A. and H. E. Zimmerman 1945. *J. Parasit.* **31** (Suppl.): 13.
125. Sprague, V. 1940. *Trans. Amer. Micr. Soc.* **59:** 460.
126. ——— 1941. *Ill. Biol. Monogr.* **18,** No. 2.
127. ——— and J. Ramsey 1942. *J. Parasit.* **28:** 399.
128. Stevenson, A. C. 1915. *Quart. J. Micr. Sci.* **61:** 127.
129. Swarczewsky, B. 1914. *Arch. f. Protistenk.* **33:** 49.
130. Thompson, P. E. and C. G. Huff 1944. *J. Inf. Dis.* **74:** 48.
131. ——— and ——— 1944. *J. Inf. Dis.* **74:** 68.
132. Tripathi, Y. R. 1948. *Parasitol.* **39:** 110.
133. Troisi, R. A. 1933. *Trans. Amer. Micr. Soc.* **52:** 326.
134. Tyzzer, E. E. 1912. *Arch. f. Protistenk.* **26:** 394.
135. ——— 1929. *Amer. J. Hyg.* **10:** 269.
136. Warren, J. and A. B. Sabin 1942. *Proc. Soc. Exp. Biol. Med.* **51:** 11.
137. Weissenberg, R. 1913. *Arch. mikr. Anat.* **82:** 81.
138. Wenyon, C. M. 1910. *Parasitol.* **3:** 63.
139. ——— 1926. *Protozoology* (London: Ballière, Tindall & Cox).
140. Weschenfelder, R. 1938. *Arch. f. Protistenk.* **91:** 1.
141. Wolf, A., D. Cowen and B. Paige 1939. *Science* **89:** 226.
142. ———, ——— and ——— 1941. *Science* **93:** 548.
143. Wolfson, F. 1940. *Amer. J. Hyg.* **32** (C): 88.
144. ——— 1941. *Amer. J. Trop. Med.* **21:** 653.

VII

Ciliophora

M EMBERS OF THIS SUBPHYLUM possess cilia or ciliary derivatives in some stage of the life-cycle. The equipment ranges from a complete covering of simple cilia to a relatively few membranelles more or less completely restricted to the peristomial area. Within this range, types of ciliary specialization and patterns of distribution form a major basis for differentiating taxonomic subdivisions. The Ciliophora are usually divided into two classes, Ciliatea and Suctorea. In the Ciliatea, cilia or their compound derivatives are present in the dominant phase of the cycle. Suctorea are non-ciliated as adults and have developed peculiar tentacles which function in feeding. The ciliated larval stages characteristic of most species establish the relationship of this group to the Ciliatea and larval ciliary patterns imply that Suctorea[1] are more closely related to the Holotrichida than to the more specialized ciliates (82, 103).

CLASS 1. CILIATEA

Cilia or compound ciliary organelles are present in active stages of the life-cycle. The ciliates show a variety of trends in specialization of the ciliature, and on this basis may be divided logically into a number of groups. The class includes the Subclasses Protociliatia and Euciliatia. The nuclei of Protociliatia are apparently similar in structure and func-

---

[1] In fact, some workers believe that the "Class Suctorea," as well as the "Order Peritrichida" and the "Order Chonotrichida," would be more appropriately placed as subdivisions of the Holotrichida, as suggested by Fauré-Fremiet (62). Rapidly accumulating data tend to support these proposals, and it now appears that such a taxonomic revision of the ciliates can be expected in the near future. The older system, as followed in the present chapter, presumably will be replaced by two major subdivisions of the ciliates, (1) a group corresponding to the Holotrichida plus the Suctorea, Chonotrichida, and Peritrichida; and (2) a group probably including the Spirotrichida as now constituted.

tion, whereas nuclear dimorphism (macronucleus and micronucleus) is characteristic of the Euciliatia.

Subclass 1. Protociliatia

These are the opalinid ciliates which, except for a few species from fishes and snakes, are parasitic in the large intestine of Amphibia. The opalinids have no cytostome, although this is not a feature exclusive to them among the Ciliatea. The distribution of cilia is practically uniform and in this respect the opalinids resemble many holotrichous ciliates with which they have sometimes been classified.

Ciliary patterns are rather simple. As described in *Opalina obtrigonoidea* (43), the dorsal rows follow sigmoid paths while the ventral rows are relatively straight (Fig. 7. 1, A). About half of the rows pass completely around the body. The rest, intercalary rows which extend from the anterior end toward one margin of the body, possibly represent stages in the development of new rows (43). Similar intercalary rows have been described in *Zelleriella elliptica* (38) and other species (152). Along the anteroventral surface in *O. obtrigonoidea,* a number of stout falcular cilia arise from the falcular fibrils (Fig. 7. 1, C, E). The latter are two subpellicular fibrils which extend along the anteroventral margin and then fuse into a single fibril which continues for some distance along the left margin of the body. The falcate fibril is connected with the first basal granule in each row of somatic cilia (Fig. 7. 1, E). Although longitudinal fibrils joining basal granules could not be detected, oblique fibrils, perpendicular to the rows of cilia, connect basal granules of different longitudinal rows (Fig. 7. 1, D). In addition to the fibrils parallel to the body surface, dorso-ventral fibrils extend inward from the basal granules, usually passing to granules on the other side of the body (Fig. 1. 11, G). In contrast to an earlier report for *Opalina ranarum* (73), no connections between the fibrils and the endoplasmic spherules could be detected in *O. obtrigonoidea.* The absence of such connections also has been reported for *Cepedea metcalfi, Opalina coracoidea,* and *O. ranarum* (8).

The pellicle of opalinids (8, 43, 152) shows numerous grooves, parallel to the rows of cilia, and each row apparently arises in such a groove. In *O. obtrigonoidea* the grooves are produced by pellicular folds (Fig. 7. 1, B) which may be a factor in maintenance of body form, "functioning much like the corrugations in corrugated cardboard" (43). Myonemes have not been demonstrated in the cortex.

The endoplasm typically contains Feulgen-negative (177) endoplasmic spherules (endospherules, endosarc bodies) which have been interpreted variously as Golgi bodies, parabasal bodies comparable to those of certain flagellates, masses of stored food, and even as stages in the development of nuclei. There is no evidence that these endoplasmic spherules are homologues of the macronuclear derivatives in *Dileptus* (Chapter I). Al-

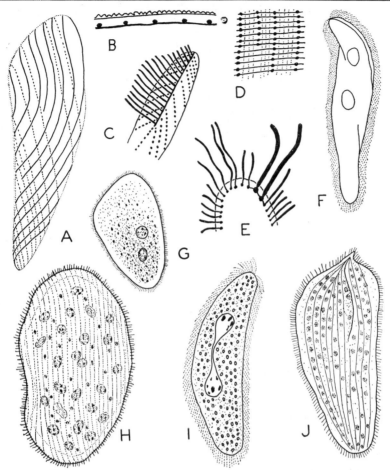

Fig. 7. 1. A-E. *Opalina obtrigonoidea* Metcalf (after Cosgrove): A. Diagram showing about half the actual number of ciliary rows. B. Cross-section showing pellicular grooves and basal granules; cilia omitted; x2160. C. Lateral view, falcular cilia, the fused falcular fibrils, basal granules of somatic cilia; semidiagrammatic. D. Surface view of basal granules and oblique fibrils; pellicular grooves indicated by dotted lines; x2160. E. Anterior end, longitudinal section; two falcular cilia arising from the falcular fibrils; somatic cilia and their basal granules; x1800. F. *Protoopalina intestinalis* (Stein) Metcalf; endoplasmic spherules not shown; x270 (after M.). G. *Zelleriella truncata* Carini, x35 (after C.). H. *Opalina ranarum* (Ehrbg.); length, 62-232μ (after Bhatia and Gulati). I. *Protoopalina montana* Metcalf, x390 (after M.). J. *Cepedea punjabensis* Bhatia and Gulati; average, 82x35μ (after B. & G.).

though the spherules may be involved in synthesis and storage of reserve food (164), the nature and significance of these inclusions are undetermined. The presence of an "excretory" canal or vacuoles, as described in *Protoopalina intestinalis* (151), has not been demonstrated in other species.

Binary fission is unusual in that the plane of division is oblique, or almost longitudinal, instead of transverse as in typical ciliates. In the binucleate *Zelleriella elliptica* (38), fission often precedes the completion of mitosis and produces temporarily uninucleate daughter organisms. Although nuclear behavior is not easily traced in multinucleate species, series of nuclear divisions apparently may precede and follow fission. Behavior of the ciliature and fibrillar system in fission of *Opalina ranarum* has been described (21).

Little is known about the life-cycles of Protociliata. However, the cycle of *Opalina ranarum,* according to one account (123), is fairly complicated. Throughout most of the year large multinucleate forms are present in the host. In the spring, plasmotomy produces small ciliates containing only a few nuclei. These stages encyst and are eliminated by the host. Such cysts are ingested by tadpoles and liberate "gametocytes." Repeated division of the "gametocytes" results in "gametes" of two sizes. According to another version (160), some ingested cysts give rise to gametes while others hatch into ciliates which merely grow to maturity. Gametes similar to those reported for *O. ranarum* have been described in *Protoopalina intestinalis* (151). Gametogenesis is said to be followed by anisogamy. The resulting zygotes encyst and are eliminated from the intestine. After ingestion by another tadpole, each zygote excysts and develops into a multinucleate ciliate. Encysted adults, as well as small cysts containing 1-4 nuclei, have been observed in *Opalina chattoni* (217).

Unfortunately, the behavior of chromosomes has not yet been traced throughout the life-cycle and meiosis remains to be described. However, a few apparently haploid specimens have been noted in *Zelleriella louisianensis* (38). These ciliates were approximately normal in size but contained four relatively small nuclei, each with 12 chromosomes, instead of the usual two nuclei with 24 chromosomes each.

Taxonomy

Flagellate affinities have been suggested for the Protociliata (73, 118). On the other hand, nuclear structure and mitosis in *Opalina ranarum* and *O. obtrigona* show features characteristic of ciliates (92) and the fibrillar system of *O. obtrigonoides* resembles that of holotrichous ciliates (43). Accordingly, retention of the opalinid ciliates in the Ciliatea appears to be sound practice at present. The evident lack of macronuclei is a logical basis for continued recognition of Metcalf's Subclass Protociliata.

The most extensive taxonomic work on the group is that of Metcalf (152, 153), who established two families on the basis of nuclear number. The Protoopalinidae include binucleate types assigned to two genera: *Protoopalina* Metcalf (8, 152; Fig. 7. 1, F, I), with cylindrical or slightly flattened bodies; and *Zelleriella* Metcalf (7, 37, 52; Fig. 7. 1, G), with distinctly flattened bodies. The multinucleate types are placed in the Opalinidae, which also include two genera: *Cepedea* Metcalf (8, 152; Fig. 7. 1, J), with cylindrical or slightly flattened bodies; and *Opalina* Purkinje and Valentin (43, 152, 153, 160; Fig. 7. 1, A-E, H), with much flattened bodies.

Geographical distribution

The geographical distribution of the Protociliatia is interesting (152, 153). The genus *Protoopalina*, supposedly the most primitive, is widely distributed and seems to be excluded only from the northeastern United States and from southern India and neighboring islands. The genus *Zelleriella*, represented in Central America, South America and southern North America, apparently does not extend north of Australia in the eastern hemisphere. *Cepedea*, although not represented in Australia, is otherwise widely distributed, whereas the genus *Opalina* apparently has not become established in Australia or South America. Metcalf (153) has attempted to correlate these peculiarities in distribution of the ciliates with the phylogeny of their hosts.

Subclass 2. Euciliatia

These are the typical ciliates with macronuclei and micronuclei. Subdivision into orders and suborders is based largely upon the distribution of cilia and their derivatives and upon the differentiation of such structures in the peristomial area. Following the practice of Kahl (100, 102, 104, 106), the subclass is now commonly divided into four orders—Holotrichida, Spirotrichida, Peritrichida, and Chonotrichida—but taxonomic treatment of the group has varied in different systems of classification (Chapter III). One of the more recent proposals would divide the Euciliatia into two groups: the "Spirotricha," the Spirotrichida as defined below; and the "Holotricha," including the rest of the Euciliatia and the Suctorea (62).

The Holotrichida lack the strongly developed adoral zone of membranelles so characteristic of the peristome in Spirotrichida. A rather uniform covering of somatic cilia is typical, although there are some genera in which the cilia are restricted to certain zones or to one surface of the body.

The Spirotrichida show an extensive development of membranelles and cirri which, in certain groups, have completely replaced simple cilia. An adoral zone of membranelles arises at the left of the cytostome and extends anteriorly, often winding around the anterior end of the body. The group as a whole shows a strong trend toward reduction of the total ciliated area.

In the Peritrichida the epistome (peristomial area) is commonly a discoid region bounded by two or more rows of cilia which, as viewed from the oral end of the body, pass counter-clockwise around the epistome and through the cytostome into the "vestibule" (pharynx). The majority are sessile and are commonly equipped with stalks.

The Chonotrichida are ectocommensals attached to their hosts by a basal disc or a short stalk. The peristome, at the distal pole, is usually surrounded by a funnel-like prolongation of the body, or sometimes by two concentric funnels. The wall of the funnel may or may not be rolled into a spiral. Cilia may be restricted to the peristome and funnel in the adult stage. Reproduction by budding is characteristic.

Order 1. Holotrichida. This large order, usually considered more primitive than the rest of the Euciliatia, shows considerable diversification of the peristomial area and in one group the cytostome has disappeared. Such specializations furnish a basis for dividing the Holotrichida into suborders.

Suborder 1. Gymnostomina. The cytostome opens directly at the surface or else into a slight depression, or oral groove, which lacks a well developed peristomial ciliature. In many genera the cytostome lies at or near the anterior end of the body. In others, the mouth has shifted posteriorly to either a compressed or a broad flattened oral ("ventral") surface.

Suborder 2. Trichostomina. The cytostome usually lies on the ventral surface at the base of a rather well defined oral groove, typically equipped with one or more fields of densely set cilia. Fusion of peristomial cilia into simple membranes or membranelles, or both, occurs in a few species.

Suborder 3. Hymenostomina. The peristomial ciliature has become modified into several membranes, perhaps derived phylogenetically from the peristomial cilia of Trichostomina.

Suborder 4. Thigmotrichina. The most characteristic feature of these commensals is an anterior group of thigmotactic cilia serving for attachment to the host. The cytostome is shifted to a position at or near the posterior end of the body. In some families there is an anterior sucker, a new organelle.

Suborder 5. Apostomina. The ventral cytostome is so reduced in size that ingestion is probably limited to very small particles. Beneath the cytostome there is a peculiar "rosette" (Fig. 7. 25, A-F) of uncertain function. The somatic ciliation includes less than 22 complete rows of cilia. Life-cycles are often fairly complex.

Suborder 6. Astomina. These are endoparasitic holotrichs without a cytostome. The body is rather uniformly ciliated as a rule, but there may be a small cilia-free area at the anterior end.

Suborder 1. Gymnostomina

Form of the body varies considerably. Ovoid, pear-shaped, spindle-shaped, and long vermiform types are common, and laterally compressed and dorso-ventrally compressed species are not unusual. The ciliation is commonly uniform except for the frequent occurrence of large cilia around the cytostome. In some genera, however, somatic cilia are limited to a few transverse bands or to one surface of the body. The cytostome usually opens at the surface. There is no well defined oral groove or peristome equipped with specialized cilia. Even if a rudimentary peristome is present, or if there are distinct preoral and postoral fields of cilia, the organization of the peristomial area is primitive as compared with that in more specialized groups. There is often a circumoral zone of cilia, somewhat longer and sometimes stouter than the somatic cilia. In addition, the pharynx is commonly surrounded by a ring of rod-like trichites, which are sometimes partially fused to form a pharyngeal basket.

The position of the cytostome varies in different families and on this basis, Kahl (100) has divided the suborder into three tribes. In one group ("Tribe Prostomata") the cytostome is anterior. Among the families listed below, this is the situation in the Actinobolinidae, Bütschliidae, Colepidae, Didiniidae, Holophryidae, Metacystidae, and Spathidiidae. In a second group ("Tribe Hypostomata") the cytostome lies on the flattened ventral surface and in the anterior half of the body. This is the case in the Chlamydodontidae, Dysteriidae, and Nassulidae. The cytostome of a third group ("Tribe Pleurostomata") lies on a compressed margin of the body—the narrow ventral surface, according to Kahl, although others have considered the cytostome lateral in position. This is the condition in the Amphibotrellidae, Amphileptidae, Loxodidae, and Tracheliidae.

Family 1. Actinobolinidae. These prostomatous ciliates possess extensible tentacles in addition to the usual ciliature. The tentacles in *Dactylochlamys pisciformis* (103) are similar to those of many Suctorea (Fig. 7. 50, C). The tentacles in *Actinobolina vorax* (221), which are slender structures emerging in the ciliary meridians (Fig. 7. 2, J), may be extended for lengths of 100μ or more, but are usually retracted is swimming ciliates. The tip of each tentacle is said to contain a toxicyst (Chapter I). In stained preparations the proximal ends of the tentacles are continuous with a system of cytoplasmic fibrils (Fig. 7. 2, I). On the basis of such tentacular equipment, Kahl (103) has suggested that the Actinobolinidae are related to the ancestral holotrichs from which the Suctorea were evolved and that *Dactylochlamys* may even represent a primitive type of Suctorea which has not developed a sessile stage.

Only three genera have been assigned to the family: *Actinobolina* Strand (103, 221; Fig. 7. 2, I, J), *Dactylochlamys* Lauterborn (103; Fig. 7. 2, B), and *Enchelyomorpha* Kahl (103; Fig. 7. 2, A). *Actinobolina* is the only genus in which a cytostome has been described. The cytostome of *A. vorax* (221) opens into a pharynx surrounded by a double ring of fibrils. These apparently converge in the rim of the cytostome (Fig. 7. 2, I).

Family 2. Amphibotrellidae. This family contains the genus *Amphibotrella* R. and L. Grandori (106; Fig. 7. 2, K), characterized by location

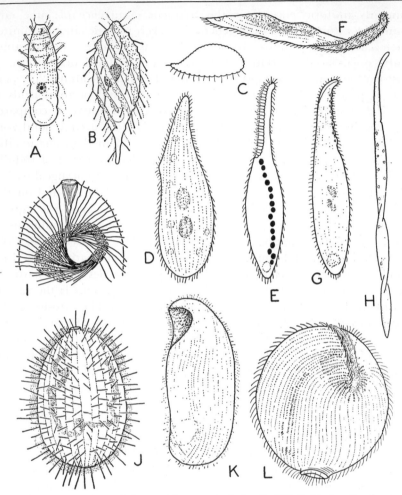

Fig. 7. 2. A. *Enchelyomorpha vermicularis* (Smith) Kahl, length about
35μ; knobbed tentacles; cytostome not described (after K.). B. *Dactylochlamys pisciformis* Lauterborn (after Kahl), about 100μ long; knobbed
tentacles, firm pellicle with rugose ribs (stippled). C. Cross-section of *Lionotus branchiarum* (Wenrich) Kahl, showing distribution of cilia (after W.).
D. *Amphileptus claparedei* Stein, 120-150μ long (after Entz). E. *Lionotus
fasciola* (O.F.M.) Wrzesniowsky, usually 300-450μ long (after De Morgan).
F, G. *Loxophyllum rostratum* Cohn, 300-400μ; lateral view showing naked
dorsal surface, and dorsal view (after De Morgan). H. *Centrophorella fascio-
lata* (Sauerbrey) Kahl, x80 (after Noland). I, J. *Actinobolina vorax* (Wenrich): anterior part of body showing circumpharyngeal fibrils and retracted
tentacles connected with inner bundle of fibrils (I); general organization of
the ciliate (J); x300 (after W.). K. *Amphibotrella enigmatica* R. and L.
Grandori, about 250μ (from Kahl, after R. & L. G.). L. *Bryophyllum carina-
tum* Gelei; sensory bristles indicated near the cytostome and in several ciliary
meridians; x375 (after G.).

of the cytostome in a non-ciliata anterior furrow which extends almost to the tip of the body. Near the posterior end of the body there is also a short ciliated groove of uncertain significance.

Family 3. Amphileptidae. In this pleurostomatous group the body is

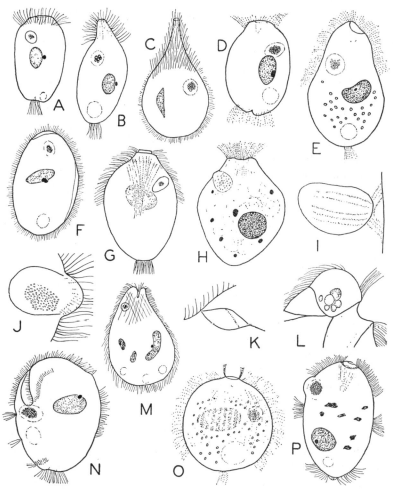

Fig. 7. 3. A. *Bundleia postciliata* (Bundle) da Cunha and Muniz, x464 (after Hsiung). B. *Polymorpha ampulla* Dogiel, x958 (after Hsiung). C. *Ampullacula ampulla* (Fiorentini) Hsiung, x363 (after H.). D. *Didesmis ovalis* Fiorentini, x484 (after Hsiung). E. *Blepharoprosthium pireum* Bundle, x484 (after Hsiung). F. *Paraisotrichopsis composita* Gassovsky, x484 (from Hsiung, after G.). G. *Blepharoconus cervicalis* Hsiung, x383 (after H.). H. *Bütschlia nana* Dogiel, x725 (after D.). I-L. Concretion-vacuoles of Bütschliidae, schematic (after Dogiel): I. *Didesmis quadrata;* J. *Bütschlia* sp., cross-section through the vacuole; K. *Polymorpha ampulla;* L. *Paraisotricha colpoidea,* anterior end of body. M. *Prorodonopsis coli* Gassovsky, x443 (after Hsiung). N. *Sulcoarcus pellucidulus* Hsiung, x533 (after H.). O. *Blepharosphaera intestinalis* Bundle, x443 (after Hsiung). P. *Alloiozona trizona* Hsiung, x363 (after H.).

laterally compressed, slightly or extensively in different genera. The slit-like cytostome lies on the typically convex "ventral" surface and is usually bordered by a zone of trichocysts. Ciliation may be uniform or may be reduced or lacking on one surface (Fig. 7. 2, C). There are usually two or more macronuclei. Carnivorous habits are characteristic, other ciliates and rotifers being common prey of various Amphileptidae.

The family includes the following genera: *Amphileptus* Ehrbg. (102; Fig. 7. 2, D), *Bryophyllum* Kahl (102; Fig. 7. 2, L), *Centrophorella* Kahl (106, 158; Fig. 7. 2, H), *Lionotus* Wrzesniowsky (102, 165; Fig. 7. 2, C, E), *Loxophyllum* Dujardin (102, 165, 167; Fig. 7. 2, F, G).

Family 4. Bütschliidae. These ciliates occur in the digestive tract of such herbivores as horses and camels. The body is more or less ovoid or pear-shaped, with the cytostome usually at the anterior end. An anterior concretion-vacuole (Fig. 7. 3, I-L)—which has been considered a statocyst (52)—and one or more contractile vacuoles are characteristic. A posterior cytopyge is typical. The cilia may be uniformly distributed or else restricted to certain areas. In fission, the concretion-vacuole is retained by the anterior daughter and a new organelle is developed by the posterior one.

Hsiung (91) has published a key to most of the following genera: *Alloiozona* Hsiung (91; Fig. 7. 3, P), *Ampullacula* Hsiung (91; Fig. 7. 3, C), *Blepharoconus* Gassovsky (91; Fig. 7. 3, G), *Blepharoprosthium* Bundle (91; Fig. 7. 3, E), *Blepharosphaera* Bundle (91; Fig. 7. 3, O), *Blepharozoum* Gassovsky (91), *Bundleia* da Cunha and Muniz (91; Fig. 7. 3, A), *Bütschlia* Schuberg (51; Fig. 7. 3, H), *Didesmis* Fiorentini (91; Fig. 7. 3, D), *Holophryoides* Gassovsky (91), *Paraisotrichopsis* Gassovsky (91; Fig. 7. 3, F), *Polymorpha* Dogiel (91; Fig. 7. 3, B), *Prorodonopsis* Gassovsky (91; Fig. 7. 3, M), and *Sulcoarcus* Hsiung (91; Fig. 7. 3, N).

Family 5. Chlamydodontidae. The cilia are restricted essentially to the ventral surface (Fig. 7. 4, D). A narrow transversely striated band borders the ciliated area in *Chlamydodon*. The cytostome is antero-ventral and the pharynx is surrounded by a pharyngeal-basket (Fig. 7. 4, J). Adoral membranes are sometimes present but are always small and poorly developed and lie anterior to the cytostome. There is no ventral protoplasmic stylus such as is found in the Dysteriidae (Fig. 7. 5, I). The Chlamydodontidae commonly feed on diatoms and other algae, phytoflagellates, and bacteria.

The family includes the following genera: *Chilodonella* Strand (102, 141, 165; Fig. 7. 4, J), *Chlamydodon* Ehrbg. (102, 140; Fig. 7. 4, E), *Cryptopharynx* Kirby (113; Fig. 7. 4, K), and *Phascolodon* Stein (102; Fig. 7. 4, C, D).

Family 6. Colepidae. These are somewhat barrel-shaped forms with an armored cortex. The armor is composed of plates (Fig. 7. 4, I), the form and arrangement of which vary with the species. The armor of *Coleps*

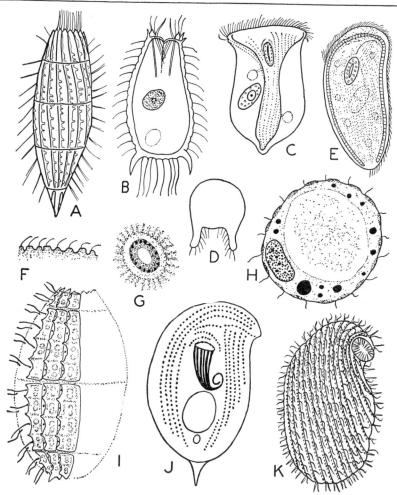

Fig. 7. 4. A. *Tiarina fusus* (Claparède and Lachmann), 110μ (after Fauré-Fremiet). B. *Coleps amphacanthus* Ehrbg. (70-90μ), longitudinal optical section showing circumpharyngeal trichites, macronucleus, contractile vacuole (after Kahl). C, D. *Phascolodon vorticella* Stein, 90-110μ; ventral view and schematic cross-section (after Kahl). E. *Chlamydodon triquetrus* (O.F.M.), 80-120μ; ventral view, striated band, ventral ciliary pattern, cytostome, macronucleus, contractile vacuoles (after Kahl). F. *Chilodonella cucullus* (Ehrbg.), cross-section of ventral cortex; x1000 (after Wetzel). G-I. *Coleps hirtus* O. F. M.: G, H. Cross-sections at level of cytostome, showing trichites, and near the equator, showing macronucleus and large mass of food; x1000 (after Wetzel). I. Diagram showing three longitudinal rows of cortical plates (after Fauré-Fremiet and Hamard). J. *Chilodonella caudata* Stokes, 40-50μ, ventral view, pharyngeal basket, basal granules, macro-, and micronucleus in outline (after MacDougall). K. *Cryptopharynx setigerus* Kahl, ventral view showing cytostome, longitudinal ribs, cilia, and marginal spines; x485 (after Kirby).

hirtus contains calcium carbonate and apparently is covered by an organic pellicle (65). Calcification of the plates is inhibited by exposure of the ciliates to benzenesulfamid (67). A ring of circumpharyngeal trichites (Fig. 7. 4, B, G) is characteristic. Although the Colepidae sometimes ingest small algae, they are primarily carnivorous.

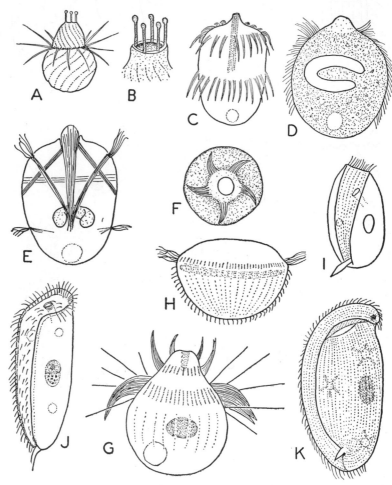

Fig. 7. 5. A, B. *Mesodinium acarus* Stein (after Noland), lateral view, x1400; anterior end, showing oral tentacles, x2800. C-E. *Didinium nasutum* O. F. M., 80-150μ: C. General organization (after Kahl). D. Freshly excysted specimen, ciliation more extensive than in the adult; x450 (after Beers). E. Schematic longitudinal section; endoplasmic fibrils, circumpharyngeal trichites, macronucleus, contractile vacuole (after ten Kate). F, G. *Askenasia volvox* (Claparède and Lachmann) Kahl, anterior and lateral views, x630 approx. (after Wang and Nie). H. *Cyclotrichium gigas* Fauré-Fremiet, specimen 160x250μ; schematic (after F-F.). I. *Trochilia marina* Mereschkowsky, x850 (after Kahl). J. *Dysteria navicula* Kahl, x650 (after Wang and Nie). K. *Hartmannula entzi* Kahl, x460 (after Wang).

The family includes two genera: *Coleps* Nitzsch (74, 99, 100, 157; Fig. 7. 4, B, G-I) and *Tiarina* Bergh (100; Fig. 7. 4, A).

Family 7. Didiniidae. These ciliates are radially symmetrical with respect to the longitudinal axis. The anterior cytostome (Fig. 7. 5, B, F) is not surrounded by cilia although there is a ring of circumoral tentacles in *Mesodinium*. A circlet of pectinellae (slender membranelles) usually lies at or near the rim of the anterior pole (Fig. 7. 5, C, E, G), and there may be one to several similar rings of pectinellae located more posteriorly. The rest of the body may be either naked or ciliated in different species. A band of circumpharyngeal trichites is characteristic. Although a few species apparently eat algae, a carnivorous diet is the usual one. *Didinium nasutum* is noted for its habit of capturing and ingesting such ciliates as *Paramecium* (150).

The family includes the following genera: *Askenasia* Blochmann (100, 165; Fig. 7. 5, F, G), *Cyclotrichium* Meunier (100, 171; Fig. 7. 5, H), *Didinium* Stein (97, 100; Fig. 7. 5, C-E), and *Mesodinium* Stein (100, 158; Fig. 7. 5, A, B). *Monodinium* Fabre-Domergue (58), with one anterior ring of pectinellae, has been considered a separate genus by some workers; others include such ciliates in *Didinium* Stein. The family includes both fresh-water and marine species, and *Cyclotrichium meunieri* has been recorded as a cause of red water in the Gulf of Maine (171).

Family 8. Dysteriidae. These hypostomes differ from the Chlamydodontidae and Nassulidae in the presence of a ventral protoplasmic stylus (Fig. 7. 5, I-K). In *Dysteria* this structure may adhere to a solid surface and serve as a temporary anchor (46), whereas the stylus in *Trochilioides* secretes a slender filament which serves the same purpose (64). The dorsal surface is not ciliated and a reduction of the ventral ciliation is often noticeable. A pharyngeal rod-apparatus is characteristic. The Dysteriidae are mainly marine ciliates which feed mostly on diatoms, other algae, or bacteria.

The family includes five genera: *Dysteria* Huxley (46, 102; Fig. 7. 5, J), *Hartmannula* Poche (102; Fig. 7. 5, K), *Scaphidion* Stein (102), *Trochilia* Dujardin (102; Fig. 7. 5, I), and *Trochilioides* Kahl (64, 102).

Family 9. Holophryidae. These are rather uniformly ciliated species in which the cytostome lies at or near the anterior pole and often opens on a rounded elevation. There is generally a circumpharyngeal zone of trichites (Fig. 7. 6, A), and an adoral row of fused cilia (syncilia) is sometimes present (Fig. 7. 6, F). Form of the body ranges from plump ovoid or cylindrical shapes to long slender types, the latter sometimes possessing a very extensible and mobile "neck" several times as long as the rest of the body. Feeding habits vary widely. Some species are rapacious carnivores, pursuing and capturing other ciliates or rotifers. Some usually eat small flagellates, others feed mainly on bacteria and small algae, while

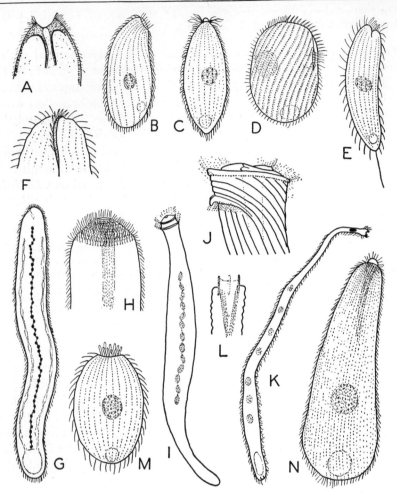

Fig. 7. 6. A. *Prorodon teres* Ehrbg., longitudinal section showing circum-pharyngeal trichites; x240 (after Wetzel). **B.** *Platophrya spumacola* Kahl, x450 (after K.). **C.** *Lagynophrya simplex* Kahl, 35-40µ (after K.). **D.** *Placus socialis* (Fabre-Domergue), slit-like cytostome, macronucleus, contractile vacuole; x680 (after Noland). **E.** *Plagiocampa longis* Kahl, 70-80µ (after K.). **F.** *P. marina* Kahl, syncilia along cytostome; x850 (after Noland). **G.** *Holophrya oblonga* Maupas, macronuclear chain, contractile vacuole and accessory canals; x60 (after De Morgan). **H.** *Holophrya* (*Trachelocerca?*) *coronata* De Morgan, anterior end of body; schematic (after De M.). **I, J.** *Helicoprorodon gigas* (Kahl) Fauré-Fremiet; lateral view, x1650; anterior end of body, schematic (after F-F.). **K, L.** *Trachelocerca entzi* Kahl, length reaches 270µ; extended specimen and longitudinal optical section of the anterior end (after K.). **M.** *Spasmostoma viride* Kahl, 50-60µ (after K.). **N.** *Prorodon parafarctus* Wang and Nie, x300 (after W. & N.).

the diet of certain species includes such a variety as bacteria, diatoms, and small nematodes.

The family includes the following genera, some of which are represented in both fresh and salt water: *Bursella* Schmidt (100), *Chaenea* Quennerstedt (46, 98, 100; Fig. 7. 7, G, H), *Chilophrya* Kahl (100), *Crobylura* André (100), *Enchelyodon* Claparède and Lachmann (100; Fig. 7. 7, D), *Enchelys* Hill (100; Fig. 7. 7, I), *Helicoprorodon* Fauré-Fremiet (61a; Fig. 7. 6, I, J), *Holophrya* Ehrbg. (46, 98; Fig. 7. 6, G, H), *Ileonema* Stokes (100), *Lacrymaria* Ehrbg. (46, 100, 165; Fig. 7. 7, B, C), *Lagynophrya* Kahl (100; Fig. 7. 6, C), *Microregma* Kahl (100), *Nannophrya* Kahl (100), *Pithothorax*

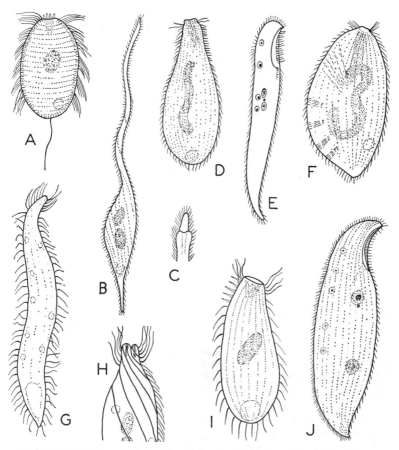

Fig. 7. 7. A. *Urotricha armata* Kahl, 40-45μ (after Kahl). B, C. *Lacrymaria olor* (O.F.M.) Bütschli, usually 110-160μ, sometimes extended to 1500μ; general organization (B); anterior end (C), schematic (after De Morgan). D. *Enchelyodon elegans* Kahl, x400 (after K.). E. *Remanella margaritifera* Kahl, 100-200μ; ciliary pattern similar to that of *Loxodes rostrum* (after K.). F. *Pseudoprorodon emmae* (Bergh) Kahl, 100-200μ (after K.). G. *Chaenea limicola* Levander, length reaches 300μ (after Kahl). H. *Chaenea teres* Dujardin, anterior end of contracted specimen; schematic (after Kahl). I. *Enchelys gasterosteus* Kahl, x1200 (after K.). J. *Loxodes striatus* Penard, two macronuclei, Müller's vesicles; x298 (after Wang and Nie).

Kahl (100), *Placus* Cohn (158; Fig. 7. 6, D), *Plagiocampa* Schewiakoff (100; Fig. 7. 6, E, F), *Platophrya* Kahl (100; Fig. 7. 6, B), *Prorodon* Ehrbg. (100, 165, 210; Fig. 7. 6, A, N), *Pseudoprorodon* Blochmann (100; Fig. 7. 7, F), *Rhopalophrya* Kahl (100), *Spasmostoma* Kahl (98; Fig. 7. 6, M), *Stephanopogon* Entz (100), *Trachelocerca* Ehrbg. (13, 100, 188; Fig. 7. 6, K, L), *Trachelophyllum* Claparède and Lachmann (100, 165), *Urotricha* Claparède and Lachmann (100, 165, 188; Fig. 7. 7, A).

Family 10. Loxodidae. As in the Amphileptidae, the body is compressed laterally but the "ventral" margin, on which the cytostome lies, tends to be slightly concave. The right surface is ciliated, the left naked. The presence of Müller's bodies (Fig. 1. 16, D; 7. 7, J) is characteristic. Algae and bacteria are the usual food.

Two genera are recognized: *Loxodes* Ehrbg. (102, 165; Fig. 7. 7, J), which includes fresh-water species; and *Remanella* Kahl (102; Fig. 7. 7, E), which includes only marine ciliates.

Family 11. Metacystidae. This family (97) is characterized by a terminal cytostome and a firm cortical layer enclosing a peculiar alveolar zone. The cytostome may be rounded or slit-like, and in certain species, opens into an endoplasmic cavity ("receptacle"). These ciliates apparently feed mainly on bacteria. A pseudochitinous lorica is characteristic, although a gelatinous lorica has been reported in rare cases.

The family includes only three genera: *Metacystis* Cohn (100, 165; Fig. 7. 8, H), *Pelatractus* Kahl (100; Fig. 7. 8, I, J), and *Vasicola* Tatem (100, 165; Fig. 7. 8, K).

Family 12. Nassulidae. In this hypostomatous family the body is completely ciliated, although the dorsal ciliation is less dense than that of the ventral surface. A pharyngeal basket is typical but there is no ventral stylus like that of the Dysteriidae. The family contains marine and fresh-water ciliates which feed mainly on diatoms and other algae.

The following genera are included: *Chilodontopsis* Blochmann (102; Fig. 7. 8, B), *Cyclogramma* Perty (102), *Eucamptocera* da Cunha (102), *Nassula* Ehrbg. (102, 165; Fig. 7. 8, C-E), *Orthodon* Gruber (102; Fig. 7. 8, A), and *Paranassula* Kahl (102; Fig. 7. 8, F, G).

Family 13. Pycnothricidae. These ciliates occur in the cecum and large intestine of various mammals. Species of *Collinella* and *Pycnothrix* are known from *Procavia* (*Hyrax*); *Buxtonella,* from cattle; *Nicollella,* and also *Collinella,* from *Ctenodactylus.* The body is completely ciliated and a long groove usually leads to the cytostome, which may lie near the middle or at the posterior end of the body. In *Pycnothrix monocystoides* (which reaches a length of 2-3 mm), there is no single cytostome. Instead, food apparently is ingested through pits in the unusually long groove. A thick layer of ectoplasm in the anterior part of the body (Fig. 7. 9, E, F) is a striking feature in *Collinella, Nicollella,* and *Pycnothrix.*

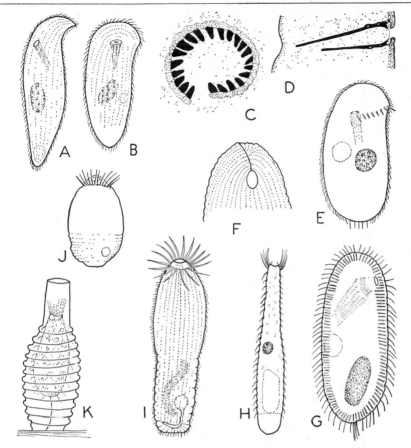

Fig. 7. 8. A. *Orthodon hamatus* Gruber, 90-260μ (after Kahl). B. *Chilodontopsis muscorum* Kahl, 65-80μ (after K.). C, D. Transverse and longitudinal sections showing circumpharyngeal trichites of *Nassula aurea* Ehrbg., x1500 and x240 (after Wetzel). E. *Nassula gracilis* Kahl, x360 (after K.). F, G. *Paranassula microstoma* (Claparède and Lachmann) Kahl; ventral view of preoral suture and cytostome (F), x600; pharyngeal apparatus, macronucleus, contractile vacuole, trichocysts (G), x450 (after Noland). H. *Metacystis elongata* Kahl, without lorica, x900 approx. (after K.). I, J. *Pelatractus constractus* Wang and Nie; extended specimen (I) showing macronucleus and canal extending posteriorly from contractile vacuole, x170; contracted specimen (J), schematic (after W. & N.). K. *Vasicola parvula* Kahl, 30-50μ, specimen in lorica (after K.).

The family includes the following genera: *Buxtonella* Jameson (94, 175; Fig. 7. 9, A, B), *Collinella* Chatton and Pérard (33; Fig. 7. 9, C, D), *Nicollella* Chatton and Pérard (33; Fig. 7. 9, E-G), and *Pycnothrix* Schubotz (33; Fig. 7. 9, H).

Family 14. Spathidiidae. These prostomatous ciliates have a slit-like cytostome generally lying in a non-ciliated ridge (Fig. 7. 10, B-D). In some genera, this ridge is continued posteriorly and spirally for some distance (Fig. 7. 10, H; 11, B, C). In others, the ridge does not extend

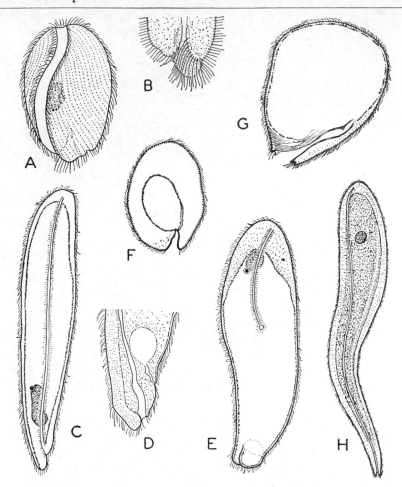

Fig. 7. 9. A. *Buxtonella sulcata* Jameson (after Rees): somatic ciliation, nuclei, groove leading to the posterior cytostome; x225. B. Longitudinal section of posterior end of *B. sulcata,* showing cytostome and gullet; x510 (after Rees). C, D. *Collinella gundii* Chatton and Pérard (after C. & P.): C. Ventral view showing preoral groove, nuclei, ectoplasmic and endoplasmic zones separated by a layer of myonemes, x125. D. Optical parasagittal section, posterior end of body, showing cytostome, gullet, and contractile vacuole, x275. E-G. *Nicollella ctenodactyli* Chatton and Pérard (after C. & P.): E. Ventral view showing preoral groove ending at the cytostome, the nuclei, contractile vacuole, thick anterior zone of ectoplasm, and layer of myonemes; x125. F. Cross-section between cytostome and anterior pole, showing preoral groove and layer of myonemes separating ectoplasm and endoplasm; x240. G. Cross-section through cytostome and pharynx, x240. H. *Pycnothrix monocystoides* Schubotz: the groove follows a slightly spiral course down one side to the posterior pole and then up on the other side almost to the anterior pole; in each groove, a number of pits which serve as cytostomes; x35 (after Chatton and Pérard).

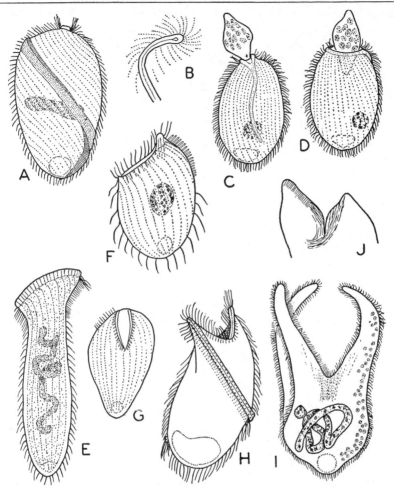

Fig. 7. 10. A-D. *Perispira ovum* Stein: A. Specimen showing spiral ridge and anterior cytostome; x513 (after Wang and Nie). B. Anterior end of ridge showing the closed cytostome (a slit ending anteriorly in a small pore); schematic (after Dewey and Kidder). C, D. Stages in ingestion of a flagellate; schematic (after Dewey and Kidder). E. *Spathidium amphoriforme* Greef, 160μ or smaller (after Kahl). F, G. *Spathidioides exsecata* Kahl, length about 60μ; lateral view (F); ventral view (G), showing slit-like cytostome opened under pressure from a coverslip (after K.). H. *Diceras bicornis* Kahl, length about 260μ; spiral ridge, posterior contractile vacuole (after K.). I, J. *Teutophrys trisulca* Chatton and de Beauchamp, x250 (after Wenrich): specimen showing proboscidial arms, macronucleus, contractile vacuole, zoochlorellae (indicated along one margin); longitudinal section through cytostome, showing circumpharyngeal fibrils and the trichocysts in one arm.

much beyond the posterior end of the cytostome (Fig. 7. 10, E-G). In any case, the oral ridge and its extension, if present, may be armed with trichites or trichocysts. In *Legendrea,* the posterior part of the body bears a number of tentacles, each equipped with trichocysts (Fig. 7. 11, D). Unlike the usual condition, the cytostome in *Teutophrys* lies at the base of three proboscis-like extensions of the body (Fig. 7. 10, I, J). Although the somatic ciliation is usually complete and uniform, except where interrupted by the oral ridge or its extension, a row of flattened "cilia" (slender membranelles?) extends along each side of the cytostome in *Spathidioides.* In addition, a more or less complete loss of cilia on the

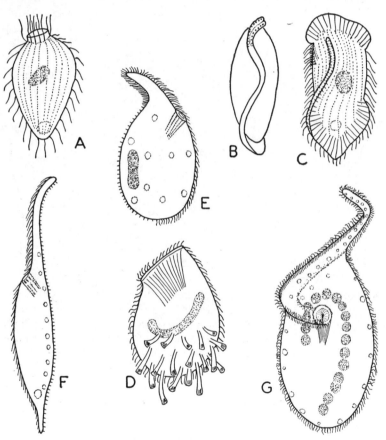

Fig. 7. 11. A. *Enchelydium amphora* Kahl, 30-45μ (after K.). B, C. *Penardiella undulata* Kahl, 90-130μ, ventral and lateral views of spiral ridge and other features (after K.). D. *Legendrea loyezae* Fauré-Fremiet, showing tentacles, macronucleus, pharyngeal fibrils (from Kahl, after F-F.). E. *Trachelius ovum* Ehrbg., 200-400μ; cytostome, circumpharyngeal trichites, macronucleus, contractile vacuoles (after Kahl). F. *Dileptus anser* (O.F.M.), 250-600μ but usually 250-400μ (after Kahl). G. *Paradileptus conicus* Wenrich, cytostome, circumpharyngeal trichites, zone of trichocysts, macronuclear chain, numerous contractile vacuoles; x250 (after W.).

left surface has occurred in *Homalozoon*. The Spathidiidae are typically foraging carnivores which commonly prey on ciliates and flagellates.

The family contains the following genera: *Cranotheridium* Schewiakoff (99), *Diceras* Eberhard (99; Fig. 7. 10, H), *Enchelydium* Kahl (99; Fig. 7. 11, A), *Homalozoon* Stokes (99), *Legendrea* Fauré-Fremiet (99, 165; Fig. 7. 11, D), *Paraspathidium* Noland (158), *Penardiella* Kahl (99; Fig. 7. 11, B, C), *Perispira* Stein (48, 99; Fig. 7. 10, A-D), *Spathidioides* Brodsky (99; Fig. 7. 10, F, G), *Spathidium* Dujardin (99, 165, 226; Fig. 7. 10, E), *Teutophrys* Chatton and Beauchamp (219; Fig. 7. 10, I, J).

Family 15. Tracheliidae. The approximately circular cytostome, located some distance from the anterior pole and at the end of a ventral row of trichocysts, is surrounded by trichites or trichocysts and sometimes by both (102). The body is completely ciliated. The Tracheliidae occur in fresh and salt water and are typically carnivorous, feeding on other ciliates and on flagellates.

Four genera have been assigned to the family: *Branchioecetes* Kahl (102), *Dileptus* Dujardin (102, 167, 215; Fig. 7. 11, F), *Paradileptus* Wenrich (220; Fig. 7. 11, G), and *Trachelius* Schrank (102, 165; Fig. 7. 11, E).

Suborder 2. Trichostomina

The cytostome usually lies at the base of a well-defined oral groove or pit, the wall of which bears one or more dense fields of adoral cilia. Such fields often contain free cilia. However, both adoral membranelles and an undulating membrane (or possibly a "pseudo-membrane") have been reported in certain genera, such as *Woodruffia* (96) and *Colpoda* (211). In some primitive Trichostomina, the cytostome lies almost at the anterior pole. More often, the mouth is shifted posteriorly on the ventral surface. Spiral torsion of the body, tending to complicate peristomial ciliary patterns, is characteristic of certain genera. Fifteen families have been recognized.

Family 1. Blepharocoridae. These ciliates occur in the digestive tract of horses and ruminants. Somatic ciliation (Fig. 7. 12, A-C) is reduced to a few anterior and posterior fields. One (*Blepharocorys*) or two (*Charon*) groups of anal cilia lie near the posterior cytopyge, and there are two or three distinct anterior groups. A band of slender adoral membranelles has been reported in *Blepharocorys* (189). The antero-ventral cytostome opens into a long ciliated pharynx.

Two genera are referred to the family: *Blepharocorys* Bundle (91, 189; Fig. 7. 12, A, B) and *Charon* Jameson (91, 93; Fig. 7. 12, C).

Family 2. Clathrostomidae. The peristome is a shallow, uniformly ciliated ventral groove, with an oval cytostome lying in the anterior half. The rim of the cytostome is a differentiated band from which circumpharyngeal fibrils extend into the endoplasm.

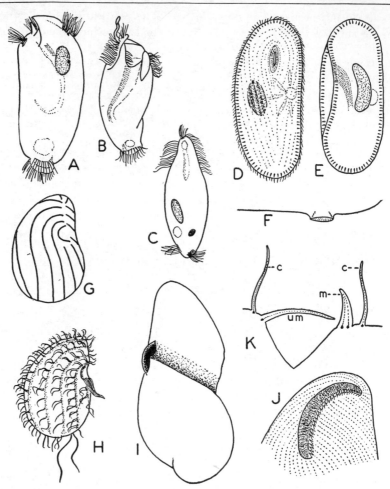

Fig. 7. 12. A. *Blepharocorys curvigula* Gassovsky, x480 (after Hsiung). B. *Blepharocorys equi* Schumacher, x940 (after S.). C. *Charon equi* Hsiung, x1000 (after Hsiung). D-F. *Clathrostoma viminale* Penard (after P.), 115-125μ: ventral view (D), lateral view (E), ventrally protruded cytostome (F). G, H. *Colpoda steinii* Maupas, ciliary meridians (G), ciliature (H); x750 (after Burt). I. *Tillina canalifera* Turner, 150-200μ, left lateral view showing oral groove and ventral lip of cytostome (after T.). J, K. *Woodruffia metabolica* Johnson and Larson: ventral view of peristomial area (J), x450; cross-section of oral groove (K) showing undulating membrane (*um*), a membranelle (*m*) and two somatic cilia (*c*), schematic (after J. & L.).

The family contains a single genus, *Clathrostoma* Penard (102, 165; Fig. 7. 12, D-F), to which three fresh-water species have been assigned.

Family 3. Colpodidae. The mouth, in the anterior half of the broad oral surface, may be funnel-shaped, approximately triangular, or sometimes elongated. The wall of the oral groove is often more or less perpendicular to the body surface, while the left wall tends to slope more gradually. The somatic ciliary rows commonly form a somewhat concentric series around the right margin of the peristome (Fig. 7. 12, G, J), while the organization of the adoral ciliature varies to some extent within the family. In *Woodruffia metabolica* (Fig. 7. 12, K), the left margin of the oral groove bears a row of membranelles, each composed of two or three fused cilia, while a delicate undulating membrane extends along the right (96). Although the undulating membrane and the membranelles are simple in structure, this type of adoral ciliation is similar to that found in Heterotrichina. Fission within a reproductive cyst (Fig. 7. 13, B-D) is typical, although it has been possible to obtain fission in the active stage in *Colpoda* under experimental conditions (198). The usual diets range from small ciliates to algae and bacteria.

The following genera have been included in the family: *Bresslau* Kahl (39, 102; Fig. 7. 13, A), *Bryophrya* Kahl (102), *Colpoda* Müller (14; Fig. 7. 12, G, H), *Tillina* Gruber (102, 213; Fig. 7. 12, I) and *Woodruffia* Kahl (96, 102; Fig. 7. 12, J, K).

Family 4. Conidiophryidae. These are ectoparasites which live attached to exoskeletal hairs of amphipod and isopod Crustacea. The adult (Fig. 7. 13, E), a non-ciliated stage in a secreted membrane, produces by terminal budding a series of small ciliated stages (Fig. 7. 13, F, G), or "tomites." The migratory stage swims about until it reaches a host and becomes impaled upon an exoskeletal hair which passes into the pharynx (Fig. 7. 13, H). The cilia then disappear and the young parasite secretes a membrane around itself and the distal portion of the hair upon which it is mounted (Fig. 7. 13, I). During growth, nourishment apparently is furnished by a secretion of the exoskeletal hair.

The family includes the genus *Conidiophrys* Chatton and Lwoff (29; Fig. 7. 13, E-I).

Family 5. Cyathodiniidae. This group, from the intestine of guinea pigs, contains several species of *Cyathodinium* da Cunha (131, 132; Fig. 7. 13, J). Cilia are limited to approximately the anterior half of the body. The non-ciliated peristome is a rather long triangular groove. From a row of papillae along the left rim of the peristome, slender trichites ("endosprits" of Lucas) extend into the endoplasm. Externally, an adoral cilium arises from each papilla.

These ciliates are unusual in that fission (Fig. 2. 4, D, F) involves reorganization with a change in polarity so that the plane of division separates the posterior ends of the two daughter organisms. Furthermore, the parental ciliature is discarded in fission and the primordial ciliature of each daughter develops in the endoplasm and then passes to the surface, where it becomes differentiated into the ciliation of the adult (132).

Family 6. Entorhipidiidae. These ciliates occur in the digestive tract of

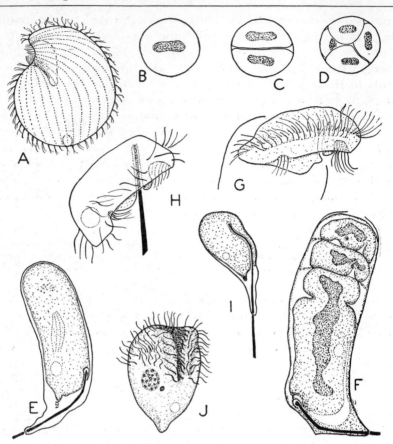

Fig. 7. 13. A. *Bresslaua sicaria* Claff, Dewey and Kidder, aboral surface, buccal region indicated in outline; x230 (after C., D. & K.). B-D. Reproductive cysts in *Tillina magna;* macronuclei shown; x112 approx. (after Beers). E-I. *Conidiophrys pilisuctor* Chatton and Lwoff (after C. & L.): E. Adult stage, secreted envelope enclosing the ciliate and distal portion of an exoskeletal "hair" of the host; contractile vacuole and field of basal granules shown; x1000. F. Adult undergoing budding; x1000. G. Ciliated larva emerging from the parental membrane; x2000. H. Larva impaled upon an exoskeletal hair which extends into the pharynx; x2000. I. Young sessile form, cilia discarded and envelope completely formed; x1000. J. *Cyathodinium piriforme* da Cunha, from guinea pig; ventro-lateral view showing peristome, macronucleus, micronucleus, contractile vacuole; x965 (after Lucas).

sea-urchins. The body is much flattened and the anterior end forms a frontal lobe which overhangs the cytostome (Fig. 7. 14, A, F). The somatic ciliation is complete and essentially uniform.

The family includes *Entodiscus* Madsen (172, 173; Fig. 7. 14, E, F) and *Entorhipidium* Lynch (136; Fig. 7. 14, A-D).

Family 7. Isotrichidae. This family is characteristic of the ungulate rumen, although a species of *Isotricha* is known from cockroaches (217). The mouth is terminal or subterminal and a ciliated pharynx has been reported (Fig. 7. 15, I, L). Longitudinal striations also have been described in the wall of the pharynx. Whether these represent trichites is uncertain, and they may be merely fibrils of the pharyngeal ciliature. The somatic ciliation is complete and practically uniform. A cytopyge lies at

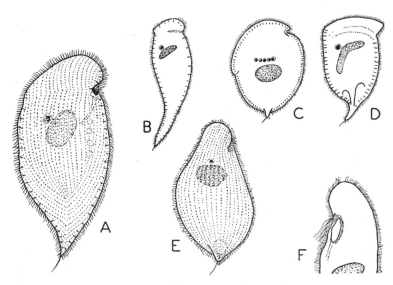

Fig. 7. 14. A. *Entorhipidium echini* Lynch, upper surface; macronucleus, micronucleus, trichocysts, and pharynx indicated; x203 (after L.). B-D. Other species of *Entorhipidium*, x110 (after Lynch): *E. tenue* Lynch (B), *E. multimicronucleatum* Lynch (C), *E. pilatum* Lynch (D). E, F. *Entodiscus borealis* (Hentschel), surface view (E), x270; longitudinal section (F) through oral cavity, showing adoral cilia, the parastyle (a rod-like structure along one margin of the peristome), and the pharynx in outline, x335 (after Powers).

the aboral end in certain species. Although the cytostome is usually considered anterior, several species swim with this end of the body directed posteriorly (4).

Two genera have been referred to the family: *Dasytricha* Schuberg (4, 12; Fig. 7. 15, I, J) and *Isotricha* Stein (4, 51; Fig. 7. 15, K, L).

Family 8. Marynidae. These are solitary or colonial ciliates with a gelatinous lorica. The peristome partially or completely encircles the free end of the body and extends posteriorly for some distance on the ventral surface (Fig. 7. 15, C). The organisms swim with the aboral end forward.

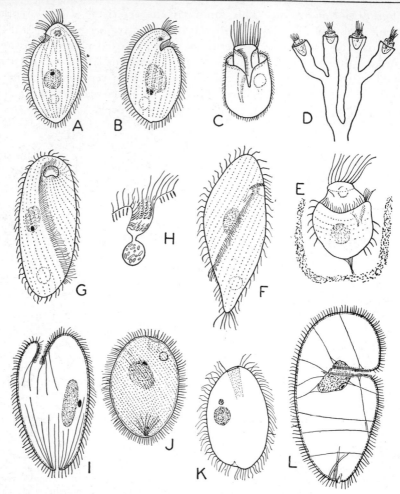

Fig. 7. 15. A, B. *Paraisotricha minuta* Hsiung, dorsal and ventral surfaces; concretion-vacuole, contractile vacuole, nuclei, and cytopharynx are
shown; x443 (after H.). C, D. *Maryna socialis* Gruber, single specimen (150μ
long) and portion of a colony (from Kahl, after G.). E. *Mycterothrix
erlangeri* Lauterborn, ciliate (50μ long) enclosed in lorica (after Kahl). F.
Spirozona caudata Kahl, specimen 80μ long (after K.). G, H. *Trichospira
inversa* (Claparède and Lachmann), ventral view of ciliate 90μ long, peripheral zone of trichocysts not shown (G), and longitudinal optical section of
oral region (after Kahl). I, J. *Dasytricha ruminantium* Schuberg: schematic
longitudinal section (I), showing nuclei, pharynx, cytopyge, and endoplasmic
fibrils (after ten Kate); surface view (J), x465 (after Becker and Talbott).
K. *Isotricha bubali* Dogiel, from camel; x325 (after D.). L. *Isotricha intestinalis* Stein, schematic sagittal section showing pharynx, nuclei, karyophore,
and endoplasmic fibrils (after ten Kate).

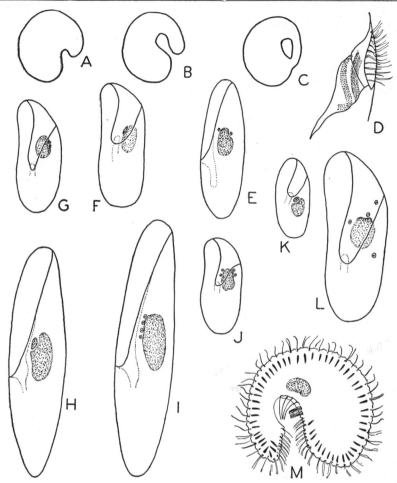

Fig. 7. 16. A-C. Transverse sections of *Paramecium caudatum*, anterior part of oral groove, posterior part of groove, and near the cytostome; x380 (after Wetzel). D. Vestibule and cytopharynx of *Paramecium bursaria*, seen from the right side, showing the dorsal "quadripartite membrane" and the penniculus; vestibular cilia shown only on the outer margin; x1000 (after v. Gelei). E-L. Various species of *Paramecium*, showing general form, oral groove, position of cytopharynx, macro- and micronuclei; x500 approx., schematic (after Wenrich): E. *P. aurelia* Ehrbg.; F. *P. bursaria* (Ehrbg.) Focke; G. *P. calkinsi* Woodruff; H. *P. caudatum* Ehrbg.; I. *P. multimicronucleatum* Powers and Mitchell; J. *P. polycaryum* Woodruff and Spencer; K. *P. trichium* Stokes; L. *P. woodruffi* Wenrich. M. Transverse section through *Paramecium caudatum* showing trichocysts, somatic cilia, double vestibular cilia, penniculus, quadripartite membrane; pharynx is not ciliated except for the quadripartite membrane; schematic (after v. Gelei).

Only two genera have been recognized: *Maryna* Gruber (102; Fig. 7. 15, C, D) and *Mycterothrix* Lauterborn (102; Fig. 7. 15, E).

Family 9. Paraisotrichidae. The mouth is subterminal, opening just posterior to the concretion-vacuole. The somatic ciliation is complete and, except for an anterior tuft of longer cilia, is uniform.

This family was erected by Hsiung (91) for *Paraisotricha* Fiorentini (Fig. 7. 15, A, B), several species of which have been reported from the cecum and colon of horses.

Family 10. Parameciidae. An oral groove (Fig. 7. 16, A-L) extends from the anterior end toward the middle of the body. The somatic ciliation is complete and essentially uniform. The adoral ciliature includes a differentiated dorsal zone of long cilia ("quadripartite membrane" of von Gelei) and a penniculus (76, 133), a dense band of cilia which extends in a shallow spiral toward the cytostome (Fig. 7. 16, D, M).

In addition to the genus *Paramecium* Hill (107, 218; Fig. 7. 16, E-L), Kahl (102) has referred his genus *Physalophrya* to this family. On the basis of general similarities in the adoral ciliature of *Paramecium* and *Espejoia,* Fauré-Fremiet (62) has suggested the possible transfer of the genus *Paramecium* to the Hymenostomina.

Family 11. Plagiopylidae. These are dorso-ventrally flattened ciliates with a central peristomial groove which lies in the anterior half of the body and extends more or less transversely from the right margin toward or past the sagittal plane. A dorsal non-ciliated striated band, representing a thickened strip of the pellicle, occurs in *Lechriopyla* and *Plagiopyla* (Fig. 7. 17, F, J). The functional significance of this band is unknown. The somatic ciliation is otherwise complete. A ciliated cytoproct has been reported in *Lechriopyla* (137).

The family includes the following genera: *Lechriopyla* Lynch (137; Fig. 7. 17, J), containing an intestinal parasite of sea-urchins; *Plagiopyla* Stein (101, 102, 137; Fig. 7. 17, F-H), including ciliates from fresh and salt water; *Sonderia* Kahl (101, 102, 113; Fig. 7. 17, I) and *Sonderiella* Kahl (102), both represented in salt water.

Family 12. Spirozonidae. The family includes *Spirozona* Kahl (102, Fig. 7. 15, F). A band of closely set cilia extends from the peristome posteriorly and spirally to the right surface of the body. In addition, the tapering posterior end bears a tuft of caudal bristles. Otherwise, the somatic ciliation is uniform. The only described species occurs in fresh water and feeds on bacteria.

Family 13. Trichopelmidae. These laterally compressed ciliates have a firm pellicle which usually shows a few longitudinal ribs and grooves, the latter sometimes limited to the left surface. The semicircular or crescentic dorsal margin is smooth in outline. The mouth may lie near the anterior

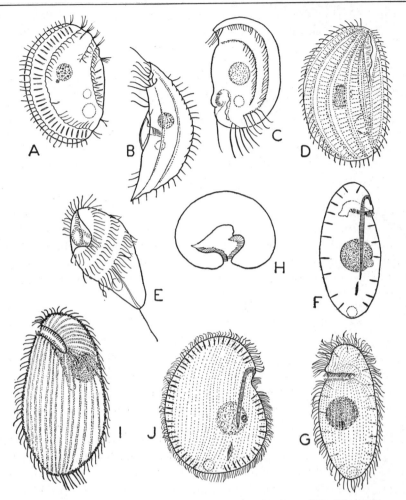

Fig. 7. 17. A. *Trichopelma sphagnetorum* Levander, x800 (after Wang and Nie). B. *Drepanomonas dentata* Fresenius, 40-65μ; lateral view of compressed body (after Penard). C. *Microthorax viridis* Penard, 35-45μ (after P.). D. *Pseudomicrothorax agilis* Mermod, longitudinal cuticular ribs, peristomial area with undulating membrane on left; cilia shown at margin of body; x630 (after Wang and Nie). E. *Trimyema compressa* Lackey, x640 (after Wang and Nie). F-H. *Plagiopyla nasuta* Stein: dorsal view (F) showing striated band, trichocysts, nuclei, cytopharynx, cytopyge anterior to contractile vacuole, x450 (after Lynch); ventral view (G) showing ciliary pattern, x450 (after Lynch); cross-section (H) at level of cytostome, schematic (after Wetzel). I. *Sonderia pharyngea* Kirby, adoral ciliature, pharynx, macronucleus, surface ridges from which cilia arise; neither bristles overhanging the margin of the peristome nor a gelatinous covering of the body are shown; x440 (after K.). J. *Lechriopyla mystax* Lynch, dorsal surface; trichocysts, striated band, nuclei, contractile vacuole, ciliary pattern, and ciliated cytoproct are shown; x250 (after L.).

or the posterior end or near the equator. There are only a few rows of somatic cilia. The Trichopelmidae resemble the Ctenostomina but lack the adoral membranelles characteristic of these heterotrichs.

The family includes the following genera from fresh water: *Drepanomonas* Fresenius (102), *Microthorax* Engelmann (102, 165; Fig. 7. 17, C), *Pseudomicrothorax* Mermod (102; Fig. 7. 17, D), and *Trichopelma* Levander (102; Fig. 7. 17, A).

Family 14. Trichospiridae. This family contains the genus *Trichospira* Roux (102; Fig. 7. 15, G, H). A band of densely set cilia, comparable to that in *Spirozona,* extends posteriorly from the peristome but spirals to the right instead of the left. The body does not taper to a point posteriorly and there are no caudal bristles. The only known species occurs in fresh water.

Family 15. Trimyemidae. The only known genus is *Trimyema* Lackey (*Sciadostoma* Kahl). Except for a caudal bristle, somatic cilia are limited to three or four spiral rows in the anterior half of the body (Fig. 7. 17, E). The cytostome is subterminal. Species are known from fresh and salt water.

Suborder 3. Hymenostomina.

Adoral cilia are fused into membranes, the number, size, and arrangement of which vary in different genera. The peristomial area also shows a certain amount of variation. In some genera there is a sort of oral pouch containing the adoral membranes (Fig. 7. 19, B, D) and opening onto the surface of the body. In others, the adoral ciliature arises in a groove which may be fairly long (Fig. 7. 18, L) or may even extend throughout most of the body (Fig. 7. 18, J). Although detailed information is not available for a number of genera, modern investigations have demonstrated several patterns of adoral organelles as well as differences in stomatogenesis during fission. Eventually, the accumulation of such data should lead to needed revisions in classification.

Kahl (102) divided the suborder into five families: Cohnilembidae (Lembidae), Frontoniidae, Ophryoglenidae, Philasteridae and Pleuronematidae. Of these, the Frontoniidae seem to be a particularly heterogeneous group which would be less so if *Tetrahymena* and certain related genera were removed. Such an improvement has been effected by Mugard (155) in transferring these ciliates to a "Family Leucophrydae." Since Corliss (42b) has concluded that none of Müller's species of *Leucophra* ("*Leucophrys*" Ehrenberg) is congeneric with any species subsequently referred to "*Leucophrys,*" and also that *Leucophra* should become a *genus dubium,* the "Leucophrydae" should be replaced by the Tetrahymenidae[2] with *Tetrahymena* Furgason as the type genus. This procedure

[2] The Family Tetrahymenidae has recently been erected by Corliss (1952. *Proc. Soc. Protozool.* 3: 4).

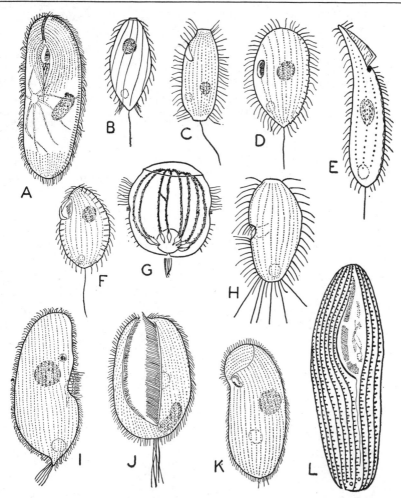

Fig. 7. 18. A. *Frontonia leucas* Ehrenberg, specimen 300μ long, showing oral region, anterior striated band, contractile vacuole, nuclei; ciliary pattern shown schematically at anterior and posterior ends; trichocysts indicated along one margin (after Kahl). B. *Homalogastra setosa* Kahl, about 30μ long (after K.). C. *Balanonema dubium* (Penard) Kahl, about 50μ long (after K.). D. *Platynematum hyalinum* Kahl, specimen 60μ long (after K.). E. *Cohnilembus (Lembus) punctatus* Kahl, 70-120μ (after K.). F. *Saprophilus putrinus* Kahl, specimen 40μ long (after K.). G. Contractile vacuole and accessory canals in *Urocentrum turbo;* silver impregnation; x250 (after Gelei). H. *Uronema pluricaudatum* Noland, left lateral view, x1190 (after N.). I. *Cryptochilidium echini* (Maupas), ventral view, x460 (after Powers). J. *Lembadion bullinum* Perty, ventral view; large membrane at left of oral groove; so-called "gullet-fibrils," just beneath the wall of the oral groove, are not shown; specimen 150μ long (after Kahl). K. *Colpidium colpoda* (Ehrbg.) Stein, specimen 150μ long (after Kahl). L. *Anophrys salmicida* Mugard, showing oral ciliature and somatic pattern; x830 approx. (after M.).

would add a sixth family to Kahl's original five, but without eliminating the need for further study of the remaining Frontoniidae.

Family 1. Cohnilembidae. This family was erected for *Cohnilembus* Kahl (102, 106; Fig. 7. 18, E). *Lembadionella* Kahl (106) was subsequently referred to the family, and more recently, *Anophrys* Cohn (Fig. 7. 18, L) has been added (155). The somatic ciliation of these ciliates is complete and rather uniform and the adoral ciliature consists of four membranes. A paroral, or lateral, membrane extends along the right margin of the elongated peristome. Three adoral membranes, which lie to the left in the oral pouch of Tetrahymenidae (Fig. 7. 19, C), are shifted to the right in *Anophrys* as a linear series parallel to the paroral membrane (Fig. 7. 18, L). There appears to be no row of somatic cilia ending at the posterior margin of the oral cavity. In stomatogenesis during fission of *Anophrys* (155), the adoral organelles of the posterior daughter are derived from basal granules which undergo multiplication at the base of the paroral membrane. This type of stomatogenesis differs from that in the Tetrahymenidae, as described below.

Family 2. Frontoniidae. Although defining the family as one in which the oral cavity does not open onto a clearly defined peristome, Kahl (102) pointed out that the lack of information concerning adoral organelles was responsible for much uncertainty in regard to the generic composition of the Frontoniidae. Later investigations have shown that Kahl's uncertainty was justified. Removal of the Tetrahymenidae still leaves the residual Frontoniidae a group probably in need of further subdivision.

After elimination of certain ciliates more or less closely related to *Tetrahymena* Furgason, the family includes the following genera: *Aristerostoma* Kahl (102), *Balanonema* Kahl (102; Fig. 7. 18, C), *Bizone* Lepsi (102), *Cardiostoma* Kahl (102), *Chasmatostoma* Engelmann (102), *Cinetochilum* Perty (102), *Cryptochilidium* Schouteden (172; Fig. 7. 18, I), *Cyrtolophosis* Stokes (102), *Dexiotrichides* Kahl (102), *Dichilum* Schewiakoff (102), *Disematostoma* Lauterborn (102; Fig. 7. 19, A), *Epimecophrya* Kahl (106), *Espejoia* Bürger (66; Fig. 7. 19, I, J), *Eurychilum* André (102), *Frontonia* Ehrbg. (102; Figs. 7. 18, A; 19, K, L), *Frontoniella* Wetzel (102), *Homalogastra* Kahl (102; Fig. 7. 18, B), *Lambornella* Keilin (102), *Leucophrydium* Roux (102), *Lembadion* Perty (102; Figs. 7. 18, J; 19, E), *Malacophrys* Kahl (102), *Monochilum* Schewiakoff (102), *Platynematum* Kahl (102; Fig. 7. 18, D), *Pseudoglaucoma* Kahl (102), *Rhinodisculus* Mansfield (102), *Saprophilus* Stokes (102; Fig. 7. 18, F), *Stegochilum* Schewiakoff (102), *Stokesia* Wenrich (219), *Turania* Brodsky (102), *Urocentrum* Nitzsch (77, 102; Figs. 7. 18, G; 19, F, G), *Uronema* Dujardin (162; Fig. 7. 18, H), *Uronemopsis* Kahl (102), *Uropedalium* Kahl (102), and *Urozona* Schewiakoff (102).

Family 3. Tetrahymenidae. As shown by Furgason (69), the adoral ciliature is composed of four membranes, three adoral ones lying to the left in the oral pouch and a paroral membrane extending along the right margin (Fig. 7. 19, C). Another feature is the presence of one or more ciliary rows ("stomatogenous rows") which end at the posterior margin of the oral pouch (Fig. 7. 20, H-L). In stomatogenesis the adoral mem-

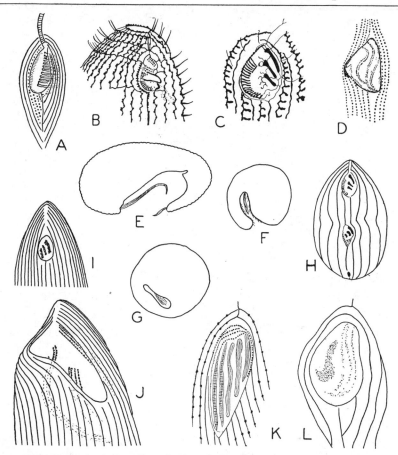

Fig. 7. 19. A. Oral region of *Disematostoma bütschlii* Lauterborn, show-ing striated preoral band; schematic (after Kahl). B. Oral region of *Loxo-cephalus colpidiopsis;* silver impregnation, showing basal granules of three adoral membranes in oral pouch; schematic (after Gelei). C. Oral ciliature of *Tetrahymena pyriformis* (Ehrbg.) Lwoff; silver impregnation, showing bases of three adoral membranes (solid black) and the paroral membrane; x125 approx. (after Corliss). D. Oral region of *Deltopylum rhabdoides* Fauré-Fremiet and Mugard, showing tetrahymenal organization; schematic (after F-F. & M.). E. Cross-section through *Lembadion bullinum* at level of cyto-stome, showing broad and narrow membranes (compare with Fig. 7. 18, J); x240 approx. (after Wetzel). F, G. Cross-section of *Urocentrum turbo* through oral groove (F) and near level of cytostome (G); x460 (after Wetzel). H. Stomatogenesis in fission of *Tetrahymena pyriformis*, differentia-tion of adoral organelles about completed in posterior daughter; schematic (after Corliss). I, J. *Espejoia mucicola* (Penard), oral regions of microstome and macrostome forms, showing differences in ciliature; schematic (after Fauré-Fremiet and Mugard). K. Oral region of *Frontonia leucas*, silver im-pregnation; schematic (after Klein). L. Oral region of *Frontonia parva* (after Klein).

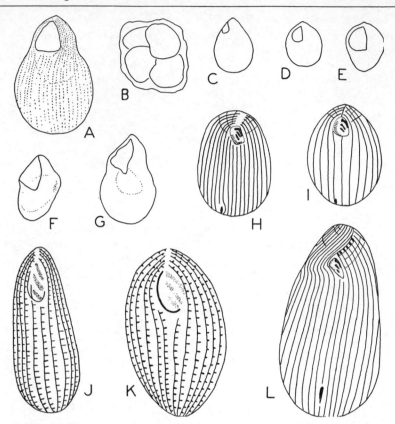

Fig. 7. 20. A-G. Changes in form observed in *Tetrahymena* (*Leuco-phrys*) *patula* (Ehrbg.) Corliss: mature macrostome (A); reproduction in cyst (B); excysted microstome (C); growth of mouth (D, E); young macrostome with ingested ciliate (F); larger macrostome (G); x325 approx. (after Corliss). H, I. Ciliary patterns in *Glaucoma scintillans* and *Tetrahymena pyriformis;* x540 approx. (after Corliss). J, K. *Paraglaucoma rostrata* Kahl (?), slender non-feeding stage ("theronte") and larger feeding stage ("trophonte"), x500 approx. (after Mugard). L. *Colpidium*-type of ciliary pattern, x540 approx. (after Corliss).

branes of the posterior daughter are derived from a field of basal granules which originate by multiplication of granules in one or more stomatogenous rows (Figs. 2. 4, G, H; 7. 19, H).

Certain species exhibit two morphological phases, the macrostome and the microstome (Fig. 7. 20, A-G). The former, equipped with a large oral pouch, is carnivorous. Both *T. patula* and *T. vorax* appear to be dimorphic in this sense.

The Family Tetrahymenidae is particularly important because several species—including *Tetrahymena patula* (Ehrbg.) Corliss, *T. pyriformis* (Ehrbg.) Lwoff and *T. vorax* (Kidder, Lilly, and Claff) Kidder—have been established in bacteria-free cultures and are being used in physiological and biochemical investigations. More than twenty strains of *T. pyriformis,* whose history has been traced by Corliss (42c), are being maintained in various laboratories.

It is not yet certain just how many of the genera in Kahl's (102) Family Frontoniidae should be transferred to the Tetrahymenidae, but the available data suggest the following list: *Colpidium* Stein (102; Figs. 7. 18, K; 20, L), *Deltopylum* Fauré-Fremiet and Mugard (155; Fig. 7. 19, D), *Glaucoma* Ehrbg. (102, 155; Fig. 7. 20, H), possibly *Loxocephalus* Eberhard (78, 102; Fig. 7. 19, B), *Paraglaucoma* Kahl[3] (102, 155; Fig. 7. 20, J, K), and *Tetrahymena* Furgason (42a, 42b, 42c, 69; Figs. 7. 19, C, H; 20, A-G, I). *Leucophra* Müller ("*Leucophrys*" Ehrenberg) is a genus of very uncertain status, and as suggested by Corliss (42b), probably will become a *genus dubium.* Accordingly, Corliss (42a) has transferred *L. patula,* the only remaining species of "*Leucophrys,*" to the genus *Tetrahymena.* In view of the similarity of this ciliate to *T. vorax,* this arrangement would seem to be a sound one unless it can be shown that *T. vorax* and *T. patula* are not congeneric with *T. pyriformis.*

Family 4. Hysterocinetidae. These are uniformly and densely ciliated, dorso-ventrally flattened ciliates with a posterior cytostome. The peristome may be merely a transverse terminal groove, along which an undulating membrane extends into the short pharynx. An anterior non-ciliated "sucker" is characteristic. These ciliates have been reported from the intestine of certain snails and fresh-water oligochaetes.

The family includes *Hysterocineta* Diesing (6; Fig. 7. 21, G-I) and *Ptychostomum* Stein (84, 181, 199; Fig. 9. 21, F).

Family 5. Ophryoglenidae. There is a ciliated vestibule (peristome), an invagination of the body wall, and a pharynx which opens into the vestibule. The vestibule is relatively deep in *Ophryoglena,* less so in *Protophryoglena,* and much reduced in *Ichthyophthirius* (155). A spiral ridge extends from the opening of the vestibule into the pharynx in *Ophryoglena.* According to Mugard (155), a tetrahymenal organization of the oral membranes is characteristic. The membranes curve along the spiral ridge before entering the pharynx in *Ophryoglena* but follow a less curved path in *Protophryoglena* and almost a straight course in *Ichthyophthirius.* In stomatogenesis, the oral membranes are derived from basal granules in a number of stomatogenous rows. A refractile "body of Lieberkühn" ("watch-glass body"), usually accompanied by a mass of pigment, lies just to the left of the vestibule.

The life-cycles follow a general pattern (155). Reproduction occurs within a cyst (Fig. 7. 21, A). The young ciliates ("tomites"), after excystment, develop into the trophic stage ("theronte") which, in free-living species, grows into a large slowly swimming stage ("trophonte") with much stored food. This mature stage then encysts in preparation for re-

---

[3] The status of the genus *Paraglaucoma* is rather confused at present, since Corliss (1952. *Proc. Soc. Protozool.* **3:** 3) has concluded that *Paraglaucoma rostrata* (the type species) is congeneric with *Tetrahymena pyriformis.*

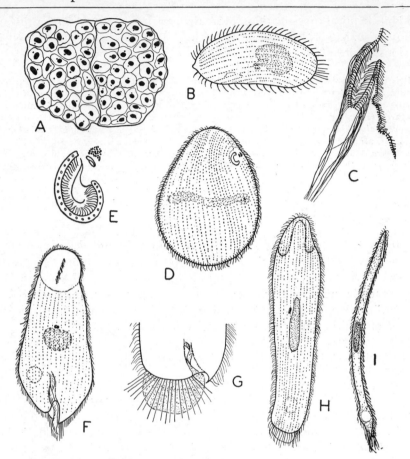

Fig. 7. 21. A. Reproductive cyst of *Ichthyophthirius multifiliis* Fouquet, cross-section, nuclei indicated but cilia not shown; x450 (after MacLennan). B. Ciliated larva of *I. multifiliis* just after excystment; "perforatorium" at anterior end, cytostome not differentiated; x750 (after MacLennan). C. Longitudinal section through oral region of mature specimen of *I. multifiliis*, embedded in epithelium of fish; x370 (after MacLennan). D, E. *Ophryoglena atra* Lieberkükn: ventral view (D) of specimen 400μ long; schematic representation (E) of vestibular ciliature and body of Lieberkühn (after Kahl). F. *Ptychostomum (Lada) pygostoma* (Rossolimo); length reaches 200μ; undulating membrane extends through posterior cytostome into pharynx (after R.). G-I. *Hysterocineta eiseniae* Beers (after B.): ventral view of posterior end (G), showing undulating membrane extending along the peristomial groove and into the pharynx, x600; dorsal view (H), the ventral sucker shown in outline at the anterior end, x285; lateral view (I), x285.

production. In *Ichthyophthirius* (145), fission produces many (100-1,000) small ciliates which are set free with an incompletely developed mouth. These active stages (Fig. 7. 21, B) swim about until they either starve to death or encounter a suitable fish. In the latter case, the ciliate apparently bores its way into the tissue as a result of strong ciliary action. After pene-

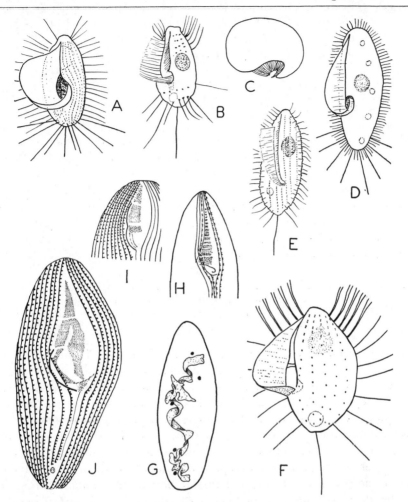

Fig. 7. 22. A. *Pleuronema setigerum* Calkins; large paroral membrane
extends around posterior end of peristome; cilia shown at margin of body;
x450 (after Noland). B. *Cristigera setosa* Kahl, specimen 30μ long (after K.).
C. Cross-section of *Pleuronema chrysalis* through posterior end of peristomial groove; x510 (after Wetzel). D. *Histiobalantium semisetatum* Noland,
inclusions omitted; x200 (after N.). E. *Ctedoctema acanthocrypta* Stokes,
specimen 35μ long (after Kahl). F. *Cyclidium glaucoma* O. F. M., cilia
shown only at margin; x1200 (after Parducz). G, H. *Porpostoma notatum*
Möbius: nuclear apparatus (G), x400; peristomial area (H), anterior ciliary
field broken up into a linear series of pseudomembranelles, schematic, x500
(after Mugard). I. Peristomial area of *Philasterides armata* Kahl, showing
deltoid, trapezoid, and falciform ciliary fields; x500 (after Mugard). J.
Philaster digitiformis Fabre-Domergue, somatic and adoral ciliary patterns;
x500 (after Mugard).

tration, the young parasite develops a functional cytostome, feeds partly on fragments of epithelial cells, and grows to a diameter of 100-1,000μ. The mature ciliate then drops off the host and encysts.

Three genera have been referred to this family: *Ichthyophthirius* Fouquet (83, 145, 155; Fig. 7. 21, A-C), *Ophryoglena* Ehrenberg (155; Fig. 7. 21, D, E), and *Protophryoglena* Mugard (155).

Family 6. Philasteridae. Members of this family are elongated ciliates with a long and approximately triangular peristomial groove. Although the adoral ciliature is basically "tetrahymenal," the three adoral membranes are replaced by three ciliary fields—the deltoid, trapezoid, and falciform fields (Fig. 7. 22, H-J) of Mugard (155). However, the paroral membrane persists as such, extending part way along the right margin of the peristome. Stomatogenesis involves multiplication of basal granules at the posterior end of the paroral membrane.

The following genera, represented by species in salt or brackish water, are referred to the family: *Helicostoma* Cohn (102), *Paralembus (Lemboides)* Kahl (102), *Philaster* Fabre-Domergue (155; Fig. 7. 22, J), *Philasterides* Kahl (155; Fig. 7. 22, I), and *Porpostoma* Möbius (155; Fig. 7. 22, G, H).

Family 7. Pleuronematidae. The paroral membrane is much enlarged and may extend around the posterior margin of the peristome (Fig. 7. 22, A-F). The rest of the adoral ciliature is less uniformly developed and may be represented by a single membrane at the left of the peristome or by a field of cilia in this region (102). In *Balantiophorus* (216) a continuous membrane extends along the right, posterior, and left margins of the peristome. When fully extended, the membrane forms a sac-like structure covering the peristome except at the anterior end. In certain Pleuronematidae, some of the dorso-lateral cilia are thigmotactic and these ciliates often become attached momentarily to a solid surface. One or more long caudal cilia also are often present.

The Pleuronematidae, which are represented in fresh and salt water, include the following genera: *Balantiophorus* Schewiakoff (216), *Calyptotricha* Phillips (102), *Cristigera* Roux (102; Fig. 7. 22, B), *Ctedoctema* Stokes (102; Fig. 7. 22, E), *Cyclidium* Müller (163; Fig. 7. 22, F), *Histiobalantium* Stokes (102, 158; Fig. 7. 22, D), *Larvulina* Penard (102, 165), *Pleurocoptes* Wallengren (102), *Pleuronema* Dujardin (102, 158; Fig. 7. 22, A, C).

Suborder 4. Thigmotrichina

These ciliates occur mostly in the mantle cavity or on the gills and palps of bivalve molluscs, although species are known also from the mantle cavity of pulmonate snails and from the tentacles of *Phoronopsis*. An anterior field of thigmotactic cilia is a general characteristic. A cytostome and the adoral ciliature, if present at all, lie in the posterior half of the body, and in certain species, the cytostome lies at the posterior pole. Some specialized genera have lost the cytostome and developed an anterior suctorial tentacle. Except in primitive types, there is reduction of the somatic ciliature and this trend reaches a climax in genera which retain only the thigmotactic cilia.

Chatton and Lwoff (30) have listed six families. In three ("Tribe Stomodea")—Conchophthiriidae, Hemispeiridae, Thigmophryidae—the cytostome is functional and the adoral ciliature is recognizable. In the others ("Tribe Rhynchodea")—Ancistrocomidae, Hypocomidae, Sphenophryidae—the adoral ciliature has undergone regression and there is no functional cytostome, although a suctorial tentacle serves for the ingestion of food much as in the Suctorea.

Family 1. Ancistrocomidae. These ciliates are ovoid, pyriform, or somewhat cylindrical, typically with a more or less pointed anterior pole. The closely set thigmotactic cilia, not as long as the somatic cilia, are limited to a few short anterior fields. The body is extensively ciliated in certain genera; in others, cilia may be limited to the thigmotactic fields. An anterior suctorial tentacle (Fig. 7. 23, B, G), continuous with an internal canal, is characteristic. This tentacle enables the organism to become attached to epithelial cells and ingest their contents.

The following genera have been referred to the family (31): *Ancistrocoma* Chatton and Lwoff (= *Parachaenia* Kofoid and Bush) (128; Fig. 7. 23, H), *Anisocomides* Chatton and Lwoff (31), *Cepedella* Poyarkoff (31), *Crebicoma* Kozloff (126; Fig. 7. 23, A), *Enerthecoma* Jarocki (129; Fig. 7. 23, J), *Goniocoma* Chatton and Lwoff (31), *Heterocineta* Mawrodiadi (125, 129; Fig. 7. 23, G), *Heterocinetopsis* Jarocki (31), *Holocoma* Chatton and Lwoff (31), *Hypocomagalma* Jarocki and Raabe (128), *Hypocomatidium* Jarocki and Raabe (31; Fig. 7. 23, E), *Hypocomella* Chatton and Lwoff (31), *Hypocomoides* Chatton and Lwoff (127; Fig. 7. 23, B), *Hypocomidium* Raabe (31), *Hypocomina* Chatton and Lwoff (126; Fig. 7. 23, D), *Insignicoma* Kozloff (127; Fig. 7. 23, C), *Isocomides* Chatton and Lwoff (31), *Raabella* Chatton and Lwoff (31), *Syringopharynx* Collin (31, 106).

Family 2. Conchophthiriidae. There is a functional cytostome in the posterior half of the body. The thigmotactic cilia are represented by the anterior portions of somatic rows instead of forming separate fields. The body is laterally compressed and the cytostome lies on the narrow ventral surface (102).

The following genera have been referred to this family: *Andreula* Kahl (106), *Cochliophilus* Kozloff (124; Fig. 7. 23, I), *Conchophthirius* Stein (106, 111; Fig. 7. 23, F), *Kidderia* Raabe (46, 108).

Family 3. Hemispeiridae. These are rather heavily ciliated types with a posterior or subterminal cytostome. The adoral ciliature shows two typical components (Fig. 7. 24, B). On the right a single row, row 1, curves slightly to the left throughout most of its length and then sharply to the

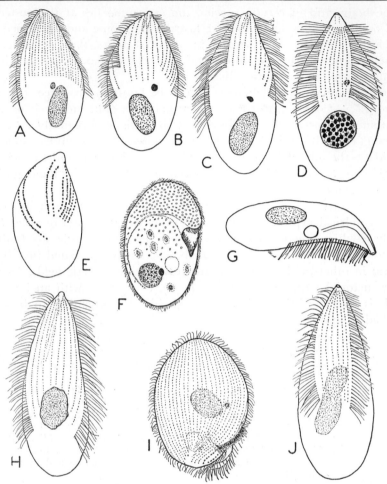

Fig. 7. 23. A. *Crebicoma carinata* (Raabe) Kozloff, ventral surface, x565 (after K.). B. *Hypocomoides mytili* Chatton and Lwoff, suctorial tentacle slightly protruded at anterior end; x935 (after Kozloff). C. *Insignicoma venusta* Kozloff, x1495 (after K.). D. *Hypocomina tegularum* Kozloff, x1400 (after K.). E. *Hypocomatidium sphaerii* Jarocki and Raabe; three fields of basal granules in the ventral thigmotactic area; silver impregnation, x900 (after J. & R.). F. *Conchophthirius anodontae* Stein; upper surface, showing peristomial area and slender pharynx; x300 (after Kidder). G. *Heterocineta phoronopsidis* Kozloff, view of right side showing macronucleus, contractile vacuole, and internal canal continuous with the suctorial tentacle; x1455 (after K.). H. *Ancistrocoma dissimilis* Kozloff, x1345 (after K.). I. *Cochliophilus depressus* Kozloff, dorsal view, x450 (after K.). J. *Enerthecoma properans* Jarocki, x1290 (after Kozloff).

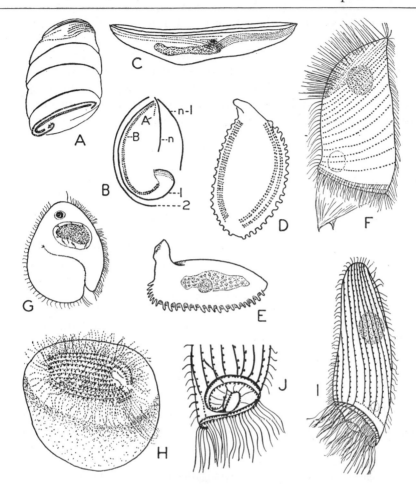

Fig. 7. 24. A, B. *Hemispeira asteriasi* Fabre-Domergue, view of right side
(A), x600; adoral ciliature and adjacent ciliary rows (*1, 2, n* and *n-1*, first,
second, last, and next to last somatic rows of cilia; *A, B,* adoral cilia),
schematic (after Chatton and Lwoff). C. *Sphenophrya dosiniae* Chatton and
Lwoff, showing long narrow sucker on upper surface, nuclei, rows of basal
granules; length reaches 120μ (after C. & L.). D, E. *Gargarius gargarius*
Chatton and Lwoff: ciliary pattern (D); view showing papillae and nuclei
(E); x900 (after C. & L.). F. *Cheissinia (Tiarella) baicalensis* (Cheissen)
Chatton and Lwoff, adoral membrane projecting beyond posterior rows of
cilia; length, 50-72μ (after Cheissin). G. *Ancistrum pernix* (MacLennan and
Connell) Chatton and Lwoff, longitudinal optical section showing nuclei and
pharynx; x490 (after MacL. & C.). H. *Hypocoma parasitica* Gruber, dorso-
lateral view, x1350 (after Chatton and Lwoff). I, J. *Boveria teredini* Nelson,
dorsal side (I), x465; posterior end (J), showing basal granules of adoral
zone, x620 approx. (after Pickard).

left at the cytostome. At the left of row 1 a double row of cilia (row B) follows much the same path but does not extend so far posteriorly. In addition, a short row of cilia lies near the anterior end of row B in some species and there are also several rows of cilia in the pharynx (30). This pattern varies in details in different species. The thigmotactic cilia of some genera are merely the anterior cilia in normal rows. In others, the posterior somatic cilia have disappeared, leaving only the thigmotactic cilia.

The family includes the following genera: *Ancistrella* Cheissen (37), *Ancistrospira* Chatton and Lwoff (30), *Ancistrum* Maupas (30, 109; Fig. 7. 24, G), *Boveria* Stevens (142, 169; Fig. 7. 24, I, J), *Cheissinia* Chatton and Lwoff (30, 37; Fig. 7. 24, F), *Hemispeira* Fabre-Domergue (30; Fig. 7. 24, A, B), *Plagiospira* Issel (30, 102), *Proboveria* Chatton and Lwoff (30), *Protophrya* Kofoid (30).

Family 4. Hypocomidae. These are ovoid to somewhat flattened ciliates in which cilia are limited to the dorsal surface. An anterior or antero-dorsal suctorial tentacle is present and there is no cytostome. However, there is an antero-lateral field of supposedly vestigial adoral cilia (31).

Three genera have been characterized by Chatton and Lwoff (31): *Heterocoma* Chatton and Lwoff, *Hypocoma* Gruber (Fig. 7. 24, H) and *Parahypocoma* Chatton and Lwoff.

Family 5. Sphenophryidae. The adult stage is not ciliated although in reproduction the "embryo" develops cilia and resembles the more specialized Ancistrocomidae (31). The suctorial tentacle is generally shorter than that of the Ancistrocomidae and Hypocomidae and tends to be funnel-shaped.

Three genera have been recognized: *Gargarius* Chatton and Lwoff (27, 31; Fig. 7. 24, D, E), *Pelecyophrya* Chatton and Lwoff (31) and *Sphenophrya* Chatton and Lwoff (31; Fig. 7. 24, C).

Family 6. Thigmophryidae. The ciliation is essentially uniform. The thigmotactic field is represented by short, closely set cilia in various somatic rows (31). *Conchophyllum caryoclada* (Kidder) Raabe shows an unusual branched macronucleus (110).

Three genera have been referred to the family: *Conchophyllum* Raabe (110), *Myxophyllum* Raabe (106), and *Thigmophrya* Chatton and Lwoff (22).

Suborder 5. Apostomina

This group was established (24) for a number of ciliates with a ventral cytostome so small that ingestion is probably limited to liquids or minute particles. A peculiar "rosette" is characteristic of the ventral surface (26, 28, 45). In *Foettingeria* (Fig. 7. 25, A-D, F) the cytostome lies

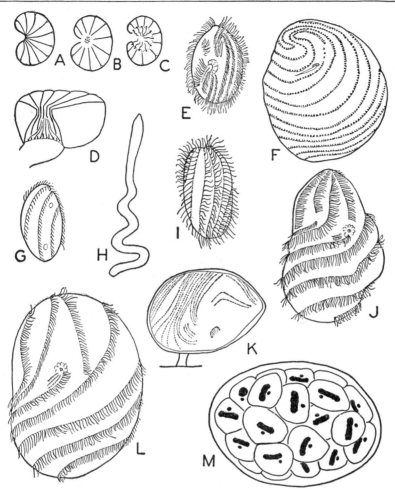

Fig. 7. 25. A-D. The rosette in *Foettingaria actinarium;* superficial and progressively deeper optical cross-sections (A-C), showing septa and cilia; vertical optical "dissection" (D), showing septa and cilia and portion of the oral pouch below; schematic (after Chatton and Lwoff). E. Young ciliated stage ("tomite") of *Spirophrya subparasitica* Chatton and Lwoff, ventral surface showing rosette and cilia; x600 (after C. & L.). F, G. *Foettingaria actinarium* (Claparède) Caullery and Mesnil: ventral side showing rosette and basal granules (F), x170; young ciliate (G) ready to leave cyst, x570 (after De Morgan). H, I. *Chromidina elegans* (Foettinger) Gonder, outline of "tropho-tomonte," x250; dorsal surface of "tomite," x1000 (after Chatton and Lwoff). J. *Synophrya hypertrophica* Chatton and Lwoff, ventral surface of young "trophonte," x800 (after C. & L.). K. Sessile stage ("phoronte") of *Foettingaria actinarium,* x990 (after Chatton and Lwoff). L. *Gymnodinioides inkystans* Chatton and Lwoff, ventral surface of "trophonte," x1400 (after C. & L.). M. Reproductive cyst of *Spirophrya subparasitica,* x530 (after Chatton and Lwoff).

at the end of a groove, in a small depression next to the rosette, and opens into a canal which leads inward, along the concave wall ("typhlosole") of the rosette, to an "oral pouch." The rosette contains 8-10 vertical septa which join the outer wall to the "typhlosole," and the base of the typhlosole is equipped with a ring of cilia (Fig. 7. 25, C). De Morgan (45) never observed movement of the rosette in living *F. actinarium* and obtained no clues in regard to its functions. There are fewer than 22 complete rows of somatic cilia but their exact number and the organization of the adoral ciliature vary in different genera.

A complex life-cycle is characteristic (28, 135). In the growth-stage, or "trophonte" (Fig. 7. 25, F, J, L), food is ingested and accumulated during growth but there is no reproduction. At maturity, the "trophonte" stops feeding, and with or without encystment in different species, becomes transformed into a "protomonte." If the "protomonte" is an encysted stage, the cilia are discarded. The "protomonte" develops into a "tomonte" in which the accumulated food is transformed into stored reserves. Then repeated fission occurs to produce many small "protomites" (Fig. 7. 25, M), each of which becomes an actively swimming "tomite" (Fig. 7. 25, E, G, I). This migratory stage becomes attached to the body of a host, usually a crustacean. However, *Chromidina elegans* has been reported from the kidney of a cephalopod (222). After attachment, the "tomite" develops into a resting cyst, or "phoronte" (Fig. 7. 25, K). When the host is ingested by a coelenterate or a ctenophore, or when the host molts, a young "trophonte" emerges from the cyst. The vegetative stage ("trophotomonte") of *Chromidina elegans* is unusual in that it may undergo fission to form chains (222) similar to those produced by Astomina.

A detailed survey of the Apostomina has been published by Chatton and Lwoff (28) who have characterized the following genera: *Calospira* Chatton and Lwoff, *Chromidina* Gonder (222; Fig. 7. 25, H, I), *Foettingaria* Caullery and Mesnil (45; Fig. 7. 25, F, G, K), *Gymnodinioides* Minkiewicz (135; Fig. 7. 25, L), *Ophiuraespira* Chatton and Lwoff, *Pericaryon* Chatton, *Phoretophrya* Chatton and A. and M. Lwoff, *Phtorophrya* Chatton and A. and M. Lwoff, *Polyspira* Minkiewicz, *Spirophrya* Chatton and Lwoff (Fig. 7. 25, E, M), *Synophrya* Chatton and Lwoff (Fig. 7. 25, J), *Traumatiophora* Chatton and Lwoff, *Vampyrophrya* Chatton and Lwoff. The genus *Chromidina* also has been assigned to the Astomina by some workers.

Suborder 6. Astomina

These are parasites without a cytostome. The body is often uniformly ciliated but there is sometimes a small naked area at the anterior pole. The average length, for the majority, probably falls within the range, 200-500μ, but such species as *Haptophrya gigantea, H. michiganensis* (225), and *Mesnilella radiata* (36) may reach lengths of 1.5-2.0 mm. The cortex shows little specialization, although it ranges from a very thin zone in some coelozoic species to a layer 1.0-2.0μ thick in certain intestinal parasites.

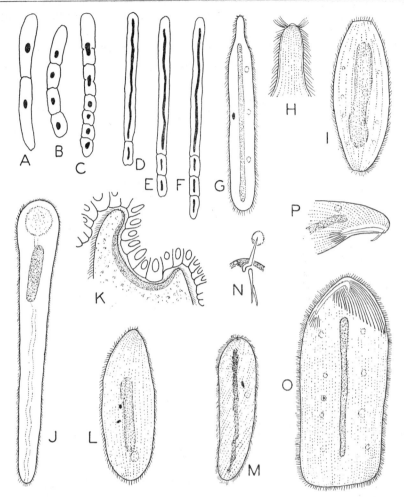

Fig. 7. 26. A-F. Formation of chains in Astomina: *Haptophrya*-type (A-C), *Radiophrya*-type (D-F), schematic (after Cheissin). G, H. *Bütschliella nasuta* Rossolimo; specimen showing nuclei and three contractile vacuoles (G); anterior end showing ciliation (H); length reaches 200μ (after R.). I. *Anoplophrya gammari* Cheissin, x490 approx. (after C.). J, K. *Haprophrya michiganensis* Woodhead: ventral view showing macronucleus, contractile canal and sucker (J), x265; section (K) showing sucker attached to intestinal epithelium of salamander, x360 (after Bush). L. *Perseia dogieli* Rossolimo; length, 114-205μ (after R.). M, N. *Buchneriella criodrili* Heidenreich; length, 110-220μ; stained specimen (M); skeletal apparatus (N), schematic (after H.). O, P. *Metaradiophrya asymmetrica* Beers: ventral view (O) showing nuclei, eight contractile vacuoles, antero-ventral fibrils and hook; lateral view of anterior end (P); x400 (after B.).

A number of the Astomina have developed holdfast organelles. Such structures usually lie at or near the anterior pole which is often in contact with an epithelium of the host. An antero-ventral sucker (Fig. 7. 26, J, K) is characteristic of certain intestinal species. In various other

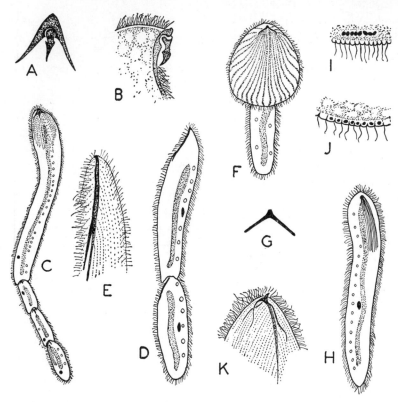

Fig. 7. 27. A, B. Holdfast apparatus of *Radiophrya lumbrici* Cheissin, ventral view (A), sagittal section through anterior end of body (B), x650 (after C.). C. *Radiophrya hoplites* Rossolimo, primite with three satellites; x100 (after Cheissin). D, E. *Protoradiophrya fissispiculata* Cheissin, primite and satellite (D), x375; tangential section of anterior end (E), showing spicules, x975 (after C.). F, G. *Mrazekiella intermedia* Cheissin: entire specimen (F), x240; holdfast apparatus (G), x975 (after C.). H-J. *Mesnilella multispiculata* Cheissin: ventral view (H) showing nuclei, skeletal spicules and row of contractile vacuoles, x210; transverse sections near anterior ends (I) and near posterior ends (J) of the spicules, x1650 (after C.). K. Anterior end of *Hoplitophrya secans* Stein, showing skeletal apparatus; x900 (after Heidenreich).

Astomina the anterior end is equipped with an apparatus composed of barbs or spicules (Figs. 7. 26, N, P; 27, B, K; 28, C, G). In addition, skeletal fibrils of unknown function may extend for some distance near the surface of the body (Fig. 7. 27, H-J) and sometimes pass from the cortex into the endoplasm (183).

Contractile vacuoles—or sometimes a contractile canal (15, 147) as in *Haptophrya* (Fig. 7. 26, J)—are generally present. There may be one contractile vacuole or, at the other extreme, many vacuoles arranged in one or more longitudinal rows (Fig. 7. 26, L, O).

Little is known about the life-cycles of Astomina. Most species are known from oligochaetes; a few, from amphipod Crustacea and from the digestive tracts of Turbellaria and Amphibia. Reproduction may involve typical binary fission, fission in which one daughter organism is a little smaller than the other, or consecutive fissions leading to the production of chains (Fig. 7. 26, A-F). In some chains both the anterior (primite) and the posterior (satellite) organisms undergo repeated fission; in others, the primite produces several satellites without undergoing a reduction in size.

The families described below represent five of the six recognized by Cheissin (36). Other workers have subdivided the Astomina in somewhat different fashion.

Family 1. Anoplophryidae. The body may be ovoid or distinctly elongated and the cilia are arranged in longitudinal rows. A poorly developed sucker is commonly present but skeletal elements are typically absent. There may be one, two, or more contractile vacuoles, or sometimes none.

Cheissin (36) has assigned the following genera to the family: *Anoplophrya* Stein (41, 84, 201; Fig. 7. 26, I), *Bütschliella* Awerinzew (84; Fig. 7. 26, G, H), *Dogielella* Poljansky, *Herpetophrya* Siedlecki, *Kofoidella* Cepède, *Metaphrya* Ikeda, *Orchitophrya* Cepède, *Perezella* Cepède, *Perseia* Rossolimo (181; Fig. 7. 26, L), *Protoanoplophrya* Mijaschita, *Rhizocarium* Caullery and Mesnil.

Family 2. Haptophryidae. A long contractile canal, instead of separate contractile vacuoles, is characteristic. An antero-ventral sucker is present in some species. Spicules or hooks may or may not be present at the anterior end.

The following genera have been referred to the family: *Haptophrya* Cepède (15, 147, 225; Fig. 7. 26, J, K), *Lachmannella* Cepède and *Steinella* Cepède.

Family 3. Hoplitophryidae. These Astomina are equipped with a holdfast apparatus, longitudinal supporting spicules, or both types of structures. There may be several to many contractile vacuoles.

The family includes the following genera: *Buchneriella* Heidenreich (84; Fig. 7. 26, M, N), *Hoplitophrya* Cepède (85; Fig. 7. 27, K), *Mesnilella* Cepède (36, 84, 183; Fig. 7. 27, H-J), *Metaradiophrya* Heidenreich (5, 84; Fig. 7. 26, O, P), *Mrazekiella* Kijenskij (36, 84; Fig. 7. 27, F, G), *Protoradiophrya* Rossolimo (36, 183; Fig. 7. 27, D, E), *Radiophrya* Rossolimo (36, 183; Fig. 7. 27, A-C).

Family 4. Intoshellinidae. These are elongated ciliates with longitudinal or spiral rows of cilia. There is a holdfast apparatus in the form of a spiny collar or a toothed disc, the area anterior to which is non-ciliated. A number of contractile vacuoles are arranged in one or two longitudinal rows or distributed irregularly. Chains are usually formed.

Two genera have been referred to the family: *Intoshellina* Cepède (36, 84; Fig. 7. 28, A-C) and *Monodontophrya* Vejdowsky (36; Fig. 7. 28, D, E).

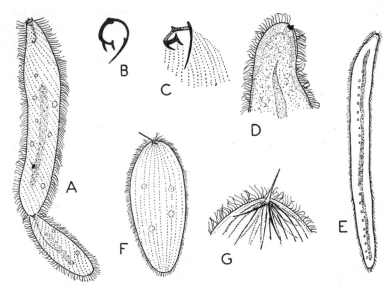

Fig. 7. 28. A-C. *Intoshellina poljansky* Cheissin: primite and satellite (A), x225; holdfast apparatus (B, C), polar and ventral views, x975 (after C.). D, E. *Monodontophrya kijenskiji* Cheissin: anterior end (D), showing thick ectoplasmic cap and holdfast organ, x650; lateral view (E), x75 (after C.). F, G. *Maupasella criodrili* Heidenreich, 50-150μ long; entire specimen (F), skeletal apparatus (G), x3300 (after H.).

Family 5. Maupasellidae. Little is known about this group which contains only two genera, *Maupasella* Cepède (84; Fig. 7. 28, F, G) and *Schulzellina* Cepède. These ciliates are similar to the Hoplitophryidae and Cheissin (36) has suggested that further investigation might justify combining the two families.

In addition to the five families described above, Cheissin (36) included the Chromidinidae, containing the genus *Chromidina* Gonder (= *Opalinopsis* Foettinger). Chatton and Lwoff (28), on the other hand, concluded that *Chromidina* belongs in the Apostomina.

Order 2. Spirotrichida. The most characteristic feature is the adoral zone of membranelles, the narrow bases of which usually lie at right or oblique angles to the long axis of the adoral zone. This series of membranelles extends anteriorly from the left margin of the cytostome, and in certain genera, may turn dorsally at the anterior pole and extend to the right for some distance along the antero-dorsal surface. The basal plate of each membranelle usually contains two rows of basal granules, although three rows (rarely, four) may be present (104). The group may be divided into six suborders.

Suborders of the Spirotrichida

Suborder 1. Heterotrichina. Somatic ciliation is usually complete. However, the dorsal surface may be sparsely ciliated in some families and shows more extensive reduction of ciliation in exceptional cases. The peristome, usually elongated and fairly narrow, bears the adoral zone of membranelles along the left wall. In addition, an undulating membrane often extends for some distance along the right margin.

Suborder 2. Oligotrichina. Although the adoral membranelles are well developed, there is a marked reduction in somatic ciliation and the peristomial field, around which the adoral zone extends, is free from cilia. An undulating membrane lies at the right margin of the adoral area in certain genera.

Suborder 3. Tintinnina. These ciliates, sometimes grouped with the Oligotrichina, are typically conical forms with a lorica. The adoral zone of membranelles follows a spiral course on the flattened oral pole.

Suborder 4. Entodiniomorphina. This group, sometimes placed in the Oligotrichina, includes parasites of the rumen and intestine of herbivores. The ciliation may be limited to the adoral zone or there may be one or more additional bands or groups of membranelles.

Suborder 5. Hypotrichina. The somatic cilia are replaced by cirri which are generally distributed in particular fields and limited essentially to the ventral surface.

Suborder 6. Ctenostomina. These are laterally compressed, wedge-shaped ciliates with a rigid pellicle decorated with longitudinal ribs. The body is sparsely ciliated, and the peristome is a pouch containing an adoral zone of eight membranelles.

Suborder 1. Heterotrichina

Since the somatic ciliation is practically complete in the majority, these ciliates are usually considered the most primitive Spirotrichida. However, there is a trend toward reduction of the dorsal ciliature in some genera, and the Peritromidae are ciliated only on the ventral surface. In addition to the adoral zone of membranelles on the left, there is often an undulating membrane at the right of the peristome. This membrane is sometimes replaced by a double row of heavy cilia. Thirteen families have been recognized.

Family 1. Balantidiidae. This family includes *Balantidium* Claparède and Lachmann (130, 139, 174, 214; Fig. 7. 29, A-E), represented by parasites of the digestive tract in both vertebrates and invertebrates. Somatic ciliation is complete and the cilia are arranged in approximately longi-

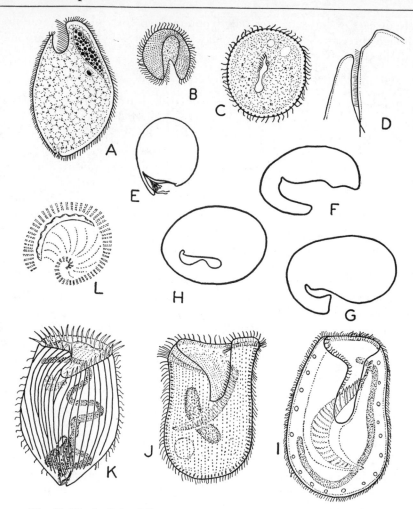

Fig. 7. 29. A. *Balantidium praenucleatum* Kudo and Meglitch, longitudinal optical section; Feulgen preparation; x475 (after K. & M.). B, C. Transverse sections of *Balantidium coli*: anterior region showing peristome (B); more posterior section through the pharynx (C), x550 (after Rees). D, E. *Balantidium sushilii* Ray: longitudinal section through peristome (D), x750; transverse section (E) through peristome near anterior end, x540 (after R.). F-H. Transverse sections of *Bursaria truncatella* O. F. M.: anterior portion of deep peristome (F), near posterior end of peristome (G), and at level of cytostome (H); x96 (after Wetzel). I. *Bursaria truncatella*, ventral view of specimen 600μ long (after Kahl). J. *Bursaridium pseudobursaria* (Fauré-Fremiet) Kahl, ventral view; part of the dorsal peristomial wall is striated but not ciliated; x260 (after Wang and Nie). K. *Chattonidium setense* Villeneuve, membranelles and undulating membrane, macronucleus, postero-axial cavity (cytoproct?); x188 (after Villeneuve-Brachon). L. *C. setense*, polar view, membrane, bases of membranelles; x250 (after V-B.).

tudinal rows. The peristome is a pouch with a triangular opening, through which the short adoral band of membranelles is not easily recognizable from the outside (214). Numerous long fibrils extend into the endoplasm from the basal granules of cilia and membranelles.

Family 2. Bursariidae. The most characteristic feature is a large funnel-shaped peristome, closed ventrally throughout part or most of its length (Fig. 7. 29, F-I). This ventral closure is perhaps the result of overgrowth of the "oral lip," a plate-like extension of the body wall which extends mediad from the right margin of the peristome in various Heterotrichina. In the Bursariidae this extension presumably has fused with the right margin of the peristome. The undulating membrane has disappeared in most species.

Three genera are referred to the family: *Bursaria* Müller (134; Fig. 7. 29, F-I), *Bursaridium* Lauterborn (104; Fig. 7. 29, J), and *Thylacidium* Schewiakoff (104).

Family 3. Chattonidiidae. These ciliates show a superficial resemblance to the Oligotrichina in that the peristome is shifted to the anterior pole. The membranelles form an almost complete spiral around the margin of the peristomial funnel, at the base of which lies the cytostome (Fig. 7. 29, K). Within the ring of membranelles, an undulating membrane extends for some distance around the peristome. The somatic ciliation is uniform.

The genus *Chattonidium* Villeneuve (214; Fig. 7. 29, K, L) is the only one assigned to the family.

Family 4. Clevelandellidae. These are completely ciliated heterotrichs which taper toward the anterior (aboral) pole. A zone of membranelles extends into the funnel-shaped peristome to the pharynx (Fig. 7. 30, G, N).

The family includes two genera, both represented by species in the digestive tract of wood roaches (*Panesthia*): *Clevelandella* Kidder (112; Fig. 7. 30, E, F, N) and *Paraclevelandia* Kidder (112; Fig. 7. 30, G).

Family 5. Condylostomidae. The large broad peristome is bordered on the left by the adoral zone of membranelles (Fig. 7. 30, D). On the right, a long undulating membrane arises from a groove hidden by a ventral ledge ("oral lip"). This ledge is extended to the left in several species to form a floor for part of the peristomial cavity. On the antero-ventral surface, there is sometimes a progressive replacement of simple cilia by fused groups of cilia, culminating in a zone of cirri at the right margin of the peristome (Fig. 7. 30, C).

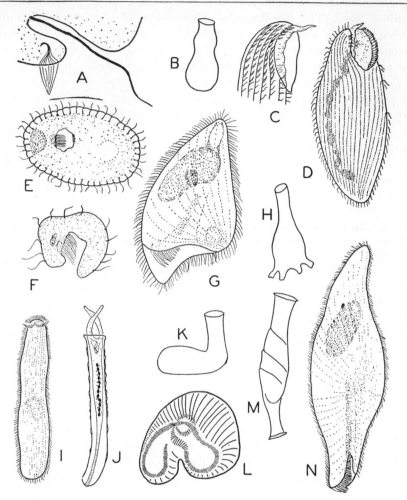

Fig. 7. 30. A. Transverse section of *Condylostoma vorax* through the undulating membrane and a membranelle; schematic, x800 (after Villeneuve-Brachon). B. Lorica of *Parafolliculina hirundo* (Kent) Kahl, 125μ long (after K.). C. Antero-ventral region of *Condylostoma arenarium* showing undulating membrane and the transition from somatic cilia to cirri; x250 (after Villeneuve-Brachon). D. *Condylostoma vorax* Villeneuve-Brachon, ventral view, x250 (after V-B.). E, F. Transverse sections of *Clevelandella elongata:* through pharynx (E), x525; through peristome (F), x640 (after Kidder). G. *Paraclevelandia brevis* Kidder, ventral view; karyophore attached to macronucleus anteriorly; x1230 approx. (after K.). H. Lorica of *Microfolliculina limnoriae* (Giard) Kahl (after K.). I. Migratory larva of *Folliculina aculeata,* x150 (after Dewey). J. *Folliculinopsis producta* (Wright) Villeneuve-Brachon, extended specimen showing macronuclear chain; x300 (after V-B.). K. Lorica of *Folliculina viridis* (Wright) Kahl, 150μ long (after K.). L. Polar view of peristome in *Folliculinopsis producta,* showing bases of adoral membranelles and rows of somatic cilia; x300 (after Villeneuve-Brachon). M. Lorica of *Pseudofolliculina arctica* (Dons) Kahl, about 430μ long (after K.). N. *Clevelandella elongata* Kidder, ventral view, x302 (after K.).

The genus *Condylostoma* Bory (13, 104, 214; Fig. 7. 30, A, C, D) is the only one assigned to the family.

Family 6. Folliculinidae. These are widely distributed marine ciliates which live attached to various plants and animals. The body is enclosed in a relatively thin "pseudochitinous" lorica. At the oral pole, the body is extended into two mobile lobes traversed by a spiral zone of membranelles extending down to the cytostome (Fig. 7. 30, L). The rest of the body is rather uniformly ciliated. Upon completion of fission in *Folliculina,* the anterior daughter leaves the lorica as a free-swimming larva (Fig. 7. 30, I) which, after a short migratory period, becomes attached and secretes a lorica (47).

The following genera, which are distinguished mainly by differences in general form of the lorica, have been recognized: *Folliculina* Lamarck (1, 47, 56, 104; Fig. 7. 30, K), *Folliculinopsis* Fauré-Fremiet (57, 214; Fig. 7. 30, J, L), *Metafolliculina* Dons (104), *Microfolliculina* Dons (104; Fig. 7. 30, H), *Parafolliculina* Dons (104; Fig. 7. 30, B), *Pebrilla* Giard (104), and *Pseudofolliculina* Dons (104; Fig. 7. 30, M).

Family 7. Lichnophoridae. Both ends of the elongated body are discoidal, while the mid-region is somewhat constricted. The zone of membranelles surrounds most of the antero-ventral, or oral, disc and extends into a depression of the peristome. The posterior disc (basal disc) is surrounded by several concentric undulating membranes, and just anterior to these, by a flexible flange, or velum. The basal disc is somewhat cup-shaped and serves for attachment to the host. With one or two exceptions, the Lichnophoridae are marine ectocommensals.

There is only one known genus, *Lichnophora* Claparède (3; Fig. 7. 31, J).

Family 8. Metopidae. These are often uniformly ciliated heterotrichs in which the peristome tends to curve to the right posteriorly. The zone of membranelles is rather straight in primitive Metopidae but spiral torsion may be marked, as in *Caenomorpha* (Fig. 7. 31, G). A relatively short undulating membrane often extends along the right margin of the peristome. Trichocysts may be present, sometimes underlying pellicular ridges or bands separating the rows of cilia.

The Metopidae, represented in fresh and salt water, include the following genera: *Bryometopus* Kahl (104), *Caenomorpha* Perty (104, 214; Fig. 7. 31, G), *Copemetopus* Villeneuve-Brachon (214), *Ludio* Penard (104, 165), *Metopus* Claparède and Lachmann (104, 214; Fig. 7. 31, A-C, I), *Palmarium* Gajevskaia (104), *Spirorhynchus* da Cunha (104; Fig. 7. 31, H), *Trochella* Penard (104, 165), and *Tropidoatractus* Levander (104).

Family 9. Peritromidae. These are marine ciliates which superficially resemble hypotrichs in their dorso-ventrally flattened bodies and the reduction of ciliation to the ventral surface. The dorsal surface may bear

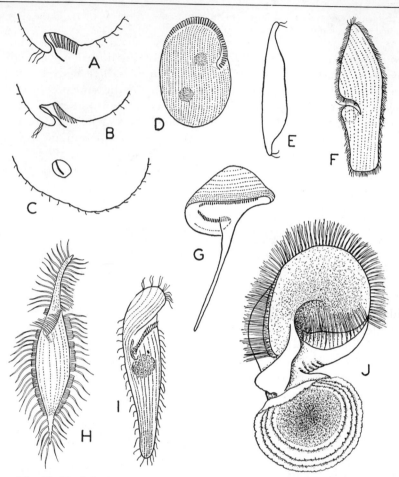

Fig. 7. 31. A-C. Cross-section of *Metopus sigmoides* through the anterior part of the peristome and more posterior levels, showing some of the membranelles (A, B) and the undulating membrane; x815 (after Wetzel). D, E. *Peritromus kahli* Villeneuve-Brachon: ventral view, x300; sagittal section, schematic, x450 (after V-B.). F. *Plagiotoma lumbrici* Dujardin, showing adoral ciliation, somatic cilia (schematic), and a contractile vacuole; x240 approx. (from Kent, after Stein). G. *Caenomorpha medusula* Perty, showing ciliary pattern and bases of membranelles; x450 (after Villeneuve-Brachon). H. *Spirorhynchus verrucosa* da Cunha, x425 (after Kirby). I. *Metopus mathiasi* Villeneuve-Brachon, ventral view, x375 (after V-B.). J. *Lichnophora macfarlandi* Stevens, showing basal and peristomial discs, adoral ciliation, lateral membrane extending toward cytostome; x565 (after Balamuth).

scattered bristles, and in some cases, so-called mucilaginous trichocysts. The band of membranelles extends across the anterior end or antero-ventral surface and then posteriorly along the left ventral margin to the cytostome, usually near the middle of the body.

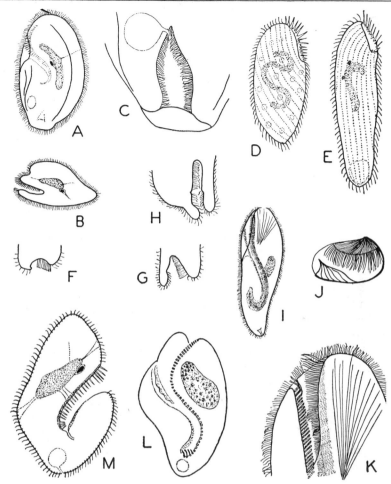

Fig. 7. 32. A-C. *Nyctotherus kyphodes* Geiman and Wichterman: A. Specimen showing nuclei, karyophore, contractile vacuole, cytoproct; x375. B. Transverse section through peristome and nuclei, x375. C. Ciliated cytoproct into which the contractile vacuole empties, x1025 approx. (after G. & W.). D. *Balantidioides muscicola* Penard, about 80μ long (after Kahl). E. *Reichenowella nigricans* Kahl, specimen 250μ long, showing adoral membranelles but no undulating membrane or distinct pharynx (after K.). F-H. Transverse sections of *Nyctotherus macropharyngeus* through anterior, middle and posterior regions of the peristome; x240 approx. (after Wetzel). I-K. *Paranyctotherus kirbyi* (Rodriguez) Sandon: view of left side (I), showing endoplasmic fibrils, macronucleus and peristome, x163; section through peristome (J), schematic; antero-ventral region (K) showing peristomial ciliature and endoplasmic fibrils (after S.). L, M. *Nyctotherus cordiformis* Stein: longitudinal section (L) showing membranelles, undulating membrane, contractile vacuole and macronucleus, x300 (after Villeneuve-Brachon); schematic sagittal section (M), showing nuclei, karyophore, peristome, and cytostome (after ten Kate).

Only two genera have been assigned to the family: *Pediostomum* Kahl (104) and *Peritromus* Stein (104, 214; Fig. 7. 31, D, E).

Family 10. Plagiotomidae. This group includes parasites of oligochaetes and other invertebrates and various vertebrates. The body is densely ciliated, the band of membranelles (Fig. 7. 32, A, B, L, M) is well developed, and an undulating membrane lies at the right margin of the peristome (Fig. 7. 32, L). A ciliated cytoproct has been described in *Nyctotherus* (Fig. 7. 32, C).

Three genera have been referred to the family. *Nyctotherus* Leidy (75, 81, 179, 214; Fig. 7. 32, A-C, F-H, L, M) is represented by intestinal parasites of vertebrates and invertebrates. *Paranyctotherus* Sandon (187; Fig. 7. 32, I-K), erected for a ciliate from a South African clawed toad, is similar to *Nyctotherus* but shows a row of membranelles along the right margin of the peristome. *Plagiotoma* Dujardin (84, 166; Fig. 7. 31, F) includes parasites of coelomic cavities in earthworms.

Family 11. Reichenowellidae. This family was erected by Kahl (104) for *Reichenowella* Kahl (Fig. 7. 32, E) and *Balantidioides* Penard (Fig. 7. 32, D). These ciliates are said to differ from other Heterotrichina in the presence of a slit-like mouth, usually closed and not easily detected, and in the lack of a definite oral pit. A band of membranelles is present, but no undulating membrane.

Family 12. Spirostomidae. Some of these are elongated, with more or less contractile bodies; certain others are dorso-ventrally flattened to some extent. A long band of membranelles (Fig. 7. 33, L, M), or a homologous double row of cilia, extends to the cytostome. An undulating membrane, sometimes fairly short, or a corresponding row of cilia extends along the right margin of the peristome. The peristome may be rather straight or may show some degree of spiral torsion. In at least certain species, bands of trichocysts alternate with rows of cilia (214).

The following genera have been assigned to the family: *Blepharisma* Perty (104, 192; Fig. 7. 33, G, I), *Gruberia* Kahl (13, 104; Fig. 7. 33, F), *Parablepharisma* Kahl (104, 214; Fig. 7. 33, L), *Phacodinium* Prowazek (104), *Protocrucia* da Cunha (214; Fig. 7. 33, H), *Pseudoblepharisma* Kahl (104), *Spirostomina* Gruber (104), and *Spirostomum* Ehrbg. (9, 104, 214; Fig. 7. 33, A-C, M).

Family 13. Stentoridae. The zone of membranelles tends to extend around the anterior pole of the body, and in some cases the peristome itself has shifted to the pole (Fig. 7. 33, D, J, K). The undulating membrane has disappeared. Somatic ciliation is relatively uniform, with the cilia arranged in longitudinal or slightly spiral rows.

The Stentoridae, represented in both fresh and salt water, include the following genera: *Climacostomum* Stein (104; Fig. 7. 33, K), *Fabrea* Henneguy (104, 113, 214; Fig. 7. 33, E), and *Stentor* Oken (104, 214; Fig. 7. 33, D, J).

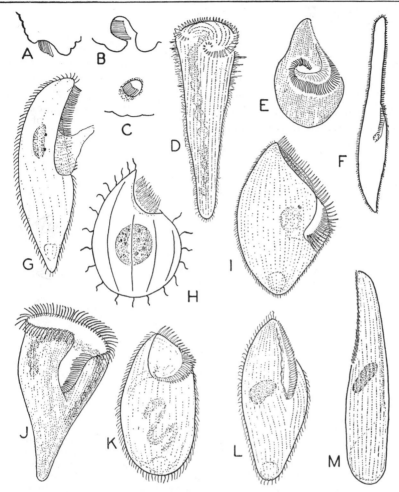

Fig. 7. 33. A-C. Transverse sections of *Spirostomum ambiguum* Ehrbg. through anterior and middle regions of the peristome and near the level of the cytostome, x510 (after Wetzel). D. *Stentor felici* Villeneuve-Brachon, showing macronuclear chain, membranelles, somatic ciliary pattern; x375 (after V-B.). E. *Fabrea salina* Henneguy; bases of membranelles, peristomial striations, somatic ciliary pattern; x125 (after Villeneuve-Brachon). F. *Gruberia calkinsi* Beltran, 200-800µ long (after B.). G. *Blepharisma hyalinum* Perty, x510 (after Wang and Nie). H. *Protocrucia tuzeti* Villeneuve-Brachon, x1320 (after V-B.). I. *Blepharisma lateritium* (Ehrbg.) Kahl, x310 (after K.). J. *Stentor auriculatus* (Gruber) Kahl, x200 (after Bullington. K. *Climacostomum virens* (Ehrbg.) Kahl, specimen 200µ long, with a broad peristome (after K.). L. *Parablepharisma bacteriophora* Villeneuve-Brachon, x300 (after V-B.). M. *Spirostomum teres* Claparède and Lachmann, showing membranelles and somatic ciliary pattern; x250 (after Villeneuve-Brachon).

Suborder 2. Oligotrichina

The somatic ciliation is either markedly reduced or has disappeared. Persisting somatic cilia are often fused into tufts. The zone of membranelles is commonly differentiated into a short oral band and an anterior spiral band of more powerful membranelles (Fig. 7. 34, A) which are the most important or else the only organelles of locomotion. The suborder is divided into two families.

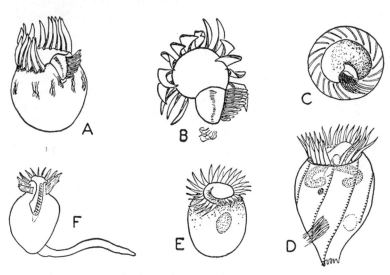

Fig. 7. 34. A, B. *Halteria geleiana* Szabó, antero-ventral view (A) showing oral membranelles and membrane, anterior locomotor membranelles, and lateral cilia ("Springborsten"), x400; polar view (B) of adoral organelles, x800 (after S.). C, D. *Strobilidium gyrans* (Stokes) Kahl, about 60μ long: polar view of peristome (C), schematic; lateral view (after K.). E. *Lohmaniella elegans* (Wulff) Kahl, specimen 25μ long (after K.). F. *Tontonia gracillima* Fauré-Fremiet, specimen 50μ long; contractile protoplasmic fibre extends from the posterior part of the body (from Kahl, after F-F.).

Family 1. Halteriidae. The peristome and the band of membranelles extend posteriorly on the ventral surface. The group is represented in fresh, salt, and brackish water.

The following genera have been referred to the family: *Halteria* Dujardin (104, 209; Fig. 7. 34, A, B), *Meseres* Schewiakoff (104), *Metastrombidium* Fauré-Fremiet (104), *Strombidium* Claparède and Lachmann (55, 60, 104), *Tontonia* Fauré-Fremiet (104; Fig. 7. 34, F).

Family 2. Strobilidiidae. The zone of membranelles forms a spiral crown at the anterior pole (Fig. 7. 34, C, D). The majority are marine, but some are known from brackish water and a few from fresh water.

Six genera have been referred to the family: *Cephalotrichium* Meunier (104), *Ciliospina* Leegaard (104), *Lohmaniella* Leegaard (104; Fig. 7. 34, E), *Strobilidium* Schewiakoff (104; Fig. 7. 34, C, D), *Parastrombidium* Fauré-Fremiet (104), and *Sphaerotrichium* Wulff (104).

Suborder 3. Tintinnina

A typical member of this group is a conical or trumpet-shaped ciliate contained in a lorica to which it is attached by the adhesive aboral tip of the body (Fig. 7. 35, M). The aboral end may or may not be drawn out into a slender contractile stalk. The peristomial field (Fig. 7. 35, A) covers most of the oral pole and is a more or less funnel-shaped area leading to the cytostome (Fig. 7. 35, B). The zone of 12-24 membranelles forms a spiral around the peristome. In some species, a protoplasmic flange lies just outside the membranelles. The adoral zone commonly bears a series of "tentaculoids," one between each pair of membranelles (Fig. 7. 35, A). Each tentaculoid is a ball- or club-shaped structure borne on a stalk, from the base of which a conical "accessory comb" extends into the peristomial area (17). Nothing is known about the functions of the tentaculoids or their appendanges. Somatic ciliation is usually sparse, sometimes limited to the anterior third of the body, sometimes extending almost to the posterior end. In certain species (18), a paroral zone of long somatic cilia lies near the oral pole. In addition, a large ciliary membrane, extending along the ventral surface from the rim of the peristome (Fig. 7. 35, M), occurs in several families. This membrane helps to mold the new lorica in fission (17, 18).

The form of the lorica (Fig. 7. 35, C-L) varies considerably. The aboral end is usually closed but both ends are open in certain species. The capacity is generally several times the volume of the enclosed ciliate. Foreign particles are sometimes incorporated in the wall of the lorica, which is composed basically of secreted organic material, including xanthoproteins (116). As fission is completed, this material is discharged through the gullet and worked into shape by the membranelles, perioral cilia and the ciliary membrane. These organelles seem to function somewhat like trowels in fashioning the new lorica, the anterior part being shaped by the anterior daughter organism and the posterior part by the posterior one.

A few Tintinnina have been described from fresh and brackish water but most of them are marine pelagic ciliates. Campbell (19) and Kofoid and Campbell (115, 116) have published systematic studies of the group, the taxonomy of which is based largely upon structure of the lorica.

The following families and genera have been characterized (19, 115, 116): (1) Codonellidae: *Codonaria* Kofoid and Campbell, *Codonella* Haeckel (Fig. 7. 35, G), *Codonopsis* K. & C., *Tintinnopsis* Stein (Fig. 7. 35, M); (2) Codonellopsidae: *Codonellopsis* Jörgensen (Fig. 7. 35, I), *Laackmanniella* K. & C., *Stenosemella* J.; (3) Coxliellidae: *Climacocyclis* J., *Coxliella* Brandt (Fig. 7. 35, H), *Helicostomella* J.,

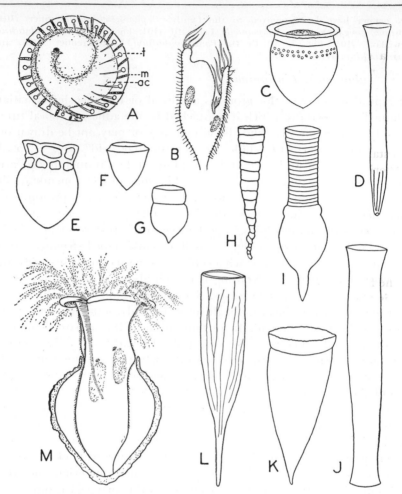

Fig. 7. 35. A. Polar view of peristome in *Tintinnopsis nucula;* bases of the membranelles alternate with tentaculoids and their accessory combs; x1075 (after Campbell). B. Longitudinal section of *Tintinnopsis campanula* (Ehrbg.), showing adoral and somatic ciliation; semidiagrammatic (after Entz). C-L. Variations in form of the lorica in Tintinnina: C. *Petalotricha ampulla;* D. *Salpingella acuminata;* E. *Dictyocysta mira;* F. *Craterella urceolata;* G. *Codonella rapa;* H. *Coxliella fasciata;* I. *Codonellopsis longa;* J. *Eutintinnus brandti;* K. *Cyttarocyclis acutiformis;* L. *Rhabdonella henseni;* F, x300; others x188 (after Campbell). M. *Tintinnopsis nucula,* lorica in optical section; ciliary membrane extends from the peristome posteriorly past the middle of the body; nuclei, cytoproct, and somatic cilia are shown; schematic, x425 (after Campbell). KEY: *ac,* accessory comb; *m,* membranelle; *t,* tentaculoid.

Metacyclis J.; (4) Cyttarocyclidae: *Cyttarocyclis* Fol (Fig. 7. 35, K); (5) Dictyocystidae: *Dictyocysta* Ehrbg. (Fig. 7. 35, E), *Luminella* K. & C., *Wailesia* K. & C., *Wangiella* Nie; (6) Epiplocylidae: *Epicanella* K. & C., *Epiorella* K. & C., *Epiplocylis* J.; (7) Favellidae: *Cymatocyclis* Laackmann, *Favella* J. (18), *Poroecus* Cleve, *Protocymatocyclis* K. & C.; (8) Pelatotrichidae: *Acanthostomella* J., *Craterella* K. & C. (Fig. 7. 35, F), *Pelatotricha*

Kent (Fig. 7. 35, C); (9) Ptychocyclidae: *Ptychocyclis* Brandt; (10) Rhabdonellidae: *Epirhabdonella* K. & C., *Protorhabdonella* J., *Rhabdonella* B., *Rhabdonellopsis* K. & C.; (11) Tintinnidae: *Albatrossiella* K. & C., *Amphorella* Daday, *Amphorellopsis* K. & C., *Brandtiella* K. & C., *Bursaopsis* K. & C., *Canthariella* K. & C., *Dadayiella* K. & C., *Daturella* K. & C., *Epicranella* K. & C., *Epirhabdosella* Campbell, *Eutintinnus* K. & C. (Fig. 7. 35, J), *Odontophorella* K. & C., *Ormosella* K. & C., *Proamphorella* K. & C., *Prostelidiella* K. & C., *Rhabdosella* K. & C., *Salpingacantha* K. & C., *Salpingella* J. (Fig. 7. 35, D), *Salpingelloides* Campbell, *Stelidiella* K. & C., *Steenstrupiella* K. & C., *Tintinnus* Schrank; (12) Undellidae: *Amplectella* K. & C., *Amplectellopsis* K. & C., *Cricundella* K. & C., *Proplectella* K. & C., *Undella* Daday, *Undellopsis* K. & C.; (13) Xystonellidae: *Parafavella* K. & C., *Parundella* J., *Xystonella* Brandt, *Xystonellopsis* J.

Suborder 4. Entodiniomorphina

These ciliates occur in the rumen of cattle, sheep and other ruminants and in the intestine of certain other herbivores. The ciliature is much reduced and in the simplest Ophryoscolecidae, as represented by *Entodinium* (Fig. 7. 36, P), is limited to the membranelles of the adoral zone. In most Ophryoscolecidae, however, there is also a dorsal zone of membranelles, ranging from a short anterior band to a longer and more or less equatorial row (Fig. 7. 36, A-E). The adoral membranelles arise in a furrow formed by an ectoplasmic fold and extend spirally to the cytostome which lies in an elevated oral disc at the anterior pole. At least the adoral zone, and in some genera the dorsal zone also, can be retracted. Between the adoral and dorsal zones there is often an elevation, the operculum (Fig. 7. 36, M, R). The Cycloposthiidae have added one or more posterior or caudal rows or tufts of membranelles (Fig. 7. 38, A).

Beneath the firm pellicle there is a distinct cortical layer (Fig. 7. 36, P) with a clear matrix containing many granules. The macronucleus, micronucleus, contractile vacuoles (143), and skeletal plates also lie in this zone, which is separated from the endoplasm by a membrane continuous anteriorly with the pharynx and posteriorly with the rectum. The cytostome (Fig. 7. 38, B) opens into the short pharynx (Fig. 7. 36, R). The endoplasmic sac, consisting of the boundary membrane and the contained endoplasm, fills most of the body posterior to the pharynx. The rectum, at the posterior end of the sac, is a thin-walled tube extending through the ectoplasm to the anus. In certain Ophryoscolecidae, the wall of the rectum apparently contains myonemes which presumably have a sphincter-like action.

Skeletal plates are present except in a few of the Ophryoscolecidae (*Diplodinium, Entodinium, Eodinium*). These structures vary in number, size, form, and arrangement in different genera (Fig. 7. 36, F-L). Each plate is a flattened structure extending posteriorly in the ectoplasm from a level shortly behind the adoral zone (Fig. 7. 36, Q). The plates of *Polyplastron multivesiculatum* consist of a protein matrix containing irregular platelets of "paraglycogen" (144).

The Entodiniomorphina are divided into two families: the Ophryo-

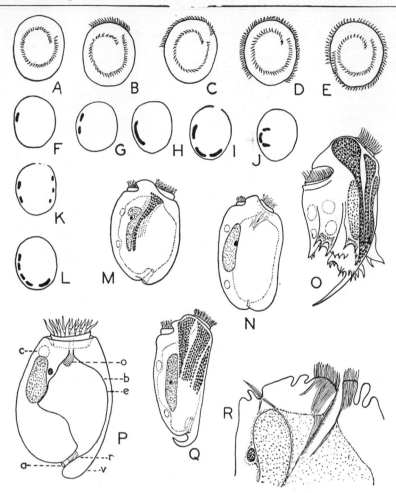

Fig. 7. 36. A-E. Arrangement of membranelles in Ophryoscolecidae, polar views: A. *Entodinium;* B. *Opisthotrichum;* C. *Diplodinium* and *Epidinium;* D. *Ophryoscolex;* E. *Caloscolex;* diagrammatic (after Dogiel). F-L. Variations in the number and arrangement of skeletal plates in Ophryoscolecidae; diagrammatic cross-sections near the anterior pole (after Dogiel). M. *Eudiplodinium maggii* (Fiorentini) Dogiel, x250 (after Kofoid and Christenson). N. *Eodinium polygonale* Kofoid and MacLennan, x600 (after M. & MacL.). O. *Ophryoscolex caudatus* Eberlein, x250 (after MacLennan). P. *Entodinium biconcavum* Kofoid and MacLennan; *a,* anus; *b,* boundary layer between ectoplasm and endoplasm; *c,* contractile vacuole; *e,* endoplasm; *o,* oesophagus; *r,* rectum; *v,* ventral lobe; schematic, x1000 (after K. & MacL.). Q. *Epidinium caudatum* (Fiorentini) Crawley, x400 (after Kofoid and Mac-Lennan). R. Longitudinal section of *Diplodinium medium* showing adoral ciliation and cilia extending into the oesophagus; x225 (after Rees).

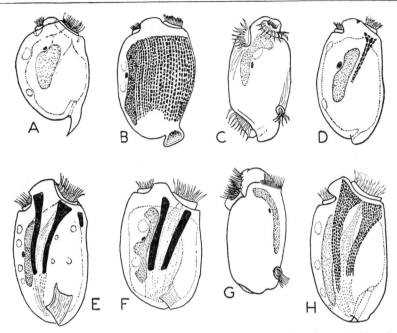

Fig. 7. 37. A. *Diplodinium monocanthum* Dogiel, x480 (after Kofoid and Christenson). B. *Ostracodinium clipeolum*, x250 (after Kofoid and MacLennan). C. *Tetratoxum unifasciculatum* (Fiorentini) Gassovsky, x222 (after Hsiung). D. *Eremoplastron bovis* (Dogiel) Kofoid and MacLennan, x375 (after K. & MacL.). E. *Polyplastron multivesiculatum*, skeletal plates indicated in solid black, x250 (after MacLennan). F. *Metadinium medium* Awerinzew and Mutafowa, x200 (after MacLennan). G. *Diloxum funinucleum* Gassovsky, x202 (after Hsiung). H. *Elytroplastron bubali* (Dogiel) Kofoid and MacLennan, x250 (after K. & MacL.).

scolecidae with not more than one "dorsal" band of membranelles in addition to the adoral zone; and the Cycloposthiidae, which have added one or more posterior or caudal groups to the maximum for Ophryoscolecidae. The Ophryoscolecidae are rumen-dwelling ciliates characteristic of cattle, sheep, and related hosts. Cycloposthiidae have been reported mostly from horses, but a few species are known from the chimpanzee, gorilla, rhinoceros, and elephant. Genera assigned to the two families are listed below.

Family 1. *Ophryoscolecidae. Amphacanthus* Dogiel, *Caloscolex* Dogiel (50), *Cunhaia* Hasselmann (50), *Diplodinium* Schuberg (50, 120, 176; Fig. 7. 36, R), *Diploplastron* Kofoid and MacLennan (120), *Elytroplastron* Kofoid and MacLennan (120), *Enoplastron* Kofoid and MacLennan (120), *Entodinium* Stein (50, 117, 119; Fig. 7. 36, P), *Eodinium* Kofoid and MacLennan (120; Fig. 7. 36, N), *Epidinium* Crawley (50, 117, 121; Fig. 7. 36, Q), *Epiplastron* Kofoid and MacLennan (121), *Eremoplastron* Kofoid and MacLennan (120; Fig. 7. 37, D), *Eudiplodinium* Dogiel (120; Fig. 7. 36, M), *Metadinium* Awerinzew and Mutafowa (120, 143; Fig. 7. 37, F), *Ophryoscolex* Stein (50, 121, 143; Fig. 7. 36, O), *Opisthotrichum* Buisson (50), *Ostracodinium* Dogiel (117, 120; Fig. 7. 37, B), *Polyplastron* Dogiel (120, 143; Fig. 7. 37, E).

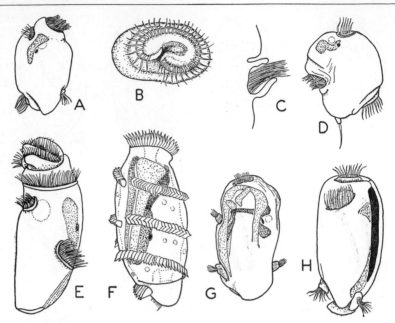

Fig. 7. 38. A. *Trifascicularia parvum* Hsiung, x322 (after H.). B. Polar view of peristome in *Tripalmaria dogieli* showing outer membranelles and basal plates of the adoral zone leading to the cytostome; x260 (after Strelkow). C. Longitudinal section through antero-dorsal group of membranelles in *Tripalmaria dogieli;* x550 (after Strelkow). D. *Triadinium caudatum* Fiorentini, x322 (after Hsiung). E. *Spirodinium equi* Fiorentini, x322 (after Hsiung). F. *Polydinium mysoreum* Kofoid, from Indian elephant; x275 (after K.). G. *Tripalmaria dogieli* Gassovsky, x322 (after Hsiung). H. *Cycloposthium bipalmatum* (Fiorentini) Bundle, x363 (after Hsiung).

Family 2. Cycloposthiidae. Cochliatoxum Gassovsky (91), *Cycloposthium* Bundle (91, 193, 194, 195; Fig. 7. 38, H), *Ditoxum* Gassovsky (91; Fig. 7. 37, G), *Polydinium* Kofoid (114; Fig. 7. 38, F), *Spirodinium* Fiorentini (91; Fig. 7. 38, E), *Tetratoxum* Gassovsky (44, 91; Fig. 7. 37, C), *Triadinium* Fiorentini (91; Fig. 7. 38, D), *Trifascicularia* Strelkow (197; Fig. 7. 38, A), *Tripalmaria* Gassovsky (91, 196; Fig. 7. 38, B, G), *Triplumaria* Hoare, *Troglodytella* Brumpt and Joyeux (208).

Suborder 5. Hypotrichina

Somatic cilia are replaced by cirri which are nearly always limited to the ventral surface. The dorsal surface often bears rows of so-called sensory bristles, which are sometimes present also on the ventral surface adjacent to cirri. The ventral cirri are typically arranged in groups (Fig. 7. 40, E, F, J): *frontal cirri,* located between the peristome and the right side of the body; *ventral cirri,* posterior to the frontal cirri; *marginal cirri,* arising from the right and left margins of the ventral surface; *caudal cirri,* arising from the posterior margin; and *anal cirri,* arising in a transverse or diagonal row a short distance from the posterior end of the body. Certain cirri, particularly the lateral ones, may be lacking in some species.

The peristomial area is large and more or less triangular in many species, but is reduced in size and fairly narrow in others. In some cases the right margin of the peristome is extended toward the left as a flange ("oral lip") which partially encloses the peristome ventrally. Such a development increases the efficiency of the peristome, especially in species which feed on bacteria.

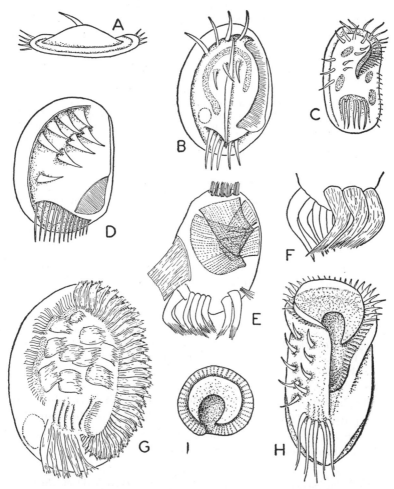

Fig. 7. 39. A, B. *Aspidisca turrita* (Ehrbg.) Claparède and Lachmann, lateral and ventral views, x765 (after Wang and Nie). C. *Certesia quadrinucleata* Fabre-Domergue, specimen 90μ long (after Kahl). D. *Aspidisca polystyla* Stein, x840 (after Wang and Nie). E, F. *Uronychia heinrothi* Buddenbrock, ventral view showing the peristomial membranes, and dorsal view of the three postero-dorsal cirri; x200 (after Bullington). G. *Euplotaspis cionaecola* Chatton and Seguela, 60-70μ long; from branchial cavity of ascidians (after C. & S.). H, I. *Euplotidium agitatum* Noland: ventral view, x600; anterior end showing bases of membranelles, x450 (after N.).

The zone of membranelles often extends from the cytostome anteriorly and then transversely across the antero-dorsal or antero-ventral surface of the body (Fig. 7. 39, H). In the Aspidiscidae, however, the membranelles are reduced to a short band (Fig. 7. 39, B). An undulating membrane often extends at least part way along the right margin of the peristome (Fig. 7. 40, A).

Family 1. Aspidiscidae. These are flattened ciliates (Fig. 7. 39, A) with an armor-like pellicle. The adoral membranelles are reduced to a short band, while the cirri are limited to a small group of frontals and a group of anal cirri (Fig. 7. 39, B). Near the anterior end there is sometimes a small depression containing a few delicate membranelles which represent the anterior remnant of the primitive adoral zone.

The type genus, *Aspidisca* Ehrenberg (104; Fig. 7. 39, A, B, D), seems to be the only one which belongs to the family. Chatton and Seguela (34) have referred their genus *Euplotaspis* (Fig. 7. 39, G) to the Aspidiscidae but such an assignment cannot be justified without major revisions in characterization of the family. Perhaps a better location for *Euplotaspis* would be the family Paraeuplotidae.

Family 2. Euplotidae. The number of ventral cirri is reduced, with a loss of the right marginal series (Fig. 7. 39, C) or both marginal rows (Fig. 7. 39, H) and usually of all except a few of the primitive ventral group. The persisting cirri are relatively stout and there is generally a group of well-developed anal cirri (usually five). A few caudal cirri also persist, either as rather slender structures or as large "rudders" in *Uronychia* and *Diophrys*. The peristome and the adoral membranelles are well developed.

The following genera are included in the family: *Certesia* Fabre-Domergue (104, 188; Fig. 7. 39, C), *Diophrys* Dujardin (104, 188; Fig. 7. 40, H), *Euplotes* Ehrenberg (104, 170; Fig. 7. 40, G), *Euplotidium* Noland (158; Fig. 7. 39, H, I), and *Uronychia* Stein (13, 104, 227; Fig. 7. 39, E, F).

Family 3. Oxytrichidae. The arrangement of the cirri follows the generalized pattern, although there is some reduction of the ventral cirri in certain species. Right and left marginal cirri are always present and the adoral membranelles are well developed.

The following genera have been referred to the Oxytrichidae: *Ancystropodium* Fauré-Fremiet (104), *Balladyna* Kowaleski (104; Fig. 7. 40, B), *Balladynopsis* Ghosh (104), *Caryotricha* Kahl (104), *Chaetospira* Lachmann (104), *Cladotricha* Gajevskaja (104), *Epiclintes* Stein (13, 104), *Eschaneustyla* Stokes (104), *Gastrocirrhus* Lepsi (13; Fig. 7. 41, K), *Gastrostyla* Engelmann (88, 104, 223; Fig. 7. 40, F), *Gonostomum* Sterki (104), *Hemicycliostyla* Stokes (104), *Holosticha* Wrzesniowski (88, 104; Fig. 7. 40, I), *Hypotrichidium* Ilowaisky (182; Fig. 7. 41, G), *Kahlia* Horvath (89, 104; Fig. 7. 41, H), *Kerona* Ehrbg. (104; Fig. 7. 41, E), *Onychodromopsis* Stokes (104), *Onychodromus* Stein (104; Fig. 7. 40, J), *Oxytricha* Ehrbg. (10, 88, 104; Fig. 7. 40, E), *Paraholosticha* Kahl (88, 104; Fig. 7. 41, A), *Pleurotricha* Stein (104; Fig. 7. 41, C), *Pseudostrombidium*

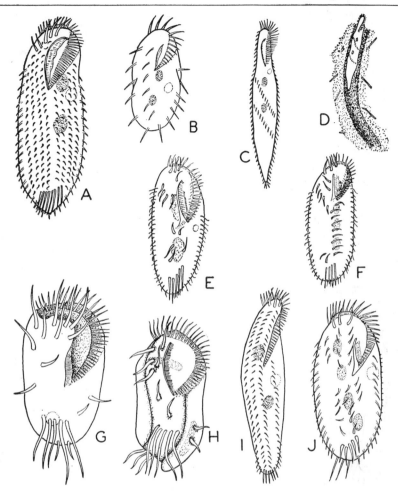

Fig. 7. 40. A. *Urostyla limboonkengi* Wang and Nie, x320 (after W. & N.). B. *Balladyna parvula* Kowalewsky, x780 (after W. & N.). C, D. *Stichotricha nankingensis* Wang and Nie, ventral view, x250; specimen in gelatinous lorica, x125 approx. (after W. & N.). E. *Oxytricha platystoma* Ehrbg., x300 (after Horvath). F. *Gastrostyla steinii* Engelmann, x300 (after Horvath). G. *Euplotes harpa* Stein, x375 (after Wang and Nie). H. *Diophrys appendiculatus* (Ehrbg.), x600 (after Wang and Nie). I. *Holosticha kessleri* (Wrzesniowski), x290 (after Wang and Nie). J. *Onychodromus grandis* Stein, specimen 250μ long (after Kahl).

Horvath (88), *Psilotricha* Stein (104), *Stichotricha* Perty (104; Fig. 7. 40, C, D), *Strongylidium* Sterki (104; Fig. 7. 41, J), *Stylocoma* Gruber (104), *Stylonethes* Sterki (71, 72), *Trachelostyla* Kahl (104; Fig. 7. 41, I), *Uncinata* Bullington (13), *Uroleptus* Ehrbg. (16, 104; Fig. 7. 41, F), *Uroleptopsis* Kahl (104), and *Urostyla* Ehrbg. (104; Fig. 7. 40, A).

In addition, *Histrio* Sterki, *Opisthotricha* Kent, *Steinia* Diesing, *Stylonychia* Ehrbg., *Tachysoma* Stokes and *Urosoma* Kowalewski are listed by Kahl (104) as sub-genera of *Oxytricha*; *Amphisiella* Gourret and Roeser, *Keronopsis* Penard, *Paruroleptus* Kahl and *Trichotaxis* Stokes, as sub-genera of *Holosticha*.

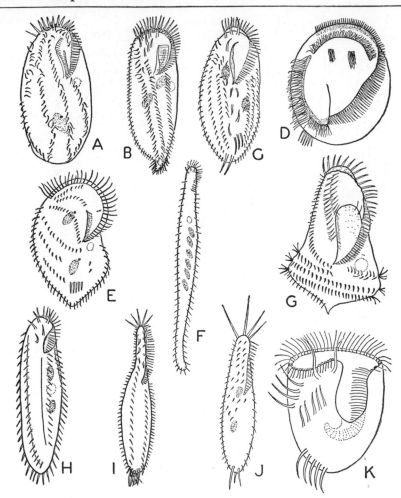

Fig. 7. 41. A. *Paraholosticha ovata* Horvath, x300 (after H.). B. *Holosticha* (*Paruroleptus*) *novitas* Horvath, x150 (after H.). C. *Pleurotricha grandis* Stein, specimen 300μ long (after Kahl). D. *Paraeuplotes tortugensis* Wichterman, ventral view, zoochlorellae not shown; x375 (after W.). E. *Kerona polyporum* Ehrbg., specimen 160μ long (after Kahl). F. *Uroleptus mobilis* Engelmann, specimen 150μ long (after Kahl). G. *Hypotrichidium conicum* Ilowaisky, x250 (from Rossolimo, after I.). H. *Kahlia costata* Kahl, x580 (after Wang and Nie). I. *Trachelostyla pediculiformis* (Cohn) Kahl, x350 (after Wang and Nie). J. *Strongylidium maritimum* Wang and Nie, x594 (after W. & N.). K. *Gastrocirrhus stentoreus* Bullington, x375 (after B.).

Family 4. Paraeuplotidae. This family contains the unusual genus, *Paraeuplotes* Wichterman (224; Fig. 7. 41, D), in which the adoral zone of membranelles is well developed but the only cirri are a group of five or six extending from the posterior end of the body. Instead of the usual ventral cirri, there are bands and tufts of free cilia. The genus is represented by a single marine species.

Euplotaspis Chatton and Seguela (34; Fig. 7. 39, G) resembles *Paraeuplotes* in several respects and possibly belongs in the same family. There seem to be two ventral rows of free cilia, and the frayed compound organelles in the frontal field may be homologous with the tufts of cilia in *Paraeuplotes*.

Suborder 6. Ctenostomina

These are small laterally compressed, wedge-shaped ciliates in which the base of the wedge (Fig. 7. 42, B) represents the ventral (oral) surface. In lateral view (Fig. 7. 42, C, H), the dorsal margin usually describes about a third of a circle but may approach a semicircle or almost a circle. Anteriorly, the dorsal keel ends in a brow-like prominence or in a spur or spine (Fig. 7. 42, E, H, J). Except for the ventral surface, and the posterior end in certain species, the body is covered with a firm pellicle differentiated into longitudinal plates (105).

The somatic ciliation is much reduced. On the left surface there are typically four rows, extending forward for varying distances from the posterior end (Fig. 7. 42, F, J), and also a fifth frontal row (exceptionally, two frontal rows) extending posteriorly for some distance from an origin near the anterior pole. In primitive species, a frontal band of five rows arises anteriorly on the lower left surface, extends across the narrow ventral surface, and then upward and posteriorly for some distance on the right side. A tuft of preoral cilia anterior to the peristome, and two adoral rows running from the frontal band almost to the peristome, may also be found on the ventral surface. Modifications of the general pattern occur in the more specialized types.

The peristome is a ventral pouch covered on the left by a thin wall (Fig. 7. 42, A, B) apparently analogous to the "oral lip" of various Spirotrichida. In contrast to most Spirotrichida, the adoral membranelles are reduced to eight in the peristome proper and a small ninth one in the pharynx (105).

All except two species are known from fresh water and all are sapropelic (or polysaprobic) types, growing well in the presence of putrefying materials. Kahl (105) recognized three families.

Family 1. Epalcidae. The posterior end of the body is unarmored, although surrounded by the spurred or spiny ends of the armor plates. Somatic ciliation is relatively complete. On the left, a frontal band and the four primitive posterior rows are always present. On the right side of the body, at least the ventral and dorsal rows are present.

Three genera are listed for this family (105): *Epalxis* Roux (Fig. 7. 42, A, D), *Pelodinium* Lauterborn (Fig. 7. 42, F), and *Saprodinium* Lauterborn (Fig. 7. 42, J).

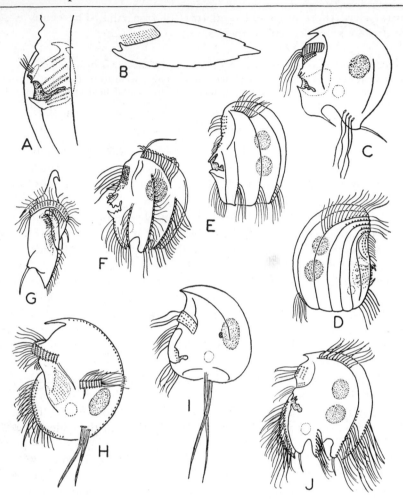

Fig. 7. 42. A. Peristome of *Epalxis* showing peristomial wall and bases of adoral membranelles; diagrammatic (after Kahl). B. Transverse section of *Epalxis bidens* through the peristome; diagrammatic (after Kahl). C. *Atopodinium fibulatum* Kahl, 35-45μ (after K.). D, E. *Epalxis striata* Kahl, 25-35μ, right and left sides (after K.). F. *Pelodinium reniforme* Lauterborn, 40-50μ (after Kahl). G, H. *Discomorpha pectinata* Levander, about 80μ long; ventral and lateral views (after Kahl). I. *Mylestoma anatinum* (Penard) Kahl, 20-28μ (after K.). J. *Saprodinium integrum* Kahl, 40-55μ (after K.).

Family 2. Mylestomidae. The right and left dorsal rows of cilia have disappeared and the ventral cilia are absent or reduced in number (Fig. 7. 42, C). The remaining posterior cilia may remain free or may be fused into one or two long "rudder-cirri" (Fig. 7. 42, I). The frontal band is limited to the ventral surface. The posterior end of the body is almost or completely covered with armor.

Two genera have been referred to the family (105): *Mylestoma* Kahl (Fig. 7. 42, I) and *Atopodinium* Kahl (Fig. 7. 42, C).

Family 3. Discomorphidae. The dorsal keel, which ends anteriorly in a spine, sweeps back over the posterior end to the ventral surface (Fig. 7. 42, H). Somatic ciliation is limited to the two ventral rows, two posterior tufts of cilia on the left, and a well-developed frontal band.

Only one genus is known (105): *Discomorpha* Levander (Fig. 7. 42, G, H).

Order 3. Peritrichida. The adult is usually attached either directly by its aboral end or by means of a secreted stalk, or else lies within a lorica which is attached to some solid surface. A number of the stalked types are colonial. A few species are free-swimming and apparently have no sessile stage.

In this order, the peristome (or "epistome") is a polar disc which, seen from the oral end of the body, is approximately circular (Fig. 7. 47, H). Encircling the peristome counterclockwise are two or more rows of cilia which usually complete a full spiral before passing through the cytostome into the vestibule. Two rows of adoral cilia have been described in *Telotrochidium* (138) and *Cyclochaeta* (146); three, in *Vorticella* (159). In all three cases, the cilia of each row are free distally but are fused basally into a continuous membrane. Each row of cilia is continued into the vestibule in *Cyclochaeta* and *Vorticella;* only the inner row, in *Telotrochidium*. Within the vestibule, a membrane may be formed by complete fusion of cilia (the outer row of *Vorticella*). The outer margin of the peristomial surface, which ranges from a narrow border to a broad projecting shelf, often forms a contractile rim which can be constricted to enclose the peristome and its ciliature.

The vestibule receives the contents of the contractile vacuole, sometimes through an intermediate "reservoir" (Fig. 7. 47, H), and also the undigested materials from old food vacuoles. As in the ordinary pharynx, incoming food particles also pass down the vestibule into the developing food vacuole at its base. Noland and Finley (159) have noted an apparent separation of incurrent and excurrent channels within the vestibule.

The scopula (54), a differentiated area at the aboral pole, is often evident as a small invagination, the wall of which sometimes shows fibrils or rod-like elements. In many of the sessile species without stalks, the scopula apparently secretes some material which insures adhesion to the substratum. In stalked species, the scopula secretes the inert matrix of the stalk. The non-contractile stalk of the Epistylidae consists entirely of secreted material. The stalk of the Vorticellidae contains, in addition, a loosely spiral myoneme, or "stalk-muscle," which appears to be an out-

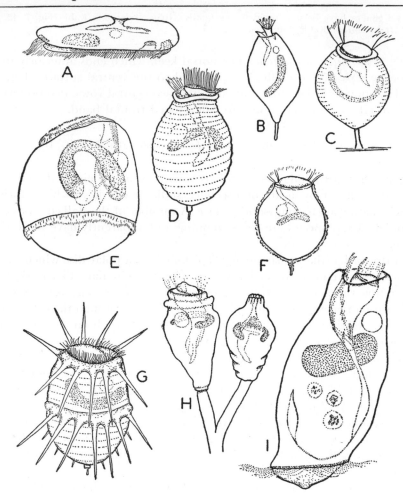

Fig. 7. 43. A. Horizontally elongated telotroch characteristic of *Epistylis horizontalis* Chatton, x500 (after C.). B. *Pyxidium cothurnoides* Kent, specimen 50μ long; stalk typically unbranched; peristomial disc similar to that in *Opercularia* (after Kahl). C. *Rhabdostyla ovum* Kent, x850 (after Wang and Nie). D. *Astylozoon piriforme* Schewiakoff, with rudimentary stalk; x560 (after Wang and Nie). E. *Telotrochidium (Opisthonecta) henneguyi* (Fauré-Fremiet) Kahl, x450 (after Kofoid and Rosenberg). F. *Geleiella vagans* Stiller, body enclosed in gelatinous mantle (after S.). G. *Hastatella radians* Ehrbg., two rings of cytoplasmic "spines"; x740 approx. (after Wang and Nie). H. *Epistylis chrysemidis* Bishop and Jahn, two zooids; x115 (after B. & J.). I. *Telotrochidium johanninae* Fauré-Fremiet, x1025 (after F-F.).

growth from the body. The stalk-muscle of colonial Vorticellidae may be continuous throughout the colony (Fig. 7. 48, D), except perhaps in the basal section of the main stalk (200), or the myonemes of individual stalks may be independent (Fig. 7. 48, E). In the former, the colony as a

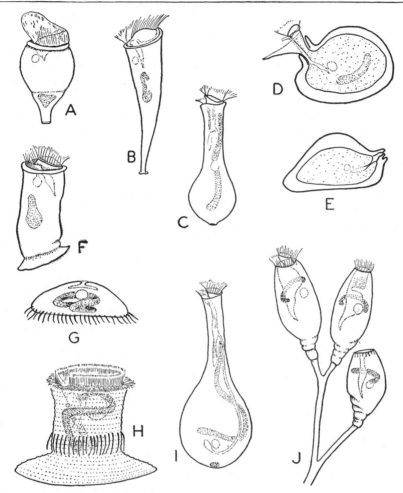

Fig. 7. 44. A. *Glossatella tintinnabulum* (Kent) Kahl, 30-43μ; large adoral membrane (after K.). B. *Paravorticella clymenellae* (Shumway) Kahl, about 100μ long (after S.). C. *Ophrydium lemnae* Kahl, specimen 70μ long (after K.). D, E. *Lagenophrys labiata* Wallengren, ventro-lateral and lateral views; x360 (after Wang and Nie). F. *Scyphidia physarum* Lachmann, about 90μ long (after Kahl). G, H. *Scyphidia ameirui* Thompson, Kirkegaard and Jahn, 34-45μ; telotroch and sessile stages (after T., K. & J.). I. *Ophrydium (Gerda) glans* (Claparède and Lachmann) Kahl, specimen 200μ long; long canal extends from reservoir of contractile vacuole to the vestibule (after K.). J. *Opercularia ramosa* Stokes, x210 approx. (after Bishop and Jahn).

whole may be retracted toward the point of attachment; in *Carchesium*, contractions of the stalks affect individual zooids separately.

The life-cycles of Peritrichida are commonly dimorphic and sometimes polymorphic. Reproduction apparently should be considered fission rather than budding, although one daughter organism is often smaller than the other. The plane of fission in *Vorticella* passes from near the center of the peristome to a point just to one side of the stalk. One daughter organism thus retains the parental stalk. The other develops an aboral band of locomotor cilia and becomes a telotroch (Fig. 7. 47, C) which swims actively for a short period. Metamorphosis into the adult follows adhesion of the scopula to a suitable surface. In this attached stage, the young peritrich resembles *Scyphidia* which lacks a stalk. However, the *Scyphidia*-stage of *Vorticella* lasts for only a short time. Soon after attachment, secretion of a stalk begins and the aboral cilia disappear within a few minutes (186). In fission during development of a colonial type, such as *Zoothamnium* (200), the daughter organism not retaining the old stalk secretes a new stalk which becomes a branch of the original one.

The telotroch is a common stage in the life-cycle and is not limited to stalked species, since it occurs in such forms as *Scyphidia* (Fig. 7. 44, H). Direct transformation of a stalked form into a telotroch sometimes occurs in *Vorticella* (Fig. 7. 47, D-F) and is a normal means of asexual propagation in such genera as *Zoothamnium* (200). After liberation from the parental colony, the migratory stage swims away and then settles down on some object to develop into a new colony. The Urceolariidae are sometimes considered highly specialized permanent telotrochs. In this connection, the telotroch of *Epistylis horizontalis* (Fig. 7. 43, A) is interesting in its superficial resemblance to the Urceolariidae and in its comparable ability to glide over surfaces (20). *Telotrochidium* (Fig. 7. 43, E) also seems to represent a permanent telotroch, although it is not impossible that this genus contains telotrochs whose sessile stages have not been recognized.

The life-cycle of the commensal *Ellobiophrya donacis* (25) is more complicated than that of most Peritrichida. The adult lives in a lamellibranch, *Donax vittatus*, attached to a gill-filament (Fig. 7. 45, A). At the completion of fission one daughter organism (the future telotroch) remains attached to the larger by a narrow isthmus of cytoplasm (Fig. 7. 45, B). A scopula soon develops in the embryonic telotroch and secretes a stalk which extends for some distance into the attached sister organism (Fig. 7. 45, D). Elongation of the developing telotroch and differentiation of the aboral cilia occur next (Fig. 7. 45, C). The telotroch then becomes free-swimming (Fig. 7. 45, E), usually breaking away at the junction of stalk and scopula, but sometimes carrying its stalk along to be discarded later. After reaching a gill-filament, this migratory stage becomes attached by its aboral end and develops the protoplasmic arms which anchor the organism to its host (Fig. 7. 45, F).

Axial homologies between the Peritrichida and other ciliates are somewhat uncertain. Although the peristome is usually considered anterior,

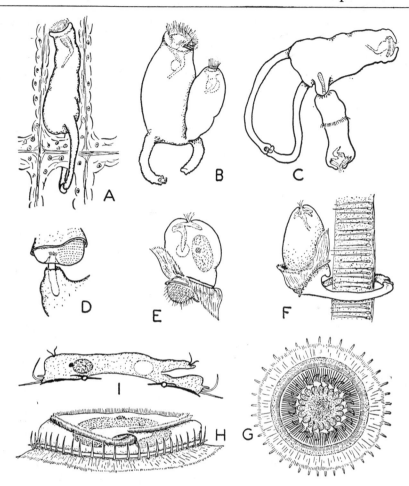

Fig. 7. 45. A-F. *Ellobiophrya donacis* Chatton and Lwoff: mature stage (A) attached to gill-filament of *Donax vittatus,* x400; completion of fission (B), x575; development of migratory larva (C), x575; stage in formation of embryonic stalk (D), x675; swimming larva (E), x675; young organism recently attached to gill-filament (F), aboral cilia still present, x675 (after C. & L.). G-I. *Cyclochaeta domerguei* Wallengren: view of aboral surface (G), x500; lateral view (H); section through vestibule and contractile vacuole (I), x750 (after MacLennan).

Telotrochidium henenguyi (138) and *Cyclochaeta domerguei* (146) both swim with the aboral pole directed forward.

Family 1. Astylozoonidae. These are actively swimming peritrichs which travel with the peristome directed forward. Instead of a stalk, one or two apparently thigmotactic bristles are developed at the aboral pole. The family has been considered a highly specialized group (106).

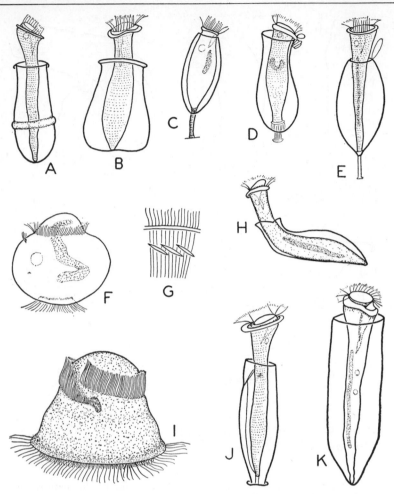

Fig. 7. 46. A. *Vaginicola annulata* Stokes, lorica reaches length of 120µ
(after Kahl). B. *Vaginicola amphora* Kahl, lorica 100µ (after K.). C. *Cothurnia canthocampti* Stokes, lorica about 80µ (after Stokes). D. *Pyxicola entzi*
(Stiller) Kahl, 70-75µ (from K., after S.). E. *Caulicola valvata* Stokes, lorica
about 50µ (after Kahl). F, G. *Urceolaria patellae* (Cuenot) Kahl, diameter
50-60µ; lateral view; portion of aboral disc (after K.). H. *Platycola longicollis* Kent, about 125µ (after Penard). I. *Trichodina spheroidesi* Padnos and
Nigrelli, x712 (after P. & N.). J. *Thuricola obconica* Kahl, about 210µ (after
K.). K. *Cothurnia acuta* Wang and Nie, x334 approx. (after W. & N.).

Three genera have been assigned to the Astylozoonidae: *Astylozoon* Engelmann (106;
Fig. 7. 43, D), *Geliella* Stiller (106; Fig. 7. 43, F), and *Hastatella* Stiller (95, 106; Fig.
7. 43, G).

Family 2. Epistylidae. In sessile stages, the scopula produces a stalk
which contains no myoneme (stalk-muscle). Some species are solitary and
others colonial.

Six genera have been referred to the family: *Ballodora* Dogiel and Furssenko (106), *Epistylis* Ehrenberg (106; Fig. 7. 43, A, H), *Opercularia* Stein (106; Fig. 7. 44, J), *Pyxidium* Kent (106; Fig. 7. 43, B), *Rhabdostyla* Kent (106; Fig. 7. 43, C) and *Telotrochidium* Kent (63, 122, 180; Fig. 7. 43, E, I). Since no stalked stage is known for *Telotrochidium*, the status of this genus as a member of the family is uncertain.

Family 3. Lagenophryidae. These are loricate ciliates in which the peristomial disc lies at the tip of a stout neck which is usually the only part of the body to be extended through the mouth of the lorica.

The family contains only the genus *Lagenophrys* Stein (2, 106; Fig. 7. 44, D, E).

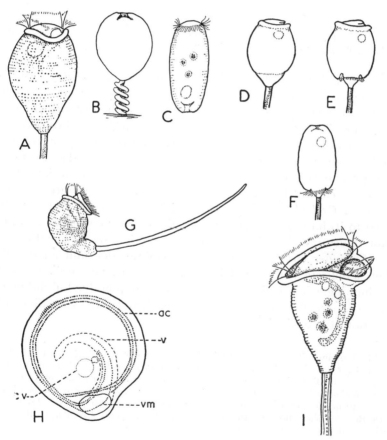

Fig. 7. 47. A-F. *Vorticella microstoma* Ehrbg.: extended form (A), contracted specimen (B), and telotroch (C), x540; development of a telotroch from a stalked stage (D-F), x360 (after Noland and Finley). G. *Vorticella mayeri* Fauré-Fremiet, x575 approx. (after Wang and Nie). H. The peristomial area in *Vorticella: ac,* basal granules of adoral ciliature; *cv,* contractile vacuole with its adjacent reservoir; *v,* vestibule; *vm,* adoral membrane in vestibule; diagrammatic (after Noland and Finley). I. *Vorticella picta* Ehrbg., x510 (after Noland and Finley).

Family 4. Ophrydiidae. The oral end of the body is prolonged into a long contractile neck. The aboral end tapers to a point in some species but is broadly rounded in others. The scopula may or may not produce a short stalk.

Only two genera have been recognized: *Ophrydium* Ehrbg. (106; Fig. 7. 44, C, I) and *Ophridiopsis* Penard (106, 165).

Family 5. Scyphidiidae. These are sessile peritrichs in which the scopula functions as a holdfast organ. The body is sometimes broadly flattened at the aboral pole; in other cases it tapers to a stalk-like basal region.

Four genera have been assigned to the family: *Ellobiophrya* Chatton and Lwoff (25; Fig. 7. 45, A-F), *Glossatella* Bütschli (106; Fig. 7. 44, A), *Paravorticella* Kahl (106; Fig. 7. 44, B), and *Scyphidia* Dujardin (87, 106, 212; Fig. 7. 44, F-H).

Family 6. Urceolariidae. This family includes specialized ectoparasites and endoparasites in which the oral-aboral axis is often much shortened. The aboral end is a flattened disc equipped with rings of cuticular elements (Fig. 7. 45, G). These skeletal elements of the basal disc seem to be composed of scleroproteins and they have no continuity in fission, each daughter organism forming a new set (68). Although the ribs and denticles (or plates) of the basal disc have sometimes been considered important in attachment to the host, their functional significance is somewhat uncertain. *Cyclochaeta domerguei* (146), for instance, is not really attached to its host. The organism is equipped with a series of aboral locomotor structures (Fig. 7. 45, H, I)—a posterior row of membranelles, a row of slender cirri just above the membranelles, and an undulating velum, a delicate membrane lying above the cirri. The cirri are important in swimming, whereas the membranelles are responsible for gliding movements, spinning the ciliate counterclockwise, and at the same time holding it in contact with the host.

Kahl (106) included three genera in the family: *Cyclochaeta* Jackson (35, 146; Fig. 7. 45, G-I), *Trichodina* Ehrbg. (49, 68, 87, 161; Fig. 7. 46, I), and *Urceolaria* Stein (87, 228; Fig. 7. 46, F, G). Hirschfield (87) has discussed the suggestion of Fauré-Fremiet that *Cyclochaeta* Jackson should be reduced to a sub-genus of *Trichodina* Ehrenberg. This simplification of the family would recognize only two genera: *Trichodina*, in which the denticles show projections (Fig. 7. 45, G); and *Urceolaria*, in which the denticles (or plates) lack such projections (Fig. 7. 46, G).

Family 7. Vaginicolidae. These are loricate peritrichs which differ from the Lagenophryidae in that the entire oral end of the body is extended beyond the mouth of the lorica.

Seven genera have been assigned to the family: *Caulicola* Stokes (106; Fig. 7. 46, E), *Cothurnia* Ehrenberg (106; Fig. 7. 46, C), *Platycola* Kent (106; Fig. 7. 46, H), *Pyxicola*

Kent (106; Fig. 7. 46, D), *Thuricola* Kent (106; Fig. 7. 46, J), *Thuricolopsis* Stokes (106), and *Vaginicola* Ehrenberg (106; Fig. 7. 46, A, B).

Family 8. Vorticellidae. This family includes four genera of typically sessile forms which develop contractile stalks.

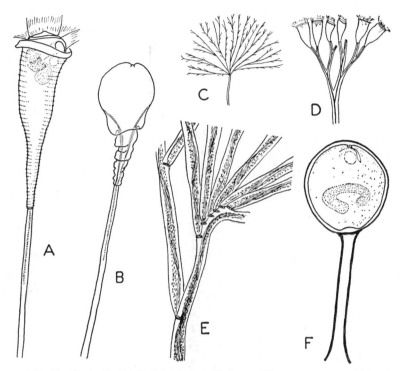

Fig. 7. 48. A, B. *Vorticella consoma* Stokes, x700 approx.: extended and contracted specimens; contraction involves the attenuated aboral portion of the body but not the stalk proper (after Fauré-Fremiet). C. *Carchesium polypinum* (Linn.) Kahl, branching pattern of large colony, zooids not shown; diagrammatic (after Kahl). D. *Zoothamnium adamsi* Stokes, continuous stalk-muscle; zooids about 60μ long (after S.). E. *Carchesium limneticum* Svec, portion of colony showing separate stalk-muscles in individual stalks; x200 approx. (after Fauré-Fremiet). F. Stalked cyst of *Zoothamnium arbuscula*, x215 approx. (after Furssenko).

Intrastylum Fauré-Fremiet (106) includes ectocommensals, either solitary or forming small colonies. In *Carchesium* Ehrenberg (61, 106; Fig. 7. 48, C, E), the stalk of each zooid in the colony is independently contractile. *Vorticella* Ehrenberg (11, 106, 159; Fig. 7. 47, A-I; 48, A, B) contains solitary types. In the colonial *Zoothamnium* Ehrenberg (70, 106, 200; Fig. 7. 48, D, F), there is a continuous stalk-muscle.

Order 4. Chonotrichida.[4] These are ectocommensals, mostly on actively swimming Crustacea. Except for *Trichochona lecythoides* (154) from the

---

[4] The life-cycles of several species have been traced in a recent paper by Y. Guilcher (1951. *Ann. Sci. Nat., Zool.*, Sér. 11, T. 13: 33).

California coast, these ciliates have been reported from European waters. Species of *Spirochona* occur on fresh-water gammarids but the other genera all seem to be marine.

The body is usually more or less vase-shaped, and is attached to the host by either a basal disc or a fairly short stalk. The peristome lies at the upper end of the body and is usually surrounded by a thin-walled funnel, near the base of which several rows of cilia extend to the cytostome. The body is generally constricted at the base of the funnel. The funnel in *Kentrochona* is a simple structure with a continuous wall (Fig. 7. 49, F). More often, the wall is incomplete and one end is rolled up to form a secondary spiral funnel (Fig. 7. 49, A, H). *Stylochona* is unusual in that a wide funnel of the *Kentrochona*-type surrounds an inner and apparently separate funnel (Fig. 7. 49, B). The general surface of the body is usually not ciliated. The contractile vacuole opens into the pharynx (vestibule), as in the Peritrichida.

Budding and conjugation (with oral ends in contact) have been reported. In *Trichochona lecythoides* there is a lateral pouch ("marsupium") into which the developing bud extends. As the bud grows, it protrudes from the marsupium and finally becomes separated from the parent (154). The bud in *Chilodochona quennerstedti* (82) is set free as a migratory larva with a ciliated ventral surface, an apparently undifferentiated cytostome, and a scopula-like organelle which will produce the stalk of the adult (Fig. 7. 49, J). Similar migratory stages have been reported for species of *Heliochona* and *Spirochona* (82).

The relationships of the Chonotrichida remain somewhat uncertain and further work is needed on the morphology and life-cycles. However, the present scanty information is believed by some workers to indicate that this group is more closely related to the Holotrichida than to any other ciliates (62). Three families have been recognized by Mohr (154).

Family 1. Chilodochonidae. This family includes *Chilodochona* Wallengren (82, 106; Fig. 7. 49, I, J) in which there is no very marked constriction ("neck") at the base of the funnel .A well-developed stalk is characteristic. The "funnel" is rudimentary and the peristome is better described as a groove bordered by two lips. This type of organization would require a rather simple metamorphosis of the migratory stage.

Family 2. Stylochonidae. Funnels are well developed but are not spirally twisted. A stalk may or may not be present.

Four genera have been assigned to the family: *Heliochona* Plate (106; Fig. 7. 49, E), *Kentrochona* Rompel (106; Fig. 7. 49, F), *Stylochona* Kent (106; Fig. 7. 49, B), and *Trichochona* Mohr (154; Fig. 7. 49, G).

Family 3. Spirochonidae. The funnel is folded into spirals and there is no stalk. The single genus, *Spirochona* Stein (106, 202, 207; Fig. 7. 49, A, C, D, H), includes species from fresh-water gammarids.

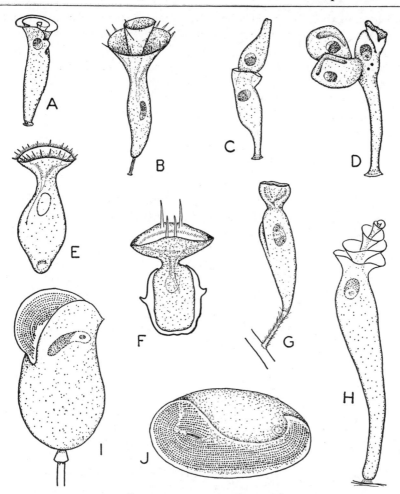

Fig. 7. 49. A. *Spirochona patella* Swarczewsky, x248 (after S.). B. *Stylochona coronata* Kent, about 60μ long (after K.). C, D. A stage in conjugation, and the formation of two buds in *Spirochona elegans,* schematic (after Swarczewsky). E. *Heliochona sessilis* Plate, about 60μ long (from Kahl, after Wallengren). F. *Kentrochona nebaliae* Rompel, a loricate type about 40μ long; pharynx and macronucleus shown in outline (from Kahl, after R.). G. *Trichochona lecythoides* Mohr, x83 (after M.). H. *Spirochona elegans* Swarczewsky, x248 (after S.). I, J. *Chilodochona quennerstedti* Wallengren: stalked form (I), showing basal granules of peristome and the macronucleus, x750; migratory larva (J), showing cytostome, ventral ciliature which will become the peristomial cilia of the adult, and the postero-lateral scopula-like organ which will secrete a stalk during metamorphosis; x875 (after Guilcher).

CLASS 2. SUCTOREA

The form of the body, in different species, may be approximately spherical, conical, club-shaped, cylindrical, vermiform, or irregularly branching. The most obvious features of the group are the presence of tentacles and the absence of cilia in the mature stage. Even the tentacles are lacking in *Endosphaera,* which includes endoparasites of certain ciliates.

Tentacles may be distributed over the surface or they may arise in

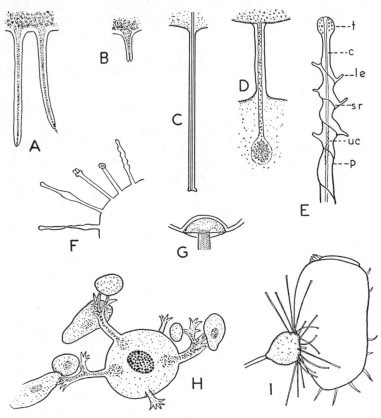

Fig. 7. 50. A, B. Tentacles of *Echinophrya horrida,* extended and partly retracted; x750 (after Swarczewsky). C, D. Tentacles of *Tokophrya lemnarum,* extended, and during feeding; x2000 approx. (after Noble). E. Tentacle of *Discophrya pisciformis: c,* internal canal; *le,* lateral expansions of the pellicle; *p,* pellicle; *sr,* spiral ridge in pellicle; *t,* tip of tentacle containing pores (?); *uc,* undulations in wall of the internal canal; diagrammatic (after Dragesco and Guilcher). F. Changes in form observed in tentacles of *Sphaerophrya magna;* diagrammatic (after Wang and Nie). G. Attachment of stalk to body in *Acineta commensalis;* x495 (after Swarczewsky). H. *Dendrocometes paradoxus* feeding on several ciliates; x295 approx. (after Pestel). I. Capture of a hypotrich by *Tokophrya lemnarum,* x268 approx. (after Noble).

clusters or from lobes or extensible arms. Two varieties are known. One type is capitate (Fig. 7. 50, C-F), ending distally in a flattened or rounded expansion. The other type tapers more or less to a point (Fig. 7. 50, A, B). In at least some species, the tentacles contain an inner tube (Fig. 7.

50, C, E) which extends into the endoplasm for a short distance. The tentacles adhere to a suitable ciliate which comes in contact with them and are powerful enough to hold prey much larger than the captor (Fig. 7. 50, H, I). Prompt paralysis of the captured organism has often been reported. Shortly after contact, protoplasm of the prey starts flowing down the tentacle to the base of the tube, where food vacuoles are formed. Whether the pellicle of the prey is ruptured by suction or undergoes lysis upon contact with the tentacle is uncertain. Ingestion is rapid. *Tokophrya lemnarum,* for instance, ingests *Euplotes patella* in about fifteen minutes (156).

The flow of material through the tentacle during feeding suggests the exertion of suction, the source of which has remained an intriguing problem. Perhaps it is significant that activity of the contractile vacuole is increased about five-fold in *Tokophrya infusionum* as the organism begins to feed (184). Dragesco and Guilcher (53) have noted, by means of phase-contrast microscopy, that the wall of the inner canal may undergo contractions suggesting a sort of peristaltic activity. Whether such activity plays a major part in ingestion is not yet certain.

The suctorian stalk, present in many species, is always non-contractile although not necessarily homogeneous in structure (156). The upper end of the stalk may be expanded as a small cup in which the base of the body rests, or in other cases, the distal end of the stalk fits into a depression in the body (Fig. 7. 50, G). In the metamorphosis of ciliated larvae, the stalk apparently arises from an organelle analogous to the scopula of Peritrichida (Fig. 7. 51, L).

Some of the Suctorea are equipped with a secreted lorica which is often open distally, leaving the apical end of the body free (Fig. 7. 56, A), or may be a fairly heavy wall enclosing the body as in *Squalophrya macrostyla* (Fig. 7. 53, H, I).

The relationships of the Suctorea to ciliates are indicated in the life-cycles of most species. Reproduction typically involves budding, either internal (Fig. 7. 51, N-P) or external. Although it appears to be unusual, both internal and external budding may occur within a single species, as reported for *Anarma multiruga* (80). The bud usually develops into a ciliated larva (Fig. 7. 51, A-K), which after a short period of swimming, undergoes metamorphosis. After the larval stage of *Tokophrya lemnarum* becomes attached (Fig. 7. 51, L, M), a stalk is secreted within a few minutes, the tentacles have grown to normal length about fifteen minutes after they are first detectable, and the adult form is fully developed within an hour (156). Even more rapid metamorphosis has been noted in *Tokophrya infusionum* (185).

The disappearance of cilia during metamorphosis apparently does not include their basal granules, which persist in the adult stage of *Podophrya fixa* (32). In reproduction, the bud receives some of the parental basal

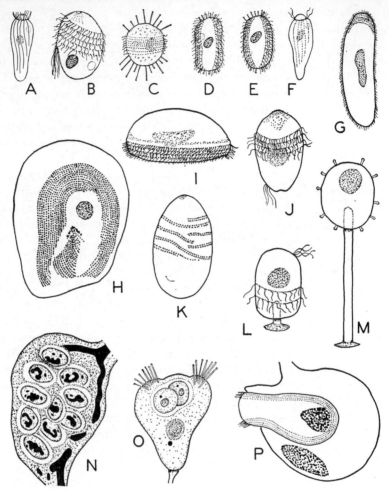

Fig. 7. 51. A-K. Ciliated larvae of various Suctorea: A. *Podophrya soliformis;* B. *Tokophrya quadripartata;* C. *Podophrya sandi;* D. *Podophrya globulifera;* E. *Podophrya fixa;* F. *Parapodophrya denticulata* (A-F, schematic, after Kahl); G. *Cyclophrya magna,* x170 (after Gönnert); H. *Ephelota gemmipara,* silver impregnation of basal granules, schematic (after Guilcher); I. *Dendrocometes paradoxus,* x380 (after Pestel); J. *Tokophrya lemnarum,* x482 (after Noble); K. *Tokophrya infusionum,* silver impregnation of basal granules, x750 approx. (after Guilcher). L, M. *Tokophrya lemnarum,* larva shortly after attachment (L), and early metamorphosis (M), x482 (after Noble). N Endogenous buds in *Gorgonosoma arbuscula,* x165 (after Swarczewsky). O. Endogenous buds in *Acineta cornuta,* x248 (after Swarczewsky). P. Emergence of larva in *Dendrocometes paradoxus,* x600 (after Pestel).

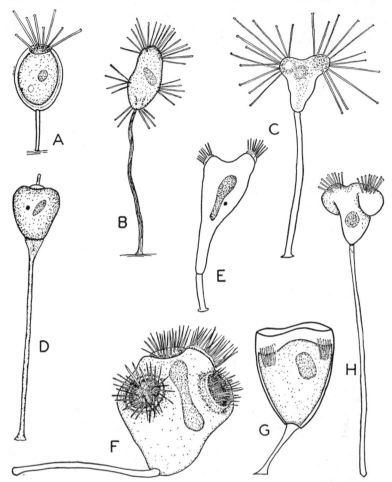

Fig. 7. 52. A. *Acineta livadiana* Mereschkowski, x548 (after Wang and Nie). B. *Multifasciculatum elegans* Goodrich and Jahn; body, 50-90x20-50μ (after G. & J.). C. *Tokophrya lemnarum* Stein, x268 (after Noble). D. *Acinetopsis elegans* Swarczewsky, x165 (after S.). E. *Acinetides varians* Swarczewsky, x165 (after S.). F. *Tokophryopsis gigantea* Swarczewsky, x165 (after S.). G. *Thecacineta baikalica* Swarczewsky, x248 (after S.). H. *Acineta cornuta* Swarczewsky, x248 (after S.).

granules, which then multiply and give rise to the larval cilia. If this case may be considered representative, there is thus a genetic continuity of basal granules throughout the life-cycle.

In the life-cycle of *Podophrya fixa* (59), an intermediate stage intervenes between the larva and the adult, parasitic on *Nassula ornata* (Fig. 7. 56, F). The result of metamorphosis is a *Sphaerophrya*-stage which floats until it makes contact with its ciliate host. *Endosphaera* also includes unusual types with an endoparasitic adult, embedded in the cytoplasm of a

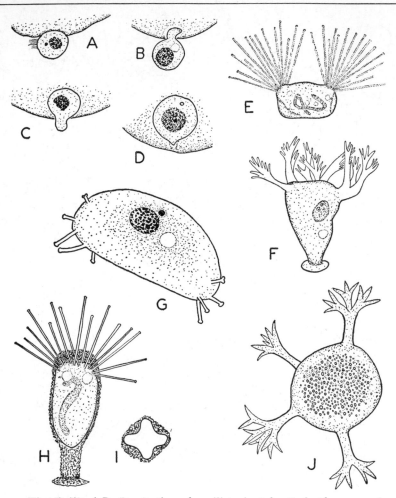

Fig. 7. 53. A-D. Penetration of a ciliate host by *Endosphaera engel-manni;* stained preparations; x600 (after Noble). E. *Anarma brevis* Good-rich and Jahn; body about 125x75μ (after G. & J.). F. *Cometodendron digitatum* Swarczewsky, x165 (after S.). G. *Allantosoma intestinalis* Gas-sovsky, from large intestine of horse; x854 (after Hsiung). H, I. *Squalo-phrya macrostyla* Goodrich and Jahn, a loricate type, lateral view and cross-section; body about 90x40μ (after G. & J.). J. *Dendrocometes para-doxus* Stein, x285 (after Pestel).

ciliate host (138). In reproduction, the parasite produces a typical ciliated larva which is set free as a migratory stage and later invades a new host (Fig. 7. 53, A-D).

In addition to the common occurrence of ciliated larvae, transforma-tion of the adult into a migratory stage also may occur, as in *Podophrya parasitica* (Fig. 7. 56, D). This migratory stage (59), in turn, becomes

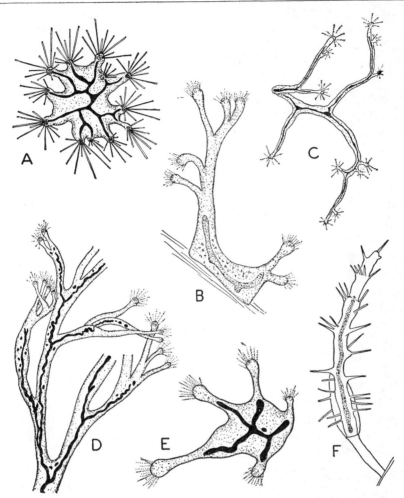

Fig. 7. 54. A. *Lernaeophrya capitata* Pérez, with branched macronucleus; x83 (after Gönnert). B. *Baikalodendron augustatum* Swarczewsky, x140 (after S.). C. *Dendrosoma radians* Ehrbg., x68 (after Gönnert). D. *Gorgonosoma arbuscula* Swarczewsky, portion of a young specimen, x31 (after S.). E. *Baikalophrya acanthogammari* Swarczewsky, x248 (after S.). F. *Dendrosomides truncata* Dons, x200 (after D.).

attached by development of a stalk, loses its cilia, and develops tentacles on its upper surface to become a *Paracineta*-stage (Fig. 7. 56, G). This stage does not feed and apparently is a temporary stage preceding encystment (Fig. 7. 56, H).

Conjugation, comparable to that in typical ciliates, has been described in several genera, including *Acineta* (148), *Dendrocometes* (86), and *Tokophrya* (156). In contrast to conjugation in *Tokophrya lemnarum,* in which the two conjugants eventually separate much as in ciliates (156), complete fusion and the production of a single synkaryon have been reported in *Lernaeophrya capitata* (79).

Encystment is known in a number of species. In *Tokophrya lemnarum* (156), encystment involves the deposition of a transparent secretion, at first basally, and finally over the apical end of the body. Specimens in early encystment resemble certain of the loricate Suctorea. Precystic withdrawal of the tentacles has not been observed. Instead, these structures remain matted over the apical surface and are engulfed by the material secreted to form the cyst membrane.

Taxonomy

The Suctorea, which are probably more closely related to the gymnostomatous Holotrichida than to other ciliates (62, 103), seem to have undergone little basic diversification in the course of their evolution. Since there seems to be no logical basis for differentiating orders, the group has usually been divided into a number of families. Even this simple arrangement might be more satisfactory if some of the families were more sharply defined so as to take care of genera which show apparently intermediate combinations of characteristics. Perhaps a more intensive study of lifecycles, with detailed comparisons of the migratory larvae, might yield useful information. For example, it is interesting that larvae of *Podophrya soliformis* and *Parapodophrya denticulata* (Family Podophryidae) have been described with a polar circlet of cilia similar to that reported for *Discophrya cybistri* (Family Discophryidae); the larva of *Podophrya sandi*, with an equatorial belt of cilia resembling that noted in species of *Tokophrya* (Family Acinetidae); larvae of *Podophrya globulifera, P. fixa,* and *P. parasitica*, with ciliary rows which parallel the long axis of the body instead of encircling it transversely.

Family 1. Acinetidae. This family is characterized by endogenous budding and by the possession of capitate tentacles, usually arranged in groups. A lorica is often present, and a stalk may be present or absent.

The following genera have been included in the family: *Acineta* Ehrbg. (148, 206; Fig. 7. 52, A, H), *Acinetides* Swarczewsky (206; Fig. 7. 52, E), *Acinetopsis* Robin (206; Fig. 7. 52, D), *Allantosoma* Gassovsky (90; Fig. 7. 53, G), *Anarma* Goodrich and Jahn (80; Fig. 7. 53, E), *Dactylophrya* Collin (40), *Endosphaera* Engelmann (138; Fig. 7. 53, A-D), *Multifasciculatum* Goodrich and Jahn (80; Fig. 7. 52, B), *Paracineta* Collin (40), *Pottsia* Chatton and Lwoff (23), *Pseudogemma* Collin (40), *Solenophrya* Claparède and Lachmann, *Squalophrya* Goodrich and Jahn (80; Fig. 7. 53, H, I), *Tachyblaston* Martin (148), *Thecacineta* Collin (206; Fig. 7. 52, G), *Tokophrya* Bütschli (156, 206; Fig. 7. 52, C), *Tokophryopsis* Swarczewsky (206; Fig. 7. 52, F).

Family 2. Dendrocometidae. These stalkless forms undergo endogenous budding. Capitate tentacles may be distributed over the surface or localized on slender extensions of the body.

The following genera have been referred to this family: *Cometodendron* Swarczewsky (204; Fig. 7. 53, F), *Dendrocometes* Stein (168, 204; Fig. 7. 53, J), *Discosoma* Swarczewsky (204), and *Stylocometes* Stein.

Family 3. Dendrosomidae. The stalkless body is irregular in form and often branched, and the basal surface is usually attached to the sub-

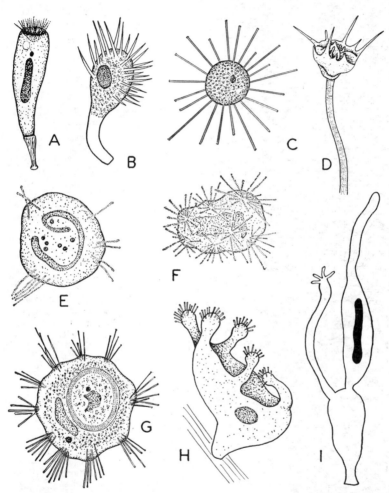

Fig. 7. 55. A. *Discophrya longa* Swarczewsky, x165 (after S.). B. *Echinophrya horrida* Swarczewsky, x248 (after S.). C. *Sphaerophrya magna* Maupas, x165 (after Wang and Nie). D. *Ephelota gemmipara* (Hertwig) Bütschli, x345 (after Wang). E. *Cyclophrya magna* Gönnert, showing macronucleus and several micronuclei; x255 (after G.). F. *Trichophrya epistylides* Claparède and Lachmann, x210 (after Gönnert). G. *Platophrya rotunda* (Hentschel) Gönnert, containing a bud; stained preparation; x386 (after G.). H. *Stylophrya polymorpha* Swarczewsky, x248 (after S.). I. Exogenous formation of a vermiform bud, characteristic of *Ophryodendron;* diagrammatic (after Collin).

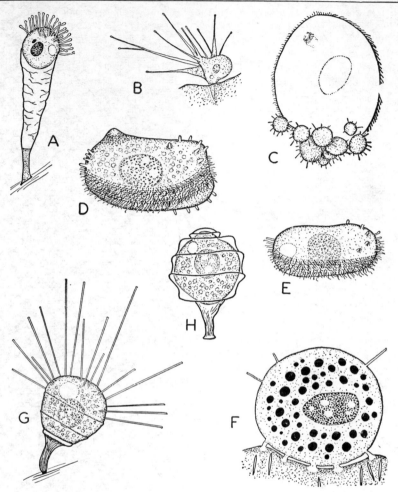

Fig. 7. 56. A. *Paracineta pleuromammae* Steuer, lorica 57-114μ (after S.). B. *Parapodophrya atypica* Gönnert, attached to a ciliate; x900 (after G.). C-H. *Podophrya parasitica* Fauré-Fremiet: C. Several specimens attached to *Nassula ornata*, x116 approx. D. Migratory stage formed by direct transformation of the adult. E. Ciliated larva produced by budding. F. Specimen attached to *Nassula ornata*, tentacles apparently penetrating the pellicle of the host. G. The *Paracineta*-stage, which does not feed. H. Encysted form, derived from the *Paracineta*-stage (after Fauré-Fremiet).

stratum. The tentacles are arranged in clusters. Reproduction typically involves endogenous budding, either single or multiple.

The family includes the following genera: *Astrophrya* Awerinzew, *Baikalodendron* Swarczewsky (203; Fig. 7. 54, B), *Baikalophrya* Swarczewsky (203; Fig. 7. 54, E), *Dendrosoma* Ehrenberg (79, 86a; Fig. 7. 54, C), *Dendrosomides* Collin (40; Fig. 7. 54, F), *Gorgonosoma* Swarczewsky (203; Fig. 7. 54, D), *Lernaeophrya* Pérez (79; Fig. 7. 54, A), *Platophrya* Gönnert (79; Fig. 7. 55, G), *Rhabdophrya* Chatton and Collin, *Staurophrya*

Zacharias, *Stylophrya* Swarczewsky (203; Fig. 7. 55, H), *Trichophrya* Claparède and Lachmann (79; Fig. 7. 55, F).

Family 4. Discophryidae. Endogenous budding and capitate tentacles are characteristic, although some species with pointed tentacles have been assigned to the family (205). A lorica is lacking and a stalk may or may not be present.

The following genera have been referred to the family: *Choanophrya* Hartog (40), *Cyclophrya* Gönnert (79; Fig. 7. 55, E), *Discophrya* Lachmann (205; Fig. 7. 55, A), *Echinophrya* Swarczewsky (205; Fig. 7. 55, B), *Rhyncheta* Zenker, *Rhynchophrya* Collin (40), and *Thaumatophrya* Collin (40).

Family 5. Ephelotidae. These are stalked marine Suctorea with capitate or pointed tentacles. Budding is typically exogenous and may be multiple. A lorica may or may not be present.

Two genera, *Ephelota* Wright (148; Fig. 7. 55, D) and *Podocyathus* Kent, have been referred to the family.

Family 6. Ophryodendridae. In these marine forms the tentacles are concentrated on one or more mobile proboscis-like extensions. In addition to the usual type of larva, so-called vermiform buds, with no tentacles or proboscis, may be produced by exogenous budding (149).

The type genus is *Ophryodendron* Claparède and Lachmann (40, 149; Fig. 7. 55, I).

Family 7. Podophryidae. Reproduction involves external budding, or in some cases "fission" in which the two daughter organisms are almost equal in size. A stalk and a lorica may be present or absent.

The following genera have been referred to the Podophryidae: *Lecanophrya* Kahl, *Metacineta* Bütschli, *Ophryocephalus* Wailes, *Paracineta* Collin (40, 191; Fig. 7. 56, A), *Parapodophrya* Kahl (79, 103; Fig. 7. 56, B), *Podophrya* Ehrbg. (59, 178; Fig. 7. 56, C-H), *Sphaerophrya* Claparède and Lachmann (Fig. 7. 55, C), *Spelaeophrya* Stammer (190), and *Urnula* Claparède and Lachmann.

LITERATURE CITED

1. Andrews, E. A. 1923. *J. Morph.* **38**: 207.
2. Awerinzew, S. W. 1937. *Arch. f. Protistenk.* **87**: 131.
3. Balamuth, W. 1941. *J. Morph.* **68**: 241.
4. Becker, E. R. and M. Talbott 1927. *Iowa St. Coll. J. Sci.* **1**: 345.
5. Beers, C. D. 1938. *J. Elisha Mitchell Sci. Soc.* **54**: 111.
6. ———— 1938. *Arch. f. Protistenk.* **91**: 516.
7. Beltran, E. 1941. *Rev. Soc. Mex. Hist. Nat.* **2**: 267.
8. Bhatia, B. L. and A. N. Gulati 1927. *Arch. f. Protistenk.* **57**: 85.
9. Bishop, A. 1923. *Quart. J. Micr. Sci.* **67**: 391.
10. Bishop, E. L. 1943. *J. Morph.* **72**: 441.
11. Brand, T. v. 1923. *Arch. f. Protistenk.* **47**: 59.
12. Braune, R. 1914. *Arch. f. Protistenk.* **32**: 111.

13. Bullington, W. E. 1940. *Carneg. Inst. Wash. Publ. No. 517:* **179.**
14. Burt, R. L. 1940. *Trans. Amer. Micr. Soc.* **59:** 414.
15. Bush, M. 1934. *Univ. Calif. Publ. Zool.* **39:** 251.
16. Calkins, G. N. 1929. *Biol. Bull.* **57:** 59.
17. Campbell, A. S. 1927. *Univ. Calif. Publ. Zool.* **29:** 179.
18. ———— 1927. *Univ. Calif. Publ. Zool.* **29:** 429.
19. ———— 1942. *The Oceanic Tintinnoina of the Plankton Gathered During the Last Cruise of the Carnegie.* Carneg. Inst. Wash. Publ. 537.
20. Chatton, E. 1936. *Mém. Musée Roy. Hist. Nat. Belg.,* Ser. 2: 913.
21. ———— and S. Brachon 1936. *C. R. Ac. Sci.* **202:** 713.
22. ———— and A. Lwoff 1923. *C. R. Ac. Sci.* **177:** 81.
23. ———— and ———— 1927. *Bull. Inst. Oceanogr.,* No. 489, 12 pp.
24. ———— and ———— 1928. *C. R. Ac. Sci.* **186:** 1381.
25. ———— and ———— 1929. *Bull. Biol. Fr. Belg.* **63:** 321.
26. ———— and ———— 1930. *Bull. Soc. Zool. Fr.* **55:** 296.
27. ———— and ———— 1934. *Bull. Soc. Zool. Fr.* **59:** 375.
28. ———— and ———— 1935. *Arch. Zool. Exp. Gén.* **77:** 1.
29. ———— and ———— 1936. *Bull. Biol. Fr. Belg.* **70:** 86.
30. ———— and ———— 1949. *Arch. Zool. Exp. Gén.* **86:** 169.
31. ———— and ———— 1950. *Arch. Zool. Exp. Gén.* **86:** 393.
32. ————, M. Lwoff, A. Lwoff and L. Tellier 1929. *C. R. Soc. Biol.* **100:** 1191.
33. ———— and C. Pérard 1921. *Bull. Biol. Fr. Belg.* **55:** 87.
34. ———— and J. Seguela 1936. *Bull. Soc. Zool. Fr.* **61:** 232.
35. ———— and S. Villeneuve 1937. *C. R. Ac. Sci.* **204:** 538.
36. Cheissin, E. 1930. *Arch. f. Protistenk.* **70:** 531.
37. ———— 1931. *Arch. f. Protistenk.* **73:** 280.
38. Chen, T.-T. 1948. *J. Morph.* **83:** 281.
39. Claff, C. L., V. C. Dewey and G. W. Kidder 1941. *Biol. Bull.* **81:** 221.
40. Collin, B. 1912. *Arch. Zool. Exp. Gén.* **51:** 1.
41. Conklin, C. 1930. *Biol. Bull.* **58:** 176.
42a. Corliss, J. O. 1951. *Proc. Amer. Soc. Protozool.* **2:** 11.
42b. ———— 1951. *Soc. Syst. Zool. News Letter* **5:** 9-10.
42c. ———— 1952. *Trans. Amer. Micr. Soc.* **71:** 159.
43. Cosgrove, W. B. 1947. *J. Parasit.* **33:** 351.
44. Davis, T. G. 1941. *Trans. Amer. Micr. Soc.* **60:** 441.
45. De Morgan, W. 1924. *Quart. J. Micr. Sci.* **68:** 343.
46. ———— 1925. *J. Mar. Biol. Assoc.* **13:** 600.
47. Dewey, V. C. 1939. *Biol. Bull.* **77:** 448.
48. ———— and G. W. Kidder 1940. *Biol. Bull.* **79:** 255.
49. Diller, W. F. 1928. *J. Morph.* **46:** 521.
50. Dogiel, V. A. 1927. *Arch. f. Protistenk.* **59:** 1.
51. ———— 1928. *Ann. Parasitol.* **6:** 323.
52. ———— 1929. *Arch. f. Protistenk.* **68:** 319.
53. Dragesco, J. and Y. Guilcher 1950. *Microscopie* **2:** 17.
54. Fauré-Fremiet, E. 1905. *Arch. f. Protistenk.* **6:** 207.
55. ———— 1932. *Biol. Bull.* **62:** 201.
56. ———— 1932. *Bull. Biol. Fr. Belg.* **66:** 77.
57. ———— 1936. *Biol. Bull.* **70:** 353.
58. ———— 1945. *Bull. Soc. Zool. Fr.* **70:** 69.
59. ———— 1945. *Bull. Biol. Fr. Belg.* **79:** 85.
60. ———— 1948. *Bull. Biol. Fr. Belg.* **82:** 5.
61. ———— 1948. *Anais Acad. Brasil Ciencias* **20:** 103.
61a. ———— 1950. *Bull. Biol. Fr. Belg.* **84:** 35.
62. ———— 1950. *Bull. Soc. Zool.* **75:** 109.
63. ———— 1950. *Bull. Soc. Zool. Fr.* **75:** 148.
64. ———— and Y. Guilcher 1948. *Bull. Soc. Zool. Fr.* **72:** 106.
65. ———— and M. Hamard 1944. *Bull. Biol. Fr. Belg.* **78:** 136.
66. ———— and H. Mugard 1949. *Hydrobiologia* **1:** 379.
67. ————, J. Stolkowski and J. Ducornet 1948. *Biochim. Biophys. Acta.* **2:** 668.

68. —— and J. Thoreaux 1944. *Bull. Biol. Fr. Belg.* **78**: 143.
69. Furgason, W. H. 1940. *Arch. f. Protistenk.* **94**: 224.
70. Furssenko, A. 1929. *Arch. f. Protistenk.* **67**: 376.
71. Garnjobst, L. 1934. *J. Mar. Biol. Assoc.* **19**: 707.
72. —— 1937. *Arch. f. Protistenk.* **89**: 317.
73. Gatenby, J. B. and S. D. King 1925. *Nature* **116**: 712.
74. Geiman, Q. M. 1931. *Trans. Amer. Micr. Soc.* **50**: 156.
75. —— and R. Wichterman 1937. *J. Parasit.* **23**: 331.
76. Gelei, J. v. 1934. *Arch. f. Protistenk.* **82**: 331.
77. —— 1937. *Zool. Anz.* **117**: 103.
78. —— 1940. *Arch. f. Protistenk.* **93**: 273.
79. Gönnert, R. 1935. *Arch. f. Protistenk.* **86**: 113.
80. Goodrich, J. P. and T. L. Jahn 1943. *Trans. Amer. Micr. Soc.* **62**: 245.
81. Grassé, P. P. 1928. *Ann. Protistol.* **1**: 55.
82. Guilcher, Y. 1950. *Année Biol.* **26**: 465.
83. Haas, G. 1933. *Arch. f. Protistenk.* **81**: 88.
84. Heidenreich, E. 1935. *Arch. f. Protistenk.* **84**: 315.
85. Hentschel, C. 1925. *Parasitol.* **17**: 217.
86. Hickson, S. J. and J. T. Wadsworth 1901. *Quart. J. Micr. Sci.* **45**: 325.
86a. —— and —— 1910. *Quart. J. Micr. Sci.* **54**: 141.
87. Hirschfield, H. 1949. *J. Morph.* **85**: 1.
88. Horvath, J. v. 1933. *Arch. f. Protistenk.* **80**: 281.
89. —— 1936. *Arch. f. Protistenk.* **86**: 482.
90. Hsiung, T.-S. 1928. *Iowa St. Coll. J. Sci.* **3**: 101.
91. —— 1930. *Iowa St. Coll. J. Sci.* **4**: 356.
92. Ivanič, M. 1936. *Arch. f. Protistenk.* **87**: 172.
93. Jameson, A. P. 1925. *Parasitol.* **17**: 403.
94. —— 1926. *Parasitol.* **18**: 182.
95. Jarocki, J. and W. Jabukowska 1927. *Zool. Anz.* **73**: 270.
96. Johnson, W. H. and E. Larson 1938. *Arch. f. Protistenk.* **90**: 383.
97. Kahl, A. 1926. *Arch. f. Protistenk.* **55**: 197.
98. —— 1927. *Arch. f. Protistenk.* **60**: 34.
99. —— 1930. *Arch. f. Protistenk.* **70**: 313.
100. —— 1930. "Urtiere oder Protozoa. I: Wimpertiere oder Ciliata (Infusoria). 1. Allgemeiner Teil und Prostomata" in *Die Tierwelt Deutschlands,* 18 Teil (Jena: G. Fischer).
101. —— 1931. *Ann. Protistol.* **3**: 111.
102. —— 1931. "Urtiere oder Protozoa. I. Wimpertiere oder Ciliata (Infusoria). 2. Holotricha" in *Die Tierwelt Deutschlands,* 21 Teil (Jena: G. Fischer).
103. —— 1931. *Arch. f. Protistenk.* **73**: 423.
104. —— 1932. "Urtiere oder Protozoa. I. Wimpertiere oder Ciliata (Infusoria). 3. Spirotricha" in *Die Tierwelt Deutschlands,* 25 Teil (Jena: G. Fischer).
105. —— 1932. *Arch. f. Protistenk.* **77**: 231.
106. —— 1935. "Urtiere oder Protozoa. I. Wimpertiere oder Ciliata (Infusoria). 4. Peritricha und Chonotricha" in *Die Tierwelt Deutschlands,* 30 Teil (Jena: G. Fischer).
107. Kalmus, H. 1931. *Paramecium. Das Pantoffeltierchen* (Jena: G. Fischer).
108. Kidder, G. W. 1933. *Arch. f. Protistenk.* **79**: 1.
109. —— 1933. *Biol. Bull.* **64**: 1.
110. —— 1933. *Biol. Bull.* **65**: 175.
111. —— 1934. *Biol. Bull.* **66**: 69.
112. —— 1937. *Parasitol.* **29**: 163.
113. Kirby, H. 1934. *Arch. f. Protistenk.* **82**: 114.
114. Kofoid, C. A. 1935. *Proc. Nat. Ac. Sci.* **21**: 501.
115. —— and A. S. Campbell 1929. *Univ. Calif. Publ. Zool.* **34**: 1.
116. —— and —— 1939. *Bull. Mus. Comp. Zool.* **84**: 1.
117. —— and J. F. Christenson 1934. *Univ. Calif. Publ. Zool.* **39**: 341.
118. —— and M. Dodds 1928. *Anat. Rec.* **41**: suppl.: 51.
119. —— and R. F. MacLennan 1930. *Univ. Calif. Publ. Zool.* **33**: 471.

120. —— and —— 1932. *Univ. Calif. Publ. Zool.* **37**: 53.
121. —— and —— 1933. *Univ. Calif. Publ. Zool.* **39**: 1.
122. —— and L. E. Rosenberg 1940. *Proc. Amer. Philos. Soc.* **82**: 421.
123. Konsuloff, S. 1922. *Arch. f. Protistenk.* **44**: 285.
124. Kozloff, E. N. 1945. *Biol. Bull.* **89**: 95.
125. —— 1945. *Biol. Bull.* **89**: 180.
126. —— 1946. *Biol. Bull.* **90**: 1.
127. —— 1946. *Biol. Bull.* **90**: 200.
128. —— 1946. *Biol. Bull.* **91**: 189.
129. —— 1946. *Biol. Bull.* **91**: 200.
130. Kudo, R. R. and P. A. Meglitch 1938. *Arch. f. Protistenk.* **91**: 111.
131. Lucas, M. S. 1932. *Arch. f. Protistenk.* **77**: 64.
132. —— 1932. *Arch. f. Protistenk.* **77**: 407.
133. Lund, E. E. 1933. *Univ. Calif. Publ. Zool.* **39**: 35.
134. Lund, E. J. 1917. *J. Exp. Zool.* **24**: 1.
135. Lwoff, A. 1950. *Problems of Morphogenesis in Ciliates* (New York: J. Wiley & Sons).
136. Lynch, J. E. 1929. *Univ. Calif. Publ. Zool.* **33**: 27.
137. —— 1930. *Univ. Calif. Publ. Zool.* **33**: 307.
138. —— and A. E. Noble 1931. *Univ. Calif. Publ. Zool.* **36**: 97.
139. MacDonald, J. D. 1922. *Univ. Calif. Publ. Zool.* **20**: 243.
140. MacDougall, M. S. 1928. *Biol. Bull.* **54**: 471.
141. —— 1936. *Bull. Biol. Fr. Belg.* **70**: 308.
142. Mackinnon, D. L. and H. N. Ray 1931. *J. Mar. Biol. Assoc.* **17**: 577.
143. MacLennan, R. F. 1933. *Univ. Calif. Publ. Zool.* **39**: 205.
144. —— 1934. *Arch. f. Protistenk.* **81**: 412.
145. —— 1935. *Arch. f. Protistenk.* **86**: 191.
146. —— 1939. *J. Morph.* **65**: 241.
147. —— 1944. *Trans. Amer. Micr. Soc.* **43**: 187.
148. Martin, C. H. 1909. *Quart. J. Micr. Sci.* **53**: 351.
149. —— 1909. *Quart. J. Micr. Sci.* **53**: 629.
150. Mast, S. O. 1909. *Biol. Bull.* **16**: 91.
151. Metcalf, M. M. 1909. *Arch. f. Protistenk.* **13**: 19.
152. —— 1923. *U. S. Nat. Mus. Bull.* 120.
153. —— 1940. *Proc. U. S. Nat. Mus.* **87**: 465.
154. Mohr, J. L. 1948. *Allan Hancock Found. Univ. S. Calif. Occ. Pap. No. 5.*
155. Mugard, H. 1948. *Ann. Sci. Nat., Zool.* (Ser. 11) **10**: 171.
156. Noble, A. E. 1932. *Univ. Calif. Publ. Zool.* **37**: 477.
157. Noland, L. E. 1925. *Trans. Amer. Micr. Soc.* **46**: 3.
158. —— 1937. *Trans. Amer. Micr. Soc.* **56**: 160.
159. —— and H. E. Finley 1931. *Trans. Amer. Micr. Soc.* **50**: 81.
160. Overbeek de Meyer, G. A. W. van 1929. *Arch. f. Protistenk.* **66**: 207.
161. Padnos, M. and R. F. Nigrelli 1942. *Zoologica* **27**: 65.
162. Parducz, B. 1939. *Arch. f. Protistenk.* **92**: 283.
163. —— 1940. *Arch. f. Protistenk.* **93**: 185.
164. Patten, R. 1932. *Proc. Roy. Irish Acad.* **41**: 73.
165. Penard, E. 1922. *Études sur les infusoires d'eau douce* (Georg & Cié: Genève).
166. Pertzewa, T. A. 1929. *Arch. f. Protistenk.* **65**: 330.
167. Peschkowsky, L. 1931. *Arch. f. Protistenk.* **73**: 179.
168. Pestel, B. 1931. *Arch. f. Protistenk.* **75**: 403.
169. Pickard, E. A. 1927. *Univ. Calif. Publ. Zool.* **29**: 405.
170. Pierson, B. F. 1943. *J. Morph.* **72**: 125.
171. Powers, P. B. A. 1932. *Biol. Bull.* **63**: 74.
172. —— 1933. *Biol. Bull.* **65**: 106.
173. —— 1933. *Biol. Bull.* **65**: 122.
174. Ray, H. 1932. *J. Roy. Micr. Soc.* **52**: 374.
175. Rees, C. W. 1930. *Parasitol.* **22**: 314.
176. —— 1931. *J. Morph.* **52**: 195.
177. Reichenow, E. 1928. *Arch. f. Protistenk.* **61**: 144.

178. Root, F. M. 1914. *Arch. f. Protistenk.* **35**: 164.
179. Rosenberg, L. E. 1937. *Univ. Calif. Publ. Zool.* **41**: 249.
180. ―― 1938. *Trans. Amer. Micr. Soc.* **57**: 147.
181. Rossolimo, L. 1926. *Arch. f. Protistenk.* **54**: 468.
182. ―― 1929. *Zool. Anz.* **86**: 69.
183. ―― and T. Perzewa 1929. *Arch. f. Protistenk.* **67**: 237.
184. Rudzinska, M. A. and R. Chambers 1951. *Biol. Bull.* **100**: 49.
185. ―― and ―― 1951. *Trans. Amer. Micr. Soc.* **70**: 168.
186. Runyan, E. M. and H. B. Torrey 1914. *Biol. Bull.* **27**: 343.
187. Sandon, H. 1941. *S. Afr. J. Med. Sci.* **6**: 116.
188. Sauerbrey, E. 1928. *Arch. f. Protistenk.* **62**: 354.
189. Schumacher, I. C. 1915. *Univ. Calif. Publ. Zool.* **16**: 95.
190. Stammer, H. J. 1935. *Arch. f. Protistenk.* **84**: 518.
191. Steuer, A. 1928. *Sitzb. Akad. Wiss. Wien.* (I) **137**: 297.
192. Stolte, H. A. 1924. *Arch. f. Protistenk.* **48**: 145.
193. Strelkow, A. 1929. *Arch. f. Protistenk.* **68**: 503.
194. ―― 1929. *Zool. Anz.* **83**: 63.
195. ―― 1931. *Arch. f. Protistenk.* **75**: 191.
196. ―― 1931. *Arch. f. Protistenk.* **75**: 221.
197. ―― 1931. *Zool. Anz.* **94**: 37.
198. Stuart, C. A., G. W. Kidder and A. M. Griffin 1939. *Physiol. Zool.* **12**: 348.
199. Studitsky, A. N. 1932. *Arch. f. Protistenk.* **76**: 188.
200. Summers, F. M. 1938. *Biol. Bull.* **74**: 41.
201. ―― and G. W. Kidder 1936. *Arch. f. Protistenk.* **86**: 379.
202. Swarczewsky, B. 1928. *Arch. f. Protistenk.* **61**: 185.
203. ―― 1928. *Arch. f. Protistenk.* **61**: 349.
204. ―― 1928. *Arch. f. Protistenk.* **62**: 41.
205. ―― 1928. *Arch. f. Protistenk.* **63**: 1.
206. ―― 1928. *Arch. f. Protistenk.* **63**: 362.
207. ―― 1928. *Arch. f. Protistenk.* **64**: 44.
208. Swezey, W. W. 1934. *J. Morph.* **56**: 621.
209. Szabó, M. 1936. *Arch. f. Protistenk.* **86**: 306.
210. Tannreuther, G. W. 1926. *Biol. Bull.* **51**: 303.
211. Taylor, C. V. and W. H. Furgason 1938. *Arch. f. Protistenk.* **90**: 320.
212. Thompson, S., D. Kirkegaard and T. L. Jahn 1947. *Trans. Amer. Micr. Soc.* **66**: 315.
213. Turner, J. P. 1937. *Trans. Amer. Micr. Soc.* **56**: 447.
214. Villeneuve-Brachon, S. 1940. *Arch. Zool. Exp. Gén.* **82**: 1.
215. Visscher, J. P. 1923. *Biol. Bull.* **45**: 113.
216. Watson, J. M. 1940. *J. Roy. Micr. Soc.* (Ser. III) **60**: 207.
217. Weill, R. 1929. *Arch. Zool. Exp. Gén.* **69** (N. et R.): 12.
218. Wenrich, D. H. 1928. *Trans. Amer. Micr. Soc.* **47**: 275.
219. ―― 1929. *Trans. Amer. Micr. Soc.* **48**: 221.
220. ―― 1929. *Trans. Amer. Micr. Soc.* **48**: 352.
221. ―― 1929. *Biol. Bull.* **56**: 390.
222. Wermel, E. 1928. *Arch. f. Protistenk.* **64**: 419.
223. Weyer, G. 1930. *Arch. f. Protistenk.* **71**: 139.
224. Wichterman, R. 1942. *Carneg. Inst. Wash. Publ.* **524**: 105.
225. Woodhead, A. E. 1928. *J. Parasitol.* **14**: 177.
226. Woodruff, L. L. and H. Spencer 1922. *J. Exp. Zool.* **35**: 189.
227. Young, D. B. 1922. *J. Exp. Zool.* **36**: 353.
228. Zick, K. 1928. *Ztschr. f. wiss. Zool.* **132**: 355.

VIII

Physiology

NUTRITIONAL REQUIREMENTS OF PROTOZOA

Pure cultures as material for research

THE ESTABLISHMENT OF various species in cultures free from other microorganisms opened a new era in the study of protozoan nutrition, making possible for the first time a realistic approach to the determination of basal food requirements. As a result, the investigation of metabolic activities in Protozoa is steadily expanding, and is leading to increasingly precise interpretations.

One of the important factors in this rapidly developing field has been the availability of many phytoflagellates in pure culture. For this, much credit is due E. G. Pringsheim[1] whose unfailing determination was responsible for maintaining an invaluable collection intact through a number of trying years. The phytoflagellates are particularly favorable material for investigation because their absolute requirements are much less extensive than those of higher Protozoa. Consequently, they afford the most direct routes to the determination of mineral requirements, and also the need for certain vitamins and organic foods. The relatively simple requirements of certain phytoflagellates (Table 8. 1), in contrast to the complex brews needed by higher Protozoa, also should expedite the study of metabolic pathways. Furthermore, the diversity of phytoflagellates, with respect to the possession or lack of chlorophyll and the presence or absence of holozoic habits, encourages consideration of the evolutionary and taxonomic aspects of protozoan nutrition.

Until recently, ciliates and Zoomastigophorea had been grown only in broths of unknown chemical composition which endangered the validity of conclusions concerning basal food requirements. The development of almost completely defined media (Table 8. 1) for at least a few of these higher Protozoa (121, 282, 349, 540, 568) insures much the same results as those now obtainable with many phytoflagellates.

Aside from the intrinsic interest to protozoologists, the study of protozoan nutrition promises significant contributions to the general fields of biochemistry and physiology. In the study of plant nutrition, the rapidly growing chlorophyll-bearing flagellates are readily adaptable to the investigation of various fundamental problems. The study of animal nutrition might be served in the same way by the typical animals among the Protozoa. As microscopic animals, which approach bacteria in rates of growth and ease of handling, Protozoa in pure cultures also offer ma-

---

[1] Pringsheim, E. G. 1946. Pure Cultures of Algae (Cambridge University Press).

TABLE 8. 1. CONSTITUENTS OF CULTURE MEDIA FOR THE COLORLESS PHYTOFLAGELLATE, *CHILOMONAS PARAMECIUM*, AND THE CILIATE, *TETRAHYMENA PYRIFORMIS*, STRAIN E (121)

Chilomonas paramecium	*Tetrahymena*	
NH_4Cl	Arginine	riboflavin
$(NH_4)_2SO_4$	histidine	pteroylglutamic acid
KH_2PO_4	isoleucine	biotin
$MgCl_2 \cdot 6H_2O$	leucine	thiamine
$CaCl_2 \cdot 2H_2O$	lysine	choline
$FeCl_3 \cdot 6H_2O$	methionine	yeast nucleic acid
Acetate (or ethyl alcohol)	phenylalanine	protogen
Thiamine	serine	$MgSO_4 \cdot 7H_2O$
	threonine	K_2HPO_4
	tryptophane	$CaCl_2 \cdot 2H_2O$
	valine	$FeCl_3 \cdot 6H_2O$
	dextrose	$Fe(NH_4)_2(SO_4)_2 \cdot 6H_2O$
	sodium acetate	$CuCl_2 \cdot 2H_2O$
	pantothenate	$MnCl_2 \cdot 4H_2O$
	nicotinamide	$ZnCl_2$
	pyridoxine	

(In addition to the listed components, various trace elements are present as impurities.)

terial for studying animal metabolism under conditions controllable to a degree not attained with tissues of higher animals. In addition, precise control of the food supply favors use of these organisms in the search for new vitamins, as in the discovery of protogen (540), as well as in microbiological assays of known growth-factors (230, 579) and amino acids (494). To the parasitologist and the pathologist, parasitic Protozoa in pure cultures offer unique opportunities for correlating metabolic activities of parasites with susceptibilities to chemotherapeutic agents and with reactions of the host's tissues to infections. To the explorer, these organisms extend a challenge to trace nutritional evolution from the possibly complete synthesis of needed vitamins to an essentially complete dependence upon external sources. Did plant-like Protozoa suddenly become "animals," with wholesale loss of synthetic abilities, or did they lose their original abilities one by one as evolution tempted them toward the animal kingdom? Or have the phytoflagellates arisen from more animal-like Protozoa, acquiring in their evolution various synthetic powers unknown to their ancestors?

General types of nutrition

For many years, general types of nutrition were classified merely as *autotrophic* (or holophytic), *saprozoic,* and *holozoic,* the last two representing varieties of heterotrophic nutrition. By definition, autotrophs could grow in inorganic media while heterotrophs required organic foods. With the exception of saprozoic types, Protozoa probably are not limited to one method in a natural environment. Chlorophyll-bearing species are often saprozoic and some can grow in darkness. A number of the green flagellates also ingest solid food, while typically holozoic organisms also may carry on saprozoic nutrition. The relative importance of one method or another depends largely upon environmental conditions.

The ecological classification of Kolkwitz and Marsson (301) divides Protozoa into *katharobes,* living in water containing almost no organic matter; and *saprobes,* found in water containing appreciable quantities of organic matter. Saprobes are divided into *oligosaprobes, mesosaprobes,* and *polysaprobes,* living in the presence of small, moderate, and large amounts of organic matter. This classification involves oxygen relationships as well as food supply, since katharobes are typically aerobic, while polysaprobes are more probably anaerobes or facultative anaerobes.

The earlier results with pure cultures soon demonstrated that these older concepts were inadequate. For instance, it became clear that the term, *autotroph,* could no longer be applied automatically to any green flagellate that occurs naturally in fairly pure water exposed to light. In fact, it is not yet certain that the existence of complete autotrophs, as originally defined, has been demonstrated. Furthermore, some of the "saprozoic" flagellates proved to be "autotrophic" with respect to nitrogen sources, although needing organic foods as a source of energy. This situation furnished the stimulus for several more modern classifications of protozoan nutrition (99, 176, 343, 358, 459). Although such classifications were a distinct improvement over the older systems and were a convenience in discussions, it now appears that even the more modern classifications have a tendency to oversimplify protozoan nutrition. From present indications, food and vitamin requirements of Protozoa will show many variations from species to species, so that much more information will be needed before definitive classification can be attempted.

The determination of food requirements

Two general methods have been followed in the study of protozoan food requirements. In one procedure the experimental media have been the simplest ones which would support growth in serial transfers. In such media, growth is often at a minimum and the organisms do little more than maintain themselves in successive transfers. In the other general procedure, media have been devised to maintain growth at a maximum and any constituent which cannot be omitted is considered essential to growth. This method is based upon the generalization that growth of any species will reach a maximum when all conditions are optimal—qualitative and quantitative aspects of the substrate, concentrations of stimulatory and essential growth-factors, concentrations of essential minerals, and non-dietary environmental factors.

On a theoretical basis, the first procedure might seem to offer the more direct analysis. In a medium reduced to bare essentials, it might be possible to recognize species capable of synthesizing required materials at a rate so slow that growth could never reach the maximum attainable in a rich medium. In the second procedure, with maximal growth as the goal, slow synthesis of a particular factor might conceivably be overlooked. In practice, however, the first method has certain limitations. Validity of the results obviously depends upon purity of the reagents and cleanliness of the culture vessels. In addition, contamination of the medium with dust or with volatile materials from the atmosphere of a laboratory could be a possibly serious source of error. Even minute contaminations might turn

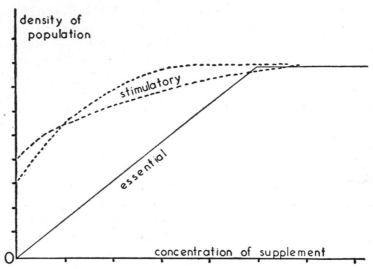

Fig. 8. 1. Hypothetical growth responses of a test organism to essential and stimulatory growth-factors.

the balance in favor of slight growth, with resulting faulty interpretations of experimental data. Hence, it is essential, in following the first procedure, to take all possible precautions. In the use of media which support maximal growth, the influence of minute contaminations would be less likely to account for positive instead of negative results. Furthermore, the response to graded increments of a given growth-factor can be traced over a wide range of growth. An approximately linear growth-response to a vitamin or a mineral in concentrations ranging from zero to an optimum (Fig. 8. 1) would indicate that the factor is essential. Omission of a stimulatory substance, on the other hand, would decrease growth but not prevent it completely.

Autotrophic nutrition

This general variety of nutrition,[2] in which inorganic nitrogen is adequate for growth, is sometimes considered a primitive type which was gradually lost during the "regressive" evolution of heterotrophs. Another

TABLE 8. 2. REPORTED CASES OF "AUTOTROPHIC" NUTRITION IN FLAGELLATES

Species	"Chemoauto-trophic"	"Photoauto-trophic"	Heteroauto-trophic
CRYPTOMONADIDA			
Chilomonas paramecium	NC(390)		NC(390)
Chilomonas paramecium			CP(220)
Chilomonas paramecium			*NC(354)
Chilomonas paramecium	NC(73)		NC(73)
PHYTOMONADIDA			
Chlamydomonas agloëformis		CP(340)	
Chlorogonium elongatum		CP(321)	
C. euchlorum		CP(321)	
Eudorina elegans		NC(108)	
Haematococcus pluvialis		CP(340)	
Haematococcus pluvialis		*CP(420)	*CP(420)
Lobomonas piriformis	CP(422)	CP(422)	CP(422)
Polytoma caudatum			*CP(352)
P. obtusum			NC(355)
P. ocellatum			*NC(353)
P. uvella			CP(340, 452)
P. uvella			NC(355)
Polytomella caeca			*NC(353)
EUGLENIDA			
Astasia longa (Jahn strain)	NC(505)		NC(503)
Euglena anabaena		CP(105, 175,	
Euglena anabaena		NC(109)	
E. gracilis		CP(104, 189)	NC(504)
E. klebsii		CP(105)	
E. stellata		CP(105)	
E. viridis		CP(177), NC(508)	

* Supplementary growth-factors said to be required; CP, cotton plugs used in culture tubes or flasks; NC, glass-covered culture vessels.

view (210, 411) is that the evolution of autotrophic organisms has involved the acquisition of synthetic abilities lacking in more primitive ancestral types which were dependent upon the environment for critical

[2] In this chapter, the following terms will be applied to species which can obtain their required nitrogen from inorganic sources: (1) *photoautotroph*, or photosynthetic autotroph, utilizing the energy of light; (2) *chemoautotroph*, or chemosynthetic autotroph, obtaining energy from inorganic substrates; (3) *heteroautotroph*, requiring an organic source of energy (e.g., acetate, lactate, ethanol).

organic materials. Whether autotrophic nutrition should be considered primitive or not, the food requirements of the supposedly autotrophic phytoflagellates differ considerably from those of other Protozoa.

Chemoautotrophic, photoautotrophic, and heteroautotrophic nutrition have been reported in various phytoflagellates (Table 8. 2). Three species have been grown under conditions suggesting chemoautotrophy—two of the three in glass-covered culture vessels. The investigation of chemoautotrophic nutrition illustrates, to an extreme degree, the difficulties inherent in the use of media supplying a bare minimum for growth. After an adequate number of transfers, it may be concluded that the food supply of the organism is limited to constituents of the test medium—*plus* any contaminants absorbed from glassware, introduced by way of distilled water, stock solutions and dust or absorbed from the air. The first obvious refinement in technique is the elimination of cotton plugs from culture tubes or flasks. Although bleached cotton may be inactive as a source of thiamine or its components (509), plugs of this material contribute significantly to the growth of *Chilomonas paramecium* in an inorganic medium and the effect is not eliminated by the addition of thiamine in excess (73). Organic pollution of distilled water and stock solutions by bacterial growth can be avoided by aseptic techniques or by the use of a volatile preservative (227). However, other difficulties remain. Certain inorganic salts used for culture media contain organic contaminants, which in terms of carbon balance could account for the observed growth in an experimental medium (73). Furthermore, there must be a demonstrable inorganic source of energy. In the case of *Chilomonas paramecium*, there is no significant oxidation of ammonia (73), although tests have not been reported for several other "chemoautotrophs." Accordingly, it must be concluded that the evidence for chemoautotrophy in Protozoa is still inadequate, and that under experimental conditions now attainable it is seemingly impossible to limit a flagellate to chemoautotrophic nutrition.

So far as photoautotrophic nutrition is concerned, it should be much less difficult to prove that organic contaminants are an unimportant factor in growth. In this connection, the failure of *Chlamydomonas moewusii* to grow without both light and carbon dioxide—even in inorganic media supplemented with a variety of nitrogen sources, vitamins and oxidizable carbon sources—seems very significant (315). Investigations are still handicapped, however, by inadequate knowledge of qualitative and quantitative mineral requirements. "Photoautotrophic" nutrition has been reported in several Phytomonadida and Euglenida (Table 8. 2). In most cases, culture vessels have been plugged with cotton, but *Eudorina elegans* (108) has been maintained in all-glass vessels. Such results (109) also have supported earlier observations on *Euglena anabaena*. Similar confirmation is needed for other reports of photoautotrophy. All-glass vessels do not eliminate all potential organic contaminants, but it is possible that such impurities could not account for the observed growth without cotton plugs.

In contrast to *Euglena anabaena, E. gracilis* is said to require the pyrimidine component (353), and *E. pisciformis,* both the pyrimidine and thiazole components of thiamine (107) for growth as "photoautotrophs." Whether or not any or all of the currently reported photoautotrophs will eventually prove to be such, it appears at present that certain green flagellates may not be photoautotrophs. For example, failures to demonstrate "photoautotrophy" have been reported for *Euglena deses* (105, 188). Such failures could have been caused by inadequate culture media. On the other hand, *E. deses* may represent a more advanced stage in the type of regressive evolution suggested for *E. gracilis* (353) and *E. pisciformis* (107).

Heteroautotrophic nutrition was first noted by Pringsheim (452) in *Polytoma uvella.* These observations have been repeated and comparable findings have been reported for *P. obtusum* (348, 353, 355). The related flagellates, *Polytoma caudatum, P. ocellatum,* and *Polytomella caeca,* have been grown in inorganic salt and acetate media with supplementary growth-factors (352, 353, 354). More recently, *Astasia longa* (503), *Euglena gracilis* (504), and *Lobomonas piriformis* (422) have been maintained as heteroautotrophs, the green species being incubated in darkness. *Chilomonas paramecium* also is a facultative heteroautotroph (73, 220, 390), although there is one report that supplementary growth-factors are required under such conditions (354). At present, it appears that certain flagellates are facultative heteroautotrophs for which thiamine and possibly other vitamins are stimulatory but not essential, while other species require one or more supplementary growth-factors under such conditions. This possibility needs further investigation with careful attention to mineral requirements and with a variety of substrates.

Mineral requirements

In contrast to older beliefs that some ten or eleven elements are essential to life, modern investigations have detected about fifty elements in the tissues of different animals and plants. It remains to be determined just how many are essential and how many are chance accumulations conditioned by a particular chemical environment. So far as the Protozoa are concerned, little is known about qualitative and quantitative mineral requirements. For microorganisms in general, certain metal requirements are related to particular enzyme systems. Such metals may be integral parts of enzymes or may serve as "activators" whose exact functions are not yet understood. Consequently, it is at least conceivable that certain mineral requirements may vary quantitatively, and possibly even qualitatively, in the presence of different substrates.

Growth in organic media cannot be expected to yield many clues because such materials contain quite a variety of trace elements. In yeast extract, for example, barium, bismuth, boron, calcium, chromium, copper, gold, iron, magnesium, manganese, phosphorus, potassium, silicon, silver, and strontium have been demonstrated by spectroscopic analysis, and a preparation of asparagine has contained as many as 21 trace metals (483). Such difficulties have been illustrated in the investigation of mineral requirements in *Tetrahymena pyriformis* (292).

For various phytoflagellates, culture media have been prepared from analyzed reagents and used in all-glass culture vessels. Within such limits of accuracy, the composition of the medium is known except for possibly significant contaminations from glassware or other sources. Some of these media contain, as impurities in the salts, barium, cobalt, chromium, copper, gold, iron, manganese, sodium, zinc, and other metals, in addition to the intentionally supplied calcium, magnesium, phosphorus, potassium, sulfur, chlorine, ammonium salts, and carbon dioxide. It has been possible, from such starting points, to detect a few trace-mineral requirements. The determination of others, merely by selecting different salts so as to exclude particular elements, has been impossible.

The purification of reagents permits some further progress. The removal of certain trace metals has been accomplished with chelating agents, such as 8-hydroxyquinoline, which form metal complexes soluble in chloroform or ethyl acetate (130). In addition, several other methods for purifying important components of culture media are available (229), and a number of purified elements and reagents can be obtained commercially.[3]

Additional advantages are promised by the use of non-toxic chelating agents in culture media (226, 229). Such substances as citrate and ethylenediamine-tetraacetic acid, which form soluble and fairly stable metal complexes, minimize and tend to eliminate certain technical difficulties. A metal-chelate complex forms a sort of metal "buffer" with an action somewhat analogous to that of pH-buffers. Since the precipitation of metals as hydroxides, phosphates, or sulfates is prevented, it is possible to add quantities sufficient for heavy growth. Metals which are toxic above certain concentrations also can be supplied at levels favoring heavy growth without danger of toxic effects. Aside from such general improvement of the simpler culture media, chelating agents can be of assistance in analyzing mineral requirements. The addition of a chelating compound to a medium containing essential trace metals in minimal amounts may induce a metal deficiency which will prevent growth. Incidentally, materials often supplied as substrates—α-amino acids, glycerol, malate, ammonium salts—also may be active enough as chelating agents to induce

---

[3] Johnson, Matthey & Co., Ltd. 1947. Catalogue of standardized substances for spectrography, chemical analysis and research (London).

metal deficiencies. Therefore, they might be considered of little value to the organism unless allowance is made for chelating activity. Intentional induction of an inhibitory metal deficiency makes it possible, by trial and error, to identify various trace elements which seem to be essential (229). After preliminary qualitative observations, individual requirements can be analyzed quantitatively by adding an excess of all needed elements except one and then determining the amounts of this element which will compensate for graded increases in the chelating agent. A curve plotted from such data and then extrapolated to zero chelate should give a fairly good approximation of the basal requirement for a particular metal. There remains to be considered the situation in which a trace element minutely contaminating a supposedly required metal may actually be the essential factor (229). This complication can be eliminated, if elimination is possible, only by the use of highly purified metal sources. However, the failure of progressive purifications to alter the apparent requirements quantitatively would suggest that the original indications were valid.

The older techniques were adequate only to the extent of indicating qualitative requirements for certain metals in a few species. Calcium—apparently needed by *Euglena anabaena* (109), *E. stellata* (105), *Hyalogonium klebsii* (457), *Chilomonas paramecium* (395), *Oikomonas termo* (192), and *Tetrahymena pyriformis* (184)—may prove to be a general requirement. Magnesium, necessary for *Chilomonas paramecium* (395) and *Tetrahymena pyriformis* (292), is a component of carboxylase and should be a general requirement. As a constituent of chlorophyll, magnesium also is obviously essential to green flagellates. Iron was found to be a requirement of *Chilomonas paramecium* (220), *Eudorina elegans* (108), *Euglena anabaena* (109), *Polytoma obtusum* and *P. uvella* (355), and *Tetrahymena pyriformis* (184, 287). Since this metal is a constituent of cytochromes, cytochrome oxidase, catalase, and peroxidase, it may be impossible to find Protozoa which do not need iron unless it can be shown that obligate anaerobes have absolutely no iron requirements. Phosphorus, essential for *Chilomonas paramecium* (423) and *Tetrahymena pyriformis* (292), is obviously a general requirement for phosphorylation of metabolites and vitamins. Observations on the phosphate cycle in *T. pyriformis* (123, 497) indicate that during the lag phase of growth there is a rapid liberation of inorganic phosphate from organic sources, whereas uptake of inorganic phosphate is more characteristic of logarithmic growth. Manganese, which favors growth of *Euglena anabaena* in inorganic media (109, 174), and apparently participates in oxidation of pyruvate and other metabolites by *Plasmodium gallinaceum* (535), may be generally needed as an activator of phosphorylases and peptidases and possibly other enzymes. Potassium, required by *Chilomonas paramecium* (423) and *T. pyriformis* (292), seems to be needed in certain phosphorylations and probably is a general requirement. The possible significance of sodium, apparently needed by *C. paramecium* (423), is uncertain. Sulfur, as a constituent of several vitamins and amino acids, is presumably essential. A variety of inorganic salts, cystine, glutathione, and cysteine are satisfactory sources for *C. paramecium* (392). Silicon stimulates growth of *C. paramecium* (398) and prolongs life in a phosphate-deficient medium (396). Whether this effect is attributable to silicon or to impurities (73) in the silicate used, remains to be determined. Vanadium also seems to accelerate growth of *C. paramecium* (25). A need for copper, apparently a component of ascorbic and phenol oxidases, became apparent in *Tetrahymena pyriformis* when natural products were replaced by purified constituents of culture media (287). Zinc, apparently involved in aldolase, carbonic anhydrase, and uricase activity, has often been included in culture media on the assumption that it is essential to protozoan growth. Cobalt, as a constituent of vitamin B_{12} (cyano-cobalamin), is required by *Euglena gracilis* (230) and probably various other Protozoa. Molybdenum, which accelerates nitrogen-fixation by bacteria and seems to be essential for certain molds, needs investigation as a protozoan requirement.

In summary, fragmentary evidence now indicates that, in addition to carbon, hydrogen, oxygen, and nitrogen, at least twelve other elements—calcium, cobalt, copper, iron, magnesium, manganese, phosphorus, potassium, silicon, sodium, sulfur, and vanadium—are either stimulatory or essential to growth of certain Protozoa. In addition, there are reasons for believing that others, such as molybdenum and zinc, may be important. Highly purified chemicals and the newer techniques of investigation may expand the list of required trace elements, and should clarify the status of some of them in protozoan metabolism. Even so, a complete list of the basal requirements apparently remains unobtainable with the inorganic materials and culture vessels now available.

Vitamin requirements[4]

The requirements of many Protozoa, although incompletely known, are probably comparable to those of Metazoa. *Colpoda steinii* (*duodenaria*) needs more than five vitamins, *Tetrahymena pyriformis* needs at least nine or ten, and not less than six are important in the metabolism of malarial parasites. At the other extreme, a few phytoflagellates have been grown in media apparently free from vitamins. There is every reason to believe that such differences depend upon the ability or inability to synthesize particular vitamins.

Among the phytoflagellates, *Chilomonas paramecium,* in an acetate, inorganic salt and thiamine medium, synthesizes nicotinic acid and the diphosphopyridine nucleotide (DPN, or coenzyme I) which contains nicotinamide and adenine (223). Microbiological assays of comparable cultures have confirmed the synthesis of nicotinic acid and demonstrated that

---

[4] Several reviews of the earlier literature are available (99, 180, 347, 348).

of pyridoxal and riboflavin (207). In addition, growth of *Tetrahymena pyriformis* on *C. paramecium* and on *Polytoma ocellatum* in similar culture media (182) suggests that these flagellates are able to synthesize a variety of vitamins needed by the ciliate. Therefore, it may be assumed, in the absence of evidence to the contrary, that metabolic activities of the phytoflagellates involve essentially the same vitamins as do those of the higher Protozoa. Under favorable conditions, which must include a medium satisfying essential mineral requirements, some species may be able to synthesize all of their needed vitamins. Present indications, that certain other phytoflagellates cannot synthesize at least one or two vitamins from simple materials, raise interesting possibilities. Perhaps it will be feasible, in this group, to trace a series of stages in the development of multiple vitamin requirements (or multiple losses in synthetic powers) as represented by ciliates, for example. As the scope of the pure-culture techniques is broadened, the ability to visualize vitamin requirements on a taxonomic framework may prove very interesting—possibly to the extent of furnishing clues to the phylogeny of the higher Protozoa. From the practical standpoint, the determination of vitamin requirements for many different Protozoa may reveal unsuspected new vitamins and may also furnish additional tools for microbiological assays. Both possibilities have already been realized to a limited extent.

Some information on vitamin requirements is now at hand for a number of species (Table 8. 3). Although the present data may be definitive for a few phytoflagellates, this is far from true for nearly all of the other Protozoa which have been investigated.

Thiamine. This vitamin is an absolute requirement for certain strains of ciliates and parasitic flagellates and probably for malarial parasites. The case of *Chilomonas paramecium* is still puzzling. Certain strains apparently require either thiamine or its thiazole and pyrimidine components, while others have been grown in all-glass vessels without added thiamine on acetate as a substrate (73, 390). Under such conditions, supplementary thiamine markedly increases growth on acetate and becomes essential instead of stimulatory when pyruvate is substituted for acetate (73). Thiamine is stimulatory for *Polytoma obtusum* and *P. uvella* in simple media, although both will grow without the added vitamin (348). In the same types of media, certain other colorless phytomonads need thiazole or both the pyrimidine and thiazole components of thiamine (Table 8. 3). Several substituted thiazoles and pyrimidine also are active for *Polytomella caeca* and *Chilomonas paramecium* (348). In addition, heavy growth of *Euglena gracilis* var. *bacillaris,* in an amino acid and inorganic salt medium containing vitamin B_{12}, depends upon an adequate concentration of thiamine (230).

Riboflavin. Earlier reports of growth-acceleration in ciliates (120, 181, 183, 283) were soon followed by evidence that this vitamin is essential for

TABLE 8. 3. VITAMIN REQUIREMENTS OF VARIOUS PROTOZOA

Species	Vitamins
PHYTOMASTIGOPHOREA	
Chilomonas paramecium	A, B (353); none (73)
Euglena gracilis	B (353); N (230)
E. pisciformis	A, B (107)
Haematococcus pluvialis	C, K (420); none (340)
Polytoma caudatum	A (352, 353)
P. obtusum	none (355)
P. ocellatum	A (353)
P. uvella	none (355)
Polytomella caeca	A, B (351)
ZOOMASTIGOPHOREA	
Eutrichomastix colubrorum	K, L, Q (49)
Leishmania agamae	M, Q (366)
L. ceramodactyli	M, Q (366)
L. donovani	K, M, Q (366)
L. tropica	K, M, Q (366)
Leptomonas ctenocephali	M (366)
L. pyrrhocoris	M (366)
Strigomonas culicidarum	C, M (366); C, D, E, M (566)
S. fasciculata	C, M (366)
S. muscidarum	M (366)
S. oncopelti	C (366)
Trichomonas columbae	K (50), L (47)
T. foetus	K, L, Q (48)
T. gallinarum	K, Q (52)
T. vaginalis	F (303), L (537)
Trypanosoma cruzi	K, M, Q (366)
T. lewisi	M (432)
T. rabinowitchi	M (410)
SARCODINA	
Acanthamoeba castellanii	A, B (345)
SPOROZOA	
Plasmodium gallinaceum	c, g, j (535)
P. knowlesi	d, j, p (11)
P. lophurae	f, h (556)
CILIATEA	
Colpidium campylum	Q (437)
Colpoda duodenaria	C, E, G (545); D, F, Q (139)
Pleurotricha lanceolata	D, E, Q (317)
Stylonychia pustulata	D, E, Q (317)
Tetrahymena pyriformis	C (120, 122, 179, 183, 357); D (179, 289, 290); E, F, G (121, 289, 290); I (122, 275); J (284); O (121, 540)

KEY: A, thiazole component of thiamine; B, pyrimidine component of thiamine; C, thiamine; D, riboflavin; E, pyridoxine; F, pantothenic acid; G, nicotinic acid or nicotinamide; H, biotin; I, pteroylglutamic acid; J, nucleic acid components (purines, pyrimidines); K, ascorbic acid; L, sterols; M, hematin; N, cyano-cobalamin (vitamin B_{12}); O, protogen; P, *p*-aminobenzoic acid; Q, unidentified growth-factors. Small letters indicate *probable* requirements.

Colpoda steinii (*duodenaria*) (139) and *Tetrahymena pyriformis* (179, 289, 290) and probably for malarial parasites (11). The synthesis of riboflavin by *Chilomonas paramecium* (207) suggests the probable importance of this vitamin in phytoflagellate metabolism.

The pyridoxine complex. In the earlier investigations, a stimulation of growth by pyridoxine was noted in several ciliates (120, 283, 317). A ciliate, *Colpoda steinii* (545), also was the first protozoon shown to need pyridoxine. *Tetrahymena pyriformis* has since been found to require pyridoxine, pyridoxal, or pyridoxamine, the two derivatives being 100-500 times as active as pyridoxine (289), a relationship similar to that previously reported for certain bacteria. Pyridoxine proved to be a component of "Factor II" (287), a concentrate of natural origin previously found essential to growth of *T. pyriformis* (92). Since pyridoxine inhibits the action of quinine and atebrin against *Plasmodium cathemerium* and *P. lophurae* in ducklings (519), the vitamin probably is a requirement of malarial parasites. Among the phytoflagellates, *Chilomonas paramecium* synthesizes pyridoxal (207).

Pantothenic acid. In the first tests on Protozoa, Elliott (117) found that growth of *T. pyriformis* was accelerated, within the pH range 5.5-6.5, by a concentrate of pantothenic acid. Garnjobst, Tatum, and Taylor (139) next found pantothenate essential for *Colpoda steinii,* and it now appears that *Tetrahymena pyriformis* has the same requirement (290, 121). Supplementary evidence involves inhibition of growth of *T. pyriformis* by α-methyl-pantothenic acid and reversal of the effect by pantothenic acid (502). This vitamin also favors survival of *P. lophurae* (556) *in vitro.* Furthermore, a pantothenate deficiency in chickens decreases the severity of infections with *P. gallinaceum,* and dosage with certain analogues is more effective than quinine therapy (28). Pantothenate analogues are active likewise against *Trichomonas foetus, T. gallinae,* and *T. vaginalis* in pure cultures (256). Supplementary pantothenate in the diet of rats also increases the populations of *Eimeria nieschulzi* (15).

Nicotinic acid. *Colpoda steinii* (545) was the first protozoan species shown to require nicotinic acid. Later on, *Tetrahymena pyriformis,* at first believed to grow without nicotinic acid (283), was found to need the vitamin (290). Diphosphopyridine nucleotide (DPN), which contains nicotinamide, also has been demonstrated in *T. pyriformis* (512). As a component of DPN and TPN, nicotinamide also is involved in oxidative metabolism of *Plasmodium gallinaceum* (535) and *Trypanosoma hippicum* (194). Among the phytoflagellates, growth of *Eugena viridis* in an asparagine medium (110) and that of *Chilomonas paramecium* as a heteroautotroph (425) are stimulated by nicotinic acid. The latter also synthesizes this vitamine (207, 223).

Biotin. Although a biotin deficiency has decreased division-rate and reduced the density of populations (283), evidence that this vitamin is essential for *Tetrahymena pyriformis* is still lacking (290). However, it seems to be important in the metabolism of malarial parasites (535, 556).

Pteroylglutamic acid and p-*aminobenzoic acid.* In the first report on Protozoa, Kidder (275) found this vitamin essential to growth of *T. pyriformis.* Calculated on the basis of free pteroylglutamic acid, the vitamin has about the same activity as it conjugates, pteroylglutamylglutamic acid and pteroylhexaglutamic acid (289). Apparently, *p*-aminobenzoic acid cannot be substituted for folic acid. This ability to use conjugates and the holozoic nature of *T. pyriformis* suggest the probable value of this ciliate in assays of natural products.

The action of sulfadiazine against *P. gallinaceum* in chickens is reversed by pteroylglutamic acid (166); *p*-aminobenzoic acid has the same effect on sulfonamides used against *P. lophurae* (520) and *P. gallinaceum* (376). Some of these sulfonamides, such as sulfanilamide (68, 562) and sulfathiazole (562), inhibit oxygen consumption of malarial parasites. In addition to the evidence obtained with analogues, growth of *P. knowlesi* is stimulated *in vitro* by *p*-aminobenzoic acid (8, 11). For the phytoflagellates, a reversal of sulfanilamide action by *p*-aminobenzoic acid has been reported in *Polytomella caeca* (359).

Nucleic acid derivatives. Ribonucleic acid contains certain purines (adenine, guanine), pyrimidines (cytosine, uracil) and D-ribose; in desoxyribonucleic acid, uracil is replaced by thymine and D-ribose by D-2-desoxyribose. Several nucleic acid derivatives have been tested on *Tetrahymena pyriformis* (284). Together with folic acid, the purines (guanine apparently being essential) form the active components of "Factor I," an undefined concentrate previously found essential to growth of *T. pyriformis* (92). Although adenine and hypoxanthine show a guanine-sparing action (286), neither can replace guanine. However, the inhibitory action of an adenine analogue (adenazolo) on growth of *T. pyriformis* is reversed specifically by adenine (293). Among various substituted purines, 1-methyl-guanine is about 75 per cent as active as guanine, several are inert, and others are inhibitory (291).

"Factor III," another concentrate which appeared necessary to growth of *T. pyriformis,* has been resolved into the pyrimidine derivatives, uracil and cytosine, or their ribosides or ribonucleotides (281, 291, 293). *T. pyriformis* is believed to synthesize thymine from non-pyrimidine precursors in reactions involving pteroylglutamic acid (293), as reported previously for bacteria (539).

Ascorbic acid. Although a need for this vitamin has been attributed to *Haematococcus pluvialis* and several parasitic flagellates (Table 8. 3), there is at present no conclusive evidence that ascorbic acid is essential to growth of Protozoa.

Sterols. Several flagellates (Table 8. 3) require sterols, a requirement which may be satisfied by cholesterol or certain other sterols. Among 66 different sterols tested on *Trichomonas gallinae* (*T. columbae*), comparable activity was shown by cholesterol, cholestanol, sitosterol, and several others. Ergosterol was moderately active if not heated, whereas irradiated ergosterol ("vitamin D") was inactive (47). Cholesterol also seems to be required by *Entamoeba histolytica* (530) and is a possible requirement of *Trichomonas vaginalis* (537). Growth of *Colpidium campylum* is slower with certain concentrations of cholesterol but reaches a greater density than in the control medium (541).

Hematin. That species of *Trypanosoma* and related flagellates need blood in culture media was first noted many years ago. Later on Salle and Schmidt (498) found that, for *Leishmania tropica,* blood could be replaced by hemoglobin, which they suggested as a probable growth-factor. This question has been investigated extensively by M. Lwoff (349, 366), who has shown that certain Trypanosomidae can grow in ordinary peptone media while others require supplementary blood or a more active substitute, hematin (Table 8. 3). The latter are unable to synthesize porphyrin groups in the production of cytochrome, cytochrome oxidase, and related enzymes (347). *Strigomonas fasciculata* apparently can combine iron and exogenous protoporphyrin to produce heme (341). On the other hand, certain Trypanosomidae and free-living Protozoa containing the cytochrome system apparently can synthesize porphyrins from simpler materials.

Vitamin B_{12} (*cyano-cobalamin*). It is interesting that the first evidence for protozoan requirements has been obtained with a phytoflagellate. Vitamin B_{12}, or "cyanocobalamin" (265), tremendously stimulates growth of *Euglena gracilis* var. *bacillaris* in the presence of adequate thiamine and is believed to be an absolute requirement (230). These findings have extended earlier observations (225) that heavy growth of *E. gracilis* depends upon certain factors present in crude casein. This growth-response of *E. gracilis* has been applied to microbiological assay of cyano-cobalamin (230, 579).

Protogen. A previously undefined "Factor II," a concentrate of natural origin essential for *Tetrahymena pyriformis* (92), has been resolved into fractions IIA and IIB (540). The name, *protogen,* was proposed for Factor IIA, which is not identical with any known vitamin or with the "animal protein factor." Protogen, which may prove to be a fundamental requirement of animals, is unique as the first vitamin to be discovered through the study of protozoan growth requirements. The search for natural sources of protogen will be facilitated by the ability of *T. pyriformis* to digest complex foods as well as by its growth in media suitable for assays.

Biosynthesis of vitamins. The synthesis of vitamins by Protozoa has been suggested occasionally, but specific evidence has been presented in only a few cases. Among the phytoflagellates, experimental evidence is available for *Chilomonas paramecium* (182, 207, 224) and *Polytoma ocellatum* (182). There is also some presumptive evidence in the case of heteroautotrophs which have been grown without exogenous thiamine. Thiazole can replace thiamine in stimulating growth of *Polytoma caudatum* (352) and *P. ocellatum* (353), while the thiazole and pyrimidine components together replace the vitamin for *Polytomella caeca* (351). Several substituted thiazoles and pyrimidines also can be utilized instead of the natural components of thiamine (348). Although actual synthesis by a phytoflagellate has not been demonstrated, it is assumed that some species can produce thiamine from simple raw materials while others need thiazole or both components. In investigating such problems, composition of the medium must be considered carefully since the supply of trace elements, such as iron (348), and the nature of the substrate may be important factors in a potential synthesis. The significance of the substrate is suggested by failure of *Chilomonas paramecium* to grow on pyruvate without added thiamine, although the flagellate grows slowly on acetate in a thiamine-free medium (73). This is an interesting parallel to *Prototheca zopfi* which can oxidize acetate in a thiamine-deficient medium but apparently requires thiamine for utilization of pyruvate (4). In general, the burden of proof seems to rest upon those who would deny that phytoflagellates can synthesize a variety of vitamins. For the higher Protozoa, such assumptions are not justified because these organisms have been grown almost exclusively in chemically undefined media. So long as materials of natural origin are included, it is unsafe to assume that a particular vitamin has been eliminated from a culture medium.

Synthesis of thiamine from its thiazole and pyrimidine components has been reported for *Acanthamoeba castellanii* (345), and from unspecified intermediates in the case of *Tetrahymena pyriformis* (277). However, *A. castellanii* was grown in peptone media of unknown vitamin content, and the interpretation of the earlier data for *T. pyriformis* has been questioned (183, 184). Although more recent data have been supplied for the ciliate (278, 282), there is no conclusive evidence that either *A. castellanii* or *T. pyriformis* can synthesize thiamine.

The Trypanosomidae which need exogenous hematin presumably are unable to synthesize the porphyrins necessary to the formation of heme. Others, which possess the cytochrome system but do not require ready made porphyrins, obviously synthesize heme from simpler constituents of culture media. The problem of obtaining suitable raw materials is a minor one because such a substrate as acetate (450) may serve as a starting point. Syntheses of this nature may be assumed for *Chilomonas paramecium, Polytoma uvella, Astasia klebsii, Euglena gracilis,* and *Tetrahymena pyriformis,* for example. As a source of direct evidence, the hematin-requiring Trypanosomidae should be useful for microbiological assays.

The synthesis of nicotinic acid (207, 223), adenine (223), pyridoxal, and riboflavin (207) has been demonstrated in *Chilomonas paramecium*. Synthesis of riboflavin, pantothenic acid and probably of biotin has been reported for *Tetrahymena pyriformis* on the basis of microbiological assays (283), but these conclusions were later withdrawn (290). The synthesis of *p*-aminobenzoic acid and inositol by *T. pyriformis* has been reported on the basis of *Neurospora* assays (276). Synthesis of the former would seem to be no advantage to the ciliate since *p*-aminobenzoic acid apparently cannot replace pteroylglutamic acid as an absolute requirement.

The requirements of various groups

At present, little has been published on two major groups of the phytoflagellates,[5] the Chrysomonadida and Dinoflagellida. Earlier work on *Oikomonas termo* (192) and dinoflagellates (13) was interrupted, and although extensive investigations are in progress, the two orders offer quite a variety of unsolved nutritional problems. Both groups include colorless and chlorophyll-bearing species and a number of holozoic types, and both are represented in fresh and salt water. Representatives of two other orders, Heterochlorida and Chloromonadida, apparently are not yet available in pure cultures.

Cryptomonadida. So far, the chlorophyll-bearing cryptomonads have been neglected in favor of *Chilomonas paramecium*, several strains of which have been investigated. As nitrogen sources, ammonium salts are satisfactory, nitrate is inadequate (73), and utilization of nitrate has not been demonstrated. Reported chemoautotrophy (390) had not been confirmed (73). Although *C. paramecium* has been grown in glycine and acetate medium (186, 390), little is known about amino acids as nitrogen sources or their possible value as sources of both carbon and nitrogen.

Excellent carbon sources,[6] added to a basal inorganic medium supplemented with thiamine (or its components), include acetate, ethanol, lactate, and pyruvate (73, 222, 354). In such a medium, about 45 per cent of the available acetate is oxidized while the rest is assimilated (224). With-

---

[5] Current data on food requirements and metabolism of the phytoflagellates have been discussed by Hutner and Provasoli (228).

[6] Extending the earlier observation of Provasoli (467) with peptone media, B. K. Swanson (1951. M. S. Thesis, University of Iowa) has tested various alcohols as carbon sources for *Chilomonas paramecium* in a simple medium. Several straight-chain alcohols —ethyl, *n*-butyl, and to a lesser degree, hexyl alcohol—were good carbon sources. Methyl, *n*-propyl and *n*-amyl alcohols were inadequate for growth, and this was true also for certain alcohols with side-chains (secondary-butyl, tertiary-butyl, *iso*-amyl, etc.). Furthermore, these non-utilizable alcohols produced significant inhibition of growth when mixed with the utilizable alcohols.

out added thiamine, acetate has supported growth in all-glass culture vessels (73, 390)—about one per cent of the growth obtained with thiamine. In thiamine-supplemented acetate medium, growth of *C. paramecium* has been tripled by raising the carbon dioxide concentration from that of the atmosphere to 100 mm Hg at atmospheric pressure (428). Similar stimulation by carbon dioxide had previously been detected in peptone media (245). Certain alcohols (467), fatty acids (299, 467), and carbohydrates (321, 327) also accelerate growth in peptone media, although a number of these supplements have not yet been tested as carbon sources in heteroautotrophic nutrition.

Phytomonadida. As inorganic nitrogen sources in "photoautotorphic" nutrition, ammonium salts have been more satisfactory than nitrates for *Haematococcus pluvialis* (340) and *Lobomonas piriformis* (422). No appreciable differences have been reported for *Chlamydomonas agloeformis* (340), *Chlorogonium elongatum,* and *C. euchlorum* (321). However, comparative tests of nitrates and ammonium salts over an adequate range of salt and hydrogen-ion concentrations have not been reported.

In heteroautotrophic nutrition *Polytoma ocellatum* has been grown in a nitrate medium (353), but species of *Polytomella* and other species of *Polytoma* apparently are limited to an ammonium-N source. This situation deserves further investigation in view of Lwoff's (347) characterization of an autotroph as an organism which can reduce nitrate in an inorganic medium.

Organic nitrogen sources have not been investigated extensively but growth on asparagine or a single amino acid has been reported for species of *Chlamydomonas* and *Haematococcus* (340, 367), *Chlorogonium* (350, 457), *Lobomonas* in darkness (422), *Polytoma* (340, 360, 452, 458), and *Polytomella* (342, 455, 458).

Acetate, butyrate, and lactate are good carbon sources in heteroautotrophic nutrition. A number of other substrates probably would be satisfactory since salts of additional acids, including propionic, valerianic, and caproic (323, 456, 463, 464, 465, 466), and also certain alcohols (467) accelerate growth of various colorless species in peptone media. Certain carbohydrates also have stimulated growth of *Polytoma* (360, 361) and *Polytomella* (342) but may or may not be adequate substrates in heteroautotrophic nutrition. The ability to use an amino acid, as the sole source of nitrogen, carbon, and energy, has not yet been demonstrated.

Several green species—*Chlorogonium elongatum* (321), *C. euchlorum* (321, 350), *Lobomonas piriformis* (422), *Chlamydomonas agloeformis,* and *Haematococcus pluvialis* (367)—have been grown in darkness, particularly in peptone media supplemented with acetate, and are obviously facultative heterotrophs. Under such conditions, acetate is a rather satisfactory substitute for photosynthesis. On the other hand, *Chlamydomonas moewusii* is an obligate phototroph in a wide variety of media (315).

Euglenida. Further study of these flagellates should prove interesting because the order includes chlorophyll-bearing species, colorless saprozoic types (*Astasia, Menoidium,* etc.), and various holozoic genera (*Heteronema, Peranema,* etc.). Furthermore, such species as *Euglena anabaena, E. deses, E. klebsii, E. pisciformis,* and *E. stellata* have failed to grow in darkness (105), whereas *Euglena gracilis* grows well under such conditions (377, 460, 549). Although investigations on holozoic types are in progress, previous reports are limited to *Euglena* and *Astasia.*

Inorganic sources of nitrogen have been tested for several species of *Euglena* (104, 105, 109, 175, 177, 189, 377, 508). The available data indicate that ammonium salts are generally more satisfactory than nitrates. However, nitrates apparently are adequate for *Euglena anabaena* (109). Among the colorless Euglenida, *Astasia longa* has been maintained on ammonium-N (503).

Organic sources of nitrogen have been investigated for several species of *Euglena* (104, 105, 549). Asparagine and various amino acids have supported growth of one species or another, but several species have shown interesting differences in their apparent abilities to utilize particular amino acids (105). Possible relations of mineral requirements and pH of the basal media to the utilization of amino acids have not been investigated adequately.

The available information on carbon sources is based mainly on growth of Euglenida in peptone media, although acetate has supported slow growth of *Astasia longa* (503) and *Euglena gracilis* (504) in heteroautotrophic nutrition. A number of organic acids—including acetic, propionic, butyric, valerianic, caproic, *iso*-caproic, octylic, nonilic, lactic, and pyruvic—have stimulated growth of *Astasia* (456, 465, 466, 467) and *Euglena* (456, 467) in peptone medium. Growth of *Euglena* (332, 456, 467) and *Astasia* (456, 467) also is stimulated by certain alcohols, including ethyl, propyl, butyl and hexanol.

Protomastigida. Pure cultures of parasitic Protomastigida have been available for many years but most investigators have been interested in these flagellates as parasites rather than in their nutrition. However, the investigations of Marguerite Lwoff (349, 363, 366) on several parasites of insects showed that *Strigomonas oncopelti* grows well in peptone media while certain other species have more complex requirements. *S. fasciculata,* from mosquitoes, requires a small amount of blood or hematin as a supplement to peptone medium. *Leptomonas ctenocephali,* from the dogflea, requires such a supplement in higher concentrations (349). Specific requirements of *S. culicidarum* include at least nine amino acids, hematin, thiamine, riboflavin, pyridoxamine, trace minerals, and possibly two or three additional vitamins (567).

Certain Trypanosomidae of vertebrates require, in addition to hematin, other growth-factors not supplied by peptone solutions (Table 8. 3).

Trypanosoma cruzi, Leishmania brasiliensis, L. donovani, and *L. tropica* need factors in serum other than thiamine, *p*-aminobenzoic acid, pyridoxine, or nicotinic acid (521). Hence, it appears that one aspect of physiological specialization among the trypanosomes and their relatives involves an increasing dependence upon the host for essential growth-factors.

Trichomonadida. Relatively little work has been reported on these flagellates (349). Peptone solutions enriched with whole blood, serum, and fragments of liver have supported growth of *Eutrichomastix colubrorum* (59), *Trichomonas gallinae* (*T. columbae*) (20), *T. foetus* (7, 163, 575), and *T. vaginalis* (255, 557, 558). Liver-infusion agar slants, overlaid with serum-enriched Ringer's solution, also have been satisfactory for *T. vaginalis.* The investigations of Cailleau have shown that the first three species need certain growth-factors apparently not required by free-living flagellates (Table 8. 3). More recently, *T. vaginalis* has been grown in a peptone solution supplemented with acetate, maltose, about 15 growth-factors, and after sterilization, diluted serum and ascorbic acid (536). In such a medium, two fractions of human serum—an ether-soluble and an ether-insoluble aqueous fraction—are essential. Linoleic acid seems to be the most active component of the ether-soluble fraction and serum albumin of the ether-insoluble one. The first fraction could be replaced by a mixture of linoleic and oleic acids, cholesterol, ergosterol, lecithin, α-estradiol, α-tocopherol, vitamin A, and β-carotene (537). *Trichomonas foetus* has been grown in a mixture of thirteen amino acids, various vitamins, and minerals (568).

Sarcodina. Published reports on the Sarcodina include little more than the development of suitable media for pure cultures, although detailed investigations are in progress. *Acanthamoeba castellanii* has been grown in a medium containing serum and liver fragments (44) and in a simpler peptone and inorganic salt medium (45). A medium containing peptone, dextrose, and inorganic salts also is satisfactory for *Mayorella palestinensis* (472, 473). Progress is also being made toward pure-culture techniques for parasitic amoebae. *Entamoeba invadens* has been maintained bacteria-free for several transfers after elimination of a single bacterial contaminant by treatment with penicillin (307). In addition, *E. histolytica* has been grown on non-viable bacteria for more than 200 transfers (500), and also in a non-particulate medium without bacterial growth (501).

Ciliates. Under natural conditions free-living ciliates feed mainly upon ingested microorganisms. In the investigation of such natural foods, strains of ciliates have been grown in cultures with other living or killed microorganisms (36, 417, 418). Such "species-pure" cultures with living bacteria involve complex relationships, and the ciliates tend to be swamped unless the initial proportions between ciliates and bacteria are satisfactory (259, 260, 261). Such relationships, particularly important when the medium supports growth of the bacteria, may be controlled by using non-nutrient basal media (14, 42, 253, 258, 315).

A wide variety of bacteria may serve as food for particular ciliates. About 20 species, as individual suspensions in salt solutions, were each adequate for growth of *Tetrahymena pyriformis* (253). Killed yeasts and washed and killed suspensions of green flagellates also were satisfactory, although living flagellates failed to support growth in serial transfers. On the other hand, *Perispira ovum* thrives on living *Euglena gracilis* (93), and *Tetrahymena pyriformis* grows on either *Chilomonas paramecium* or *Polytoma ocellatum* (182). For *Colpidium colpoda,* species of Enterobacteriaceae are more satisfactory than Bacillaceae (42). Killed bacteria seem to be an inadequate diet for *Colpoda duodenaria* (548). Likewise, *Pleurotricha lanceolata* and *Stylonychia pustulata* can be grown on living *Tetrahymena geleii* but not on killed ciliates (317). Just what heat-labile factors, supplied by living organisms, are significant in such cases is still unknown. However, *Didinium nasutum* is said to have lost the ability to synthesize peptidases and must obtain these enzymes from the living *Paramecium* which it ingests (101).

Definitive observations on food requirements of ciliates awaited, first of all, the establishment of pure cultures. This step was taken some thirty years ago when A. Lwoff isolated *Tetrahymena (Glaucoma) pyriformis*[7] in a peptone medium. Comparative data on various culture media were published later (340). These observations furnished a timely stimulus, and within a relatively few years, additional bacteria-free strains— referred to the genera *Colpidium, Colpoda, Glaucoma, Tetrahymena, Loxocephalus,* and *Paramecium*—were isolated by other workers (274). With a few exceptions, culture media included solutions of commercial peptones, yeast-extract or yeast autolysates, usually supplemented with inorganic salts. Such media as those of Glaser and Coria (160, 161, 162) were more complex. Although *Paramecium bursaria* has been maintained in peptone media (322), cultivation of other species of *Paramecium* has proven more difficult. However, *P. aurelia* (564) and *P. multi-micronucleatum* (262) are now in pure culture and investigations on their food requirements are in progress.

The next progressive step led toward the development of chemically defined culture media (349). The first apparently successful results were those of Kline (298) with *Colpidium striatum.* Unfortunately, Kline's strain of *C. striatum* seems to have been lost and several other strains have failed to grow in his medium.

Much better results have been obtained with somewhat similar media

---

[7] This ciliate is a strain of *Tetrahymena gelii,* a genus and species erected by Furgason (138) to include strains of "*Colpidium campylum,*" "*C. striatum,*" "*Glaucoma pyriformis.*" Letter designations for various strains, such as *T. geleii* H and *T. geleii* W, have since been proposed (72, 279). The name of the species apparently should be *Tetrahymena pyriformis* (see Chapter VII).

developed for *Tetrahymena geleii* W (280, 282). The simpler of these media contained eleven amino acids (arginine, histidine, isoleucine, leucine, lysine, methionine,[8] phenylalanine, serine, threonine, tryptophane, valine), glucose, eleven known vitamins, several inorganic salts, and in the proportion of 1:10, a plant or animal tissue extract apparently containing a number of amino acids, certain unidentified growth factors and known vitamins and several minerals. Further progress has made possible the gradual substitution of known growth-factors (Table 8. 3) for supplements of natural origin. This general type of medium, which has proven satisfactory for several strains of *Tetrahymena* (121, 122, 494), is illustrated in Table 8. 1, although nucleic acid may be replaced by known purines and pyrimidines. Such media are now almost completely defined in a chemical sense and are potentially useful in the assay of certain vitamins and also such amino acids as histidine, isoleucine, lysine, and tryptophane (494).

OXYGEN RELATIONSHIPS AND OXIDATIONS

Ecological distribution

The distribution of Protozoa suggests that some species are obligate aerobes, that others are microaerophiles (requiring only a little oxygen), and that many intestinal parasites and some free-living types may be obligate or facultative anaerobes. Natural waters containing much putrefying material are anaerobic at their lower levels, and such artificial environments as Imhoff sewage tanks also insure anaerobiosis beneath the surface (304, 305). Species characteristic of such a fauna, sometimes termed polysaprobic or sapropelic, are at least facultative anaerobes. They include Ctenostomina and scattered species of other ciliates, as well as a few flagellates and Sarcodina. Another practically anaerobic environment is found near the bottom of deep fresh-water lakes, but very little is known about this fauna. Other Protozoa, typical of clean waters with a high oxygen content, are aerobes and some may be obligate aerobes. However, such ciliates as *Coleps hirtus* and *Frontonia leucas,* which are not sapropelic, may survive anaerobically for several weeks (318).

Oxygen relationships of parasites doubtless vary with the usual site of infection. Species which invade the blood and other tissues probably have access to about as much oxygen as the surrounding tissue cells and may be predominantly aerobic. Oocysts of *Eimeria stiedae* and *E. magna,* for instance, apparently cannot sporulate under strictly anaerobic con-

---

[8] The reported ability of *T. geleii* to use homocystine, with supplementary "liver-fraction," as a replacement for methionine (285) has been refuted (150) on the basis that the observed growth in the presence of homocystine can be attributed to the methionine content of the liver-fraction used by Kidder and Dewey.

ditions (61). On the other hand, conditions in the vertebrate intestine suggest that intestinal parasites are anaerobes. Experimental evidence indicates that the rumen ciliate, *Eudiplodinium neglectum,* is an obligate anaerobe (218). Such is true also for flagellates of termites (217, 555). *Entamoeba histolytica,* in contrast to many other intestinal parasites, normally invades the wall of the colon. Yet this species grows as an anaerobe in cultures (56).

Relationships between oxygen tension and growth of laboratory populations have been investigated in a few cases. Aeration of flask cultures increases growth of *Tetrahymena pyriformis* (245, 440), reduction of the oxygen supply (pyrogallol technique) decreases populations to about half the normal density (171), and complete anaerobiosis prevents growth (340). Growth of *Chilomonas paramecium,* on the other hand, is retarded by aeration of cultures (245). Quantitative data also have been reported for *Trichomonas vaginalis* (255) and for *C. paramecium* and *T. pyriformis* (428). Growth of *T. vaginalis* is heaviest in complete anaerobiosis and is inhibited progressively by increasing oxygen tensions. Oxygen pressures of 0.5 to 500 mm Hg permit growth of *C. paramecium,* with an optimum at about 75 mm Hg (about half the normal atmospheric concentration of oxygen), while pressures of 600 mm Hg and higher are lethal. Growth of *T. pyriformis* increases from 10 mm Hg to a maximum (about twice the growth with atmospheric concentrations of oxygen) in an atmosphere of pure oxygen (739 mm Hg).

Oxidation-reduction potentials[9]

The oxidation-reduction potential of the culture medium is another factor related to the growth of microorganisms. In a general sense, this potential is a measure of the reducing intensity or oxidizing intensity of a given system. Examples of such systems—each of which consists of a more reduced and a less reduced substance—are leuco-methylene blue/ methylene blue, lactate/pyruvate, and reduced cytochrome *a*/oxidized cytochrome *a*. If a platinum electrode and a calomel electrode, in a potentiometer hookup, are immersed in such a system, a potential difference can be measured. Since the calomel electrode is standardized against the hydrogen electrode, measurements are expressed in millivolts in terms of the hydrogen electrode potential. The more negative the potential, the greater is the reducing power of the system; the more positive, the greater the oxidizing power (and the lower the reducing power). Each system has a characteristic E_0' value at which it is half reduced at a particular temperature and pH. Consideration of pH is necessary because the potential

---

[9] Compact discussions of oxidation-reduction potentials have been published by Johnson (257) and Stephenson (538). In addition, there is available a table of potentials for more than 200 different systems (6). Early literature on Protozoa has been reviewed by Jahn (246).

varies with pH. For the methylene blue system, E_0' at pH 7 is 11 mv; for the cytochrome a system, 290 mv at pH 7.4; for lactate/pyruvate, -180 mv at pH 7. If two systems with different E_0' values are mixed together, a reaction, which may be considered the transfer of electrons from one system to the other, continues until equilibrium is reached. The higher potential is lowered and the lower potential raised to a common level; or reduction of the first system (gain of electrons) and oxidation of the second (loss of electrons) take place.

The potential of the culture medium undoubtedly influences the growth of microorganisms. For bacteria, it is possible to lower the potential of a liquid medium with a suitable reducing agent so as to inhibit growth of aerobes and permit growth of anaerobes. In the case of *Chilomonas paramecium*, appropriate additions of the sulfhydryl radical ($-SH$) both lower the oxidation-reduction potential of the medium and stimulate growth (238). Influence of the potential on *Entamoeba histolytica* apparently varies with the type of medium. According to one worker, growth of *E. histolytica* decreases from a maximum, at a potential below -300 mv, to almost none at -200 mv; unencysted amoebae die after an hour or more at -50 mv (56). Jacobs (234), on the other hand, found that the potential of the medium was about -25 mv while *E. histolytica* was growing most rapidly in cultures containing "organism t." In contrast to *E. histolytica*, *Trypanosoma cruzi* and several species of *Leishmania* grow best in cultures at a potential of about 330 mv (57). Growth of microorganisms themselves also may modify the potential. For instance, a drop of about 290 mv has been traced in cultures of *Chilomonas paramecium* (241). It is uncertain just how extensively the potential of the medium influences internal oxidations and reductions, although the "internal potential" of *Amoeba proteus*, as measured by injected indicators, may be changed from about -70 mv (pH 7) under aerobic conditions to -143 mv in anaerobiosis (55, 70).

Oxygen consumption[10]

Measurements of oxygen consumption make it possible to trace effects of environmental factors on metabolic rates, to investigate the utilization of particular substrates, and to correlate stages in the life-cycle with metabolic activity. Such measurements are necessary in the study of oxidative mechanisms by the use of poisons or stimulants, and may indicate the relative importance of particular systems, such as the cytochrome system, in the metabolism of a particular species. Manometric techniques can be used also in the estimation of specific enzyme systems and metabolites. Comparative data on oxygen consumption of different species

---

[10] A monograph by Umbreit and his associates (560) supplies a comprehensive survey of manometric techniques and their various applications. The earlier literature on Protozoa has been reviewed by Jahn (246).

should be interpreted cautiously, since extensive variations apparently occur even in single species. For example, oxygen consumption of *Paramecium caudatum* has been recorded as 0.00014 (339), 0.0004 (213) and 0.0052 mm^3/hour/organism (266). In addition to differences attributable to different manometric techniques, the physiological condition of the test organisms may be a significant factor. Starvation significantly reduces oxygen consumption of *Paramecium caudatum* (339) and *Pelomyxa carolinensis* (526). Likewise, a marked decrease occurs in old cultures of *Colpidium colpoda* (563), *Bodo caudatus* (310), *Chilomonas paramecium* (221), *Tetrahymena pyriformis* (9, 431), *Trichomonas foetus* (484), and *Trypanosoma cruzi* (33). In *T. pyriformis* the change occurs after the logarithmic phase of growth (421) and is not correlated with any decrease in cytochrome content (9). Changes in consumption also have been traced during conjugation of *Paramecium caudatum* (585).

Environmental conditions also may influence oxygen consumption. For *Tetrahymena pyriformis* consumption is at a maximum in media at pH 5.5 and is distinctly lower on each side of the optimum (170). Increasing temperatures, within physiological limits, stimulate oxygen consumption of ciliates (267, 563) and *Strigomonas fasciculata* (341). The oxygen consumption of *Spirostomum ambiguum* increases with increasing oxygen concentration of the atmosphere to which cultures are exposed. The maximum, observed with pure oxygen, was about 50 per cent higher than for ciliates exposed to air (532). On the other hand, changes in oxygen tension within fairly wide limits have produced little effect on *Paramecium caudatum* (4).

Respiratory quotients

The ratio of the carbon dioxide produced to the oxygen consumed —the respiratory quotient (R.Q.)—has interested physiologists as a theoretical index to the type of material being consumed. The R.Q. for complete oxidation of carbohydrate is 1.0 and is about the same for acetate; for butyrate, about 0.8; for fats, approximately 0.7; for proteins, about 0.8 (urea as the nitrogenous waste) or about 0.9 (ammonia as the nitrogenous waste). Quotients well above 1.0 may indicate synthesis and storage of fat produced from carbohydrate. Low values (0.4-0.6) might indicate conversion of protein to carbohydrate, or incomplete oxidation of carbohydrate.

Most of the R.Q. values reported for Protozoa (Table 8. 4) fall within the usual range. This is especially true of Trypanosomidae, some of which have shown a higher R.Q. with glucose than without (415, 531), as would be expected. Unusually low values for several phytoflagellates have been attributed to synthesis of carbohydrates from carbon dioxide (398) and to the conversion of protein into carbohydrate or the incomplete oxidation of carbohydrate (247). Varying quotients for a species may reflect

TABLE 8. 4. RESPIRATORY QUOTIENTS REPORTED FOR VARIOUS PROTOZOA

Species	R.Q.
PHYTOMASTIGOPHOREA	
Astasia longa (strain J)	0.34 (247)
Chilomonas paramecium	0.28-0.37 (398); 0.74-0.93 (221)
Khawkinea halli	0.56 (247)
ZOOMASTIGOPHOREA	
Leishmania tropica	0.84-0.95 (531)
Strigomonas fasciculata	1.0 (341)
S. oncopelti	1.0 (341)
Trypanosoma cruzi	0.74-1.06 (33)
T. equiperdum	0.60 (126)
T. lewisi	0.74-0.94 (531)
T. rhodesiense	0.2 (64)
SARCODINA	
Amoeba proteus	1.03 (124)
Pelomyxa carolinensis	0.56-0.87 (526); 0.45-0.94 (430)
SPOROZOA	
Plasmodium knowlesi	0.87-0.93 (63)
CILIATEA	
Balantidium coli	0.84 (85)
Blepharisma undulans	1.12 (124)
Paramecium aurelia	0.73-0.90 (429)
P. caudatum	0.69 (4); 0.62 (495); 0.70-0.99 (429)
P. multimicronucleatum	0.72 (398)
Spirostomum ambiguum	0.84 (532)
Tetrahymena pyriformis	0.81-1.27 (431)

differences in condition of the organisms. An R.Q. of 0.87 has been reported for well-fed *Pelomyxa carolinensis* and one of 0.56 for starved specimens (526). Age of the culture also is a factor. The R.Q. of *Chilomonas paramecium* drops from 0.91-0.93 in 24-hour cultures to 0.75 at 72 hours (221); that of *Tetrahymena pyriformis* from 1.21-1.27 at three days to 0.81 after seven days (431); that of *Trypanosoma cruzi,* from a maximum of 1.06 to a low of 0.74 after the population reaches its peak. In the last case, the lower quotient is attributed to exhaustion of carbohydrates and subsequent utilization of proteins (35). The R.Q. also may vary with temperature—0.73 at 20° to 0.90 at 30° for *Paramecium aurelia;* 0.70 at 15° to 0.99 at 35° for *P. caudatum* (429); 0.45 at 10° to 0.94 at 30° for *Pelomyxa carolinensis* (430).

Oxidations[11]

Most biological oxidations consist of series of oxidations and reductions catalyzed by a variety of enzymes, and may be pictured as

[11] For detailed discussions of oxidative enzyme systems, the reader is referred to such sources as Baldwin (10), Lardy (308), and Stephenson (538).

involving the transfer of hydrogen step by step from one acceptor to another. Each step involves an oxidation-reduction system and each dehydrogenation yields energy for anabolism. For cells in general, a number of enzymes and oxidation-reduction systems are known to be involved in metabolism. Gradually accumulating evidence indicates that at least some of these are operative in Protozoa, as would be expected.

The cytochrome system. In aerobes the final stages of the oxidative reactions—the transfer of hydrogen to oxygen (2H to O_2)—involve the cytochrome system. This system includes several cytochrome pigments which, in their reduced forms, show different absorption bands spectroscopically. Each cytochrome is an iron-porphyrin-protein which can exist in either the oxidized or the reduced form. The oxidation-reduction potentials (E_0') of cytochromes *a* and *c* are about 290 and 270 mv; that of cytochrome *b*, about -40 mv. The oxidation of reduced cytochrome *c*, catalyzed by cytochrome oxidase, involves the transfer of 2H to atmospheric oxygen:

cytochrome-H_2 + cyt. oxidase $\rightarrow$ cytochrome + cyt. oxidase-H_2
cyt. oxidase-H_2 + $\frac{1}{2}O_2$ $\rightarrow$ cytochrome oxidase + H_2O

The reduction of cytochrome *c* is catalyzed by dehydrogenases which bring about oxidation of reduced DPN, reduced TPN, and such substrates as succinate. Cytochrome *b* also may be involved in the reduction of cytochrome *c*. Reduction of cytochrome *c* may be blocked by heat and by such reagents as alcohol, formalin, and urethanes. The transfer of hydrogen from cytochrome to cytochrome oxidase is inhibited by cyanide and azide, thus maintaining cytochrome in the reduced condition. Transfer of hydrogen from cytochrome oxidase to oxygen is inhibited by carbon monoxide.

As would be expected, aerobic Protozoa resemble other aerobic microorganisms in possessing cytochrome pigments. Cytochromes *a*, *b*, and *c* have been reported in *Astasia klebsii* (83) and *Tetrahymena pyriformis* (9); cytochromes *b* and *c*, in *Euglena gracilis*, *Tetrahymena* (*Glaucoma*) *pyriformis*, *Polytoma uvella*, *Strigomonas fasciculata*, and *S. oncopelti* (341); cytochrome *c*, in *Colpidium campylum* (510, 512), and with cytochrome oxidase, in *Chilomonas paramecium* (220). Cytochrome oxidase is said to occur in the pigment granules (mitochondria) of *Stentor coeruleus* (569). In contrast to the typical aerobes, *Trichomonas foetus* apparently contains no cytochrome (484).

Poisoning techniques have supplied additional information. The respiration of *Tetrahymena pyriformis* is decreased by 9-57 per cent in different concentrations of methyl-, ethyl-, and propylurethanes (364). Cyanide decreases oxygen consumption about 61-64 per cent in *Astasia longa* and *Khawkinea halli* (247), about 90 per cent in *Polytoma uvella* (364), and about 95 per cent in *Astasia klebsii,* for which azide is almost as inhibitory (83). A number of Trypanosomidae (349) also are susceptible to such poisons. *Leptomonas ctenocephali, Strigomonas fasciculata,* and *S. oncopelti* show 83-95 per cent inhibition with cyanide and are about as sensitive to carbon monoxide (341). Cyanide in certain concentrations inhibits respiration about 90 per cent in *Trypanosoma cruzi* (33), 11-82 per cent in *T. congolense* (34), 97-98 per cent in *Leishmania tropica, L. brasiliensis,* and *L. donovani,* 85-88 per cent in *T. lewisi* from cultures, and 66-69 per cent in *T. conorhini* (32). Certain other Trypanosomidae are relatively insensitive to cyanide—*T. equiperdum* (127), *T. brucei, T. hippicum, T. rhodesiense* (32, 64, 126), *T. evansi,* and *T. equinum* (34). Although the oxygen consumption of *T. gambiense* from blood is not decreased by cyanide (34), flagellates from cultures are moderately sensitive (32). Among the Sarcodina, *Pelomyxa carolinensis* is sensitive to cyanide (427), and sensitivity increases with temperature in the range, 10-35° (430). Respiration of *Plasmodium knowlesi* also is inhibited by cyanide (64, 371) and carbon monoxide (371). Earlier reports (338, 364, 526) that free-living ciliates are insensitive to cyanide, are contradicted by later observations. Respiration of *Tetrahymena pyriformis* is sensitive both to carbon monoxide (9) and to cyanide (9, 170), while that of well-fed, but not of starved specimens, also is cyanide-sensitive in *Paramecium aurelia* (424) and *P. caudatum* (66, 424).

The results obtained with poisoning techniques indicate that in general, aerobic Protozoa are cyanide-sensitive and presumably oxidize substrates mainly through the cytochrome system. On the other hand, some questions are unanswered. Why are starved ciliates, in contrast to well-fed ones, relatively insensitive to cyanide? What converts insensitive *T. gambiense* from the blood into cyanide-sensitive flagellates in culture media? Is it necessary for these organisms to oxidize certain substrates only partially ("anaerobically") in the blood but completely, or nearly so, in culture media? And what are the biochemical differences between the cyanide-sensitive *"lewisi* group" of trypanosomes and such insensitive species as *T. brucei* and *T. evansi?* Such problems are of practical as well as theoretical interest, since the response of parasites to chemotherapeutic agents may depend to an important extent upon the oxidative mechanisms of particular species.

Pyridine nucleotide enzymes. The pyridine nucleotides are coenzymes for a number of important oxidative enzymes. Diphosphopyridine nucleotide (DPN), or coenzyme I, contains nicotinamide, D-ribose, adenine, and two phosphoric acid groups. Triphosphopyridine nucleotide (TPN), or coenzyme II, contains a third phosphoric acid group. Both coenzymes are involved in protozoan metabolism. *Chilomonas paramecium* (223) and *Tetrahymena pyriformis* S (510, 512) contain DPN, while *Trypanosoma hippicum* requires DPN for glycolysis *in vitro* (194). In addition, supplementary DPN and TPN accelerate oxidation of pyruvate by *Plasmodium gallinaceum* in the presence of dicarboxylic acids (535).

Diphosphothiamine enzymes. This phosphoric acid ester of thiamine is the coenzyme of carboxylase which catalyzes the decarboxylation of pyruvic acid and probably certain other α-keto monocarboxylic acids. Supplementary thiamine is necessary for the oxidation of pyruvate by *Tetrahymena pyriformis* (552), is essential to growth of *Chilomonas paramecium* on pyruvate (73), and accelerates oxidation of pyruvate by *Plasmodium gallinaceum* (535). The thiamine content of *Tetrahymena pyriformis* is at least 60 per cent that of yeast (574), and the vitamin is essential to growth of this and certain other Protozoa (Table 8. 3). Therefore, thiaminoprotein enzymes are probably of general importance in protozoan metabolism.

Flavoprotein enzymes. In these enzymes the prosthetic groups contain riboflavin, either as riboflavin-phosphate or as flavin dinucleotide (a union of riboflavin-phosphate and adenylic acid). Enzymes of the first type apparently catalyze the oxidation of reduced TPN and oxidation of L-amino acids (L-amino acid dehydrogenase). Enzymes of the second type include xanthine oxidase, D-amino acid dehydrogenase, glycine dehydrogenase, and apparently "diaphorase I" (catalyzing oxidation of reduced DPN). These flavoprotein enzymes, which are not significantly affected by cyanide poisoning, are probably present in Protozoa. Riboflavin occurs in high concentration in *Tetrahymena pyriformis* (574) and is essential to growth of several ciliates (Table 8. 3), although synthesized by *Chilomonas paramecium* (207).

Pyridoxine enzymes. Pyridoxal phosphate appears to be the coenzyme for transaminases, tryptophanase, and certain amino-acid decarboxylases. The presence of comparable enzymes in Protozoa may be suspected since pyridoxine is essential to growth of certain ciliates (Table 8. 3) and inhibits the antimalarial action of quinine and atebrine against *P. lophurae* (519), and also since pyridoxal is synthesized by *Chilomonas paramecium*.

Peroxidase and catalase. These are iron-porphyrin-protein enzymes. Catalase probably catalyzes coupled oxidations by means of the hydrogenperoxide formed in some primary reaction (271), the peroxide being decomposed to water and molecular oxygen. Peroxidase catalyzes the oxidation of such substrates as tyrosine, adrenaline, bilirubin, pyrogallol, and various other phenols in the presence of hydrogen peroxide. Peroxidase has been demonstrated in *Tetrahymena pyriformis* (311) and catalase in certain related ciliates (43, 204), but the activities of neither enzyme in protozoan metabolism have been investigated.

Glutathione. In the reduced form, this is a tripeptide of glycine, cysteine, and glutamic acid. Although reduced glutathione has been demonstrated in *Tetrahymena pyriformis* (311, 512) and may play a part in respiration of this ciliate (364), its functions in protozoan metabolism are still unknown.

Pantothenic acid enzymes. Pantothenic acid is a component of *coenzyme A* (319) which may be involved in acetylation reactions in general and perhaps in the utilization of acetylmethylcarbinol by certain bacteria. Although pantothenate is essential to growth of certain ciliates and malarial parasites, its possible functions in protozoan metabolism have not been investigated.

Adenosine phosphate system. The adenosine phosphate system includes *adenylic acid* (adenosine monophosphate), *adenosine diphosphate* (ADP), and *adenosine triphosphate* (ATP). Each contains adenosine (a riboside of adenine) and one, two, or three phosphoric acid groups, respectively. The system functions in phosphorylation of metabolites and enzymes and especially in the transfer of high-energy phosphate bonds.[12] This system apparently makes available for anabolic activities the energy derived from oxidation of metabolites. Essentially, TPN serves as a participant common to a variety of exergonic and endergonic reactions, making it possible for reactions of the first type to drive those of the second variety. Little is known about the adenosine-phosphate system in Protozoa. However, adenylic acid, ADP, and ATP have all been demonstrated in *Euglena gracilis* (1). In addition, *Trypanosoma hippicum* needs ATP in the formation of hexose-phosphates (194), and *Tetrahymena pyriformis* contains adenosine triphosphatase (510).

Tricarboxylic acid cycle.[13] This so-called cycle (Fig. 8. 2) involves the oxidation of various metabolites through a common catalytic system to carbon dioxide and water under aerobic conditions. The cycle is fed by glycolysis, leading to pyruvate and thence to acetyl; by the breakdown of fats, yielding acetyl from fatty acids; and by the breakdown of proteins, through the deamination of certain amino acids to α-keto acids which enter the cycle. At each turn of the oxidative cycle, CO_2 and H_2O are produced as end-products in certain reactions, and energy is made available by the generation of high-energy phosphate bonds in several dehydrogenations. Aside from its importance in the oxidation of substrates, the tricarboxylic acid cycle may also be considered a basic reservoir of important materials which can be drawn upon for the synthesis of amino acids, carbohydrates, and fatty acids.

The tricarboxylic acid cycle has been studied both by the use of isotopes (578) and by the control of enzyme systems with blocking reagents. In the presence of cyanide at a suitable concentration, oxalacetate is trapped;

---

[12] For a discussion of the energetics of high-energy phosphate bonds, a review by Ogsdon and Smithies (419) may be consulted.

[13] Representative discussions (10, 165, 416) may be consulted for details of the tricarboxylic acid cycle and its general importance in metabolism.

in the presence of sufficient malonate, which inhibits succinic dehydrogenase, the cycle stops with the accumulation of succinate. Arsenite checks the cycle by inhibiting the oxidation of malate to oxalacetate. In addition, the ability of a species to use components of the cycle may be tested by

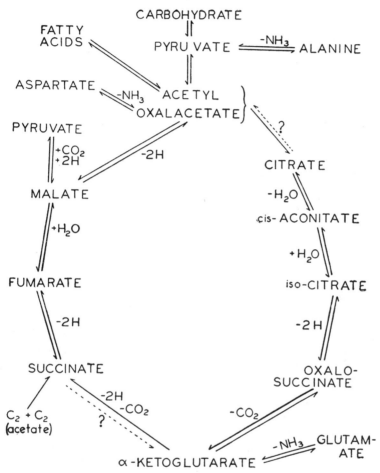

Fig. 8. 2. The tricarboxylic acid cycle.

measuring oxygen consumption with each as a substrate or by determining possible stimulation of growth.

Little work has been done on the tricarboxylic acid cycle in protozoan metabolism. There is no reason *a priori,* for suspecting that all aerobic Protozoa must complete the oxidation of metabolites through a typical tricarboxylic acid cycle; there may be some species which do not. There apparently are such reactions as $C_2 + C_2$ condensations which skip the C_6 acids of the typical cycle. *Rhizopus nigricans* can carry out this condensation, producing succinate and fumarate from labeled acetate or ethanol with essentially quantitative recovery of radioactive carbon, indicating no decarboxylation of intermediate C_6 acids (131). In relation to hetero-autotrophic nutrition of phytoflagellates, it is interesting that a mutant form of *Azotobacter agilis* has lost the ability to use glucose, lactate, pyruvate, and various Krebs-cycle acids, but retains the ability to use acetate and ethanol (269, 270).

Evidence for the occurrence of the tricarboxylic acid cycle in certain ciliates seems conclusive. *Tetrahymena pyriformis* takes up carbon dioxide with formation of succinate in the anaerobic dissimilation of glucose (561). Studies on oxygen consumption show that pyruvate, succinate, α-ketoglutarate, fumarate, malate, and oxalacetate are utilized, and that malonate produces typical inhibition (513, 528). It is interesting that malonate in low concentrations (5 $\mu g/ml$) serves as a substrate for *T. pyriformis* (528), although it is distinctly inhibitory at high concentrations. With the exception of citrate and *cis*-aconitate, the various intermediates of the cycle are readily utilized by *Plasmodium gallinaceum* (407, 535), and fumarate, pyruvate, and succinate are known to be oxidized by *P. lophurae* (21). The evidence for such a cycle in phytoflagellates is not yet conclusive. Added to a peptone medium, malate stimulates growth of *Astasia longa, Euglena gracilis,* and *Polytoma ocellatum,* while succinate stimulates growth of these and six other species (565), and also accelerates growth of *E. gracilis* in darkness (244). In addition, fumarate, malate, and succinate are satisfactory substrates for *E. gracilis* var. *bacillaris* at pH 3.0-3.6 (228). Occasional failures to use Krebs-cycle acids have been observed but these cases probably should be reconsidered. Experimental data for *Tetrahymena pyriformis* (516) indicate that permeability of the surface to the substrate is a major factor to be considered. Such a factor may explain the reported inability of *Polytoma uvella* to use malate and pyruvate (456), and that of *Astasia klebsii* to oxidize succinate or citrate at a significant rate (83). The need for carbon dioxide, established for several phytoflagellates (471), might suggest that carboxylation occurs as an essential part of the cycle but such an assumption is yet to be confirmed experimentally. The data for Zoomastigophorea also are fragmentary. *Trypanosoma lewisi* oxidizes several of the intermediates rather slowly (403), although the basal "medium" used for such tests may not be the most favorable one for reactions which depend upon a variety of growth-factors. *Trypanosoma cruzi* and the species of *Leishmania* from man form succinate as one of the products in oxidation of glucose and levulose (57).

DIGESTION

Digestion in holozoic species occurs typically within vacuoles which enclose the food after ingestion. The mechanical features of ingestion vary with the species and with the type of food. Ingestion in Amoebida commonly involves extension of pseudopodia or formation of "food cups" to engulf the food. A food cup may be quite deep, as in *Amoeba vespertilio* (233) in which the food is taken in through a temporary "cytostome" (Fig. 1. 15, C) similar to the permanent structures in more specialized Protozoa. In shelled types ingestion is limited to an area of naked protoplasm. If there is a large enough opening, ingested particles may be passed into the shell, as in *Arcella*. If the shell contains only small pores, as in many Foraminiferida, the fusion of already extended pseudopodia to enclose trapped food is the essential feature. A comparable process often follows the adherence of food particles to axopodia in Heliozoida and Radiolarida. Ingestion by pseudopodial activity has been reported in various holozoic phytoflagellates and other simple flagellates, while fairly large particles are ingested without marked pseudopodial activity in *Lophomonas* and *Trichonympha* (125). In certain flagellates and in typical ciliates, ingestion is limited to a cytostome. In simple cases, this appears to be merely a thin region of the cortex. More often, the cytostome lies at the base of a groove or pit. The oral groove, or the peristomial area, of ciliates is often equipped with strong cilia, membranelles, or undulating membranes which drive particles into the cytostome (Chapter I).

Food vacuoles

The wall of the vacuole in *Amoeba* and similar types is derived from the surface layer of the body. In ciliates feeding on small particles, the vacuole develops at the inner end of the cytopharynx as an enlarging bulb which is eventually pinched off (103, 300). Formation of the vacuole apparently is stimulated by the passage of solid particles through the cytostome into the cytopharynx, since ciliates in a non-particulate medium contain few, if any, food vacuoles (340). The ingestion of large masses, as in the engulfment of *Paramecium* by *Didinium nasutum*, is a less simple process. In Suctorea (Chapter VII), a food vacuole is formed at the base of a tentacle which is usually attached to the prey and sucks its protoplasm into the captor's body. Food vacuoles apparently may fuse or divide. Fusion of small vacuoles (391) and the division of large vacuoles into several smaller ones (387) have been noted in *Amoeba proteus*. Also, the collection of small ingested particles into one mass, which becomes surrounded by a common vacuolar membrane, has been described in *Ichthyophthirius multifiliis* (372).

A continuous "digestive tract," in which successively formed food vacuoles remain joined with one another by slender tubes, has been described in *Paramecium* and *Vorticella* (300). In addition, a coiled "canal," extending from cytostome to cytopyge, has been described in *Colpidium* (74), cyclosis of food vacuoles being merely an optical illusion caused by movement of food along this canal. Such a canal resembles to some extent the long sausage-shaped food vacuoles formed by *Paramecium* in certain salt solutions (94), but other workers have failed to find a tubular digestive system in ciliates (103, 182).

After formation of the food vacuole, the contents apparently become acid sooner or later. As reported in *Paramecium caudatum* (103, 522) and *Actinosphaerium eichorni* (212), a drop to pH 4.0-4.3 occurs after a time. In *Amoeba*, the pH of the vacuolar fluid falls to some point between 4.0 and 6.5 (389). The acidity of the vacuole in *P. caudatum* is said to approach that of 0.8N hydrochloric acid; in certain other ciliates, less than that of 1×10^{-4} N acid (413). The origin of this acid is uncertain, although Mast (389) attributed it to the respiration of ingested organisms and their later autolytic changes. During later stages of digestion and absorption, there is a gradual rise in pH, sometimes to about pH 7.0 in old vacuoles containing undigested residues.

Undigested materials are usually eliminated through a definite area (*cytopyge*) in Protozoa with a well-developed cortex. In various Peritrichida the contents of the old vacuole are discharged into the vestibule (Chapter VII). In many other ciliates, the cytopyge lies at the surface somewhere in the posterior half of the body. A similar differentiation also may be found in such flagellates as *Peranema trichophorum,* in which the supposed cytopyge is a small area in the postero-lateral body wall lacking the usual cortical inclusions.

Digestion of proteins[14]

Protozoa which ingest solid food presumably are equipped with digestive enzymes, and would thus be expected to produce both endopeptidases (proteinases) and exopeptidases (peptidases). *Didinium nasutum* seems to be an interesting exception which depends upon its ingested prey for a supply of peptidases (101). *"Glaucoma" pyriformis* produces an endopeptidase active in the pH range, 2.2-9.6, with an optimum at about pH 6.0 (311, 312); comparable enzymes of *Plasmodium gallinaceum* are more active at pH 6.5 than at 7.4 (408). Exopeptidases have been reported in *Paramecium caudatum, Frontonia* sp., and *Amoeba proteus* (204). Certain trypanosomes likewise produce exopeptidases and also an endopeptidase of the kathepsin type, but no enzymes of the pepsin or trypsin types (302).

The ability to digest proteins also has been reported for *Euglena gracilis* (173, 237, 377) and for such a saprozoic flagellate as *Leishmania tropica* (498). Digestion in such cases is presumably extracellular but it is uncertain whether the enzymes are eliminated during life or are released by disintegration of the flagellates.

---

[14] A brief general discussion of digestive enzymes will be found in Baldwin's (10) monograph.

Digestion of carbohydrates

Enzymes catalyzing the digestion of carbohydrates are of two general types—*polysaccharidases,* or polysaccharases, acting on cellulose, starch, and similar large molecules, and the *glycosidases,* acting on such small molecules as disaccharides and trisaccharides.

The digestion of cellulose has been reported for several Protozoa (Table 8. 5) and the same ability may be assumed for species which feed on plant materials or those which invade plant tissues. The demonstration of cellulases in certain flagellates of termites (216, 217, 555) and the wood roach (554), and in certain ciliates of ruminants (218, 219),

TABLE 8. 5. UTILIZATION OF POLYSACCHARIDES

Species	Cellulose	Starch	Inulin	Dextrin	Glycogen
MASTIGOPHORA					
Eutrichomastix colubrorum (47)	?	?	—	—	—
Leishmania tropica (102)	?	?	+	—	—
Strigomonas media (365)	?	?	+	—	?
S. muscidarum (365)	?	?	+	+	?
S. parva (365)	?	?	—	—	?
Trichomonas columbae (47)	?	+	+	+	?
T. foetus (47)	?	+	+	+	?
T. termopsidis (555)	+	?	?	?	?
flagellates of termites (217)	+	?	?	?	?
flagellates of wood roach (554)	+	?	?	?	?
SPOROZOA					
Plasmodium knowlesi (133)	?	?	—	—	—
CILIATEA					
Chilodon cucullus (162)	+	+	?	?	?
Colpidium campylum (272)	?	—	?	?	?
Diplodinium denticulatum (219)	+	?	?	?	?
D. maggii (219)	+	?	?	?	?
D. multivesiculatum (219)	+	?	?	?	?
Entodinium caudatum (219)	—	?	?	?	?
Eudiplodinium neglectum (219)	+	?	?	?	?
Glaucoma scintillans (272)	?	+	?	?	?
Paramecium caudatum (162)	+	+	?	?	?
P. multimicronucleatum (162)	+	+	?	?	?
Saprophilus oviformis (162)	+	+	?	?	?
Tetrahymena pyriformis E (114)	?	+	+	+	?
T. pyriformis E (279)	?	+	—	+	+
T. pyriformis GF-J (251)	?	+	—	+	?
T. pyriformis GHH (279)	?	+	—	+	?
T. pyriformis GP (251)	?	+	—	+	?
T. pyriformis H (114)	?	+	+	+	?
T. pyriformis H (279)	?	+	—	+	+
T. pyriformis L (71)	?	—	—	?	?
T. pyriformis R (311)	?	+	?	?	?
T. pyriformis T, T-P, W (279)	?	+	—	+	+
T. vorax (272, 279)	?	+	—	+	+
Trichoda pura (162)	+	+	?	?	?

presumably qualifies these organisms as symbiotes of their respective hosts. In addition to the Protozoa in which other polysaccharidases have been reported (Table 8. 5), the many species which store and utilize starch and glycogen doubtless have enzymes capable of splitting these reserve foods into simple sugars. However, the utilization of stored polysaccharides may involve phosphorolysis rather than digestive hydrolysis. Starch, for example, would yield α-glucose-1-phosphate instead of maltose or glucose. This situation raises the possibility that some of the phytoflagellates which store starch may be unable to use exogenous starch as a substrate.

The utilization of disaccharides (Table 8. 6) has been reported on the basis of fermentation reactions, the activity of extracts prepared from Protozoa, or the effects of sugars on oxygen consumption. Such abilities also may be inferred for species which digest polysaccharides.

Digestion of lipids

Little is known about the utilization of lipids by Protozoa, although the production of lipases by many species seems probable in view

TABLE 8. 6. UTILIZATION OF DISACCHARIDES

Species	Cellobiose	Lactose	Maltose	Sucrose
MASTIGOPHORA				
Eutrichomastix colubrorum (47)	?	+	+	+
Leishmania tropica (102)	?	?	±	+
Strigomonas media (365)	?	−	−	+
S. muscidarum (365)	?	+	+	+
S. parva (365)	?	−	−	+
Trichomonas columbae (47)	?	+	+	+
T. foetus (47)	?	+	+	+
T. termopsidis (555)	+	?	?	?
flagellates of termites (217)	+	?	?	?
flagellates of wood roach (554)	+	?	?	?
SPOROZOA				
Plasmodium knowlesi (133)	?	−	−	−
CILIATEA				
Colpidium campylum (272)	−	−	+	+
Diplodinium denticulatum (219)	+	?	?	?
D. maggii (219)	+	?	?	?
D. multivesiculatum (219)	+	?	?	?
Eudiplodinium neglectum (219)	+	?	?	?
Glaucoma scintillans (272)	+	−	+	−
Saprophilus oviformis (162)	+	?	+	?
Tetrahymena pyriformis E, GF-J, GP, H, L (71, 114, 251)	?	−	+	−
T. pyriformis E, GHH, H, T, T-P (279)	−	−	+	−
T. pyriformis W, T. vorax (272)	+	−	+	−
T. pyriformis W, T. vorax (279)	−	−	+	−

Key: +, utilized; ±, utilized very slowly; −, not utilized; ?, data not reported.

of the common storage of cytoplasmic fats and oils, and the absence of evidence that different enzyme systems are involved in storage and utilization of lipids. *Amoeba proteus* apparently hydrolyzes several animal and vegetable oils after their injection into the cytoplasm (89), and also digests fats in food vacuoles (387). The products of digestion pass into the cytoplasm and are combined there to form droplets of neutral fat (387). Unlike amoebae, certain trypanosomes apparently do not produce lipases (302).

NITROGEN METABOLISM

For certain phytoflagellates no amino acid need be supplied from external sources. Therefore, the major feature of nitrogen metabolism presumably is the assimilation of ammonium-N in synthesis of the amino acids needed for growth. In *Chilomonas paramecium* and *Polytoma ocellatum,* these syntheses apparently include all the amino acids which are absolute requirements for *Tetrahymena geleii* (182). Such flagellates may have some promise in tracing the intermediate stages and the growth-factors involved in synthesis of amino acids. Perhaps the general technique of "inhibition analysis" (525) will prove applicable here.

The fact that certain phytoflagellates can grow on a single amino acid indicates that transaminations may be as effective, in a general way, as the assimilation of ammonium-nitrogen from an inorganic source. Utilization of an amino acid as the sole source of energy has not been demonstrated and the dissimilation of amino acids has not yet been traced. A little more is known about the metabolism of amino acids in other Protozoa. Strains of *Tetrahymena pyriformis* seem to need eleven amino acids, ten of which are considered irreplaceable for higher animals (10). *T. pyriformis* undoubtedly synthesizes additional amino acids. In a chemically defined medium stripped to essentials, these syntheses must involve transaminations with at least certain number of the eleven serving as nitrogen-donors. However these reactions have not yet been traced.

The production of ammonia—reported for *Bodo caudatus* (310), *Leishmania tropica* (498), *Acanthamoeba castellanii* (46), *Plasmodium gallinaceum* (408), *Didinium nasutum* (567), "*Glaucoma*" *pyriformis* (100, 362), *Paramecium caudatum* (77), *Spirostomum ambiguum* (532)—indicates that such species can deaminate amino acids but nothing is known about the specific dehydrogenases involved.

For Protozoa in pure cultures there is little critical information on nitrogenous excretory products. The rather general production of ammonia, and also the failure of tests for urea and uric acid in cultures of *Tetrahymena pyriformis* (362) and in washed suspensions of *Paramecium caudatum* fed powdered fibrin (77), have suggested ammonia as the probable excretory product.

CARBOHYDRATE METABOLISM

The utilization of various carbohydrates by ciliates, trichomonad flagellates, trypanosomes and related forms is well known. On the other hand, the significance of sugars in the metabolism of phytoflagellates remains problematical. Quantitative techniques have not demonstrated utilization of glucose by *Chilomonas paramecium* and *Chlorogonium euchlorum* (327). Furthermore, sugars do not accelerate growth of *Polytomella agilis* and *Polytoma ocellata* in peptone media (454), and sugars apparently cannot replace acetate in the synthesis of reserve carbohydrates by phytoflagellates (344). In a few cases, stimulation of growth has been reported in peptone media supplemented with certain sugars.

TABLE 8. 7. UTILIZATION OF MONOSACCHARIDES

Species	Sugars
MASTIGOPHORA	
Eutrichomastix colubrorum (47)	a, **B, D, E, I,** j, l
Leishmania donovani (71)	**B, E**
Leishmania tropica (102)	a, **B, D, E, G, I,** l
Leptomonas ctenocephali (71)	**B, E**
Strigomonas media (365)	a, **B, D, E, G, I,** j, l
S. muscidarum (365)	**A, B, D, E, G, I,** j, l
S. parva (365)	a, **B, D, E, G, I,** j, l
Trichomonas columbae (47)	*A,* **B, D,** *E, I,* j, *L*
Trichomonas foetus (47)	a, **B, D, E, I,** j, l
Trichomonas vaginalis (557)	a, **B, D, E,** j, l
Trypanosoma brucei (29, 30)	**B, D, E, G**
SARCODINA	
Acanthamoeba castellanii (45)	b
SPOROZOA	
Plasmodium knowlesi (133)	a, **B,** d, **E, G,** h, i, j, l
CILIATEA	
Colpidium campylum (272)	a, **B,** d, **E,** l
Glaucoma scintillans (272)	a, **B,** d, **E,** l
Tetrahymena pyriformis E (114)	a, **B,** d, **E, G,** h, j, l
T. pyriformis E (279)	a, **B,** c, **D, E,** f, **G,** h, i, j, k, l
T. pyriformis GF-J (251)	a, **B, D,** e, g, h, j, l
T. pyriformis GHH (279)	a, **B,** c, d, **E,** f, **G,** h, i, j, k, l
T. pyriformis GP (251)	a, **B, D, E,** g, h, j, l
T. pyriformis H (279)	a, **B,** c, d, **E,** f, **G,** h, i, j, k, l
T. pyriformis L (71)	a, **B, D, E,** l
T. pyriformis T, T-P (279)	a, **B,** c, d, **E,** f, **G,** h, i, j, k, l
T. pyriformis W (272, 279)	a, **B,** c, d, **E,** f, **G,** h, i, j, k, l
Tetrahymena vorax D (272)	a, **B,** d, **E,** l
T. vorax PP, V (279)	a, **B,** c, **D, E,** f, **G,** h, i, j, k, l
Trichoda pura (162)	**B**

A, arabinose; B, dextrose; C, fucose; D, galactose; E, levulose; F, lyxose; G, mannose; H, melizitose; I, raffinose; J, rhamnose; K, ribose; L, xylose. Bold-face capitals indicate utilization; italicized capitals, slow utilization; small letters, no utilization.

However, such effects have been minor ones and cannot, with any assurance, be attributed to utilization of sugars as substrates. This situation has been puzzling in view of the fact that these flagellates store carbohydrates and evidently utilize such reserves. Perhaps the difficulty lies in some fundamental deficiency such as the lack of an adequate phosphorylating mechanism for utilizing exogenous carbohydrates. Or possibly the permeability of the body wall is too low for effective absorption. Low rates of absorption presumably would not be a hindrance in holozoic species. Consequently, the investigation of polysaccharides and disaccharides as substrates for holozoic Euglenida and Chrysomonadida might yield significant information.

Utilization of monosaccharides (Table 8. 7) has been demonstrated by fermentation reactions, by measuring stimulation of growth or oxygen consumption, and by quantitative sugar determinations. The decomposition of a monosaccharide[15] involves a series of reactions catalyzed by a number of enzymes (Fig. 8. 3), the initial step being phosphorylation of the sugar to glucose-6-phosphate. This reaction precedes the dissimilation of exogenous sugar and often its storage as polysaccharide. In this connection, it is interesting that hexokinase has not been found in *Polytomella caeca* (356), and also that hexosediphosphate but not glucose can be oxidized by *Astasia klebsii* (83). Although utilization of glucose also has not been demonstrated for *Euglena gracilis,* this species does contain the following compounds which appear in glycolysis: glucose-1-phosphate, fructose-6-phosphate, fructose-1,6-diphosphate, and glycerophosphoric acid (1).

In organisms equipped with hexokinase, glucose-6-phosphate is produced and also may be stored, presumably by conversion into glucose-1-phosphate and thence into polysaccharide. Or, glucose-6-phosphate may undergo dissimilation, the next step being conversion into fructose-6-phosphate. Phosphorylation of this ester yields fructose-1,6-diphosphate. The diphosphate then undergoes cleavage into two interconvertible triose-phosphates. Later reactions are traced to pyruvate in Figure 8. 3. The series of reactions up to this point yields a certain amount of utilizable energy. Aerobically, pyruvate may be oxidized through the tricarboxylic acid cycle, with more efficient utilization of the original free energy in the glucose molecule. Anaerobically, pyruvate may be converted into lactate or into ethanol.

Glycolysis has been traced, at least to some extent, in a number of Protozoa. Trypanosomes apparently vary in their methods of attacking glucose. In the earlier work, no evidence was obtained for phosphorylation. More recently, *Trypanosoma equiperdum* has been shown to phosphorylate glucose to fructose-1,6-diphosphate, which is split into triose-

---

[15] For details of glycolysis, discussions by Baldwin (10) and Lardy (308) may be consulted.

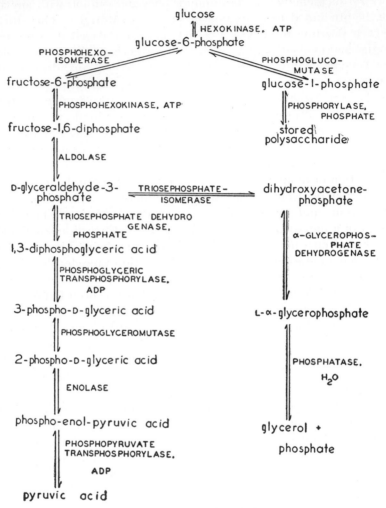

Fig. 8. 3. Dissimilation of glucose.

phosphates (63). Glycolysis is similar in *T. evansi* (379) and *T. hippicum* (194). In the latter, hexokinase, aldolase, triose-phosphate dehydrogenase, glycerol dehydrogeanse, and glycerophosphate dehydrogenase have been demonstrated. The activity of hexokinase in certain trypanosomes is inhibited significantly by arsenicals (194, 379) and in malarial parasites by quinacrine (22, 534).

The products of dissimilation vary in different species of *Trypanosoma* (31). Certain species decompose glucose mainly, or even quantitatively (194), to pyruvate. *Trypanosoma equiperdum* (475) produces pyruvate and glycerol; glycerol accumulates under anaerobic conditions but is converted almost completely to pyruvate aerobically (475). Sugar metabolism of *T. evansi* (379) and *T. hippicum* (194) is essentially similar to that of *T. equiperdum*. It has been suggested that *T. hippicum,* which lacks cytochrome oxidase, is dependent upon the host for removal of waste pyruvate. However, it might be interesting to test *T. hippicum* and *T. equiperdum* under conditions which would insure an adequate supply of thiamine and other growth-factors *in vitro*. Such species as *T. lewisi* (475, 517, 518) and *T. rhodesiense* (135) produce several intermediates. Succinic forms about 40 per cent of the acids recovered from *T. rhodesiense* suspensions in glucose-Ringer's solution, and is also a major product for *T. lewisi*. Both species also produce acetic, lactic, pyruvic, and formic acids, ethanol and CO_2, and *T. rhodesiense* produces glycerol in addition. Formate and CO_2 appear only under aerobic conditions in *T. lewisi* suspensions. Whether succinate is produced through the tricarboxylic acid cycle is uncertain. Since succinic dehydrogenase is cytochrome-linked and *T. rhodesiense* presumably lacks the cytochrome system (32), this trypanosome may be unable to oxidize succinate after producing it. This may not be true for *T. lewisi* which is rather sensitive to cyanide poisoning and presumably contains the cytochrome system.

Certain flagellates of termites decompose glucose anaerobically to carbon dioxide, hydrogen, acetic acid, and certain unidentified products. Lactic and pyruvic acids, acetaldehyde, methyl glyoxal, and ethanol have not been detected in significant amounts (217).

In *Plasmodium gallinaceum,* hexokinase has been demonstrated (533), and glucose, lactate, and pyruvate all seem to be oxidized through the tricarboxylic acid cycle (535). The oxidation of pyruvate is inhibited by malonate, with accumulation of succinate. Parasitized erythrocytes oxidize pyruvate almost completely to CO_2 and H_2O by way of the Krebs cycle and accumulate very little acetate. Cell-free suspensions of *P. gallinaceum* produce considerable acetate, as well as CO_2 and H_2O, under aerobic conditions and the acetate is not further decomposed; anaerobically, pyruvate does not disappear and acetate is not formed (535). In *P. knowlesi,* lactate is produced from glucose and can be oxidized (371, 570), and the increase in lactate is more or less parallel to the production of pyruvate (571).

Little is known about sugar metabolism of ciliates. *Paramecium caudatum* decomposes glucose to unidentified organic acids which account for about a third of the sugar utilized (77). *Tetrahymena pyriformis* produces lactic, acetic, and succinic acids from glucose under anaerobic conditions (550). When *T. pyriformis* was supplied with glucose and radioactive CO_2, all the radioactive carbon appeared in the carboxyl groups of succinic acid, indicating that CO_2 is assimilated in the production of succinate (550, 412), as previously reported for *Trypanosoma lewisi* under anaerobic conditions (518). The oxidation of substrates through the tricarboxylic acid cycle in ciliates is indicated by the presence of succinic dehydrogenase in *Tetrahymena pyriformis* (311) and *Paramecium caudatum* (215), and by the stimulatory effects of fumarate, succinate, and α-ketoglutarate on oxygen consumption of the former (513).

Synthesis of carbohydrates and lipids

Many Protozoa synthesize and store carbohydrates and lipids as visible deposits. Little is known about the relations of particular substrates and other factors to such syntheses. Photosynthesis[16] makes an important contribution in many phytoflagellates, but those without chromatophores also store carbohydrates. In pure cultures, lipids may accumulate as the cultures grow older, whereas carbohydrates may be predominant in young cultures.

The lipids synthesized by *Tetrahymena pyriformis* have been estimated quantitatively (511); sterols make up about 0.05 per cent of the total (514). A mixture of fatty acids extracted from *T. pyriformis* has shown bacteriostatic activity against several Gram-positive bacteria *in vitro* but not *in vivo*. Similar material from *Chilomonas paramecium* showed activity against pneumococcus type III *in vitro* (370). Acetate is an effective substrate for the synthesis of lipids and carbohydrates by *T. pyriformis*. Although arsenite and malonate inhibit oxidation of acetate, they do not influence synthesis of either carbohydrates or lipids (515).

CONTRACTILE VACUOLES IN HYDROSTATIC REGULATION

The major function of contractile vacuoles seems to be that of hydrostatic regulation. Although they probably do eliminate some soluble wastes, their excretory function is of doubtful importance. The many Protozoa which lack contractile vacuoles must carry on excretion through the general body surface or some permeable portion, and the same mechanism probably is operative in species with contractile vacuoles.

The nature of the excretory products is uncertain for most Protozoa. So-called excretion-crystals have been described in various species, but the chemical nature of these inclusions has been disputed and their excretory significance has not been demonstrated satisfactorily. In attempts to identify less problematical waste products, Howland (211) was unable to demonstrate uric acid in the vacuoles of *Amoeba, Paramecium* and *Vorticella,* but did detect it in fluid from cultures of *Amoeba* and *Paramecium*. Weatherby (565) found urea in culture fluid but not in the contractile vacuole or cytoplasm of *P. caudatum*. However, urea has been reported in the vacuolar fluid of *Spirostomum,* the low concentration suggesting that only about 1.0 per cent of the theoretical urea produc-

---

[16] Major experimental investigations on photosynthesis in phytoflagellates are yet to be completed. Reviews of photosynthesis in general have been published by Rabinowitch (470) and by Franck and Loomis (132).

tion could be eliminated by the contractile vacuole (566). Ammonia, rather than urea, seems to be the nitrogenous waste product for a number of species.

The assumption that the contractile vacuole is a hydrostatic regulator is based upon the fact that, in a system involving two fluids of different densities separated by a semipermeable membrane, water should pass from the less dense into the denser medium until equilibrium is reached. The cytoplasm would represent the denser medium in fresh-water Protozoa, and the occurrence of endosmosis would necessitate a mechanism for preventing excessive dilution of the cytoplasm. The general occurrence of contractile vacuoles in fresh-water Protozoa and the absence of such structures in many marine and parasitic species support this assumption. An osmoregulatory function also is indicated by certain experimental data. Injection of distilled water into *Amoeba dubia* increases rate of pulsation and water output of the contractile vacuole (214). A decrease in frequency of contraction with increasing salinity of the medium has been observed in *Amoeba verrucosa* (582), species of *Paramecium* (144, 197), *Gastrostyla steinii* (197) and *Blepharisma undulans* (144). In *A. verrucosa*, pulsation ceases at a salt concentration of 1.5-2.5 per cent; in *G. steinii*, at 1.25 per cent (197). Conversely, the rate of pulsation in certain marine and parasitic species rises with decreasing salinity, as in *Amphileptus guttula* (268), *Nyctotherus cordiformis* (197), and *Balantidium entozoon* (112). Under similar conditions, appearance *de novo* of contractile vacuoles has been described for *Amoeba biddulphiae* (583) and *Vahlkampfia calkinsi* (203). However, *Flabellula mira* develops no contractile vacuoles even in a 1:20 dilution of sea water. This species seems to eliminate water by way of large food vacuoles which are emptied at intervals (209).

The water eliminated by the contractile vacuole may be traced to several sources. Endosmosis may account for much of it in fresh water species. Such a process demands the maintenance of a difference in osmotic pressure across a selectively permeable membrane. The internal electrolyte concentration of *Amoeba proteus* and various ciliates, determined with microelectrodes for measurement of intracellular conductivity, is equivalent to 0.01-0.068N KCl (148, 149). The internal osmotic pressure of *Spirostomum ambiguum*, determined by the vapor pressure method, is equivalent to that of 0.15 per cent NaCl (448), and the difference of osmotic pressure across the body wall of fresh water peritrichs approximates that of a 0.05M sucrose solution (295). Formation of food vacuoles is another source of water in holozoic Protozoa, although there is some compensation in the evacuation of old vacuoles. This source accounts for 8-20 per cent of the water eliminated by contractile vacuoles of marine ciliates (297). Another source of water is that arising in metabolism, but the relative amount has not been estimated.

The vacuolar cycle

In the simplest cases, small vacuoles appear in the cytoplasm and fuse to form a new vacuole which increases in volume (diastole) and then collapses (systole) in discharging its contents to the outside. Canal-fed vacuoles receive fluid during diastole from feeder canals which may persist throughout the cycle. As described by Lloyd and Beattie (320) in *Paramecium caudatum*, diastole involves: (1) an early rapid phase, coinciding with contraction of the canals to force fluid into the vacuole; and (2) a slow phase, in which further distension involves diffusion of water into the vacuole from the cytoplasm. In systole there are: (1) a preliminary slow phase, in which fluid passes from the vacuole into the canals, distending them; and (2) a rapid phase, in which the remaining fluid is expelled from the vacuole to the outside. Fluid of relatively high osmotic pressure—that derived from the vacuole at the beginning of systole—supposedly remains in the canals and facilitates withdrawal of water from the cytoplasm in the next cycle. On the other hand, Gelei (146) believed that connections between the vacuole and the canals are closed before systole. This is also the case in *Paramecium multimicronucleatum* (294).

The frequency of pulsation, in general, is greater in fresh-water species than in marine or parasitic forms. Cycles range from 6 seconds to 20 minutes for fresh-water species, 45 seconds to 32 minutes for marine and brackish water types, and 72 seconds to 16 minutes for endoparasitic forms (296). Fresh-water species eliminate a volume of water equivalent to body volume in 4-45 minutes, whereas marine ciliates require 2.75-4.75 hours. In a given species, frequency of pulsation increases as the temperature rises within non-injurious limits. Temperature characteristics (μ values), calculated from the equation of Arrhenius, have been reported for *Spirostomum ambiguum, Blepharisma undulans,* and four species of *Paramecium* over the range, 16-26.8° (145).

According to the *osmotic theory* of diastole, water passes into the contractile vacuole by osmosis from the cytoplasm. This mechanism would require an osmotic gradient favoring the contents of the contractile vacuole. Since it is not clear just how such a gradient would be maintained, it is difficult to account for diastole on this basis alone (296). The *filtration theory* (129, 448) holds that hydrostatic pressure forces water through the vacuolar membrane. Haye (195) and Kitching (296) have pointed out that hydrostatic pressure would not be relieved by passage of water into the contractile vacuole, since this organelle is surrounded by cytoplasm during diastole. The *secretion theory,* favored by Kitching (296), postulates secretion of water into the contractile vacuole by the membrane. This assumption seems logical enough and it conflicts with no available data.

The discharge of the contractile vacuole has been explained in two general ways: (1) that the process involves contraction of the vacuolar membrane; and (2) that systole is produced by cytoplasmic pressure on the vacuole. Although the change from a sol to a gel in the vacuolar membrane might exert enough contraction to initiate systole (147), this mechanism could not in itself bring about complete discharge. Cytoplasmic pressure theories maintain that contraction of the vacuole is brought about by pressure of the cytoplasm against the vacuolar wall. Observations on *Amoeba dubia* (214) and *A. proteus* (382), in which the vacuole becomes embedded in a zone of gelated cytoplasm just before systole, suggest that pressure from this zone brings about systole. For such ciliates as *Paramecium,* it appears that hydrostatic pressure is exerted by a more or less fluid cytoplasm and that systole may be initiated by some other factor, such as adjustment of the vacuole to the excretory pore. Adjustment to the pore, as a preliminary step, would presumably insure discharge of a full vacuole rather than a partially filled one.

GROWTH OF PROTOZOA

Individuals and populations

The growth of individual Protozoa has been traced in very few cases. In some species, a constant growth-rate has been reported, as in *Plasmodium praecox* (193) and *Ichthyophthirius multifiliis* (373); in others, a decreasing rate which may or may not follow a sigmoid curve. Investigations on this phase of protozoan growth have been reviewed by Richards (482).

Cultures of Protozoa are essential for investigating a variety of problems. *Pure cultures,* containing one species of Protozoa and no other microorganisms, are a necessity for tracing many biochemical and physiological activities and for determining basal food requirements. *"Species-pure" cultures,* containing one strain of Protozoa and one or more strains of other microorganisms, also have been used to advantage in many investigations. The maintenance of such cultures with known bacteria in known concentrations has insured reproducible experimental conditions. In the case of *Entamoeba histolytica,* cultures of this type show promise for preliminary investigations on growth requirements and amoebacidal drugs (27, 477, 478). *Mixed cultures,* containing two species of Protozoa either bacteria-free (37, 93, 182, 462) or with bacteria, also have been used in a few investigations. An interesting example is the growth of *Entamoeba histolytica* with *Trypanosoma cruzi* (442, 443). Gause (140, 141, 142, 143) has been interested in the struggle for existence between competitors for the same food supply (e.g., *Paramecium caudatum* and *Stylonychia mytilus* feeding on bacteria) and in captor and prey relationships (*Didinium* and *Paramecium*). In the competition between *S. mytilus* and *P. caudatum,* mutual inhibition was noted, *S. mytilus* being the stronger competitor. The observations of Brown (37), Dewey and Kidder (93), and Provasoli (462) involve the captor-prey relationship in bacteria-free media. Loefer (325, 326, 328) was dealing with analogous problems in his bacteria-free cultures of *Paramecium bursaria,* in which conditions optimal for growth of *Chlorella paramecii* were not those most favorable to growth of the ciliate-algal partnership.

Experimental data based upon cultures are to be interpreted in terms of protozoan populations. Growth of populations in microorganisms[17] may consist of several phases (Fig. 8. 4): an *initial stationary phase,* with no increase in number of organisms; a *lag phase,* during which the rate

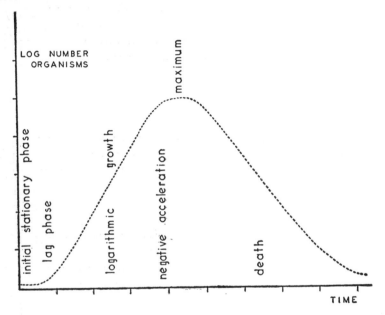

Fig. 8. 4. Generalized growth curve for populations of microorganisms.

of population-growth increases to a maximum; a *phase of logarithmic growth,* during which the population increases at a constant rate; a *phase of negative growth acceleration,* in which the growth-rate decreases progressively; a *maximal stationary phase,* in which the population remains essentially constant; and various *phases of death,* in which the density of population decreases. The first two phases are sometimes lumped together under the one term, *lag.*

The early phases in growth of populations have been investigated in *Euglena* (235, 236) and *Tetrahymena* (37, 116, 439, 440), while more

---

[17] Recent discussions of bacterial growth have been published by Hinshelwood (202) and Monod (401).

extended curves have been traced for *Paramecium bursaria* (326), *Polytoma* (467), *Astasia longa* (506), and *Tetrahymena pyriformis* (190, 263). The histories of such populations show essentially the same phases as those reported for bacteria.

Initial stationary phase. The occurrence of this phase in cultures of *T. pyriformis* is related to the age of the inoculum. No stationary phase follows inoculation of fresh media from cultures in logarithmic growth, but with older inocula, length of this phase varies with age of the stock (439). A similar relationship has been observed in *Chilomonas paramecium* (393). The responsible factors remain unknown, although organisms in old cultures show lower reproductive ability than those in young cultures. This difference in *C. paramecium* has been attributed to storage of an "X-substance" in excessive amounts. After inoculation of fresh medium with old flagellates, fission is delayed until the excessive X-substance diffuses into the medium (393). Another possibility is that the activity of important enzymes is impaired in old cultures, perhaps by progressive vitamin or mineral deficiency or by the accumulation of injurious substances. Upon inoculation of fresh medium, the regeneration or reactivation of essential enzymes would have to precede growth. A change to a radically different medium might demand the development of "adaptive" enzymes before growth could occur, or perhaps the environmental selection of types adapted to growth in the new medium. If the fresh medium contains mainly complex foods, some preliminary digestion might be a prerequisite for growth. Under certain conditions, changes in the organisms must be the major factor, since no relationship between length of the initial stationary phase and size of the inoculum has been observed in *Tetrahymena pyriformis* (439).

The lag phase. The occurrence of lag has been explained in various ways. According to one view, favorable changes are produced by the organisms in a "biological conditioning" of the medium. This possibility is supported by the stimulatory effects of old culture fluid added to fresh media for *Chilomonas paramecium* (393, 397), *Colpidium striatum* (378), and *Tetrahymena pyriformis* (187, 273) in pure cultures. An analogous "conditioning" has been noted in bacterized cultures of ciliates (260, 337). Another explanation is that the inoculated organisms are still recovering from damage suffered in the stock culture. Therefore, lag is a period of physiological recovery leading to the accumulation of metabolic intermediates essential for synthesis of protoplasm. During lag in cultures of *Tetrahymena pyriformis* there is marked phosphatase activity, with liberation of inorganic phosphate into the medium (123). The condition of the organisms evidently is the important factor in some cases, since inocula from cultures of *T. pyriformis* in the logarithmic phase show no lag while those from older stock cultures usually do (439). Such a relationship has been noted also in *Chilomonas paramecium* (222). The duration of lag in bacterized cultures of ciliates also may increase, up to a maximum, with age of the inoculum (491).

In addition to changes in fission-rate, changes in individual size may occur during lag. Inocula containing small *T. pyriformis* show a gradual increase to a mean size which is later maintained during the logarithmic phase. If the inoculated ciliates are large, the size decreases to about the same average as that reached by small ciliates (421).

Phase of logarithmic growth. In late lag the rate of growth increases to a maximum as the population enters the logarithmic phase. During this period the average size of individual organisms as well as the growth-rate may remain essentially constant, as in *T. pyriformis* (421). Length of this phase is influenced by various factors, and within such a genus as *Leishmania* (58), may vary with the species in a particular medium. The initial concentration of food is a major influence in cultures of *Astasia klebsii* (82), *Glaucoma scintillans* (272), and *T. pyriformis* (19, 116, 440), although the rate of fission may be independent of food concentration within wide limits (82, 440). Supplementary thiamine extends the logarithmic phase for *Chilomonas paramecium* in an acetate and ammonium-N medium (73), and any essential vitamin, food, or metal presumably could become a limiting factor during this phase of growth. A pure culture also may accumulate waste products or undergo other unfavorable changes which bring the logarithmic phase to an end.

Phase of negative growth acceleration. Such unfavorable changes as depletion of the food supply or marked changes in pH of the medium sooner or later become significant and the rate of fission decreases, as in *Euglena* (235, 236). Lower rates of oxygen consumption in this phase have been reported for *Chilomonas paramecium* (221), *Trypanosoma cruzi* (33), and *Tetrahymena pyriformis* (431). Changes in the respiratory quotient for *T. pyriformis* (431) also indicate qualitative changes in oxidative metabolism. There is also a gradual increase in size of individual ciliates in populations of *T. pyriformis* (421).

Phase of maximal density. Progressive changes in the culture medium finally check increase in number and the population reaches its maximum. Maximal density has been correlated with initial concentration of food in *Astasia klebsii* (82), *Glaucoma scintillans* (272), *Mayorella palestinensis* (473), *Paramecium bursaria* (326), and *T. pyriformis* (19, 116, 272, 440).

For certain organisms at least, the vitamin supply may be a more critical factor than the total amount of food. *T. pyriformis* shows almost no growth in a filtered and autoclaved peptone medium which has previously supported a population of the same species. With added thiamine and riboflavin, however, this used medium supports populations approximating those obtained with fresh peptone (181). Maximal density also may be limited by adverse changes in pH, as noted for *Chilomonas para-*

mecium in an acetate and inorganic-salt medium. As the medium becomes increasingly alkaline, growth ceases and death of the flagellates soon follows (73, 222). Periodic addition of acetic, hydrochloric, or lactic acid increases maximal density two- to four-fold (222).

Duration of the stationary phase may depend upon a variety of factors. The thiamine content of the medium is important for *T. pyriformis* (190, 552), and the pH of the medium is a limiting factor for *C. paramecium* (222). It is somewhat uncertain just how the population is maintained during this phase. Fission may continue at a rate which balances the losses from death, or the life of individual organisms may be prolonged.

Phases of death. Little is known about this phase in protozoan populations. Morphological changes often accompany the decline in population, and a gradual decrease in individual size to about half the maximum, observed in the maximal stationary phase, has been traced in *T. pyriformis* (421). Death may be accelerated by a sharp drop in pH, related to thiamine deficiency in a medium containing sugar (552). For some species the decline in numbers is described by a fairly smooth curve; in other cases, the curve is more or less irregular. Populations of *Paramecium bursaria* show a steady decline over a period of three weeks or more in certain media (326). Populations of *T. pyriformis,* in a casein-peptone medium, have decreased in two major steps separated by a period of several weeks in which the population remains almost constant. Following the second step, in which most of the ciliates die, a small population may persist at least six months longer (190). The longevity of such small populations is related to the available thiamine. *T. pyriformis* lives for about four months in a certain gelatin medium, while added thiamine extends life of the populations to 11-12 months. With peptone culture fluid which has previously supported growth, supplementary thiamine extends life of the cultures from a maximum of one week to a minimum of at least nine months (185).

Size of the inoculum in relation to growth. There are three possible relationships between the initial density of population and the rate of growth. (1) The rate of growth may be independent of the initial density under a given set of conditions. (2) The growth-rate may be higher with large than with small inocula. (3) The growth-rate may vary inversely with initial density of population.

A relationship of the first type has been noted in pure cultures of *T. pyriformis* (439). With optimal bacterial concentrations, a similar relationship has been observed in species-pure cultures of *Stylonychia pustalata* (16).

A relationship of the second type involves the so-called *allelocatalytic effect* of Robertson (488, 489, 490, 492, 493). According to Robertson's views, fission is stimulated by a nuclear autocatlyst which is liberated only during fission. Once fission has occurred, the autocatalyst which reaches the cytoplasm during nuclear division soon passes into the culture medium, there to accelerate later fissions. When the inoculum contains more than one organism, the liberation of more catalyst would cause mutual stimulation of fission, or *allelocatalysis*. Accordingly, the fission-rate varies more or less directly with size of the inoculum. An apparent allelocatalytic effect has been reported for bacterized cultures of certain ciliates (258, 436), *Chilomonas paramecium* (393), and *Mayorella palestinensis* (474). The case of *C. paramecium* has been questioned (178) because interpretations were based upon terminal counts without any information concerning the earlier history of populations.

Various explanations have been proposed for the Robertson effect. Cutler and Crump (78, 79, 80, 81) believed that Robertson's findings resulted from failure to control the bacterial flora of his cultures. The importance of the bacterial concentration also has been stressed by Johnson (258) who showed that, in cultures of *Oxytricha fallax*, the initial concentration of bacteria may determine whether a culture is to show a Robertson effect. Another possibility is that the initial pH of Robertson's poorly buffered medium was not optimal for his ciliates, which could change the pH toward the optimum (64). On this basis, two ciliates should produce such a change more rapidly than one and cause an allelocatalytic effect. Jahn (240) has suggested that, in similar fashion, the oxidation-reduction potential of the medium might be responsible for an allelocatalytic effect.

An inverse relationship between growth-rate and initial density was observed by Woodruff in *Paramecium aurelia* and *P. caudatum*. The more rapid reproduction with lower initial densities was attributed to less rapid accumulation of waste products (580). A comparable relationship has since been reported for cultures of *P. aurelia*, *P. caudatum*, and *Pleurotricha lanceolata* (167), *Stylonychia pustulata*, *P. caudatum* (88), and *Euglena* sp. (235). This so-called Woodruff effect is variously attributed to the accumulation of waste products in the medium, exhaustion of a scanty food supply, and changes in oxygen tension and pH away from the optimum.

Initial pH of the culture medium

The observed relations to growth indicate that pH of the medium influences utilization of food and synthesis of protoplasm, perhaps through effects on solubility and ionization of substrates and on permeability of the organism to components of the medium. Activities of extracellular enzymes also may be influenced by pH of the medium. The "internal" pH may be relatively independent of environmental pH, since immersion of *Amoeba dubia* in liquids at pH 5.5 and 8.0 induces no change in cytoplasmic pH (54) from the normal level of about 6.9 (479). However, the activity of a proteinase from *Tetrahymena pyriformis* varies with pH of the medium (312). Likewise, the rate of oxygen consumption by *Trypanosoma rhodesiense* decreases as pH of the medium falls, and both changes can be prevented by buffering the medium (64). Accelerating effects of carbohydrates on growth of *Tetrahymena pyriformis* are marked below pH 7.0, but are insignificant in alkaline media (114). The effect of plant auxins on growth of *Euglena gracilis* varies with pH of the medium and stimulation is greatest at pH 5.6 (118). The rate of locomotion in *Amoeba proteus* is related to pH of the medium (208, 449), and pseudopodial activity in ingestion of food may be influenced likewise. Also, the rate at which food vacuoles are formed in *Colpidium* increases from pH 4.5 to 6.0, and then decreases to zero at pH 8.0 (399).

For Protozoa in general growth in pure cultures has been reported

TABLE 8. 8. GROWTH-pH RELATIONSHIPS OF VARIOUS PROTOZOA IN PURE CULTURES

Species	pH Range	Optimum
MASTIGOPHORA		
Astasia klebsii, peptone (82)	3.2-8.2	4.2-6.0
Chilomonas paramecium, peptone (324)	4.2-8.4	4.8-5.1; 6.8-7.1
C. paramecium, peptone, acetate (324)	5.8-8.4	7.0
C. paramecium, heteroautotrophy (453)	5.7-6.7	
Chlorogonium elongatum, peptone (324)	4.9-8.7	7.6
C. elongatum, heteroautotrophy (453)	5.7-8.5	—
C. euchlorum, peptone (324)	4.9-8.7	7.4
C. euchlorum, heteroautotrophy (453)	5.7-8.5	—
Euglena anabaena, peptone (172)	4.5-8.3	6.9
E. deses, peptone (172)	5.3-8.0	7.0
E. gracilis, peptone (2)	3.0-7.7	6.7
E. gracilis, peptone (104)	3.5-9.0	—
E. gracilis, peptone (237)	3.9-9.9	6.6
E. gracilis var. *bacillaris* (331)	2.5-8.8	—
E. klebsii, peptone (105)	5.5-7.5	6.5
E. mutabilis, peptone (84)	2.1-7.7	3.4-5.4
E. pisciformis, peptone (105)	6.0-8.0	—
E. stellata, peptone (105)	4.5-8.0	5.5
E. viridis, inorganic (508)	4.0-7.2	—
Polytoma uvella (453), heteroautotrophy	7.1-8.5	—
Polytomella caeca (346), peptone	2.2-9.2	—
Trichomonas vaginalis (254)	4.9-7.5	5.4-5.8
SARCODINA		
Mayorella palestinensis (472)	6.4-7.2	6.8
CILIATEA		
Colpidium campylum (272)	—	5.4
Glaucoma scintillans (272)	—	5.6-6.8
Paramecium bursaria (328)	4.9-8.0	6.8
Tetrahymena pyriformis E (113)	4.5-8.5	5.5; 7.4
T. pyriformis GF-J (252)	4.9-9.5	5.1-6.0
T. pyriformis GP (252)	4.0-8.9	4.8-5.3
T. pyriformis H (114)	4.5-8.5	5.5; 7.4
T. pyriformis W (272)	—	5.6-8.0
Tetrahymena vorax (272)	—	6.2-7.6

between the pH limits 2.1 and 9.9 (Table 8.8). Survival for at least short periods may be possible within a wider range, such as pH 2.3-11.0 for *Euglena gracilis* (2), 2.0-9.65 for *E. gracilis* var. *bacillaris* (331), and 1.4-9.6 for *Polytomella caeca* (346). *Euglena mutabilis* apparently can survive in polluted waters at pH 1.8 (306), and in pure cultures, for at least 12 days within the range, 1.4-7.9 (84). Growth throughout most of the general range seems to have been observed only in *Euglena gracilis* and *Polytomella caeca,* and the specific range varies considerably in other species.

The pH optimum also varies from species to species and within one species under different conditions. Unfortunately, it is sometimes uncertain just what a reported "optimum" means in terms of protozoan growth. The apparent optimum may depend upon the time of observation, as in *Euglena gracilis* which showed heaviest growth at pH 6.6 after 8-9 days, but at pH 7.7-7.4 after seven weeks (237). Present knowledge of growth-pH relationships should be extended by tracing growth curves in media at different pH levels. Most of the available information does not eliminate the possibility that within reasonable limits, a pH above or below an apparent optimum may retard growth without modifying the eventual density of population.

The growth of *Astasia longa* in acid media throws some light on such questions (507). Growth in peptone medium at pH 3.7, for example, is rapid for the first few days and then ceases for a period of 3-5 weeks. Later, a second period of growth produces populations comparable in density to those obtained much sooner at higher pH levels (Fig. 8. 5). This resumption of growth apparently cannot be attributed to the slight rise in pH (0.1) during incubation. Only the first phase of growth is observed in a medium at pH 3.1 and second transfers in medium at the same pH show no significant growth after four months. A delayed growth phase seems to be limited to distinctly acid media since it has not appeared within the pH range, 6.0-9.6. A particularly interesting feature of these populations is the early increase in acid media, even at a pH level which inhibits later growth. The data suggest the possibility that inocula from a healthy culture may contain enough critical reserves to insure a 20- to 25-fold increase in number, in an unfavorable environment. This reserve apparently is exhausted before the flagellates are completely adjusted to the new environment, and in media which are not too acid, a period of "adaptation" precedes the resumption of growth.

Two periods of logarithmic growth separated by an appreciable stationary phase—Monod's phenomenon of "diauxie"—have been observed also in bacteria grown on a mixture of two carbohydrates (401). In such cases, it has been assumed that the first phase of growth ends with exhaustion of the more readily utilized substrate, and that the bacteria must become adapted to the second sugar before growth is resumed.

Relationships between growth and pH are further complicated by the occasional observation of two "optima" at the end of a given period. Such bimaximal relationships, which remain unexplained, have appeared in bacterized cultures of *Stylonychia pustulata* (87) and in pure cultures of *Tetrahymena pyriformis* (113, 252) and *Chilomonas paramecium*

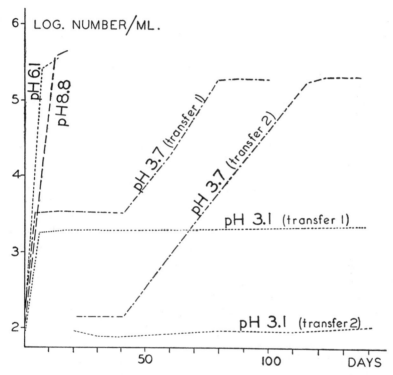

Fig. 8. 5. Growth of *Astasia longa* (strain J) in relation to pH of the medium. The curves are based on data of Schoenborn (507).

(324). The two optima are replaced by one in *T. pyriformis* (113) and *C. paramecium* (324) grown in the presence of acetate, and *T. pyriformis* also shows only one optimum in certain protein and peptone media (113, 114, 115, 252). Additional questions are raised by variations of the apparent optimum with the type of medium (113, 115, 252, 324). This may be the case in bacterized as well as in pure cultures. For instance, *Paramecium aurelia* has been assigned a pH optimum in certain cases, whereas the fission-rate of this ciliate fed on *Serratia marcescens* is practically the same between pH 5.9 and 7.7 (438). Growth of *Tetrahymena*

pyriformis on *Serratia marcescens* also was about the same between pH
4.5 and 8.6, but yields were greatest at about pH 5.0 and 7.4 in similar
suspensions of *Klebsiella pneumoniae, Pseudomoans fluorescens* and
Proteus vulgaris (253).

Temperature

The biothermal range, or range of temperature permitting growth,
extends from about 54 to aproximately 0° C. for Protozoa. Adaptation
to the higher temperatures within this range is rare, although certain
flagellates (at 54°), shelled rhizopods (at 51°), amoebae (at 50-52°) and
ciliates (at 46°) have been reported from hot springs (232).

Except for the unusual thermophilic species, active stages are killed
by temperatures approaching or exceeding 45°. *Euglena gracilis,* at pH
7.0, is killed within eight minutes at 44° (239); *Entamoeba gingivalis,*
within 20 minutes at 45° (299); *Paramecium caudatum,* within nine
seconds at 40° (451); *Spirostomum ambiguum,* at 36° (524); *Colpoda
cucullus,* at 37-45° after exposures of 0.5-10.0 minutes (17). Termite
flagellates are eliminated from their hosts after 24 hours at 36° (67),
and gregarine trophozoites from *Tenebrio* larvae after six days at 37.5°
(369). Lethal exposures depend upon time as well as temperature, and
the thermal death time at a given temperature also varies with pH of
the medium. The resistance of *Euglena gracilis* to high temperatures is
greatest at pH 5.0 and is less above pH 7.0 than below (239). *Paramecium
caudatum,* on the other hand, shows greater resistance to 40° above and
below pH 7.0 than at the neutral point (53). Both *E. gracilis* (239) and
P. multimicronucleatum (98) have shown increasing resistance with increasing density of population. After the maximum is reached, however,
resistance decreases gradually in older cultures of the latter.

Cysts are generally more resistant than corresponding active forms.
Dried cysts of *Colpoda cucullus,* for example, resist 100° dry heat for three
hours, although moistened cysts die within 30 minutes at temperatures of
49-55°. Excystment is retarded by non-lethal exposures to 37-48° (17).
Somewhat higher lethal temperatures, in 5-minute exposures to moist
heat, have been reported for intestinal parasites: *Entamoeba coli,* 76°;
E. histolytica, 68°; *Endolimax nana,* 64°; *Giardia lamblia,* 64°; *Chilomastix mesnili,* 72°; *Iodamoeba büschlii,* 64° (18). Unsporulated oocysts
of *Eimeria miyairii* are quickly killed at 53° (476).

Short exposure to temperatures below 0° C. is often not lethal to
active stages (111, 239, 576). Cultures of *Leishmania donovani* have remained viable after intermittent exposure to −12° over a period of 10
days (200) and *Entamoeba gingivalis* may live almost 18 hours at 0° (299).
Fission may continue slowly—for example, a fission every two weeks in
Paramecium caudatum (111)—at temperatures just below zero. Cytoplasmic division is more susceptible than nuclear division to extremes of

temperature in *Amoeba proteus,* so that binucleate forms are occasionally seen toward the limits of the range (86). Freezing (111, 239, 576) and prolonged exposure to sub-zero temperatures (111) are fatal to active stages of many species, although cysts of *Colpoda* have survived exposure to liquid air (546).

Little is known about biothermal ranges of individual species. However, fission occurs in *Amoeba proteus* at 11-30° (86); in *Astasia longa* at 15-30° in peptone media and at 22-30° in ammonium-N media (506); and in *Chilomonas paramecium* between 9.5 and 35° (529). An optimum for fission has been reported in a few species: *Paramecium aurelia,* 24-28.5° (581); *Chilomonas paramecium,* 26-30.5° (531); *Astasia longa,* 30° (506); *Tetrahymena geleii,* 28.5° in the range, 7.8-28.5° (441). *Euglena gracilis,* in peptone medium, has shown an optimum of 10° in darkness. With supplementary acetate, the optimum is shifted to about 23° which is approximately that for growth in light (243).

Temperature coefficients (Q_{10} values) and thermal increments (μ values) for fission have been calculated in several cases. For *Paramecium aurelia,* $Q_{10} = 2.7$ at 21.5-31.5° (581); for *P. aurelia,* $\mu = 23,000$ calories at 12-25° (400); for fission of *Amoeba proteus* (86), $\mu = 16,500$ calories at 11-30°, and for cytoplasmic division $\mu = 20,500$ (11-21°) and 7,300 (21-30°). For *Tetrahymena pyriformis,* Q_{10} and μ values vary with the temperature range: at 7.8-12.3°, $Q_{10} = 9.7$ and $\mu = 35,800$ cal.; at 12.3-20°, $Q_{10} = 3.0$ and $\mu = 18,400$; at 20-28.5°, $Q_{10} = 1.5$ and $\mu = 7,350$ (441). Reported Q_{10} values (22-28°) for *Astasia longa* vary with the medium— 2.10 in peptone, 2.17 in acetate and peptone, 1.28 in acetate and ammonium-N, and 8.03 in an inorganic medium (506).

The use of thermal coefficients and thermal increments in biology has been based upon the assumption that Q_{10} and μ values are related to the nature of a reaction, and upon the hope that a study of such data might furnish clues to the fundamental nature of various biological phenomena. The Q_{10} value is the coefficient of increase in the velocity of a reaction for each 10° increase in temperature. Q_{10} values are calculated from the equation,

$$\log Q_{10} = \frac{10 (\log k_1 - \log k_2)}{t_1 - t_2},$$

in which k_1 represents the reaction velocity at temperature t_1 and k_2 the velocity at temperature t_2. Log k is a linear function of temperature (Centigrade). For a particular reaction, Q_{10} values vary with temperature and usually increase as the temperature decreases. For example, Q_{10} may be 10 or greater for a given reaction at low temperatures, as compared with 2 or less for a higher range.

The thermal increment, described by the law of Arrhenius, is calculated from the equation,

$$\mu = \frac{4.6 \, (\log k_2 - \log k_1)}{\dfrac{1}{T_1} - \dfrac{1}{T_2}},$$

in which T_1 and T_2 are absolute temperature values. The μ value represents the heat of activation, or the number of calories required to transform one gram equivalent of "inactive molecules" of the reacting substance into "active" ones. There is a close relationship between μ and Q_{10} values, and the latter may be derived from the former for short temperature ranges. A Q_{10} value of 2.0 corresponds to a μ of about 13,200; a Q_{10} of 10, to a μ of about 44,000 calories. Unfortunately, the biological significance of thermal coefficients and thermal increments is uncertain.

Light and darkness

A source of light is obviously important for chlorophyll-bearing flagellates, in which the relation to photosynthesis doubtless accounts for various effects on growth. However, Dusi (106) has reported that under constant illumination *Euglena gracilis* grew well in peptone medium but poorly in inorganic medium, whereas *E. klebsii* grew well in inorganic medium under the same conditions. *E. viridis,* on the other hand, failed to grow under constant illumination. Temperature as the significant factor, rather than illumination, apparently was not completely excluded in these cases.

Light and darkness also may influence the effects of other factors on growth. Thus the thermal optimum for *Euglena gracilis* in peptone medium is about 10° in darkness and 25° in light (243). Accelerating effects of certain organic acids are relatively greater in darkness, while oxalate is slightly stimulatory in light and without effect in darkness (244). Plant auxins also have accelerated growth of *E. gracilis* in light but not in darkness (119).

Even less is known about growth of higher Protozoa in relation to light. Richards (481), in analyzing data on growth of several ciliates, noted that the seasonal rhythms reached a peak in July. On this basis, he suggested that temperature is less important than sunlight when both are variables. On the other hand, light of high intensity is lethal to pigmented *Blepharisma undulans,* the effect being attributed to a photooxidation of the pigment with irreversible damage to protoplasmic components (159). Indirect effects have been reported for *Plasmodium cathemerium.* Exposure of the hosts to artificially prolonged periods of "day" and "night" lengthen the cycle of merogony (26).

Effects of certain toxins and venoms

Bacterial exotoxins are relatively inactive against Protozoa. Exposure of *Paramecium aurelia, P. calkinsi,* and *P. caudatum* to diphtheria toxin has not affected fission-rate or death-rate (444), although undiluted culture filtrates containing this toxin may be lethal (559). Tetanus toxin (150 MLD) and botulinus toxin in various concentrations are without action on *P. caudatum* (445). On the other hand, a thermostable cytolysin produced by *Pseudomonas aeruginosa* is lethal to *Glaucoma scintillans* (60). Although ricin is inactive, certain snake venoms, in minimal concentrations of 1.4-150 µg/ml, are lethal to *P. caudatum*. Locomotion is inhibited and rupture of the cortex and disintegration of the ciliate occur sooner or later. Susceptibiltiy to *Crotalus atrox* venom varies with the species. *Bursaria truncatella*, *P. aurelia*, and *Stentor coeruleus* are killed within an hour, *Frontonia leucas*, *Oxytricha fallax*, and *Volvox* after longer periods, while certain other species are not harmed (445). This apparent resistance of certain species may be largely a matter of degree. For example, the MLD (minimum lethal dose) of *Crotalus atrox* venom for *Coleps hirtus* is nine times that for *Oxytricha fallax*. Sensitivity of 14 species to *Cobra* venom shows no apparent correlation with sensitivity to *Crotalus* venom (446). Adequate doses of antiserum completely protect *Paramecium multimicronucleatum* against lethal concentrations of *Cobra* venom (447).

Effects of certain therapeutic drugs

In addition to their action on growth of Protozoa, certain drugs have shown specific effects on metabolic activities (349). From a practical standpoint, such results are of interest because they help to plan attacks against parasites at vulnerable points. As more is learned about food requirements and metabolic activities, the development of specific drugs for particular parasites more closely approaches realization. Another interesting possibility is that the determination of specific effects of chemotherapeutic drugs may reveal additional tools for the analysis of protozoan metabolism.

Specific effects of certain therapeutic drugs have been reported for malarial parasites (349, 406) and trypanosomes. Hydrolysis of proteins by *Plasmodium gallinaceum* is retarded by atebrin and quinine (408), and the oxidation of carbohydrates also is retarded by these drugs (527). The antimalarial activity of a series of naphthoquinones seems to be related to their effects on succinic dehydrogenase (128, 199). Oxygen consumption of *Plasmodium cathemerium* is inhibited by sulfanilamide and sulfathiazole (562), and that of *P. knowlesi* by sulfanilamide (68) and quinine (134). Surprisingly, however, sulfanilamide has no effect on respiration of *P. inui*, and little or no therapeutic action, whereas the drug eradicates infections with *P. knowlesi* in the same host (69). Trivalent arsenicals (halarsol, reduced atoxyl, reduced tryparsamide) are powerful inhibitors of respiration in *Trypanosoma rhodesiense* (134).

Triose-phosphate dehydrogenases of *T. hippicum* are sensitive to oxophenarsine (194), and the activity of hexokinase also is inhibited by arsenicals in trypanosomes (62, 194, 379).

The susceptibility of Protozoa to certain antibiotics varies with the species. *Euglena gracilis* var. *bacillaris* remains viable in concentrations of penicillin at least five times as great as those tolerated by *Tetrahymena geleii* and the difference in resistance to streptomycin is of the same order (330). Tyrothricin, in chickens, has shown parasiticidal activity against extracellular merozoites of *Plasmodium gallinaceum* (544). Aureomycin likewise has shown activity against *Entamoeba histolytica* (374), and comparable effects have been reported more recently for terramycin (Chapter XI). One of the most interesting effects reported so far is the bleaching action of streptomycin on certain green flagellates, first reported in *Euglena gracilis* var. *bacillaris* (468). The effect, which involves a loss of the ability to synthesize chlorophyll, presumably is the result of specific damage to certain enzyme systems.

As mentioned above for pantothenic acid, pteroylglutamic acid and nucleic acid derivatives, certain vitamin analogues retard or inhibit growth and oxygen consumption of several Protozoa. In addition to the general interest of such findings and their bearing on the determination of vitamin requirements, the therapeutic value of certain pantothenate analogues in chickens infected with *Plasmodium gallinaceum* (28) indicates that results of practical value may be expected in further exploration of this field.

Effects of carcinogenic hydrocarbons

Stimulation of fission by several carcinogenic hydrocarbons has been reported for *Paramecium* (577), but these findings have not been confirmed (553). In the only investigation on ciliates in pure culture, Tittler (551) has obtained no evidence that 3,4-benzpyrene, methylcholanthrene, or 1,2,5,6-dibenzanthrene significantly influences growth of *Tetrahymena pyriformis*.

EFFECTS OF IRRADIATION

Irradiation is a tool of potential value in the study of various problems. One of the least explored is the possibility of inducing biochemical mutations in Protozoa, and the prospects grow more intriguing as protozoan food requirements become better known. Effects on rates of fission, as well as the immediate and pathological effects of irradiation, have interested a number of workers, so that such information is available for a few species.

Beyond the violet end of the visible spectrum extend the overlapping *ultraviolet*, *X-ray*, and *gamma-ray* spectra. The ultraviolet spectrum includes radiation from wave-lengths of about 390 mμ (3900 A., or Angstrom units) to 1.5 mμ or less. Rays of 390-200 mμ are transmitted through quartz and are sometimes termed the "quartz spectrum." Below 200 mμ lies the Schumann-Lyman-Millikan region in which the rays are absorbed by water, air, and most other materials. In the Schumann range (approximately 200-125mμ), fluorite is used for transmission.

The reported effects of ultraviolet irradiation vary with the wave length, the dosage, the species, and physiological condition of the organisms (155). In the quartz spectrum, radiation is relatively harmless at the longer wave lengths. Heavy dosage at 313 mμ is not lethal to *Paramecium multimicronucleatum* (157), and there is almost no effect on *Euglena* at 313 and 365 mμ (543). Excystment of *Colpoda duodenaria* is slightly retarded at 313 mμ in a dosage of not less than 30,000 ergs/mm^2, but tripled dosage at 366 mμ is without effect (153). *Peranema trichophorum* is killed at 253 mμ but not at longer wave lengths (523). Radiation at 302 mμ in a dosage of 28,000 ergs/mm^2, and also the shorter wave lengths in lighter dosage, are lethal to *P. multimicronucleatum* (157). Selective effects of particular wave lengths have been noted. Motor responses of *P. trichophorum* are most rapid at 302 mμ (523). Fission of *Paramecium caudatum* is retarded more markedly at 280.4 than by equivalent dosage at 265.4 mμ, although recovery from exposure to the longer wave lengths is more rapid. This difference in rate of recovery is attributed to greater absorption by nucleoproteins at 265.4. Since absorption is essentially the reverse for cytoplasmic proteins, fission is delayed to a greater extent at the longer wave length (152). At a particular wave length, the specific effects may vary with the dosage. At 280.4 mμ, immobilization of *P. caudatum* requires about 11,800 ergs/mm^2, while fission is retarded by 2,000-3,000 (154).

Effects of ultraviolet vary also with the species. *Fabrea salina* is about six times as resistant as *Tetrahymena pyriformis* and the latter is twice as resistant as *Blepharisma undulans* and *Spirostomum ambiguum* to radiation at 253.7 mμ (151). Differences also have been noted within the genus *Paramecium* and among several strains of *P. multimicronucleatum* (158). Physiological condition of the organisms also influences susceptibility. *Tetrahymena pyriformis* in old cultures is much less resistant than in young populations (151), and starved specimens of *Paramecium* are more susceptible than well-fed ciliates (158). Sensitivity of *P. caudatum* seems to be greatest in early stages of fission (201). Sensitivity of *Paramecium* also increases with rising temperature within the range, 0-30° (96), and preliminary exposure to ultraviolet increases susceptibility to high temperatures (23).

Effects on fission also have been noted. Fission of *P. caudatum* may be accelerated by light dosages (3, 201), and in the absence of serious injury, recovery from heavier dosage may be accompanied by accelerated fission (24). Still heavier dosages retard or inhibit fission (3, 152, 201, 524), and successive exposures may interrupt fission of *P. caudatum* to form chains of several individuals (201). The ultraviolet action spectrum for *Paramecium* has been described by Giese (154).

Certain morphological effects are to be expected. Liquefaction of the cortex in *Amoeba dubia* and *A. proteus* is followed by temporary liquefaction of the endoplasm and then, after heavier dosage, by gelation of the endoplasm (196). Comparable changes occur in *Spirostomum ambiguum* (524). After short exposures the endoplasm becomes fluid and cyclosis is accelerated, while prolonged exposure causes gradual increase in viscosity, and finally coagulation and vacuolation. Locomotion is accelerated at first, but ceases as lethal dosage is approached. Fragmentation of the macronuclear chain is common. The cortex eventually ruptures after lethal exposure. Vacuolation and cytolysis, following immobilization, also have been described in 11 other species of ciliates (151, 157). Cytolysis has not been observed in *Peranema trichophorum*, although immobilization, distortion of the body and coagulation of the endoplasm are characteristic effects (523). *Euglena gracilis* disintegrates after heavy dosage with quartz ultraviolet, but green flagellates are less sensitive than colorless strains of the species (250).

Beyond the ultraviolet, the X-ray spectrum extends into the region of gamma-rays emitted by radium, decreasing wave length being correlated with increasing power of penetration ("hardness"). Of the radium emanations (alpha, beta, and gamma rays), alpha-rays are softest and gamma-rays hardest. X-rays produced at 1,000 kv or more extend into the gamma-ray region.

The morphological effects of X-rays and radium are similar to those of ultraviolet. Movement of *Paramecium* (95) and *Colpidium* (76) is first accelerated and then retarded in lethal exposure to X-rays, and amoeboid movement is similarly affected by radium (435). Vacuolation of the cytoplasm, upon exposure to radium, has been noted in *Amoeba diploidea* (584), *A. vahlkampfia* (435), *Entamoeba histolytica* (409), and *Spirostomum ambiguum* (496), and the effect of X-rays on *Euplotes taylori* is similar (38). Cytolysis of *Paramecium* (95), although not of *Peranema trichophorum* (523), is caused by lethal dosage with X-rays, and lethal exposure to radium induces cytolysis of *Spirostomum ambiguum* (496). Heavy dosage with alpha rays (polonium source) causes immobilization and cytolysis of *Polytoma uvella*. Lighter dosage may be followed by fission, but the daughter flagellates undergo cytolysis (206). Sublethal exposure of *Eudorina elegans* to radium induces deformed daughter colonies containing less than the normal number of flagellates (169). Unusually large organisms, resulting from continued growth but retarded fission, occur in *Colpidium colpoda* after exposure to X-rays (76), and in *Bodo caudatus* (485, 487) and *Entamoeba histolytica* (409) after exposure to radium. The sensitivity of *Paramecium* to X-rays is increased by preliminary treatment with vital dyes and other reagents (97), and is less at 15° than at lower or higher temperatures (84a). *Paramecium bursaria* seems to be less sensitive to X-rays than its symbiotic algae, which are sometimes eliminated at certain dosages (572). Lethal effects of X-rays on *Tetrahymena pyriformis* in pure culture have been attributed to the production of H_2O_2 in culture media, which become toxic whether irradiated directly or prepared from irradiated distilled or tap water (547).

Effects of radium and X-rays on growth of populations have been described for several species. Growth of *Entamoeba histolytica,* exposed to gamma-rays primarily or to unscreened radium for 24-48 hours, reaches a maximum one 'to several days sooner than in the controls (409). Exposure of *P. caudatum* and *P. multimicronucleatum* to X-rays for 10 minutes to four hours has retarded fission for 2-5 days. Longer exposures, or exposures repeated at intervals of several days, may increase the fission-rate (191). *Bodo caudatus,* exposed continuously to gamma-rays in serial transfers, shows retarded fission and no acclimatization. Such effects may persist for several weeks after removal of the radium, although recovery is complete after three months. In a given transfer, the lag phase is prolonged almost three hours in irradiated cultures (485), and the period of greatest sensitivity occurs about 2.0-2.5 hours before the first fission in a new culture (486). Although the generation time is essentially normal thereafter, irradiated populations cannot catch up with the controls before the end of the incubation period. Slower growth in the young irradiated population is correlated with larger individual size. Irradiation for part of the incubation period, so as to allow 8-11 subsequent hours of growth, is followed by acceleration of growth to produce populations exceeding 90 per cent of the normal density (487). The production of ammonia (per culture and per flagellate) by *B. caudatus* is increased after exposures which produce maximal effects on size and fission-rate (313).

Locomotion

Locomotion in free-living Protozoa is of two basic types: *swimming,* which depends upon the activity of flagella, cilia, or their derivatives; and *creeping,* which is dependent upon direct contact with a substratum. Creeping in Amoebida and similar organisms usually involves pseudopodial activity and is termed *amoeboid movement.*

AMOEBOID MOVEMENT

Several explanations have been proposed for amoeboid movement (90, 382, 499). According to one view, locomotion in *Amoeba proteus* is a "walking" process in which extended pseudopodia become attached to the substratum and then contract to pull the body forward (91). A rolling movement has been attributed to *Amoeba verrucosa.* A given point on the surface passes forward on the upper surface, downward at the anterior end, remains on the lower surface for a time as the body rolls forward, and then passes upward at the posterior end to repeat the cycle (248). Locomotion in *Amoeba limax* has been interpreted as "fountain streaming," in which there is a forward streaming of endoplasm through a tubular layer of ectoplasm. During movement, endoplasm is continually converted into ectoplasm at the anterior end, and ectoplasm into endoplasm posteriorly. According to this interpretation, the flow on the upper surface is backward, instead of forward as in rolling movement (480).

Mast (382, 384) has resolved the ectoplasm of *A. proteus* into a thin elastic *plasmalemma*, or surface layer, and a thicker *plasmagel*. Between the two there is usually a hyaline fluid, except where the plasmalemma is attached to the substratum. During locomotion the plasmalemma flows forward, as in rolling movement. The plasmagel remains a tube which is converted into endoplasm (*plasmasol*) posteriorly and is formed from plasmasol anteriorly as a pseudopodium grows. Locomotion is attributed to several processes: (1) The plasmalemma becomes attached to the substratum. (2) There is a local, partial liquefaction of the plasmagel. (3) The rest of the plasmagel, which is under tension, forces the plasmasol against this weakened area to produce a bulge, the beginning of a pseudopodium. (4) Posteriorly, the inner surface of the contracting plasmagel is converted into plasmasol. (5) Anteriorly, the plasmagel tube is continuously regenerated by gelation of the plasmasol as the pseudopodium grows. The major factor is thus assumed to be a contraction of the ectoplasm, or plasmagel of Mast. The nature of this contraction remains uncertain, although it has been suggested that contraction represents the elastic recoil of a plasmagel under continuous tension (382), that syneresis of the plasmagel causes contraction (383, 433), and that the process of gelation involves or causes a contraction (231, 316).

In locomotion of shelled rhizopods, such as *Arcella* and *Difflugia,* a developing pseudopodium extends from the mouth of the shell and swings about freely until it makes contact with the substratum and adheres to it. Contraction of the pseudopodium then pulls the body forward (91, 383). If movement is to continue, a new pseudopodium is extended to repeat the process. Locomotion of creeping Foraminiferida, by means of myxopodia, is similar. The myxopodia are extended, become attached to the substratum, and then contract to pull the organism toward the point of attachment. Axopodia also may function to a limited extent in movement along a substratum. The mechanism in *Acanthocystis* (434) apparently involves terminal adhesion of axopodia, followed by a contraction which rolls the body toward the point of attachment.

FLAGELLAR LOCOMOTION

The mechanical aspects of flagellar activity have been disputed and various explanations have been suggested for locomotion in flagellates. Perhaps the most plausible mechanism is that suggested by Lowndes (333, 334, 335), whose data indicate that the basic function of the flagellum, at least in uniflagellate species, is to produce rotation of the organism on its major axis as well as gyration about an axis which marks the general direction of locomotion. In flagellar activity, waves pass spirally along the flagellum with increasing amplitude from base to tip, producing two distinct components of force. The resultant of these two components, acting on the anterior end of the flagellate, causes both rotation and gyration which, in an elongated organism, supply the force for propulsion, the principle being that of the screw or propeller. An additional forward component may be supplied by the flagellum itself if it is swung backward as in *Euglena viridis,* but not if it is merely swung outward more or less at a right angle as in *Rhabdomonas incurvum* (334). In such colonies as *Volvox,* the flagella are believed to act as propellers, drawing water toward the points of attachment and thus creating forward components of force. The stroke of the flagellum is so directed that the *Volvox* colony usually rotates in swimming, although rapid swimming without rotation also may occur (388). The ingenious experiments of Brown (36) produced data which agree with the interpretations of Lowndes, and indicate further that gyration of a flagellum alone also may produce a fairly effective locomotor force. This possibility may explain gliding in *Peranema trichophorum,* which Lowndes (333, 335) apparently could not reconcile with his observations on other flagellates.

Swimming in ciliates

In two respects, rotation of the body on its long axis and the usually spiral path of locomotion, swimming in ciliates resembles that in various flagellates. Therefore, the principle of the screw or propeller would seem applicable to swimming in ciliates also. However, the cilia themselves apparently contribute a major forward component of force in addition to causing rotation and gyration. This is indicated in the "browsing" movements of ciliates along a surface during feeding. Movement may be slower than in ordinary swimming, and particularly in various hypotrichs, rotation of the body does not occur. The activity of cilia, or their derivatives, is solely responsible for such movements. The analysis of ciliary behavior in moving ciliates is a more difficult problem than that of tracing flagellar movements. However, the activity of individual cilia seems to be quite variable (36, 499), and may even include spiral, flagellum-like undulations (36). Such a range of activity is presumably correlated with the variety of maneuvers to be observed in ciliates.

The spiral path followed in swimming, as traced by Bullington (39) in 164 species, shows a width, length, and direction rather characteristic of each species. Both rotation and gyration are attributed to the combined action of all the body cilia rather than a particular group. In ciliates normally tracing left spirals, the cilia beat obliquely backward to the right for forward movement. When the same ciliate swims backward, the cilia beat obliquely forward to the left. Although a given type of spiral is more or less characteristic of a species, five species of *Paramecium* (40) and four of *Frontonia* (41) may follow either right or left spirals, although swimming is always more rapid in one direction than in the other. Certain other ciliates swim either in right or in left spirals, but not in both. A right spiral is characteristic of backward swimming in both *Paramecium* and *Frontonia,* and is independent of the spiral followed in forward locomotion.

RESPONSES TO STIMULI

Reactions of Protozoa to different stimuli vary with the species as well as with the nature and intensity of the stimulus. Some species may show no reaction to a stimulus which evokes marked reactions in others. The responses studied most extensively are motor reactions which usually tend to move a sensitive organism toward or away from the source of stimulation with some regularity. The response typically involves the organism as a whole, and the morphological nature of the response depends upon and is limited by the structure of the organism. In other words, the response is a stereotyped reaction which depends primarily upon structural features of the species rather than upon the nature of the stimulus. The character of the response seems to be one of "trial and error" (248), rather than an immediate and directly induced orientation to the stimulus as would be required in the usual concept of *tropisms.*

In a typical species of *Euglena,* which rotates on its long axis and also follows a spiral path in swimming, the reaction to moderate stimulation usually shows the following pattern (248). Following stimulation, the gyrations of the anterior end of the body are suddenly widened, presumably by an increase in the transverse thrust of the flagellum, and then normal swimming is resumed in a new spiral path. If the stimulus is still encountered, the reaction is repeated until the organism enters a path in which there is no stimulating effect. If stimulation is intense enough, the flagellate temporarily stops forward movement or may move backward a short distance before turning into a new path. The reaction of a swimming ciliate is comparable to that of *Euglena.* Stimulation causes the organism to swim backward for a short distance, stop, and then swim forward in a new spiral. Or backward swimming may be omitted. If the stimulus is still effective, the characteristic reaction is repeated until the path of the organism eliminates the stimulating effect. Such hypotrichs as *Oxytricha* often creep about on the substratum without rotation of the body on the long axis. If stimulated while creeping, *Oxytricha* swims backward, swerves to the right, then swims forward again. The process is repeated until the stimulating effect disappears. In spiral swimming and in creeping the characteristic gyration or swerving occurs in a particular direction presumably determined by structure of the body. The reactions of amoeboid organisms are less complicated in that locomotion is by "creeping," without the rotation and gyration characteristic of freely swimming flagellates and ciliates. Changes in direction are brought about by formation of new pseudopodia at a different point on the body surface.

Responses to light

The reactions of Protozoa to light have been reviewed by Mast (380, 388). The stimulating intensity of light varies with the wave length as well as with the intensity of illumination. Within the visible spectrum, light at about 485 mμ produces the maximal effect on species of *Chlamydomonas, Euglena, Gonium, Phacus,* and *Trachelomonas,* while light at 535 mμ is most effective for *Eudorina, Pandorina,* and *Spondylomorum* (381). The stimulatory spectrum for *Volvox* (309) is similar to that for *Euglena.* Many flagellates—species of *Euglena, Chlamydomonas, Cryptomonas,* and *Gonium,* among others—react so that the path of locomotion is definitely oriented to the source of light. Others, such as *Peranema,* may show merely a shock reaction which is not followed by definite orientation. Species of *Euglena* (248, 380) respond to a sudden change in the intensity of illumination by their characteristic motor reaction, and the response is repeated until the stigma is equally illuminated at each point in the spiral path of locomotion. As a result, photopositive specimens swim toward the source, and photonegative specimens away from the source of light. Illumination of *Amoeba proteus* (386), which is photonegative in strong light, causes an increase in thickness of the plasmagel by inducing gelation of the adjacent plasmasol in the stimulated region. This increase in elastic strength causes a contraction of the plasmagel in the stimulated area. Therefore, the formation of pseudopodia in this region is inhibited and new pseudopodia will tend to develop at the opposite end of the body. A small increase in illumination may do nothing more than retard temporarily the growth of a pseudopodium. The result of the first type of reaction is a photonegative response, while the second type produces only a delay in locomotion. The photonegative *Stentor coeruleus* (248, 380), one of the few ciliates known to react definitely to light, shows a typical motor reaction to increased illumination, and the response is repeated until the organism is equally illuminated throughout its spiral course and is moving away from the source of light.

Reactions to electric current

Although reactions to the electric current can scarcely be considered part of the adjustment to natural environments, many Protozoa show rather specific responses. In the genus *Amoeba,* reactions vary with the species. *Amoeba proteus* shows a well defined orientation in direct current and moves toward the cathode, whereas *A. dofleini* shows no response (385). The reaction of *A. proteus* (168, 385) depends upon an induced solation at the cathodal surface, resulting in a decreased elastic strength of the plasmagel in this area. The response of the organism depends upon its orientation when stimulated. Amoebae moving toward the anode show reversal of protoplasmic flow at the cathodal end, followed by cessation of flow at the anodal end. If the current is too strong and the medium is not acid, disintegration of the organism begins at the anodal surface, whether the amoeba is moving toward or away from the cathode. With weaker currents, the direction of locomotion is reversed. Ciliates (249, 388) usually react to a direct current by reversal of the ciliary stroke on the cathodal surface. As a result, the body is turned so that the organism swims toward the cathode. In a strong but sub-lethal current, ciliary reversal may be so extensive that the ciliate swims backward toward the anode.

Responses to temperature

Reactions to unfavorable temperatures, as described for various ciliates, involve typical motor responses similar to those noted under stimulation of light in certain species. The response is repeated until the path of locomotion takes the organism into a region with a more favorable temperature.

LITERATURE CITED

1. Albaum, H. G., A. Schatz, S. H. Hutner, & A. Hirshfield 1950. *Arch. Biochem.* **29**: 210.
2. Alexander, G. 1931. *Biol. Bull.* **61**: 165.
3. Alpatov, W. W. and O. K. Nastjukova 1933. *Protoplasma* **18**: 281.
4. Amberson, W. R. 1928. *Biol. Bull.* **55**: 79.
5. Anderson, E. H. 1945. *J. Gen. Physiol.* **28**: 297.
6. Anderson, L. and G. W. E. Plaut 1949. "Table of oxidation-reduction potentials" in *Respiratory Enzymes* (Minneapolis: Burgess).
7. Andrews, J. M. and H. S. Lyford 1940. *Amer. J. Hyg.* **31**, C: 43.
8. Anfinsen, C. B., Q. M. Geiman, R. W. McKee, R. A. Ormsbee and E. G. Ball 1946. *J. Exp. Med.* **84**: 607.
9. Baker, E. G. S. and J. P. Baumberger 1941. *J. Cell. Comp. Physiol.* **17**: 285.
10. Baldwin, E. 1947. *Dynamic Aspects of Biochemistry* (Cambridge: The University Press).
11. Ball, E. G., C. B. Anfinsen, Q. M. Geiman, R. W. McKee and R. A. Ormsbee 1945. *Science* **101**: 542.
12. ———, ——— and O. Cooper 1947. *J. Biol. Chem.* **168**: 257.
13. Barker, H. A. 1935. *Arch. Mikrobiol.* **6**: 157.
14. ——— and C. V. Taylor 1931. *Physiol. Zool.* **4**: 620.
15. Becker, E. R. and L. Smith 1942. *Iowa St. Coll. J. Sci.* **16**: 443.
16. Beers, C. D. 1933. *Arch. f. Protistenk.* **80**: 36.
17. Bodine, J. H. 1923. *J. Exp. Zool.* **37**: 115.
18. Boeck, W. C. 1921. *Amer. J. Hyg.* **1**: 365.
19. Bond, R. M. 1933. *Bull. Bingham Oceanogr. Coll.* 4, Art. 4.
20. Bos, W. 1933. *Zentralbl. f. Bakt.*, Orig. **130**: 221.
21. Bovarnick, M. R., A. Lindsay and L. Hellerman 1946. *J. Biol. Chem.* **163**: 523.

22. ———, ——— and ——— 1946. *J. Biol. Chem.* **163**: 535.
23. Bovie, W. T. and G. A. Daland 1923. *Amer. J. Physiol.* **66**: 55.
24. ——— and D. M. Hughes 1918. *J. Med. Res.* **39**: 223.
25. Bowen, W. J. 1940. *Biol. Bull.* **79**: 114.
26. Boyd, G. H. 1929. *J. Exp. Zool.* **54**: 111.
27. Brackett, S. and H. Bliznick 1947. *J. Parasit.* **33**: 154.
28. ———, E. Waletsky and M. Baker 1946. *J. Parasit.* **32**: 453.
29. Brand, T. V. 1933. *Ztschr. vergl. Physiol.* **19**: 587.
30. ——— 1938. *Quart. Rev. Biol.* **13**: 41.
31. ——— 1950. *J. Parasit.* **36**: 178.
32. ——— and E. M. Johnson 1947. *J. Cell. Comp. Physiol.* **29**: 33.
33. ———, ——— and C. W. Rees 1946. *J. Gen. Physiol.* **30**: 163.
34. ——— and E. J. Tobie 1948. *J. Cell. Comp. Physiol.* **31**: 49.
35. ———, ——— and B. Mehlman 1950. *J. Cell. Comp. Physiol.* **35**: 273.
36. Brown, H. P. 1945. *Ohio J. Sci.* **45**: 247.
37. Brown, M. G. 1940. *Physiol. Zool.* **13**: 277.
38. ———, J. M. Luck, G. Sheets and C. V. Taylor 1933. *J. Gen. Physiol.* **16**: 397.
39. Bullington, W. E. 1925. *Arch. f. Protistenk.* **50**: 219.
40. ——— 1930. *J. Exp. Zool.* **56**: 423.
41. ——— 1939. *Arch. f. Protistenk.* **92**: 10.
42. Burbanck, W. 1942. *Physiol. Zool.* **15**: 342.
43. Burge, W. 1924. *Amer. J. Physiol.* **69**: 304.
44. Cailleau, R. 1933. *C. R. Soc. Biol.* **113**: 990.
45. ——— 1933. *C. R. Soc. Biol.* **114**: 474.
46. ——— 1934. *C. R. Soc. Biol.* **116**: 721.
47. ——— 1937. *Ann. Inst. Pasteur* **59**: 137.
48. ——— 1938. *C. R. Soc. Biol.* **127**: 861.
49. ——— 1938. *C. R. Soc. Biol.* **127**: 1421.
50. ——— 1939. *C. R. Soc. Biol.* **130**: 319.
51. ——— 1939. *C. R. Soc. Biol.* **131**: 964.
52. ——— 1940. *C. R. Soc. Biol.* **134**: 32.
53. Chalkley, H. W. 1930. *Physiol. Zool.* **3**: 425.
54. Chambers, R. 1928. *Biol. Bull.* **55**: 369.
55. ———, B. Cohen and H. Pollack 1932. *Protoplasma* **17**: 376.
56. Chang, S. L. 1946. *Parasitol.* **37**: 101.
57. ——— 1948. *J. Inf. Dis.* **82**: 109.
58. ——— and W. O. Negherbon 1947. *J. Inf. Dis.* **80**: 172.
59. Chatton, E. 1918. *C. R. Soc. Biol.* **81**: 343.
60. ——— and M. Chatton 1927. *C. R. Soc. Biol.* **97**: 289.
61. Cheissen, E. 1935. *Arch. f. Protistenk.* **85**: 426.
62. Chen, G. 1948. *J. Inf. Dis.* **82**: 226.
63. ——— and E. M. Geiling 1946. *Proc. Soc. Exp. Biol. Med.* **63**: 486.
64. Christophers, S. R. and J. D. Fulton 1938. *Ann. Trop. Med. Parasit.* **32**: 43.
65. ——— and ——— 1939. *Ann. Trop. Med. Parasit.* **33**: 161.
66. Clark, A. M. 1945. *Austral. J. Exp. Biol. Med. Sci.* **23**: 317.
67. Cleveland, L. R. 1924. *Biol. Bull.* **46**: 177.
68. Coggeshall, L. T. 1940. *J. Bact.* **39**: 30.
69. ——— 1940. *J. Exp. Med.* **71**: 13.
70. Cohen, B., R. Chambers and P. Reznikoff 1928. *J. Gen. Physiol.* **11**: 585.
71. Colas-Belcour, J. and A. Lwoff 1925. *C. R. Soc. Biol.* **93**: 1421.
72. Corliss, J. O. 1950. *Proc. Amer. Soc. Protozool.* **1**: 2.
73. Cosgrove, W. B. 1950. *Physiol. Zool.* **23**: 73.
74. Cosmovici, N. L. 1932. *Ann. Sci. Univ. Jassy* **17**: 294.
75. Craig, G. M. 1936. *Amer. J. Hyg.* **23**: 114.
76. Crowther, J. A. 1926. *Proc. Roy. Soc.*, B, **100**: 390.
77. Cunningham, B. and P. L. Kirk 1941. *J. Cell. Comp. Physiol.* **18**: 299.
78. Cutler, D. W. and L. M. Crump 1923. *Biochem. J.* **17**: 174.
79. ——— and ——— 1923. *Biochem. J.* **17**: 878.
80. ——— and ——— 1924. *Biochem. J.* **18**: 905.

81. —— and —— 1925. *Biochem. J.* **19**: 450.
82. Dach, H. v. 1940. *Ohio J. Sci.* **40**: 37.
83. —— 1942. *Biol. Bull.* **82**: 356.
84. —— 1943. *Ohio J. Sci.* **43**: 47.
85. Daniel, G. E. 1931. *Amer. J. Hyg.* **14**: 411.
86. —— and H. W. Chalkley 1933. *J. Cell. Comp. Physiol.* **2**: 311.
87. Darby, H. 1929. *Arch. f. Protistenk.* **65**: 1.
88. —— 1930. *J. Exp. Biol.* **7**: 308.
89. Dawson, J. A. and M. Belkin 1929. *Biol. Bull.* **56**: 80.
90. De Bruyn, P. P. H. 1947. *Quart. Rev. Biol.* **22**: 1.
91. Dellinger, O. P. 1906. *J. Exp. Zool.* **3**: 337.
92. Dewey, V. C. 1944. *Biol. Bull.* **87**: 107.
93. —— and G. W. Kidder 1940. *Biol. Bull.* **79**: 225.
94. Dogiel V. and M. Issakowa-Keo 1927. *Biol. Centralbl.* **47**: 577.
95. Dognon, A. and C. Piffault 1931. *C. R. Soc. Biol.* **107**: 1272.
96. —— and —— 1931. *C. R. Soc. Biol.* **107**: 1501.
97. —— and —— 1931. *C. R. Soc. Biol.* **107**: 1503.
98. Doudoroff, M. 1936. *J. Exp. Zool.* **72**: 369.
99. Doyle, W. L. 1943. *Biol. Rev.* **18**: 119.
100. —— and J. P. Harding 1937. *J. Exp. Biol.* **14**: 462.
101. —— and E. K. Patterson 1942. *Science* **95**: 206.
102. Dubois, A. 1936. *C. R. Soc. Biol.* **123**: 141.
103. Dunihue, F. W. 1931. *Arch. f. Protistenk.* **75**: 476.
104. Dusi, H. 1933. *Ann. Inst. Pasteur* **50**: 550.
105. —— 1933. *Ann. Inst. Pasteur* **50**: 840.
106. —— 1937. *Arch. f. Protistenk.* **89**: 94.
107. —— 1939. *C. R. Soc. Biol.* **130**: 419.
108. —— 1940. *Ann. Inst. Pasteur.* **64**: 340.
109. —— 1941. *Ann. Inst. Pasteur* **66**: 159.
110. —— 1944. *Ann. Inst. Pasteur* **70**: 311.
111. Efimoff, W. W. 1925. *Arch. f. Protistenk.* **49**: 433.
112. Eisenberg-Hamburg, E. 1929. *Arch. f. Protistenk.* **68**: 451.
113. Elliott, A. M. 1933. *Biol. Bull.* **65**: 45.
114. —— 1935. *Arch. f. Protistenk.* **84**: 156.
115. —— 1935. *Arch. f. Protistenk.* **84**: 225.
116. —— 1935. *Arch. f. Protistenk.* **84**: 472.
117. —— 1935. *Biol. Bull.* **68**: 82.
118. —— 1938. *Physiol. Zool.* **11**: 31.
119. —— 1939. *Trans. Amer. Micr. Soc.* **58**: 385.
120. —— 1939. *Physiol. Zool.* **12**: 363.
121. —— 1949. *Physiol. Zool.* **22**: 337.
122. —— 1950. *Physiol. Zool.* **23**: 85.
123. —— and R. L. Hunter 1950. *Proc. Amer. Soc. Protozool.* **1**: 7.
124. Emerson, R. 1929. *J. Gen. Physiol.* **13**: 153.
125. Emik, L. O. 1941. *Trans. Amer. Micr. Soc.* **60**: 1.
126. Fenyvessy, B. v. and L. Reiner 1924. *Ztschr. Hyg. Infekt.* **102**: 109.
127. —— and —— 1928. *Biochem. Ztschr.* **202**: 75.
128. Fieser, L. F. and H. Heymann 1948. *J. Biol. Chem.* **176**: 1363.
129. Fortner, H. 1926. *Arch. f. Protistenk.* **56**: 295.
130. Foster, J. W. 1949. *Chemical Activities of Fungi* (New York: Academic Press).
131. ——, S. F. Carson, D. S. Anthony, J. B. Davis, W. E. Jefferson and M. V. Long 1949. *Proc. Nat. Acad. Sci.* **35**: 663.
132. Franck, J. and W. E. Loomis (editors) 1949. *Photosynthesis in Plants* (Ames: Iowa State College Press).
133. Fulton, J. D. 1939. *Ann. Trop. Med. Parasit.* **33**: 217.
134. —— and S. R. Christophers 1938. *Ann. Trop. Med. Parasit.* **32**: 177.
135. —— and T. S. Stevens 1945. *Biochem. J.* **39**: 317.
136. —— and W. Yorke 1941. *Ann. Trop. Med. Parasit.* **35**: 221.
137. —— and —— 1941. *Ann. Trop. Med. Parasit.* **35**: 233.

138. Furgason, W. 1940. *Arch. f. Protistenk.* **94**: 224.
139. Garnjobst, L., E. L. Tatum and C. V. Taylor 1943. *J. Cell. Comp. Physiol.* **21**: 199.
140. Gause, G. F. 1934. *Zool. Anz.* **105**: 219.
141. ———— 1935. *Arch. f. Protistenk.* **84**: 207.
142. ————, O. K. Nastjukova and W. W. Alpatov 1934. *J. Anim. Ecol.* **3**: 222.
143. ———— and A. A. Witt 1935. *Amer. Nat.* **69**: 596.
144. Gaw, H. Z. 1936. *Arch. f. Protistenk.* **87**: 185.
145. ———— 1936. *Arch. f. Protistenk.* **87**: 201.
146. Gelei, J. v. 1937. *Mikrokosmos* **30**: 111.
147. ———— 1937. *Arch. f. Protistenk.* **88**: 295.
148. Gelfan, S. 1927. *Univ. Calif. Publ. Zool.* **29**: 453.
149. ———— 1928. *Protoplasma* **4**: 192.
150. Genghof, D. S. 1949. *Arch. Biochem.* **23**: 85.
151. Giese, A. C. 1938. *J. Cell. Comp. Physiol.* **12**: 129.
152. ———— 1939. *J. Cell. Comp. Physiol.* **13**: 139.
153. ———— 1941. *J. Cell. Comp. Physiol.* **18**: 272.
154. ———— 1945. *J. Cell. Comp. Physiol.* **26**: 47.
155. ———— 1945. *Physiol. Zool.* **18**: 223.
156. ———— 1946. *J. Cell. Comp. Physiol.* **28**: 119.
157. ———— and P. A. Leighton 1935. *J. Gen. Physiol.* **18**: 557.
158. ———— and E. A. Reed 1940. *J. Cell. Comp. Physiol.* **15**: 395.
159. ———— and E. Zeuthen 1949. *J. Gen. Physiol.* **32**: 525.
160. Glaser, R. W. and N. A. Coria 1930. *J. Exp. Med.* **51**: 787.
161. ———— and ———— 1933. *J. Parasit.* **20**: 33.
162. ———— and ———— 1935. *Amer. J. Hyg.* **21**: 111.
163. ———— and ———— 1935. *Amer. J. Hyg.* **22**: 221.
164. Granick, S. 1949. *J. Biol. Chem.* **179**: 505.
165. Green, D. E. 1949. "The Citric Acid Cycle and the Cyclophorase System" in *Respiratory Enzymes* (Minneapolis: Burgess).
166. Greenberg, J. 1949. *Proc Soc. Exp. Biol. Med.* **71**: 306.
167. Greenleaf, W. E. 1926. *J. Exp. Zool.* **46**: 143.
168. Hahnert, W. F. 1932. *Physiol. Zool.* **5**: 491.
169. Halberstaedter, L. and A. Luntz 1929. *Arch. f. Protistenk.* **68**: 177.
170. Hall, R. H. 1941. *Physiol. Zool.* **14**: 193.
171. Hall, R. P. 1933. *Anat. Rec.* **57** (suppl.): 95.
172. ———— 1933. *Arch. f. Protistenk.* **79**: 239.
173. ———— 1937. *Trans. Amer. Micr. Soc.* **56**: 285.
174. ———— 1937. *Arch. f. Protistenk.* **90**: 178.
175. ———— 1938. *Arch. f. Protistenk.* **91**: 465.
176. ———— 1939. *Quart. Rev. Biol.* **14**: 1.
177. ———— 1939. *Arch. Zool. Exp. Gén.* **80** (N. et R.): 61.
178. ———— 1941. *Amer. Nat.* **75**: 419.
179. ———— 1942. *Physiol. Zool.* **15**: 95.
180. ———— 1943. *Vitamins and Hormones* **1**: 249.
181. ———— 1944. *Physiol. Zool.* **17**: 200.
182. ———— 1950. *Proc. Amer. Soc. Protozool.* **1**: 5.
183. ———— and W. B. Cosgrove 1944. *Biol. Bull.* **86**: 31.
184. ———— and ———— 1945. *Physiol. Zool.* **18**: 425.
185. ———— and ———— 1947. *Anat. Rec.* **99** (suppl.): 130.
186. ———— and J. B. Loefer 1936. *Protoplasma* **26**: 321.
187. ———— and ———— 1940. *Proc. Soc. Exp. Biol. Med.* **43**: 128.
188. ———— and H. W. Schoenborn 1938. *Arch. f. Protistenk.* **90**: 259.
189. ———— and ———— 1939. *Physiol. Zool.* **12**: 76.
190. ———— and A. Shottenfeld 1941. *Physiol. Zool.* **14**: 384.
191. Hance, R. T. and H. Clark 1926. *J. Exp. Med.* **43**: 61.
192. Hardin, G. 1942. *Physiol. Zool.* **15**: 466.
193. Hartman, E. 1927. *Amer. J. Hyg.* **7**: 407.
194. Harvey, S. C. 1949. *J. Biol. Chem.* **179**: 435.

195. Haye, A. 1930. *Arch. f. Protistenk.* **70**: 1.
196. Heilbrunn, L. V. and K. Daugherty 1933. *Protoplasma* **18**: 596.
197. Herfs, A. 1922. *Arch. f. Protistenk.* **44**: 227.
198. Hetherington, A. 1936. *Biol. Bull.* **70**: 426.
199. Heymann, H. and L. F. Fieser 1948. *J. Biol. Chem.* **176**: 1359.
200. Hindle, E. and W. S. Patton 1926. *Proc. Roy. Soc. London,* B, **100**: 385.
201. Hinrichs, M. A. 1928. *Physiol. Zool.* **1**: 394.
202. Hinshelwood, C. N. 1946. *The Chemical Kinetics of the Bacterial Cell* (Oxford: Clarendon Press).
203. Hogue, M. J. 1923. *J. Elisha Mitchell Sci. Soc.* **39**: 49.
204. Holter, H. and W. L. Doyle 1938. *J. Cell. Comp. Physiol.* **12**: 295.
205. —— and M. J. Kopac 1937. *J. Cell. Comp. Physiol.* **10**: 423.
206. Holweck, F. and A. Lacassagne 1931. *C. R. Soc. Biol.* **107**: 812.
207. Holz, G. 1950. *Physiol. Zool.* **23**: 213.
208. Hopkins, D. L. 1928. *J. Morph.* **45**: 97.
209. —— 1928. *Biol. Bull.* **75**: 337.
210. Horowitz, N. H. 1945. *Proc. Nat. Ac. Sci.* **31**: 153.
211. Howland, R. B. 1924. *J. Exp. Zool.* **40**: 231.
212. —— 1928. *Protoplasma* **5**: 127.
213. —— and A. Bernstein 1931. *J. Gen. Physiol.* **14**: 339.
214. —— and H. Pollack 1927. *J. Exp. Zool.* **48**: 441.
215. Humphrey, B. A. and G. F. Humphrey 1948. *J. Exp. Biol.* **25**: 123.
216. Hungate, R. E. 1938. *Ecology* **19**: 1.
217. —— 1939. *Ecology* **20**: 230.
218. —— 1942. *Biol. Bull.* **83**: 303.
219. —— 1943. *Biol. Bull.* **84**: 157.
220. Hutchens, J. O. 1940. *J. Cell. Comp. Physiol.* **16**: 265.
221. —— 1941. *J. Cell. Comp. Physiol.* **17**: 321.
222. —— 1948. *J. Cell. Comp. Physiol.* **32**: 105.
223. ——, B. J. Jandorf and A. B. Hastings 1941. *J. Biol. Chem.* **138**: 321.
224. ——, B. Podolsky and M. F. Morales 1948. *J. Cell. Comp. Physiol.* **32**: 117.
225. Hutner, S. H. 1936. *Arch. f. Protistenk.* **88**: 93.
226. —— 1948. *Trans. N. Y. Acad. Sci.,* Ser. II, **10**: 136.
227. —— and C. A. Bjerknes 1948. *Proc. Soc. Exp. Biol. Med.* **67**: 393.
228. —— and L. Provasoli 1951. "Phytoflagellates" in *Physiology and Biochemistry of Protozoa* (New York: Academic Press).
229. ——, ——, A. Schatz and C. P. Haskins 1950. *Proc. Amer. Philos. Soc.* **94**: 152.
230. ——, ——, S. L. R. Stokstad, C. E. Hoffman, M. Belt, A. Franklin and T. H. Jukes 1949. *Proc. Soc. Exp. Biol. Med.* **70**: 118.
231. Hyman, L. H. 1917. *J. Exp. Zool.* **24**: 55.
232. Issel, R. 1910. *Intern. Rev. Ges. Hydrobiol. Hydrogeog.* **3**: 178.
233. Ivanič, M. 1933. *Arch. f. Protistenk.* **79**: 200.
234. Jacobs, L. 1950. *Amer. J. Trop. Med.* **30**: 803.
235. Jahn, T. L. 1929. *Biol. Bull.* **57**: 81.
236. —— 1930. *Biol. Bull.* **58**: 281.
237. —— 1931. *Biol. Bull.* **61**: 387.
238. —— 1933. *Protoplasma* **20**: 90.
239. —— 1933. *Arch. f. Protistenk.* **79**: 249.
240. —— 1934. *Cold Spr. Harb. Symp. Quant. Biol.* **2**: 167.
241. —— 1935. *Arch. f. Protistenk.* **86**: 225.
242. —— 1935. *Arch. f. Protistenk.* **86**: 238.
243. —— 1935. *Arch. f. Protistenk.* **86**: 251.
244. —— 1935. *Arch. f. Protistenk.* **86**: 258.
245. —— 1936. *Proc. Soc. Exp. Biol. Med.* **33**: 494.
246. —— 1941. "Respiratory Metabolism" in *Protozoa in Biological Research* (New York: Columbia Univ. Press).
247. Jay, G. 1938. *Anat. Rec.* **72** (suppl.): 164.
248. Jennings, H. S. 1904. *Publ. Carneg. Inst. Wash.,* No. 16.

249. ——— 1906. *Behavior of the Lower Organisms* (New York: Columbia Press).
250. Jírovec, O. 1934. *Protoplasma* **21**: 577.
251. Johnson, D. F. 1935. *Anat. Rec.* **64** (suppl.): 106.
252. ——— 1935. *Arch. f. Protistenk.* **86**: 263.
253. ——— 1936. *Arch. f. Protistenk.* **86**: 359.
254. Johnson, G. 1940. *Proc. Soc. Exp. Biol. Med.* **45**: 567.
255. ——— 1942. *J. Parasit.* **28**: 369.
256. ——— and A. B. Kupferberg 1948. *Proc. Soc. Exp. Biol. Med.* **67**: 390.
257. Johnson, M. J. 1949. "Oxidation-reduction Potentials" in *"Respiratory Enzymes* (Minneapolis: Burgess).
258. Johnson, W. H. 1933. *Physiol. Zool.* **6**: 22.
259. ——— 1937. *Amer. Nat.* **71**: 5.
260. ——— 1941. *Amer. Nat.* **75**: 438.
261. ——— 1941. *Quart. Rev. Biol.* **16**: 336.
262. ——— 1950. *Proc. Amer. Soc. Protozool.* **1**: 9.
263. ——— and E. G. S. Baker 1943. *Physiol. Zool.* **16**: 172.
264. Jones, E. P. 1930. *Biol. Bull.* **59**: 274.
265. Kaczka, E. A., D. E. Wolf, F. A. Kuehl, Jr. and K. Folkers 1950. *Science* **112**: 354.
266. Kalmus, H. 1927. *Biol. Zentralbl.* **47**: 595.
267. ——— 1928. *Ztschr. vergl. Physiol.* **7**: 314.
268. ——— 1929. *Arch. f. Protistenk.* **66**: 409.
269. Karlsson, J. L. and H. A. Barker 1948. *J. Bact.* **56**: 670.
270. ——— and ——— 1948. *J. Biol. Chem.* **175**: 913.
271. Keilin, D. and E. F. Hartree 1945. *Biochem. J.* **39**: 293.
272. Kidder, G. W. 1941. *Biol. Bull.* **80**: 50.
273. ——— 1941. *Physiol. Zool.* **14**: 220.
274. ——— 1941. "The Technique and Significance of Control in Protozoan Culture" in *Protozoa in Biological Research* (New York: Columbia Press).
275. ——— 1946. *Arch. Biochem.* **9**: 51.
276. ——— 1947. *Ann. N. Y. Acad. Sci.* **49**: 99.
277. ——— and V. C. Dewey 1942. *Growth* **6**: 405.
278. ——— and ——— 1944. *Biol. Bull.* **87**: 121.
279. ——— and ——— 1945. *Physiol. Zool.* **18**: 136.
280. ——— and ——— 1945. *Arch. Biochem.* **6**: 425.
281. ——— and ——— 1945. *Arch. Biochem.* **6**: 433.
282. ——— and ——— 1945. *Biol. Bull.* **89**: 131.
283. ——— and ——— 1945. *Biol. Bull.* **89**: 229.
284. ——— and ——— 1945. *Arch. Biochem.* **8**: 293.
285. ——— and ——— 1948. *Proc. Nat. Acad. Sci.* **34**: 81.
286. ——— and ——— 1948. *Proc. Nat. Acad. Sci.* **34**: 566.
287. ——— and ——— 1949. *Arch. Biochem.* **20**: 433.
288. ——— and ——— 1949. *J. Biol. Chem.* **178**: 383.
289. ——— and ——— 1949. *Arch. Biochem.* **21**: 58.
290. ——— and ——— 1949. *Arch. Biochem.* **21**: 66.
291. ——— and ——— 1949. *J. Biol. Chem.* **179**: 181.
292. ———, ——— and R. E. Parks 1951. *Physiol. Zool.* **24**: 69.
293. ———, ———, ——— and M. R. Heinrich 1950. *Proc. Nat. Ac. Sci.* **36**: 431.
294. King, R. L. 1933. *Trans. Amer. Micr. Soc.* **52**: 103.
295. Kitching, J. A. 1938. *J. Exp. Biol.* **15**: 143.
296. ——— 1938. *Biol. Rev.* **13**: 403.
297. ——— 1939. *J. Exp. Biol.* **16**: 34.
298. Kline, A. P. 1943. *Physiol. Zool.* **16**: 405.
299. Koch, D. 1927. *Univ. Calif. Publ. Zool.* **31**: 17.
300. Koehring, V. 1930. *J. Morph.* **49**: 45.
301. Kolkwitz, R. N. and M. Marsson 1908. *Ber. deutsch. bot. Ges.* **26a**: 505.
302. Krijgsman, B. J. 1936. *Ztschr. vergl. Physiol.* **23**: 664.
303. Kupferberg, A. B., G. Johnson and H. Sprince 1948. *Proc. Soc. Exp. Biol. Med.* **67**: 304.
304. Lackey, J. B. 1929. *Bull. N. J. Agr. Exp. St.,* No. 417.

305. ——— 1932. *Biol. Bull.* **63**: 287.
306. ——— 1938. *U. S. Publ. Health Rep.* **53**: 1499.
307. Lamy, L. 1948. *C. R. Soc. Biol.* **142**: 633.
308. Lardy, H. A., et al 1949. *Respiratory Enzymes* (Minneapolis: Burgess).
309. Laurens, H. and H. D. Hooker 1920. *J. Exp. Zool.* **30**: 345.
310. Lawrie, N. R. 1935. *Biochem. J.* **29**: 547.
311. ——— 1935. *Biochem. J.* **29**: 2297.
312. ——— 1937. *Biochem. J.* **31**: 789.
313. ——— and M. Robertson 1935. *Biochem. J.* **29**: 1017.
314. Leslie, L. D. 1940. *Physiol. Zool.* **13**: 243.
315. Lewin, J. C. 1950. *Science* **112**: 652.
316. Lewis, W. H. 1939. *Arch. exp. Zellforsch.* **23**: 1.
317. Lilly, D. M. 1942. *Physiol. Zool.* **15**: 146.
318. Lindeman, R. L. 1942. *Ecology* **23**: 1.
319. Lipmann, F., N. O. Kaplan, G. D. Novelli, L. C. Tuttle and B. M. Giurard 1947. *J. Biol. Chem.* **167**: 869.
320. Lloyd, F. E. and J. Beattie 1928. *Biol. Bull.* **55**: 404.
321. Loefer, J. B. 1934. *Biol. Bull.* **66**: 1.
322. ——— 1934. *Science* **80**: 206.
323. ——— 1935. *Arch. f. Prótistenk.* **84**: 456.
324. ——— 1935. *Arch. f. Protistenk.* **85**: 209.
325. ——— 1936. *Arch. f. Protistenk.* **87**: 142.
326. ——— 1936. *J. Exp. Zool.* **72**: 387.
327. ——— 1938. *J. Exp. Zool.* **79**: 167.
328. ——— 1938. *Arch. f. Protistenk.* **90**: 185.
329. ——— 1942. *Physiol. Zool.* **15**: 333.
330. ——— 1949. *Texas J. Sci.* **1**: 92.
331. ——— 1950. *Texas J. Sci.* **2**: 225.
332. ——— and R. P. Hall 1936. *Arch. f. Protistenk.* **87**: 123.
333. Lowndes, A. G. 1941. *Proc. Zool. Soc. London* **111** (A): 111.
334. ——— 1943. *Proc. Zool. Soc. London* **113** (A): 99.
335. ——— 1944. *Proc. Zool. Soc. London* **114**: 325.
336. Luck, J. M., G. Sheets and J. O. Thomas 1931. *Quart. Rev. Biol.* **6**: 46.
337. Ludwig, W. and C. Boost 1939. *Arch. f. Protistenk.* **92**: 453.
338. Lund, E. J. 1918. *Amer. J. Physiol.* **45**: 365.
339. ——— 1918. *Amer. J. Physiol.* **47**: 167.
340. Lwoff, A. 1932. *Recherches biochimiques sur la nutrition des protozoaires* (Paris: Masson).
341. ——— 1934. *Zentralbl. Bakt., Orig.* **130**: 498.
342. ——— 1935. *C. R. Soc. Biol.* **119**: 974.
343. ——— 1938. *Arch. f. Protistenk.* **90**: 194.
344. (See: 353).
345. ——— 1938. *C. R. Soc. Biol.* **128**: 455.
346. ——— 1941. *Ann. Inst. Pasteur* **66**: 407.
347. ——— 1943. *L'évolution physiologique* (Paris: Hermann).
348. ——— 1947. *Ann. Rev. Microbiol.* **1**: 101.
349. ——— (editor) 1951. *Physiology and Biochemistry of Protozoa* (New York: Academic Press).
350. ——— and H. Dusi 1935. *C. R. Soc. Biol.* **119**: 1260.
351. ——— and ——— 1937. *C. R. Ac. Sci.* **205**: 630.
352. ——— and ——— 1937. *C. R. Ac. Sci.* **205**: 756.
353. ——— and ——— 1938. *C. R. Soc. Biol.* **127**: 53.
354. ——— and ——— 1938. *C. R. Soc. Biol.* **127**: 1408.
355. ——— and ——— 1941. *Ann. Inst. Pasteur* **67**: 229.
356. ———, H. Ionesco and A. Gutman 1949. *C. R. Ac. Sci.* **228**: 342.
357. ——— and M. Lwoff 1938. *C. R. Soc. Biol.* **127**: 1170.
358. ———, C. B. van Niel, F. J. Ryan and E. L. Tatum 1946. *Cold Spr. Harb. Symp. Quant. Biol.* **11**: 302.
359. ———, F. Nitti, J. Trefouël and V. Hamon 1941. *Ann. Inst. Pasteur* **67**: 9.

360. ———— and L. Provasoli 1935. *C. R. Soc. Biol.* **119**: 90.
361. ———— and ———— 1937. *C. R. Soc. Biol.* **126**: 279.
362. ———— and N. Roukhelman 1929. *C. R. Ac. Sci.* **183**: 156.
363. Lwoff, M. 1933. *Ann. Inst. Pasteur* **51**: 55.
364. ———— 1934. *C. R. Soc. Biol.* **115**: 237.
365. ———— 1936. *C. R. Soc. Biol.* **121**: 419.
366. ———— 1940. *Recherches sur le pouvoir de synthèse des flagellés trypanosomides* (Paris: Masson).
367. ———— and A. Lwoff 1929. *C. R. Soc. Biol.* **102**: 569.
368. Lyford, H. S. 1941. *Amer. J. Hyg.* **33, C**: 69.
369. MacDougall, M. M. 1942. *J. Parasit.* **28**: 233.
370. McKee, C. M., J. D. Dutcher, V. Groupé and M. Moore 1947. *Proc. Soc. Exp. Biol. Med.* **65**: 326.
371. McKee, R. W., R. A. Ormsbee, C. B. Anfinsen, Q. M. Geiman and E. G. Ball 1946. *J. Exp. Med.* **84**: 569.
372. MacLennan, R. F. 1936. *Arch. f. Protistenk.* **86**: 404.
373. ———— 1942. *J. Exp. Zool.* **91**: 1.
374. McVay, L. V., R. L. Laird and D. H. Sprunt 1949. *Science* **109**: 590.
375. Maier, J. and L. T. Coggeshall 1941. *J. Inf. Dis.* **69**: 87.
376. ———— and E. Riley 1942. *Proc. Soc. Exp. Biol. Med.* **50**: 152.
377. Mainx, F. 1928. *Arch. f. Protistenk.* **60**: 355.
378. Marbarger, J. P. 1943. *Physiol. Zool.* **16**: 186.
379. Marshall, P. B. 1948. *Brit. J. Pharmacol.* **3**: 8.
380. Mast, S. O. 1911. *Light and the Behavior of Organisms* (New York: Wiley).
381. ———— 1917. *J. Exp. Zool.* **22**: 471.
382. ———— 1926. *J. Morph.* **41**: 347.
383. ———— 1931. *Biol. Bull.* **61**: 223.
384. ———— 1931. *Protoplasma* **14**: 321.
385. ———— 1931. *Ztschr. vergl. Physiol.* **15**: 309.
386. ———— 1932. *Physiol. Zool.* **5**: 1.
387. ———— 1938. *Biol. Bull.* **75**: 389.
388. ———— 1941. "Motor Responses in Unicellular Animals" in *Protozoa in Biological Research* (New York: Columbia Press).
389. ———— 1942. *Biol. Bull.* **83**: 173.
390. ———— and D. M. Pace 1933. *Protoplasma* **20**: 326.
391. ———— and ———— 1935. *Physiol. Zool.* **8**: 255.
392. ———— and ———— 1935. *Protoplasma* **23**: 297.
393. ———— and ———— 1938. *Physiol. Zool.* **11**: 359.
394. ———— and ———— 1938. *J. Exp. Zool.* **79**: 429.
395. ———— and ———— 1939. *J. Cell. Comp. Physiol.* **14**: 261.
396. ———— and ———— 1942. *J. Cell. Comp. Physiol.* **20**: 1.
397. ———— and ———— 1946. *Physiol. Zool.* **19**: 223.
398. ————, ———— and L. R. Mast 1936. *J. Cell. Comp. Physiol.* **10**: 1.
399. Mills, S. M. 1931. *J. Exp. Biol.* **8**: 17.
400. Mitchell, W. H. 1929. *J. Exp. Zool.* **54**: 383.
401. Monod, J. 1949. *Ann. Rev. Microbiol.* **3**: 371.
402. Morea, L. 1927. *C. R. Soc. Biol.* **97**: 49.
403. Moulder, J. W. 1948. *J. Inf. Dis.* **83**: 33.
404. ———— 1948. *J. Inf. Dis.* **83**: 42.
405. ———— 1948. *J. Inf. Dis.* **83**: 262.
406. ———— 1948. *Ann. Rev. Microbiol.* **2**: 101.
407. ———— 1949. *J. Inf. Dis.* **85**: 195.
408. ———— and E. A. Evans, Jr. 1946. *J. Biol. Chem.* **164**: 145.
409. Nasset, E. C. and C. A. Kofoid 1928. *Univ. Calif. Publ. Zool.* **31**: 387.
410. Nattan-Larrier, L. and J. Dufour 1936. *C. R. Soc. Biol.* **122**: 514.
411. Niel, C. B. van 1949. "The Comparative Biochemistry of Photosynthesis" in *Photosynthesis in Plants* (Ames: Iowa St. Coll. Press).
412. ————, J. O. Thomas, S. Ruben and M. D. Kamen 1942. *Proc. Nat. Acad. Sci.* **28**: 157.

413. Nierenstein, E. 1925. *Ztschr. wiss. Zool.* **125:** 513.
414. Noland, L. E. 1925. *Ecology* **6:** 437.
415. Novy, F. G. 1932. *J. Lab. Clin. Med.* **17:** 731.
416. Ochoa, S. 1951. *Physiol. Rev.* **31:** 56.
417. Oehler, R. 1919. *Arch. f. Protistenk.* **40:** 16.
418. ———— 1920. *Arch. f. Protistenk.* **41:** 34.
419. Ogsdon, A. G. and O. Smithies 1948. *Physiol. Rev.* **28:** 283.
420. Ondratschek, K. 1940. *Arch. Mikrobiol.* **11:** 219.
421. Ormsbee, R. A. 1942. *Biol. Bull.* **82:** 423.
422. Osterud, K. L. 1946. *Physiol. Zool.* **19:** 19.
423. Pace, D. M. 1941. *J. Cell. Comp. Physiol.* **18:** 243.
424. ———— 1945. *Biol. Bull.* **89:** 76.
425. ———— 1947. *Exper. Med. Surg.* **5:** 140.
426. ———— and W. H. Belda 1944. *Biol. Bull.* **86:** 146.
427. ———— and ———— 1944. *Biol. Bull.* **87:** 138.
428. ———— and R. L. Ireland 1945. *J. Gen. Physiol.* **28:** 547.
429. ———— and K. K. Kimura 1944. *J. Cell. Comp. Physiol.* **24:** 173.
430. ———— and T. E. Kimura 1946. *Proc. Soc. Exp. Biol. Med.* **62:** 223.
431. ———— and E. D. Lyman 1947. *Biol. Bull.* **92:** 210.
432. Pannier, R. 1936. *C. R. Soc. Biol.* **122:** 29.
433. Pantin, C. F. A. 1923. *J. Mar. Biol. Assoc.* **13:** 24.
434. Penard, E. 1904. *Les héliozoaires d'eau douce* (Genève: Kündig).
435. Petschenko, B. 1926. *Ann. Roentgenol. Radiol.* **2:** 40.
436. Petersen, W. A. 1929. *Physiol. Zool.* **2:** 221.
437. Peterson, R. E. 1942. *J. Biol. Chem.* **146:** 537.
438. Phelps, A. 1934. *Arch. f. Protistenk.* **82:** 134.
439. ———— 1935. *J. Exp. Zool.* **70:** 109.
440. ———— 1936. *J. Exp. Zool.* **72:** 479.
441. ———— 1946. *J. Exp. Zool.* **102:** 277.
442. Phillips, B. P. 1950. *Science* **111:** 8.
443. ———— and C. W. Rees 1950. *Amer. J. Trop. Med.* **30:** 185.
444. Philpott, C. H. 1928. *J. Morph.* **46:** 85.
445. ———— 1930. *J. Exp. Zool.* **56:** 167.
446. ———— 1931. *Biol. Bull.* **60:** 64.
447. ———— 1931. *Science* **74:** 157.
448. Picken, L. E. R. 1936. *J. Exp. Biol.* **13:** 387.
449. Pitts, R. F. and S. O. Mast 1934. *J. Cell. Comp. Physiol.* **4:** 237.
450. Panticorvo, L., D. Rittenberg, and K. Bloch 1949. *J. Biol. Chem.* **179:** 839.
451. Port, J. 1927. *Protoplasma* **2:** 401.
452. Pringsheim, E. G. 1921. *Beitr. allg. Bot.* **2:** 88.
453. ———— 1934. *Naturwiss.* **22:** 510.
454. ———— 1935. *Naturwiss.* **23:** 110.
455. ———— 1935. *Naturwiss.* **23:** 197.
456. ———— 1937. *Nature* **139:** 196.
457. ———— 1937. *Planta* **26:** 631.
458. ———— 1937. *Planta* **26:** 665.
459. ———— 1937. *Planta* **27:** 61.
460. ———— 1948. *New Phytol.* **47:** 52.
461. ———— and F. Mainx 1926. *Planta* **1:** 583.
462. Provasoli, L. 1935. *C. R. Soc. Biol.* **119:** 93.
463. ———— 1937. *C. R. Soc. Biol.* **126:** 280.
464. ———— 1937. *C. R. Soc. Biol.* **126:** 847.
465. ———— 1938. *C. R. Soc. Biol.* **127:** 51.
466. ———— 1938. *C. R. Soc. Biol.* **127:** 190.
467. ———— 1938. *Boll. Zool. Agr. Bachicolt.* **9:** 1.
468. ————, S. H. Hutner and A. Schatz 1948. *Proc. Soc. Exp. Biol. Med.* **69:** 279.
469. Pruthi, H. S. 1926. *J. Exp. Biol.* **4:** 292.
470. Rabinowitch, E. I. 1945. *Photosynthesis and Related Processes* (New York: Interscience).

471. Rahn, O. 1941. *Growth* **5**: 197.
472. Reich, K. 1935. *J. Exp. Zool.* **69**: 497.
473. ——— 1936. *Physiol. Zool.* **9**: 254.
474. ——— 1938. *Physiol. Zool.* **11**: 347.
475. Reiner, L., C. V. Smythe and J. T. Pedlow 1936. *J. Biol. Chem.* **113**: 75.
476. Reinhardt, J. F. and E. R. Becker 1933. *Iowa St. Coll. J. Sci.* **7**: 505.
477. Rees, C. W., J. Bozicevich, L. V. Reardon and F. S. Daft 1944. *Amer. J. Trop. Med.* **24**: 189.
478. ———, ———, ——— and F. Jones 1942. *Amer. J. Trop. Med.* **22**: 581.
479. Reznikoff, P. and H. Pollack 1928. *Biol. Bull.* **55**: 377.
480. Rhumbler, L. 1898. *Arch. Entwickl. Org.* **7**: 103.
481. Richards, O. 1929. *Biol. Bull.* **56**: 298.
482. ——— 1941. "The Growth of Protozoa" in *Protozoa in Biological Research* (New York: Columbia Univ. Press).
483. ——— and M. C. Troutman 1940. *J. Bact.* **39**: 739.
484. Riedmüller, L. 1936. *Zentralbl. Bakt., Orig.* **137**: 428.
485. Robertson, M. 1932. *Quart. J. Micr. Sci.* **75**: 511.
486. ——— 1935. *Brit. J. Radiol.* **8**: 502.
487. ——— 1935. *Brit. J. Radiol.* **8**: 570.
488. Robertson, T. B. 1921. *Biochem. J.* **15**: 595.
489. ——— 1921. *Biochem. J.* **15**: 612.
490. ——— 1922. *J. Physiol.* **56**: 404.
491. ——— 1924. *Austral. J. Exp. Biol. Med. Sci.* **1**: 105.
492. ——— 1924. *Austral. J. Exp. Biol. Med. Sci.* **1**: 151.
493. ——— 1924. *Biochem. J.* **18**: 1240.
494. Rockland, L. B. and M. S. Dunn 1949. *J. Biol. Chem.* **179**: 511.
495. Root, W. S. 1930. *Biol. Bull.* **59**: 48.
496. Roskin, G. 1929. *Arch. f. Protistenk.* **66**: 340.
497. Roth, J. S., A. M. Elliott and R. L. Hunter 1950. *Proc. Amer. Soc. Protozool.* **1**: 7.
498. Salle, A. J. and C. L. A. Schmidt 1928. *J. Inf. Dis.* **43**: 378.
499. Schaeffer, A. A. 1920. *Amoeboid Movement* (Princeton Univ. Press).
500. Schaffer, J. G. and W. W. Frye 1948. *Amer. J. Hyg.* **47**: 214.
501. ———, F. W. Ryden and W. W. Frye 1948. *Amer. J. Hyg.* **47**: 345.
502. Schinazi, L. A., W. Drell, G. H. Ball and M. S. Dunn 1950. *Proc. Soc. Exp. Biol. Med.* **75**: 229.
503. Schoenborn, H. W. 1940. *Ann. N. Y. Acad. Sci.* **40**: 1.
504. ——— 1942. *Physiol. Zool.* **15**: 325.
505. ——— 1946. *Physiol. Zool.* **19**: 430.
506. ——— 1947. *J. Exp. Zool.* **105**: 269.
507. ——— 1949. *J. Exp. Zool.* **111**: 437.
508. ——— 1950. *Trans. Amer. Micr. Soc.* **69**: 217.
509. Schopfer, W. H. and W. Rytz, Jr. 1937. *Arch. Mikrobiol.* **8**: 244.
510. Seaman, G. R. 1949. *J. Cell. Comp. Physiol.* **33**: 1.
511. ——— 1949. *J. Cell. Comp. Physiol.* **33**: 137.
512. ——— 1949. *J. Cell. Comp. Physiol.* **33**: 441.
513. ——— 1949. *Biol. Bull.* **96**: 257.
514. ——— 1950. *J. Cell. Comp. Physiol.* **36**: 129.
515. ——— 1950. *J. Biol. Chem.* **186**: 97.
516. ——— and R. K. Houlihan 1950. *Arch. Biochem.* **26**: 436.
517. Searle, D. B. and L. Reiner 1940. *Proc. Soc. Exp. Biol. Med.* **43**: 80.
518. ——— and ——— 1941. *J. Biol. Chem.* **141**: 563.
519. Seeler, A. O. 1945. *J. Nat. Mal. Soc.* **4**: 13.
520. ———, O. Graessle and E. D. Dusenbery 1943. *J. Bact.* **45**: 205.
521. Senekjie, H. A. and R. A. Lewis 1945. *Amer. J. Trop. Med.* **25**: 345.
522. Shapiro, N. N. 1927. *Trans. Amer. Micr. Soc.* **46**: 45.
523. Shettles, L. B. 1938. *J. Cell. Comp. Physiol.* **12**: 263.
524. Shirley, E. S. and H. E. Finley 1949. *Trans. Amer. Micr. Soc.* **68**: 136.
525. Shive, W. and J. Macow 1946. *J. Biol. Chem.* **162**: 451.
526. Shoup, C. S. and J. T. Boykin 1931. *J. Gen. Physiol.* **15**: 107.

527. Silverman, M., J. J. Ceithaml, L. G. Taliaferro and E. A. Evans, Jr. 1944. *J. Inf. Dis.* **75**: 212.
528. Slater, J. V. 1950. *Proc. Amer. Soc. Protozool.* **1**: 7.
529. Smith, J. A. 1940. *Biol. Bull.* **79**: 379.
530. Snyder, T. L. and H. E. Meleney 1943. *J. Parasit.* **29**: 278.
531. Soule, M. H. 1925. *J. Inf. Dis.* **36**: 245.
532. Specht, H. 1934. *J. Cell. Comp. Physiol.* **5**: 319.
533. Spek, J. F. and E. A. Evans, Jr. 1945. *J. Biol. Chem.* **159**: 71.
534. ———— and ———— 1945. *J. Biol. Chem.* **159**: 83.
535. ————, J. W. Moulder and E. A. Evans, Jr. 1946. *J. Biol. Chem.* **164**: 119.
536. Sprince, H. and A. B. Kupferberg 1947. *J. Bact.* **53**: 435.
537. ———— and ———— 1947. *J. Bact.* **53**: 441.
538. Stephenson, M. 1949. *Bacterial Metabolism* (London: Longmans, Green & Co.).
539. Stokstad, E. L. R. 1941. *J. Biol. Chem.* **139**: 475.
540. ————, C. E. Hoffman, M. A. Regan, D. Fordham and T. H. Jukes 1949. *Arch. Biochem.* **20**: 75.
541. Sullivan, W. D. 1948. *Trans. Amer. Micr. Soc.* **67**: 262.
542. Sutherland, E. W., T. Z. Posternak and C. F. Cori 1949. *J. Biol. Chem.* **179**: 501.
543. Swann, W. F. G. and G. del Rosario 1932. *J. Franklin Inst.* **213**: 549.
544. Taliaferro, L. G., F. Coulston and M. Silverman 1944. *J. Inf. Dis.* **75**: 179.
545. Tatum, E. L., L. Garnjobst and C. V. Taylor 1942. *J. Cell. Comp. Physiol.* **20**: 211.
546. Taylor, C. V. and A. H. R. Strickland 1935. *Physiol. Zool.* **9**: 15.
547. ————, J. O. Thomas and M. G. Brown 1933. *Physiol. Zool.* **6**: 467.
548. ———— and W. J. van Wagtendonk 1941. *J. Cell. Comp. Physiol.* **17**: 349.
549. Ternetz, C. 1912. *Jahrb. wiss. Bot.* **51**: 435.
550. Thomas, J. O. 1943. *Thesis*, Stanford University.
551. Tittler, I. A. 1948. *J. Exp. Zool.* **108**: 309.
552. ———— 1949. *Anat. Rec.* **105** (suppl.): 21.
553. ———— and M. Kobrin 1942. *Proc. Soc. Exp. Biol. Med.* **50**: 95.
554. Trager, W. 1932. *Biochem. J.* **26**: 1763.
555. ———— 1934. *Biol. Bull.* **66**: 182.
556. ———— 1943. *J. Exp. Med.* **77**: 411.
557. Trussell, R. E. and G. Johnson 1941. *Proc. Soc. Exp. Biol. Med.* **47**: 176.
558. ———— and E. D. Plass 1940. *Amer. J. Obstetr. Gynecol.* **40**: 883.
559. Tunnicliff, R. 1928. *Proc. Soc. Exp. Biol. Med.* **26**: 213.
560. Umbreit, W. W., R. H. Burris and J. F. Stauffer 1949. *Manometric Techniques and Tissue Metabolism* (Minneapolis: Burgess).
561. ———— and I. C. Gunsalus 1945. *J. Biol. Chem.* **159**: 333.
562. Velick, S. F. 1942. *Amer. J. Hyg.* **35**: 152.
563. Wachendorff, T. 1912. *Ztschr. allg. Physiol.* **13**: 105.
564. Wagtendonk, W. J. and P. L. Hackett 1949. *Proc. Nat. Acad. Sci.* **35**: 155.
565. Weatherby, J. H. 1927. *Biol. Bull.* **52**: 208.
566. ———— 1929. *Physiol. Zool.* **2**: 375.
567. Weber, M. M., J. Cowperthwaite and S. H. Hutner 1950. *Proc. Amer. Soc. Protozool.* **1**: 2.
568. Weiss, E. D. and G. H. Ball 1947. *Proc. Soc. Exp. Biol. Med.* **65**: 278.
569. Weisz, P. B. 1950. *J. Morph.* **86**: 177.
570. Wendel, W. B. 1943. *J. Biol. Chem.* **148**: 21.
571. ———— and S. Kimball 1942. *J. Biol. Chem.* **145**: 343.
572. Wichterman, R. 1948. *Biol. Bull.* **94**: 113.
573. Wildeman, É. de 1928. *Ann. Protistol.* **1**: 127.
574. Williams, R. J. 1943. *Vitamins and Hormones* **1**: 229.
575. Witte, J. 1933. *Zentralbl. Bakt., Orig.* **128**: 188.
576. Wolfson, C. 1935. *Ecology* **16**: 630.
577. Wolman, M. 1940. *Growth* **3**: 387.
578. Wood, H. G. 1946. *Physiol. Rev.* **26**: 198.
579. Wooley, D. W. 1951. *J. Exp. Med.* **93**: 13.
580. Woodruff, L. L. 1911. *J. Exp. Zool.* **10**: 558.
581. ———— and G. A. Baitsell 1911. *Amer. J. Physiol.* **29**: 147.

582. Zuelzer, M. 1910. *Arch. Entwickl. Org.* **27**: 632.
583. ———— 1927. *Arch. f. Protistenk.* **57**: 247.
584. ———— and E. Philipp 1925. *Biol. Zentralbl.* **45**: 557.
585. Zweibaum, J. 1921. *Arch. f. Protistenk.* **44**: 99.

IX

Heredity in Protozoa[1]

INHERITANCE WITHIN THE STRAIN

Strains, races, biotypes

A PROTOZOAN SPECIES is composed of strains (races, biotypes, or stocks) which differ among themselves in hereditary traits. Such races have long been known in *Paramecium* (24, 25), *Difflugia* (27), *Arcella* (21) and *Centropyxis* (70). Observations on mating types of ciliates (Chapter II) have shown that a conventional species also may include varieties which are completely, or almost completely, unable to interbreed. This situation creates taxonomic problems which cannot be solved until more is known about mating types and the comparative characteristics of these different ciliate strains. Racial characteristics are of various kinds. Dif-

---

[1] Reviews of protozoan genetics have been published by Jennings (28, 29, 30) and Sonneborn (76, 81).

ferences in size and fission-rate are well known in various ciliates. Strains of *Tetrahymena* in pure cultures have shown minor differences in biochemical activities (Chapter VIII), and in the extent to which they can become acclimatized to salt solutions (42). Differences in pathogenicity, noted among strains of parasitic species, may be paralleled by morphological differences. Strains of *Entamoeba histolytica* with relatively low pathogenicity may show a small average size (16). In *Plasmodium vivax*, relatively low and high degrees of pathogenicity may be correlated with slow and rapid reproduction. That these racial characteristics are inherited is indicated by their persistence in cultures or in infected animals.

Tendency toward genetic uniformity

Although non-hereditary differences, induced perhaps by environmental factors, may be expected within a race, reproduction by fission or budding should insure exact duplication of genes from generation to generation, barring mutations or mitotic accidents. Therefore, genetic constancy of the race would be expected in the absence of sexual phenomena. In general, this expectation has been realized. Such was the case in the early work of Jennings (24) on *Paramecium*. Although separation of wild populations into several races was usually possible, selection for size within the race was no longer effective. Similar findings of Ackert (1) and Jollos (33) also indicated that the race is relatively constant. However, certain apparent exceptions have been reported.

Apparently spontaneous changes

Selection within the race, continued for many generations, has produced distinct stocks of *Difflugia corona* differing in number and length of spines, diameter and height of the shell, and diameter of the mouth (27). Comparable effects have been observed in *Centropyxis aculeata* (70) and *Arcella dentata* (21). These results remain unexplained. Although it is possible that gene mutations were involved, undetected environmental differences might have been perpetuated under the experimental conditions of continued selection. In the latter case, the different types probably could be considered results of acclimatization rather than mutations.

Comparable changes within the race have been reported in a few ciliates. By opposite selection through more than 150 generations, Middleton (48) established two strains of *Stylonychia pustulata* differing in rate of fission. During selection there was a gradual increase in the average difference, indicating that the effects of selection were cumulative. Since these differences persisted after conjugation and also through fission for several months after selection was discontinued, Middleton suggested that the selection of small variations may be "an effective evolutionary procedure." Similar changes, involving size, division-rate, and resistance to environmental factors, were observed by Raffel (65, 66) in a clone of *Paramecium aurelia*. The new types did not revert to normal, even after conjugation, and were believed to have arisen by gene mutation. The origin of two unusual biotypes—differing from the parent stock in rarity of conjugation, lower division-rate, higher mortality, and frequency of morphological abnormalities—also has been reported by Sonneborn and Lynch (92) in *P. aurelia*.

Some of these hereditary changes in ciliates were attributed to endomixis (5, 15, 92). Diller's (11) report of autogamy in *P. aurelia* was discounted as a possible explanation on the grounds that his evidence for autogamy was far from convincing and that extraordinary assumptions would be necessary in relating autogamy to the appearance and subsequent disappearance of particular traits (92). The recent conclusion of Sonneborn (81), that autogamy (and *not* endomixis) occurs in his strains of *P. aurelia*, evidently leaves some of these intraracial changes in ciliates unexplained for the present. The effects of selection described in *Stylonychia pustulata* cannot be ascribed to endomixis or autogamy because neither process seems to have been observed in this species.

Certain morphological changes in ciliates have been interpreted as mutations. An example is Hance's (19) race of *Paramecium caudatum* with 2-7 extra contractile vacuoles, an abnormality inherited in fission and unaffected by selection or conjugation. Likewise, hereditary changes in number of nuclei have been observed in *P. bursaria* (101). A truncated type of *P. aurelia* has shown similar behavior, persisting through more than 400 generations without being influenced by conjugation or endomixis (9). MacDougall's (43) tetraploid mutant in *Chilodonella uncinatus* also bred true.

Environmentally induced changes

A variety of changes may be induced by modification of environmental conditions. Although some cases of acclimatization may represent merely the selection of a resistant strain from a genetically mixed population, serologically distinct types evidently can arise within a pure line, as in *Trypanosoma brucei* (67).

Changes in resistance to chemical agents have been investigated in parasitic and free-living species. Among the parasites, most of the work has been done on trypanosomes[2] in which antigenic modifications, occurring during an infection, are especially interesting. After inoculation of a guinea pig, for example, with *Trypanosoma rhodesiense*, the flagellates increase in number for a time. Suddenly, most of them are killed by a newly developed antibody. The survivors continue to multiply, so that

[2] Papers by Dobell (14) and Taliaferro (93) may be consulted for references to the earlier literature.

the blood is repopulated by a *relapse strain*. This relapse strain is resistant to the trypanocidal antibody which is still present in the host and is still active against the original strain (*passage strain*). Two explanations have been suggested: (1) the activity of the antibody brings about selection of a resistant strain (the relapse strain) from an originally mixed population; (2) as the result of an antigenic change, the trypanocidal antibody is no longer specific for flagellates which give rise to the relapse strain. The second interpretation receives support from the fact that an infection started with a pure line of *T. brucei* showed the usual development of a relapse strain (67). The treatment of different strains of *Paramecium aurelia* with homologous antisera also has induced antigenic changes which are inherited (89).

Similar phenomena have been observed in chemotherapy of trypanosomiasis. Most of the flagellates are killed, but a few may survive to produce a resistant strain—often termed an "arsenic-fast" or "antimony-fast" strain, depending upon the type of drug, although such a designation may not be entirely accurate. In tests of several substituted phenylarsenoxides, for instance, trypanosomes have seemed to develop resistance to substituent basic or acidic groups on the phenylarsenoxide molecule rather than to the arsenoxide group as such (72). This drug resistance may persist for long periods. Strains of *T. rhodesiense* have remained resistant to atoxyl, tryparsamide, and acriflavine for 7.5 years through 900 mouse transfers (52), and to atoxyl for 12.5 years through 1,500 mouse transfers (17). A strain of *T. brucei* was still tryparsamide-resistant after 59 transfers through guinea pigs and four through *Glossina morsitans* (52). A tryparsamide-resistant strain of *T. rhodesiense* has been produced also by repeated treatment of the flagellates *in vitro*. The trypanosomes were exposed to the drug, washed, and then inoculated into a mouse. The strain was recovered from the mouse and the procedure was repeated a number of times, with the result that the flagellates became at least 500 times as resistant as the original stock (103). Among the malarial parasites, *Plasmodium gallinaceum* has inherited paludrine-resistance in five cyclical transfers through mosquitoes without intervening drug treatment (4). The mechanism involved in development of resistance to drugs is unknown. One suggestion is that resistant trypanosomes have lost their normal ability to absorb active drugs (23). In addition, differences in stainability of normal and resistant strains have been demonstrated, and the development of resistance may accompany shifts in isoelectric points of various trypanosomal proteins (72).

Although genetic significance has not been considered in many studies of acclimatization in free-living Protozoa, inherited modifications have been reported in a few instances. Neuschloss (53, 54) acclimatized *Paramecium caudatum* to quinine, arsenic and antimony compounds, and various dyes by exposing the ciliates to gradually increasing concentrations. The developed resistance was specific except for some reciprocal effects of arsenic and antimony compounds. Similar results have been obtained in *P. aurelia* and *P. caudatum* by a combination of selection and acclimatization (33). For example, a strain was grown in a non-lethal concentration of an arsenical and then subjected to a dosage lethal for most of the ciliates. The survivors were returned to a non-lethal arsenic medium for a time before heavy dosage was repeated. As the procedure was continued, the strain became progressively more resistant. Resistance was inherited for long periods after a return to normal culture media. Such modifications—although inherited through hundreds of fissions, through endomixis (or autogamy?), and in rare cases through conjugation—eventually disappeared after removal of the stimulus. Accordingly, Jollos (33, 34) called such changes "Dauermodifikationen," distinguishing them from true mutations. The more recent acclimatization of both amicronucleate and normal strains of *Colpoda steinii* to arsenicals indicates that the micronucleus is not necessarily involved in "Dauermodifikationen" (71).

Comparable acclimatization has been reported in *Bodo caudatus*, strains of which developed a tolerance to acriflavine in concentrations of 1:500, as compared with the normal susceptibility to dilutions of 1:50,000 to 1:10,000. This resistance was inherited, in decreasing degree, for at least a year in drug-free media (68).

Morphological modifications have been reported in several cases. Loss of the kinetoplast, induced in *Trypanosoma brucei* by inoculating infected mice with certain dyes, became an apparently fixed characteristic (98). Loss of the parabasal body also was induced in *Bodo caudatus* by treatment with acriflavine, but no permanently abnormal strain was obtained (68). Various structural changes have been reported in *Chlamydomonas debaryana* (49). One type could be transformed into another by maintenance in an appropriate medium for a period varying with the length of time the original strain had been exposed to the conditions which produced it. In view of these findings, Moewus suggested that many of the varieties found in natural populations are merely "Dauermodifikationen" induced by specific environmental conditions.

Morphologically distinct types of *Chilodonella uncinatus* have been induced by ultraviolet irradiation. These changes, believed to be mutations, persisted through fission and conjugation (44, 45). Likewise, a physiological change, expressed as a lowered fission rate, has been induced in *P. aurelia* by treatment with X-rays (40). Homozygous strains were obtained in autogamy, and the abnormality was transmitted through both exconjugants in matings between normal and abnormal clones. This induced change was attributed to a micronuclear mutation (41).

Aside from the rare cases which may have involved true mutations, the genetic significance of these induced changes remains uncertain. Jollos considered them the result of cytoplasmic modification rather than gene mutation—an interpretation with interesting implications. In reproduction by fission, an original mass of modified cytoplasm would already be diluted several million times at the twentieth generation, and some of these induced modifications have persisted for several hundred generations after removal of the stimulus. It is inconceivable that modified cytoplasm could exert significant effects in such high dilutions. If "Dauermodifikationen" are strictly cytoplasmic, the modified cytoplasm obviously must reproduce itself in a sort of cytoplasmic inheritance.

GENETIC EFFECTS OF
SYNGAMY

Syngamy in haploid flagellates

Meiosis appears to be zygotic in Phytomonadida, with the result that heterozygous vegetative stages are eliminated by persistence of the haploid chromosome number throughout most of the life-cycle. Since the genotypic composition of the flagellate is indicated by its phenotype after division of the zygote, the phytomonads may be favorable material for the study of biochemical genetics because so many species can be grown bacteria-free in media of known composition. The induction of mutations in autotrophic and heterotrophic types might produce physiological changes which could be analyzed genetically. Experimentally induced loss of chlorophyll might make possible crosses between green and colorless strains of the same species. Such matings might supply significant data on the genetics and biochemistry of chlorophyll formation and perhaps on cytoplasmic inheritance. Although such aspects of phytomonad genetics have not been explored, the inheritance of morphological traits has been traced in a few species.

The first observations were reported by Pascher (55, 56) in two strains of *Chlamydomonas*. In some cases, the lines derived from hybrid zygotes were essentially identical with one parental type or the other. Occasionally, some of the lines showed combinations of parental characteristics and apparently represented new genetic combinations.

Essentially the same pattern of inheritance was reported by Moewus (50) in intraspecific and interspecific crosses of *Polytoma pascheri* and *P. uvella*. Linkage of such features as size of the body and length of flagella was described, and occasional crossing-over was reported. Similar results were obtained with *Chlamydomonas eugametos, C. paradoxa, C. paupera,* and *C. pseudoparadoxa* (51). Although these observations are very interesting, they need confirmation because the validity of the data on crossing-over has been questioned (58).

Syngamy in diploid Protozoa

A number of Protozoa undergo gametic meiosis and are diploid throughout most of the life-cycle (Chapter II). Except for the ciliates, which carry on conjugation instead of syngamy, the genetics of diploid species is yet to be investigated.

GENETIC EFFECTS OF CONJUGATION

The significance of conjugation in heredity was discussed by Bütschli, R. Hertwig, and Maupas long before adequate experimental data were available. It was suggested that conjugation, in bringing about biparental inheritance, forms new combinations and thus increases variation. At the same time, conjugation was believed to level out major differences arising in other ways, and in this sense, to limit the range of variation.

General effects of conjugation

The work of Pearl (57) indicated that exconjugants are less variable than non-conjugants, and that conjugation tends to prevent extreme variation instead of inducing variation. However, Jennings (26) found that exconjugants were more variable than non-conjugant lines with respect to fission-rate. Since these differences were inherited, conjugation in a population apparently gave rise to new biotypes, although the descendants of a single pair were closely similar as a result of biparental inheritance. The appearance of new combinations after conjugation within a population was reported also in later investigations (7, 32, 64). The effects may vary with the strain of *Paramecium aurelia*, variation being increased in some strains but not in others (90).

The other general effect of conjugation is the production of similarities through biparental inheritance in single pairs of exconjugant lines. In tracing the effects of hybridization on viability, body-length, and fission-rate of *Paramecium aurelia*, Sonneborn and Lynch (92) found that some lines resembled one parental type, some resembled the second, and others were intermediate. Inbreeding showed that the intermediate types were heterozygous; the others were apparently homozygous. It was concluded that the inheritance of these traits in *P. aurelia* is basically mendelian.

Cytoplasmic lag in biparental inheritance

An unusual feature of hybridization has been the occurrence of a "cytoplasmic lag" in the exconjugant phenotypes of *P. aurelia*. In the experiments of Sonneborn and Lynch (91), the two lines from each pair of conjugants did not become phenotypically identical until ten generations or so had passed. A similar lag characterizes inheritance of body-size in *P. caudatum* (10), the original size being retained in a hybrid exconjugant line for 10-36 generations. Since the two lines derived from a pair of conjugants were considered genotypically identical, this lag in appearance of the new phenotypes supposedly represented the time required for elimination of the old cytoplasm and the production of new cytoplasm under the influence of the heterozygous synkaryon. Assuming that the volume of old cytoplasm is halved at each fission, a dilution of at least 1:1,000 would seem to be required in these cases before the new zygotic nucleus can assert itself by producing a new phenotype.

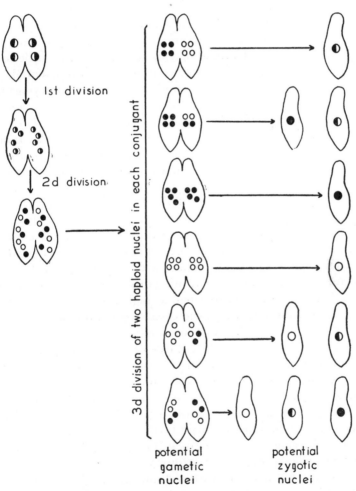

Fig. 9. 1. Theoretical genetic effects of conjugation in *Paramecium aurelia*, based on Diller's (11) account of micronuclear behavior. In the diagram, it is assumed that the two conjugants are heterozygous for some particular trait and that only two haploid nuclei undergo the third pregamic division. Only the micronuclei are indicated.

The micronucleus in conjugation

The behavior of the micronucleus and its derivatives must be considered in relation to the potential genetic effects of conjugation. For instance, it is often assumed that the two gametic nuclei in a conjugant are derived from the same parental haploid nucleus. If this is the case, the nuclear contributions of a heterozygous conjugant to the two zygotic nuclei of the conjugating pair would be identical. So far as cytological evidence goes, this is not necessarily true in *Paramecium aurelia* because "two to five products of the second division continue to divide" (11), and thus produce a number of potential gametic nuclei. Therefore, it is possible that the two successful gametic nuclei of a heterozygous conjugant could originate from different nuclei and thus be genetically different (Fig. 9. 1). In *P. caudatum* also, a variable number of nuclei undergo the third pregamic division to produce more than two potential gametic nuclei, and both cross-fertilization and self-fertilization (cytogamy) are believed to occur in conjugation (12). Two products of the second maturation division normally undergo the third division in *Euplotes,* so that there are four potential gametic nuclei (37, 94). Are the functional gametic nuclei derived from one second-division nucleus or from two? Genetic data indicate that both methods of origin occur in *Euplotes* (8).

Behavior of mating types in conjugation

The effects of conjugation on mating types apparently vary with the species and the variety of ciliates. In variety I of *Paramecium bursaria* (31) the descendants of each pair of conjugants have belonged to the same mating type in most cases. The few exceptional pairs show various results. In some cases, the two exconjugants may produce clones of different mating types. In other pairings, a single exconjugant has produced two different mating types. In some cases, these two types were parental types; in others, they were not. Five crosses, of the six possible for the four types in variety I, have produced descendants belonging to all four mating types. Jennings concluded that mating types are controlled by the genetic composition of the synkaryon and that the appearance of nonparental types might represent new nuclear combinations. Chen (6) has suggested that inheritance of mating types in *P. bursaria* is probably independent of the chromosomes count, which may vary as much among races within the same mating type as it does among different types.

Inheritance of mating types in group A of *P. aurelia* (81, 86)—types I and II (variety 1), V and VI (variety 3) and IX and X (variety 5)—may be illustrated by crosses between types I and II (74). Three results are possible (Fig. 9. 2). All of the exconjugant lines may be type I; all may be type II; or an individual exconjugant may differentiate into types I and II, usually at the first exconjugant fission. The third type of result was believed to indicate that mating types are controlled by the macro-nucleus (74), although it is not clear how this can explain the production of two types from one exconjugant. The possible action of cytoplasmic factors (*plasmagenes*) in variety 1 seems to have been dismissed in the statement that "mating is determined by the genes and is not affected by whatever initial differences in cytoplasm may have existed" (86).

Mendelian inheritance has been reported in matings between a per-manently type I strain and a "two-type" strain in which both types I and II appear within a clone (74). The hybrid exconjugant lines usually showed the two-type condition, indicating its dominance over the one-type trait. In back-crosses between the recessive (one-type) and the hybrid

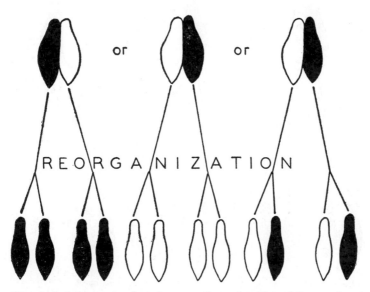

Fig. 9. 2. Inheritance of mating types in conjugation of *Paramecium aurelia,* group A, mating types I (solid black) and II.

(two-type) progeny, about half of the exconjugant lines showed the one-type and the rest the two-type condition, as in a mendelian back-cross. Certain exceptional results were later attributed to cytogamy, which may occur in about 60 per cent of the conjugating pairs at 27° (81), a tem-perature within the optimal range (25-30°) for conjugation of variety 1 (87). The method of inheritance, in this "first discovery of inheritance in Mendelian ratios in the ciliate Protozoa" (74), is not altogether clear. Individual matings, in crosses between the one-type (type I) and the two-type strains, doubtless involved type I and type II ciliates. These type II ciliates presumably were hybrids because the exconjugant lines, instead of belonging only to type II or type I, included both mating types. The progeny, in back-crosses to the parental type I (one-type) stock, must have been represented only by type II phenotypes which were type II/I hybrids, since the back-cross produced both mating types. However, such assumptions do not explain the occasional origin of two mating types from a single exconjugant, as reported in the back-crosses.

In group B of *P. aurelia*—types III and IV (variety 2), VII and VIII (variety 4), XI and XII (variety 6), and XV and XVI (variety 8)—mating types usually do not change at conjugation (87). In crosses between types VII and VIII (Fig. 9. 3), the type VII exconjugant usually produces type VII, and the other exconjugant type VIII lines. Cytogamy, which seems to occur occasionally in variety 4 (77), might account for such behavior

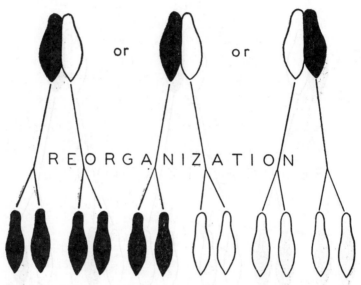

Fig. 9. 3. Inheritance of mating types in conjugation of *Paramecium aurelia*, group B, mating types VII (solid black) and VIII.

of mating types. However, both exconjugants may sometimes produce type VII lines, or both may give rise to type VIII lines. At present, the combined results cannot be explained logically on the basis of nuclear behavior in conjugation. Consequently, Metz (47) has insisted that cytoplasmic factors afford the only mechanism which can account for the behavior of mating types in group B.

The inheritance of mating types in *Euplotes patella* (types I-VI) has been explained by a system of triple alleles in which the genotypes are represented as follows: type I, mt_1mt_2; type II, mt_1mt_3; type III, mt_3mt_3; type IV, mt_1mt_1; type V, mt_2mt_3; type VI, mt_2mt_2. Crosses between types I and II yield types I, II, IV, and V, while IV x VI crosses yield only type I (38). The crosses I x III, II x VI, and III x IV, also have produced the expected results (60). An interesting feature of *E. patella* is that amicronucleate strains have retained their type characteristics and have shown mating reactions with other amicronucleate *E. patella* (37). Mating types in this ciliate are correlated with the production of specific substances which are released into the culture fluid and can induce conjugation in certain combinations. Induction of conjugation by a given substance is restricted to strains which cannot produce that substance, and may occur within a clone previously showing only one mating type. For instance, mating-type substance 1, from a type IV culture, induces conjugation within a clone of type III, V, or VI (Chapter II). The relation of this phenomenon to the results obtained in crosses of two mating types is not yet clear.

Behavior of antigenic types in conjugation

At least four, and possibly six, antigenic types have been identified within killer stock 51 of *P. aurelia* and its variants (82, 86). In crosses between antigenic types A and B (82, 89), three different results may be

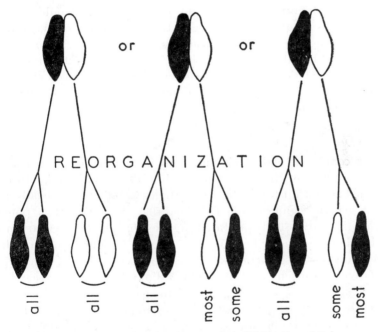

Fig. 9. 4. Inheritance of antigenic types A (solid black) and B in conjugation of *Paramecium aurelia*.

expected (Fig. 9. 4). (1) The progeny of the type A conjugant remain type A and those of the other remain type B, even through autogamy. (2) The type A conjugant gives rise to type A lines, while the type B conjugant produces some type A, but mostly type B. (3) Descendants of the type A conjugant remain type A, while the other conjugant produces mostly type A and few or no type B lines. If a different type B strain is mated with type A, the proportions may be exactly reversed. The behavior of micronuclei affords no apparent basis for all these results.

GENETIC SIGNIFICANCE OF ENDOMIXIS, AUTOGAMY, AND CYTOGAMY

Endomixis

As described in *Paramecium aurelia* (102), endomixis involves: (1) a periodic disintegration and resorption of the macronucleus; (2) division of the micronuclei to produce eight daughter nuclei, all but two of which usually disintegrate; (3) a fission which produces two ciliates, each with a functional nucleus; (4) division of this nucleus to produce four, two of which become macronuclei; (5) division of both micronuclei at the next fission to restore the normal equipment.

From the genetic standpoint, the significance of such a process is uncertain. The absence of meiosis and nuclear fusion should eliminate recombinations of genes, and the genetic implications of macronuclear replacement under such conditions are unknown. Although genetic effects have been attributed to endomixis in *P. aurelia* (5, 66, 92), more recent data afford no evidence for the occurrence of endomixis in this species (81). The "endomixis" induced by Sonneborn (73) in *P. aurelia* apparently represents some other type of nuclear reorganization.

Autogamy

In contrast to endomixis, autogamy in *P. aurelia* (11) involves not only replacement of the macronucleus, but also meiosis and subsequent fusion of haploid nuclei in the same ciliate. Certain other details are of possible genetic significance.[3] The fact that more than two potential gametic nuclei are usually produced suggests that the new synkaryon may be either homozygous or heterozygous (Fig. 9. 5). The former condition would result if both gametic nuclei are produced from the same haploid second-division nucleus, or if the original diploid micronuclei were homozygous. If the stock is heterozygous and the gametic nuclei have different origins, the resulting synkaryon would often be heterozygous. In other words, there is no cytological assurance that autogamy invariably results in a homozygous synkaryon. In contrast to this lack of cytological evi-

---

[3] Two, three, four, or five nuclei may undergo the third prezygotic division, the division which produces the potential gametic nuclei. "I do not have clear-cut cases of just a single one of the eight nuclei going ahead to form the gametic nuclei, but probably this condition does occur at times." Furthermore, ". . . in most cases at least four potential gametic nuclei are formed in the region of the paroral cone" (11).

dence, it has been concluded from genetic data that the two gametic nuclei in *P. aurelia* are always genotypically identical (81).

Genetic changes in autogamy have been reported in *Paramecium*. A clone of *P. bursaria* may differentiate into two mating types after autogamy (31). After autogamy in variety 1 of *P. aurelia*, all of the progeny usually belong to either mating type I or mating type II, and heterozygous

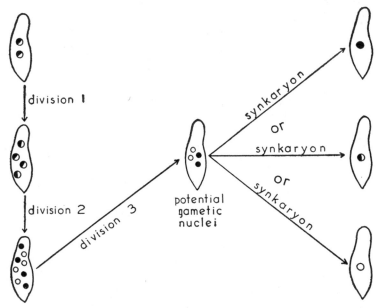

Fig. 9. 5. Theoretical genetic effects of autogamy in a heterozygous ciliate, based on Diller's (11) description of autogamy in *Paramecium aurelia*. In the diagram, it is assumed that four nuclei undergo a second pregamic division and that only one haploid nucleus of each type completes the third division.

strains apparently become homozygous (35, 74). A lag has been noted in the transformation of heterozygous type II into type I. The change occurs at different times in different ciliates, so that cultures come to contain organisms of both types and may show mating reactions. Such a lag was not observed in the change from heterozygous type I to type II. In addition to the usual production of all type I or all type II, both mating types sometimes arise after autogamy. These unusual cases are not readily explained since the lines arising from one ciliate all contain micronuclei and macronuclei derived from the same synkaryon.

Cytogamy

In addition to autogamy, cytogamy is believed to occur in *P. aurelia* (81). Cytogamy (Chapter II) is essentially incomplete conjuga-

tion in which the exchange of pronuclei is inhibited and each "conjugant" undergoes autogamy (99). The occasional occurrence of cytogamy
in *Euplotes patella* also is suggested by genetic data (38, 60); autogamy,
as described for other ciliates, does not occur in this species (36). Cytogamy has the same genetic significance as autogamy.

GENETIC SIGNIFICANCE OF
THE MACRONUCLEUS

The role of the macronucleus in heredity remains problematical,
although Sonneborn at one time believed that in *P. aurelia,* "the phenotype is controlled exclusively by the macronuclear genes" (81). In addition, the detection of macronuclear mutations has been discussed and
conditions for their appearance have been postulated (81). However,
such mutations apparently have not been demonstrated.

The supposed macronuclear control of phenotypes in *P. aurelia* seems
to be based upon the correlation of macronuclear "regeneration" with
certain results in crosses of *killer* and *non-killer* strains (discussed below).
Macronuclear regeneration was induced by exposing conjugants (variety
1) to temperatures of 38.0-38.5° for not less than 3-5 hours following
"fertilization" (75). Such treatment seems rather rigorous, since *P. caudatum* may be killed in nine seconds at 40° (59). Among various abnormalities (81), there was a retarded division of differentiating macronuclei.
In the postconjugant fissions, some ciliates received new macronuclei and
others only the fragments of the old macronuclei. The latter developed
macronuclei from the fragments, each of which became a complete nucleus. The resulting macronuclei were distributed in subsequent fissions
until the normal nuclear situation was restored.

In applying this process to the study of genetic problems, Sonneborn
(80) crossed non-killers (*kk*) with homozygous killers (*KK*). Macronuclear
regeneration was induced in the exconjugants derived from the non-
killers. These were supposed to have received from their mates an excess
of *kappa,* a cytoplasmic factor essential to development of the killer condition. The zygotic nucleus of each exconjugant was a *Kk* genotype, and
the macronuclei derived from the synkaryon had the same genotype. The
non-killers which regenerated their macronuclei had to use fragments of
the old *kk* macronucleus. Only ciliates with new *Kk* macronuclei developed into killers. Furthermore, non-killers (*Kk* micronuclei and *kk*
macronuclei) produced no killers after autogamy, although some must
have developed *KK* micronuclei and macronuclei. Their supply of kappa
presumably was exhausted before autogamy occurred. Accordingly, the
presence of gene *K* in the macronucleus was considered essential to the
continued production of kappa in the cytoplasm. It might be interesting
to extend these observations to such a combination as *Kk* micronuclei

and regenerated *KK* macronuclei, or *kk* micronuclei and regenerated *Kk* macronuclei, since the production of kappa is inhibited at temperatures above 33.5° (62, 83).

It has been suggested that the macronucleus controls mating types in group A of *P. aurelia* (76, 81). This assumption does not explain the origin of two mating types from one ciliate after autogamy, a phenomenon implying formation of two genotypically different macronuclei from one zygotic nucleus. The least improbable explanation, according to Sonneborn (81), involves macronuclear mutation, an assumption which cannot be tested experimentally at present.

THE CYTOPLASM IN INHERITANCE

There is a growing tendency to relate inheritance of certain traits in *Paramecium aurelia* to cytoplasmic factors which may, in different cases, be dependent upon or independent of nuclear genes. These characteristics include the *killer* trait, mating types, and antigenic varieties. Cytoplasmic inheritance is, in a rather real sense, a phenomenon familiar to all protozoologists in the self-perpetuation of blepharoplasts in flagellates and basal granules in ciliates. Therefore, there is nothing very startling in the possibility that self-perpetuating cytoplasmic particles may induce the appearance of specific substances which show physiological activity without assuming the concrete form of new organelles. The current investigations on ciliates are being followed with much interest and with the hope that future developments may furnish logical explanations for some of the unsolved puzzles in protozoan genetics.

The *killer* trait in *Paramecium aurelia*

A *killer* strain of *P. aurelia,* as described in variety 4, gives off into the culture fluid a substance, *paramecin,* which is lethal to sensitive strains but without effect on killers (74, 77, 78, 79). As an antibiotic substance, paramecin is interesting in that it shows differential effects within a single variety. Different strains of *P. aurelia* seem to produce different quantities and different kinds of paramecin (13, 62, 74, 77). A single particle of paramamecin (stock 51, variety 4), produced by a killer about once every five hours, may be enough to kill a sensitive ciliate (2), whereas Sonneborn (84) has found that as many as half of the sensitive ciliates may survive when exposed singly or in small numbers to 10,000 or more particles of paramecin. Paramecin seems to be a desoxyribonucleoprotein which is inactivated by pepsin, chymotrypsin, and desoxyribonucleases and shows a sensitivity to high temperatures comparable to that of various enzymes (95, 96, 97).

The ability to produce paramecin is said to depend upon the presence of a dominant gene *K* and a self-reproducing plasmagene, *kappa*. Non-killer strains may be genotypes *KK, Kk* or *kk* which lack the factor kappa. Although gene *K* may occur in the absence of kappa, maintenance of kappa in the cytoplasm depends upon the presence of gene *K*, perhaps in the macronucleus as well as the micronucleus. Sonneborn (81) suggested that kappa particles are distributed as single molecules throughout the body. Later calculations of Preer (61), however, indicate a size of 0.3–3.0μ for kappa particles. Comparable particles, present only in killer strains, have been identified as granules stainable by Feulgen and Giemsa techniques and containing desoxyribonucleic acid (61, 63). Treatment of *P. aurelia* with nitrogen mustard inactivates kappa and at the same time reduces the number of these granules (18). Kappa particles apparently lose the power to reproduce at temperatures above $33.5°$ (62, 83). Some of these characteristics suggest close chemical similarity between kappa and paramecin. Under optimal conditions, kappa in variety 2 of *P. aurelia* is quadrupled daily. Consequently, it is possible to decrease the kappa content by increasing fission-rate, or even to eliminate kappa completely and permanently from strains of variety 2 (62). This apparently is not possible for the kappa of variety 4 which increases fast enough to keep up with rapid fission (79, 83). By depressing the fission-rate, the kappa content of a low-kappa strain may be increased progressively, at a rate which apparently varies with the strain or with the kind of kappa. Mutations of kappa have been reported in variety 4 of *P. aurelia*. The mutant plasmagenes stimulated production of a new kind of paramecin with a different lethal action on sensitive cilates (13).

The behavior of kappa in autogamy and conjugation has been described (77, 79). After autogamy in a *Kk*-kappa line, the persistence of the killer trait for a few generations in homozygous recessive (*kk*-kappa) lines suggests that kappa can maintain the production of paramecium even without gene *K*. Sooner or later, however, the recessives become non-killers, presumably because kappa cannot increase in the absence of gene *K*. The disappearance of kappa thus shows a "lag" analogous to that described for inheritance of size in conjugation. If gene *K* is reintroduced, by crossing the recessive with a homozygous killer (*KK*) strain, before all the kappa has been lost, the hybrid (*Kk*-kappa) descendants remain killers. If the cross, *kk* x *KK*-kappa, is made after the recessive has become a non-killer strain upon exhausting its original supply of kappa, the heterozygous (*Kk*) descendants of the non-killer conjugants remain non-killers. Such results are said to demonstrate that gene *K* cannot initiate the production of kappa after it has disappeared from the cytoplasm. Therefore, cytoplasmic inheritance is very important in transmission of the killer trait.

It has been reported more recently that, in certain crosses of *KK*-kappa x *kk*, both exconjugant lines become killers (*Kk*-kappa). This result is said to depend upon transfer of cytoplasm from the killer to the non-killer conjugant (86). When autogamy occurs in such lines, some of the descendants remain killers, presumably as *KK*-kappa genotypes, while the rest become non-killers after kappa has disappeared from the cytoplasm.

The status of the killer and non-killer traits is further complicated by the conclusion that another pair of genes, *S* and *s*, and a corresponding plasmagene, *sigma,* are involved. The relationships between sigma and its homologous alleles are comparable to those between kappa and its related genes. Sigma supposedly has the ability to compete with kappa and to replace it under certain conditions, but is "not actually a factor for sensitivity" (82). It now appears that a homozygous killer (*KKSS*) strain can yield pure killer and pure sensitive strains differing only in cytoplasmic factors.

Mating types and cytoplasmic inheritance

The difficulty of explaining inheritance of mating types in variety 4 of *P. aurelia* (Fig. 9. 3) is responsible for the conclusion that plasmagenes are involved (47, 84). The usual appearance of the original mating type in each exconjugant line would have to be explained on the basis of cytogamy rather than interchange of gametic nuclei, if nuclear genes are responsible. The production of type VIII from conjugants belonging originally to types VII and VIII would imply that type VIII is dominant to VII, if nuclear control exists. Other matings, in which the results are exactly reversed, would indicate that type VII is dominant to type VIII. Furthermore, the origin of both mating types from one exconjugant can scarcely be explained on a micronuclear basis, although a similar phenomenon has been attributed tentatively to macronuclear mutation in group A (81).

These peculiarities in the inheritance of group B mating types are attributed to the occurrence or the lack of cytoplasmic transfer during conjugation (84), although such a process has not been detected in cytological studies on *P. aurelia* (11) and *P. bursaria* (100). According to this hypothesis, no transfer of cytoplasm has occurred when type VII conjugants produce only type VII descendants, and type VIII only type VIII. If the exconjugant lines are all type VIII, in a VII x VIII mating, cytoplasm has been transferred from the type VIII to the VII conjugant. If the results are reversed, cytoplasm has been transferred from type VII to type VIII. If one exconjugant produces two mating types, interchange of cytoplasm has been followed by segregation of plasmagenes in postconjugant fissions. Sonneborn assumes that there are two kinds of plasmagenes in variety 4, one controlling type VII and the other type VIII. The same explanation is believed to hold for other varieties of group B.

Antigenic types and cytoplasmic inheritance

Hereditary antigenic variations in *Paramecium aurelia* have been reported by several workers. According to Harrison and Fowler (20), such variations may arise spontaneously. The stability of the variant differs with the strain and has ranged from less than three months to about four years. Similar variations have been induced in *P. aurelia* (stock 51) by exposure to X-rays (82) and to homologous antisera (82, 89). Temporary changes, lost after 1-15 fissions, also have been induced by exposure to trypsin and by maintenance of cultures at 14° for a number of generations (39). Antigenic types may be modified in different ways by different experimental methods. Types B, C, and D may be converted into A by incubation at 32°, and types A, C, and D may be changed to B by incubation at 12°. All the various types remain stable at 27° if the food supply is controlled to maintain one fission a day (85). The antigenic type in variety 4 of *P. aurelia* is said to depend upon competition between plasmagenes (85, 89).

In the only experiments with bacteria-free cultures, an antigenic modification, exhibited as insensitivity to antiserum, has been produced by exposure of *Tetrahymena* to homologous antiserum, but the ciliates reverted to the original type after two transfers in normal culture medium (69).

The status of antigenic varieties in *P. aurelia* is not yet settled. Since there is no evidence for micronuclear control, it has been suggested that cytoplasmic inheritance determines the observed behavior in conjugation and autogamy (82, 86). Results obtained in conjugation of types A and B (Fig. 9. 4) are attributed to a lack of cytoplasmic transfer in some cases, and to the transfer of large or small amounts of cytoplasm in others. After an A x B cross, the inbreeding of type A exconjugant lines yields only type A; that of type B exconjugants, only type B. Cytoplasmic inheritance is believed to offer the most logical explanation for these various results.

Possible mechanisms involved in the antigenic transformations of *P. aurelia* have been discussed by several workers (3, 22, 89), and Beale has suggested that the potsulated plasmagenes are the antigens themselves (3).

LITERATURE CITED

1. Ackert, J. E. 1916. *Genetics* 1: 387.
2. Austin, M. L. 1948. *Physiol. Zool.* 21: 69.
3. Beale, G. H. 1948. *Proc. Nat. Ac. Sci.* 34: 418.
4. Bishop, A. and B. Birkett 1948. *Parasitol.* 39: 125.
5. Caldwell, L. 1933. *J. Exp. Zool.* 66: 371.
6. Chen, T.-T. 1940. *J. Hered.* 31: 249.
7. Cohen, B. M. 1934. *Genetics* 19: 25.
8. ——— 1934. *Genetics* 19: 40.

9. Dawson, J. A. 1926. *J. Exp. Zool.* **44**: 133.
10. De Garis, C. F. 1935. *J. Exp. Zool.* **71**: 209.
11. Diller, W. F. 1936. *J. Morph.* **59**: 11.
12. ——— 1940. *J. Morph.* **66**: 605.
13. Dippell, R. V. 1948. *Amer. Nat.* **82**: 43.
14. Dobell, C. C. 1912. *J. Genet.* **2**: 201.
15. Erdmann, R. 1920. *Arch. Entw.-Mech. Org.* **46**: 85.
16. Frye, W. W. and H. E. Meleney 1938. *Amer. J. Hyg.* **27**: 580.
17. Fulton, J. D. and W. Yorke 1941. *Ann. Trop. Med. Parasit.* **35**: 221.
18. Geckler, R. P. 1949. *Science* **110**: 89.
19. Hance, R. T. 1917. *J. Exp. Zool.* **23**: 287.
20. Harrison, J. A. and E. H. Fowler 1945. *J. Immunol.* **50**: 115.
21. Hegner, R. W. 1919. *Genetics* **4**: 95.
22. Irwin, M. R. 1949. *Quart. Rev. Biol.* **24**: 109.
23. Jansco, N. von 1932. *Zentralbl. Bakt., Orig.* **124**: 167.
24. Jennings, H. S. 1908. *Proc. Amer. Philos. Soc.* **47**: 393.
25. ——— 1911. *J. Exp. Zool.* **11**: 1.
26. ——— 1913. *J. Exp. Zool.* **14**: 279.
27. ——— 1916. *Genetics* **1**: 407.
28. ——— 1920. *Life and Death, Heredity and Evolution in Unicellular Organisms* (Boston: Badger).
29. ——— 1929. *Bibliogr. Genet.* **5**: 105.
30. ——— 1941. "Inheritance in Protozoa" in *Protozoa in Biological Research* (New York: Columbia Univ. Press), pp. 710-771.
31. ——— 1942. *Genetics* **27**: 193.
32. ———, D. Raffel, R. S. Lynch and T. M. Sonneborn 1932. *J. Exp. Zool.* **62**: 363.
33. Jollos, V. 1921. *Arch. f. Protistenk.* **43**: 1.
34. ——— 1934. *Arch. f. Protistenk.* **83**: 197.
35. Kimball, R. F. 1937. *Proc. Nat. Acad. Sci.* **23**: 469.
36. ——— 1939. *Amer. Nat.* **73**: 451.
37. ——— 1941. *J. Exp. Zool.* **86**: 1.
38. ——— 1942. *Genetics* **27**: 269.
39. ——— 1947. *Genetics* **32**: 486.
40. ——— 1949. *Genetics* **34**: 210.
41. ——— 1949. *Genetics* **34**: 412.
42. Loefer, J. B. 1939. *Physiol. Zool.* **12**: 161.
43. MacDougall, M. S. 1925. *Quart. J. Micr. Sci.* **69**: 361.
44. ——— 1929. *J. Exp. Zool.* **54**: 95.
45. ——— 1931. *J. Exp. Zool.* **58**: 229.
46. Metz, C. B. 1947. *J. Exp. Zool.* **105**: 115.
47. ——— 1948. *Amer. Nat.* **82**: 85.
48. Middleton, A. R. 1915. *J. Exp. Zool.* **19**: 451.
49. Moewus, F. 1934. *Arch. f. Protistenk.* **83**: 220.
50. ——— 1935. *Ztschr. indukt. Abstamm.-u. Vererbungsl.* **69**: 374.
51. ——— 1936. *Ber. deutsch. Botan. Gesellsch.* **54**: 45.
52. Murgatroyd, F. and W. Yorke 1937. *Ann. Trop. Med. Parasit.* **31**: 165.
53. Neuschloss, S. 1919. *Pflüger's Archiv* **176**: 223.
54. ——— 1920. *Pflüger's Archiv* **178**: 61.
55. Pascher, A. 1916. *Ber. deutsch. botan. Gesellsch.* **34**: 228.
56. ——— 1918. *Ber. deutsch. botan. Gesellsch.* **36**: 163.
57. Pearl, R. 1906. *Proc. Roy. Soc., B,* **77**: 377.
58. Philip, N. and J. B. S. Haldane 1939. *Nature* **143**: 334.
59. Port, J. 1927. *Protoplasma* **2**: 401.
60. Powers, E. L., Jr. 1943. *Amer. Mid. Nat.* **30**: 175.
61. Preer, J. R., Jr. 1948. *Amer. Nat.* **82**: 35.
62. ——— 1948. *Genetics* **33**: 348.
63. ——— 1948. *Genetics* **33**: 625.
64. Raffel, D. 1930. *Biol. Bull.* **58**: 293.
65. ——— 1932. *Biol. Bull.* **62**: 244.

66. ——— 1932. *J. Exp. Zool.* **63**: 371.
67. Ritz, H. 1916. *Arch. Schiffs- u. Tropenhyg.* **20**: 392.
68. Robertson, M. 1929. *Parasitol.* **21**: 375.
69. ——— 1939. *J. Pathol. Bact.* **48**: 305.
70. Root, F. M. 1918. *Genetics* **3**: 174.
71. Schuckmann, W. v. and G. Piekarski 1940. *Arch. f. Protistenk.* **93**: 355.
72. Schueler, F. W. 1947. *J. Inf. Dis.* **81**: 139.
73. Sonneborn, T. M. 1937. *Biol. Bull.* **72**: 196.
74. ——— 1939. *Amer. Nat.* **73**: 390.
75. ——— 1940. *Anat. Rec.* **78** (suppl.): 53 (abstract).
76. ——— 1942. *Amer. Nat.* **76**: 46.
77. ——— 1943. *Proc. Nat. Acad. Sci.* **29**: 329.
78. ——— 1945. *Ann. Missouri Botan. Gard.* **32**: 213.
79. ——— 1945. *Amer. Nat.* **79**: 318.
80. ——— 1946. *Genetics* **31**: 231 (abstract).
81. ——— 1947. *Advances in Genetics* **1**: 263.
82. ——— 1947. *Growth* **11**: 291.
83. ——— 1947. *Cold Spr. Harb. Symp. Quant. Biol.* **11**: 236.
84. ——— 1948. *Amer. Nat.* **82**: 26.
85. ——— 1948. *Proc. Nat. Acad. Sci.* **34**: 413.
86. ——— 1949. *Amer. Sci.* **37**: 33.
87. ——— and R. V. Dippell 1946. *Physiol. Zool.* **19**: 1.
88. ———, ——— and W. Jacobson 1947. *Genetics* **32**: 106.
89. ——— and A. LeSuer 1948. *Amer. Nat.* **82**: 69.
90. ——— and R. S. Lynch 1932. *Biol. Bull.* **62**: 258.
91. ——— and ——— 1934. *J. Exp. Zool.* **67**: 1.
92. ——— and ——— 1937. *Genetics* **22**: 284.
93. Taliaferro, W. H. 1926. *Quart. Rev. Biol.* **1**: 246.
94. Turner, J. P. 1930. *Univ. Calif. Publ. Zool.* **33**: 193.
95. Wagtendonk, W. J. van 1948. *Amer. Nat.* **82**: 60.
96. ——— 1948. *J. Biol. Chem.* **173**: 691.
97. ——— and L. P. Zill 1947. *J. Biol. Chem.* **171**: 595.
98. Werbitski, F. W. 1910. *Zentralbl. Bakt.* **53**: 303.
99. Wichterman, R. 1940. *J. Morph.* **66**: 423.
100. ——— 1946. *Science* **104**: 505.
101. Woodruff, L. L. 1931. *Quart. J. Micr. Sci.* **74**: 537.
102. ——— and R. Erdmann 1914. *J. Exp. Zool.* **17**: 425.
103. Yorke, W., F. Murgatroyd and F. Hawking 1931. *Ann. Trop. Med. Parasit.* **25**: 521.

X

Host-Parasite Relationships

PARASITISM

Protozoa which have become adapted to life in or on the body of another organism, the *host,* are commonly referred to as *parasites.* *Parasitism,* in a correspondingly broad sense, designates the association of such a parasite with its host. This is also the original meaning of *symbiosis,* as proposed by de Bary,[1] but recent usage has generally restricted this term to the special relationship of "mutualism" (van Beneden). Since the problematical benefits of revising accepted terminology probably would not balance the resulting misunderstandings, the prevailing usage will be followed here.

Types of parasites

Protozoa which normally live on the surface of the host's body may be called *ectoparasites—*or *ectocommensals,* if they neither damage nor benefit the host. Ectocommensalism, obviously limited to aquatic hosts, may involve definite attachment of the commensal or merely the

[1] A concise historical discussion of terminology has been published by Kirby (56).

527

adherence of a motile organism to the surface of the host's body. The latter condition is not easily distinguished from casual association of a free-living species with a pseudo-host. Many other parasites occur in such body cavities as the mouth and other parts of the digestive tract, the mantle cavity of Mollusca, and the cloaca of aquatic vertebrates. So long as these Protozoa are both harmless and useless, they may be considered *endocommensals,* or *inquilines* (14). Endocommensals may be expected in terrestrial as well as aquatic hosts. Endoparasites which participate in *symbiosis,* an association involving mutual benefits to host and parasite, are known as *symbiotes.* Parasites which destroy the tissues of their hosts or damage them in other ways may be called *pathogens.* Such terms as "strict parasite" and "true parasite" have been used in the same sense.

Although some such terminology is convenient for purposes of discussion, there may be practical difficulties in distinguishing symbiosis from endocommensalism or commensals from pathogens. It has even been suggested that in a single host species, a pathogen may occasionally become a commensal, or a commensal may sometimes harm the host. However, the former change does not necessarily occur in the usual *carrier* of a normally pathogenic species. It is quite likely that the carrier shows no obvious symptoms because an effective although incomplete immunity has been developed.

Commensalism as an evolutionary goal

The evolutionary aspects of pathogenicity and commensalism have interested many parasitologists. According to one theory, the evolutionary goal of the parasite is adjustment to commensalism, an association which tends to conserve available hosts, and in this sense, favors survival of the well-adapted parasite. This hypothesis implies that endocommensals, as the product of long-continued adaptation to a particular species of host, are phylogenetically older than pathogens invading the same host. Pathogenic species would represent newly acquired parasites which have not had time to evolve into commensals.

Certain objections to this hypothesis have been discussed by Ball (4). So far as experimental data are suggestive, there is little reason for assuming that mere passage of time is a major influence in the loss of pathogenicity. Packchanian's (75) results with *Trypanosoma brucei* in *Peromyscus* have shown that a given parasite may cause experimental infections which range, in different species of hosts, from acute lethal types to chronic infections followed usually by spontaneous recovery. Furthermore, investigations on avian malaria have shown that one species of *Plasmodium,* upon inoculation into a variety of hosts, may produce lethal infections in one species, malaria of moderate severity in another and yet fail to induce symptoms in a third, although completing a normal cycle and producing gametocytes in each type of host. Thus, under experimental conditions, a parasite may in a single transfer become a dangerous pathogen or show almost no pathogenicity, depending upon the host. Therefore, long association between a parasite and a host is not necessary for the reduction or practical elimination of pathogenicity. In addition, the present pathogenicity of a parasite would seem to be no real guarantee of its amateur standing. As applied to the Endamoebidae, the hypothesis of progressive adjustment to commensalism would imply that man and certain other primates have each acquired *Entamoeba histolytica* much more recently than their other amoebae, which may approach the status of commensals. It seems just as likely that *E. histolytica* was pathogenic and certain other amoebae were non-pathogenic when they first invaded the ancestral primates, and that the various species have merely retained their original characteristics during the subsequent evolution of their hosts. In this connection, the occurrence of a *histolytica*-like pathogen (*Entamoeba invadens*) in various reptiles (28, 81a, 84) may have some significance.

Symbiosis

As an abstract concept, *symbiosis* (mutualism) is an interesting association. However, examples involving Protozoa as the symbiotes are rare.[2] The most likely candidates are certain intestinal flagellates of wood-eating termites and wood-roaches (*Cryptocerus*). The ability to digest cellulose has been reported for some of the termite flagellates (43, 91, 92) and flagellates of the wood-roach (22, 91). In addition, the results of defaunation indicate that both types of hosts are dependent, to a considerable extent and perhaps completely, upon certain of their intestinal flagellates (19, 20, 21, 22). The status of the rumen ciliates of herbivores has been disputed (7). There is some morphological evidence that ingested cellulose is digested by certain species (96), and the production of cellulases also has been reported (44, 45). The results of defaunation have varied from no significant effects (10) to a decreased digestion of roughage (101). Growth-rates of lambs have remained normal in the absence of ciliates (9). If the definition of a symbiote merely requires an organism to be beneficial to its host and not necessarily its major means of support, the possession of cellulases might qualify some of these ciliates for participation in symbiosis. If the definition is restricted, as it has been occasionally (37), to an organism which is indispensable to its host, then there is no justification for listing ciliates of the rumen in this category.

[2] The literature on flagellates of termites and ciliates of ruminants has been reviewed by Hungate (45a).

The evolution of parasites

Speculations concerning the origin and development of protozoan parasites have been based upon certain assumptions and upon rather limited observational and experimental data. Within the phylum, parasites are not limited to exclusively parasitic groups but are also scattered in various orders which contain mostly free-living species. Such taxonomic distribution suggests that parasitic Protozoa have arisen frequently and independently from different groups of free-living ancestors.

The origin of ectoparasites from free-living species may be assumed as a matter of course. Endoparasites also may have arisen directly from free-living ancestors. Another possibility is that endoparasites have developed from ectoparasites whose prior origin was favored by the minor adaptive changes required for the transition to ectoparasitism.

As pointed out by Wenrich (98), it is difficult, with protozoological data, to support the origin of endoparasites from ectoparasites. Ectoparasites include mostly primitive flagellates, certain Peritrichida and a number of Suctorea. Genera containing both ectoparasitic and endoparasitic species are rare and it is difficult to trace possible connecting links. It is more probable that endoparasites have arisen directly from free-living species. The primary invasion probably led to colonization of the digestive tract in most cases. Invasion of the blood and other tissues by many species followed eventually in the course of evolution. Opportunities for entering the digestive tract are certainly abundant enough, although the primary invader must overcome new environmental hazards and must also establish an infection if it is to succeed as a parasite. The latter step involves satisfying food requirements and carrying on reproduction. Furthermore, the probationary parasite must possess or develop methods for insuring a safe passage from the first host to new ones if it is to become anything more than a sporadic invader.

It is often assumed that the original host of certain parasites, which now have two hosts, was the one termed the *intermediate host* (or vector), and that parasitism in the *final host* may be regarded as a secondary adaptation. Whether this hypothesis can be applied to the genus *Leishmania* is somewhat uncertain. Among the species found in reptiles, *L. chamaeleonis* is an intestinal flagellate retaining the leptomonad form (100), while certain other species invade the blood of gekkos and are found also in sandflies (Chapter XII).

The occasional occurrence of sporadic endoparasitism by normally free-living species suggests that direct transition may not have been too difficult for some Protozoa. Sporadic paratism by Euglenida has been reported in tadpoles (36, 97) and millipedes (98). Experimental infection with *Tetrahymena pyriformis* has been established in the haemocoel of insects (47, 65). Natural invasion by this ciliate or related species has been observed in the haemocoel of insects (29, 34, 67, 93), in the gills of *Gammarus pulex* (78), in the haemocoel of crabs (79), in the coelom of sea-urchins (64), and in the digestive tract of slugs (82). Such temporary invasions may be comparable to the initial step in the origin of endoparasitism.

The transition from sporadic invasion to the establishment of natural parasitism need not have required any marked morphological changes. This is obvious in many parasitic species which belong to predominantly free-living groups. Both free-living and parasitic species sometimes occur within a single genus. Species of *Astasia* have been reported as parasites of rhabdocoeles (5), rotifers (95), and Crustacea (1), although others are free-living. *Euglena leucops* (35), parasitic in a rhabdocoele, has lost its chlorophyll but resembles free-living Euglenidae in other respects. "*Astasia*" *chaetogastris*, found in lethal infections of an oligochaete, retains the stigma but discards the flagellum of the free-living stage (23). Another example, *Euglenamorpha hegneri* (97), occurs in the rectum of tadpoles as two varieties, one with chlorophyll and the other without. Loss of chlorophyll can scarcely be considered an adaptation to parasitism, since the same change has occurred in free-living Euglenidae exposed to darkness and other experimental conditions. *Hexamita* apparently represents an extreme case in which free-living species and parasites of the digestive tract in various invertebrates and vertebrates have been assigned to one genus. Likewise, members of the ciliate genera *Anophrys*, *Colpidium*, *Colpoda*, *Metopus*, and *Uronema*, which include mostly free-living species, have been reported as intestinal parasites of sea-urchins. Even such genera as *Balantidium* and *Nyctotherus*, which include parasites only, cannot be distinguished from free-living ciliates by morphological criteria. Obviously, the initial stages in development of endoparasitism do not demand appreciable changes in structure. Accordingly, it may be assumed that the primary adaptations have been physiological rather than morphological.

There are, however, parasites which have undergone more or less extensive morphological specialization, and thus seem to show structural adaptations to parasitism. The absence of feeding organelles in the Opalinida and Astomina is sometimes considered an example of regressive evolution in ciliates, which are predominantly holozoic organisms. However, the loss of holozoic habits is not a universal feature of specialized parasites. The Cycloposthiidae and Ophryoscolecidae, for example, include highly differentiated ciliates which are distinctly holozoic. Organelles of attachment have appeared in such parasites as gregarines, the peritrich *Ellobiophyra donacis* (18), various dinoflagellates (16, 74, 89), and such termite flagellates as *Streblomastix* (59), and *Microrhopalodina* (*Proboscidiella*) (50). Another common feature is the occurrence of rapid multiplication at certain periods in the life-cycle, as in merogony and sporogony of Coccidia and Haemosporidia. The dinoflagellate, *Amyloodinium ocellatum* (74), and the ciliate, *Ichthyophthirius multifiliis* (69), also undergo a period of rapid fission following prolonged growth. In general, such morphological pecularities should perhaps be considered adaptive features which have been preserved and augmented through natural selection.

One of the most interesting phases of adaptation to parasitism, that of physiological and biochemical modifications, must await exploration until more is known about food requirements and metabolism of parasites. This field of investigation may be expected to yield clues to fundamental factors in the evolution of parasites and in the maintenance of more or less obligatory parasitism.

Host-specificity

The development of host-relationships has shown two general trends (99). In various instances, small groups of parasites have become adapted to a wide variety of hosts. Examples are found in different groups of Protozoa. Species of *Trypanosoma* parasitize some five hundred different species of vertebrates (100) and the genus *Entamoeba* also is represented in many hosts. The genus *Eimeria* includes more than two hundred species distributed among such hosts as annelids, insects, myriapods, fishes, Amphibia, reptiles, birds, and mammals (62).

In the second type of development, a small group of parasites has become restricted to a few hosts and may, in some cases, have undergone extensive evolution within this limited environment. The Entodiniomorphina contain many ciliates living in ruminants and in the cecum of horses. Extensive speciation has been noted in some hosts. For *Bos indicus*, 13 genera containing about 100 species have been listed (58), while nine species of *Cycloposthium* have been described from the horse (42). Certain genera of Hypermastigida and Trichomonadida also have undergone extensive speciation in a limited group of termites (53), and the opalinid ciliates are limited almost entirely to Amphibia (72).

The host-specificity of individual species ranges from well-marked to relatively slight in different cases. The Coccidia of mammals, in experimental cross-infections, generally show a high degree of specificity (8), although *Isospora felis* and *I. rivolta* can infect both cats and dogs (2). The malarial parasites of man also show a fairly rigid host-specificity, except for reports that they occasionally produce mild infections in experimentally inoculated apes. Perhaps to a lesser degree, species of *Giardia* may be restricted in their distribution among mammalian hosts (37). At the other extreme, a species may be adaptable to a wide variety of hosts— *Herpetomonas muscarum* may invade flies belonging to a number of different genera (6, 24); *Trypanosoma brucei* occurs in various wild and domesticated mammals and may be transferred to certain laboratory animals; malarial parasites of birds generally can parasitize a variety of avian hosts; *Balantidium coli* occurs naturally in man, apes, monkeys, and pigs; *Toxoplasma,* recovered from man, is infective for a number of mammals (70).

TAXONOMIC DISTRIBUTION OF PARASITIC PROTOZOA

The Phytomastigophorea are represented by only a few parasitic species and the authentic cases apparently are limited to two orders. The Dinoflagellida include about 15 genera of parasites. Parasitic Euglenida are represented by *Euglenamorpha* (97) and *Hegneria* (12) and by several species of *Euglena* and *Astasia*. In contrast to the Phytomastogophorea, many Zoomastigophorea are parasitic—the orders Hypermastigida and Trichomonadida and a number of smaller groups are exclusively parasitic.

Among the Sarcodina, the Proteomyxida include a few parasitic species and a number of the Mycetozoida also are parasitic. The Endamoebidae are all parasitic, and Wenyon (100) has suggested that every vertebrate species probably will be found to harbor parasitic amoebae. The majority of these amoebae seem to be endocommensals. However, man is not the only host of a pathogenic species, since reptiles (81a) also may suffer from amoebiasis.

All known Sporozoa are parasitic and the majority cause appreciable damage to their hosts. Certain groups have become adapted to particular environments within the host. The Gregarinidia live primarily in such cavities as the digestive tract and coelom of invertebrates. The Coccidia are mainly invaders of epithelial cells, while the Haemosporidia occur in blood cells and, as exoerythrocytic stages, in certain other tissue cells of vertebrates.

Among the Ciliatea, the Protociliatia, Astomina, and Entodiniomorphina are exclusively parasitic. In addition, a number of parasitic genera and species are scattered among the rest of the ciliates. Some parasitic ciliates, such as *Ichthyophthirius multifiliis* and *Balantidium coli,* normally invade and destroy tissues of the host. Many others appear to be commensals, while certain ciliates of ruminants have been considered possible symbiotes. The Suctorea include only a few ectoparasites, presumably ectocommensals, and a few endoparasites.

PROTOZOA AS HOSTS

In addition to their representation among parasites, Protozoa also serve as hosts of microorganisms.[3] Hyperparasitism, in which parasitic Protozoa are invaded by their own parasites, is not uncommon (57, 86). Some combinations, involving algae in free-living Protozoa, are possibly

[3] An extensive review of this subject has been published by Kirby (57).

symbiotic. Various other cases of parasitism may result in destruction of the protozoan host.

Protozoan parasites of Protozoa

Some of the most interesting of these parasites are Suctorea which, at one time, were believed to be embryonic stages of ciliates. Species of *Endosphaera* (31, 66) differ from free-living Suctorea in the absence of tentacles throughout the life-cycle. There are also a few parasitic species of *Sphaerophrya* which have tentacles in the free-living stage but discard them upon invading a protozoan host. In addition to Suctorea, various other parasites of Protozoa are known. Dinoflagellates have been reported from dinoflagellate (17), ciliate (39), and radiolarian hosts. A species of *Astasia* has been observed in *Stentor* and *Spirostomum* (41) and unidentified Zoomastigophorea have been found in ciliates, Suctorea, and Myxosporida. Small amoebae have been reported from opalinid ciliates (88) and from *Trichodina*; Microsporida, from Myxosporida (60), ciliates, gregarines, and Hypermastigida; several Haplosporidia, from gregarine hosts (68). Some of these associations are examples of hyperparasitism (86).

Bacterial parasites of Protozoa

Certain bacteria are ectoparasitic on flagellates of termites (25, 32, 48, 52, 54). Fusiform bacilli, adherent lengthwise to the cortex of the host and often regularly spaced, have sometimes been mistaken for cortical ridges in *Devescovina, Lophomonas, Polymastix, Caduceia,* and *Staurojoenia*. Similarly attached bacteria also have been reported from ciliates, including a species of *Cyclidium* (80). Spirochetes, attached terminally to their hosts (21, 25, 48), have been mistaken occasionally for flagella or cilia. Although less common than spirochetes, terminally attached bacilli have been observed on such flagellates as *Microrhopalodina (Proboscidiella) kofoidi* (50) and *M. inflata* (26).

Endoparasitic bacteria also occur in certain flagellates of termites— *Trichonympha* (51), *Pseudodevescovina* (54, 33), and *Bullanympha* (55). Both nuclear and cytoplasmic parasites have been reported from *Paramecium* (11, 27), for which invasion of the macronucleus is often fatal.

Other plants as parasites of Protozoa

This group includes such Fungi as Chytridiales which sometimes occur as cytoplasmic (*Sphaerita*) and nuclear parasites (*Nucleophaga*) in Protozoa. Species of *Sphaerita* have been described from Euglenida (30, 46, 73), *Amoeba* (71), flagellates of termites, species of *Entamoeba, Zelleriella, Nyctotherus,* and *Diplodinium* (57). The young form of *Sphaerita* is a uninucleate amoeboid stage. Growth and nuclear division result in a plasmodium, which eventually produces a number of small spores, or sometimes flagellated "zoospores." *Nucleophaga* (61) has been reported from *Endolimax nana* (13), *Endamoeba disparata* (49), *Amoeba* (71), and from flagellates of termites (57).

Certain algae also parasitize Protozoa. Blue-green algae occur in the testacean, *Paulinella chromatophora* (77), and species of *Chlorella* in *Frontonia leucas* (40) and *Paramecium bursaria* (63, 76, 81). Although these algal-protozoan associations are often considered examples of symbiosis, the experimental evidence is not entirely conclusive.

INFECTIONS

Upon reaching a suitable host, a parasitic protozoon which is not promptly eliminated may give rise to an infection. The establishment of an infection requires multiplication of the parasite at a rate rapid enough to overbalance any destructive forces which may be encountered, and the result is a net increase in parasite population. The ability to establish an infection in a particular host, or the *infectivity* of the parasite for that host, is somewhat variable. To what extent the apparent infectivity may depend upon individual variations in the internal environment or in natural resistance of the host is uncertain, although it may be assumed that such factors are important. For instance, the change from a normal to a high-carbohydrate diet makes the rat susceptible to infection with *Balantidium coli,* a ciliate which ordinarily shows little or no infectivity for this rodent (38). In such a case, the normal intestinal environment obviously is a factor limiting infectivity. In other cases, infectivity may be modified by changes in the parasite. An example is the loss of infectivity for kittens by two strains of *Entamoeba histolytica* which had ceased producing cysts in cultures. Modification of the culture medium so as to restore the ability to encyst was followed by the recovery of infectivity (15).

In the terminology of Justin Andrews, protozoan infections may be described in terms of *prepatent, patent,* and *subpatent* periods. The *prepatent period* precedes the appearance of parasites in numbers large enough for detection by routine examinations. The apparent absence of parasites is often the result of failure to find the few parasites actually present in the material examined. In a malarial infection, however, the parasites may be developing as exoerythrocytic stages prior to invasion of the blood.

The *patent period* opens with the finding of parasites in material from the host. During this period, the parasite density usually continues to rise for some time and the transfer of parasites by vectors is most likely to be successful in this stage. Eventually, the infection may lead to death of the host, the number of parasites may be sharply reduced by immunological reactions of the host, or the surviving parasites may leave the host upon completion of the life-cycle. The patent period passes into the subpatent period when the parasites are no longer detectable.

The *subpatent period* varies in significance. It may represent a marked decrease in number of parasites as the infection is brought under control prior to elimination. In tertian malaria, on the other hand, a subpatent period may parallel continued development of exoerythrocytic parasites. A new patent period may follow the subpatent period, and the sequence may be repeated several times before the infection is terminated.

Infections which induce the appearance of definite symptoms in the host also may be characterized in terms of several clinical periods—period of incubation, period of symptoms and period of convalescence.

The *incubation period,* initiated by introduction of the parasites, ends when symptoms are recognizable. In malignant tertian malaria, symptoms may appear at or near the end of the prepatent period. In various other infections, the correlation between incubation period and prepatent period is not necessarily close. Parasites are often detectable some time before the appearance of symptoms. At the other extreme, characteristic symptoms appear and reach a peak before the end of the prepatent period in infections with *Isospora hominis.*

The *period of symptoms* opens typically with the appearance of mild (or prodromal) symptoms. As the infection progresses, the symptoms become progressively more severe and more characteristic of the particular host-parasite association. During this phase, the parasites are producing more or less specific effects, the nature of which varies with the parasite. Variations in the severity of the effects produced may reflect differences in resistance of the hosts and in virulence of the parasites (Chapter XIV). Mechanical irritation may be caused by movements of intestinal Protozoa, and tissues are destroyed by many parasites. Invasion of individual cells may lead to extensive destruction of tissues—an epithelium by Coccidia, or blood cells by malarial parasites. Tissues also may be destroyed without invasion of cells, as in ulceration of the intestine by *Entamoeba histolytica* and *Balantidium coli.* Whether such ulceration is brought about solely by histolytic enzymes of the parasites or partly by mechanical means is uncertain. The production of toxic substances has been suggested for some parasites, although specific toxins have not been isolated. However, the production of a potent toxin has been reported for a free-living dinoflagellate. *Gonyaulax catanella* apparently is the source of the poison found occasionally in the edible California mussel (87), and concentrates of this substance have shown a toxicity of 1.65 mouse units per microgram (83).

The *period of convalescence,* marked by the gradual disappearance of symptoms, extends to clinical recovery of the host. In some protozoan infections, apparent convalescence may be merely a period of *latency* during which a low-grade infection persists. Latency may be interrupted sooner or later by a *relapse,* in which symptoms reappear following renewed multiplication of the parasites.

TRANSFER OF PARASITIC PROTOZOA

Protozoan parasites reach new hosts in various ways. Active migration may lead to invasion of aquatic hosts—*Endosphaera* (66) of ciliates, *Amyloodinium* (74), and *Ichthyophthirius* (69) of fishes. *Contact transfer* is the characteristic method for some parasites—oral contact for *Entamoeba gingivalis* and *Trichomonas tenax;* transfer in coitus for *Trichomonas vaginalis, Tritrichomonas foetus,* and *Trypanosoma equiperdum.* *Contaminative transfer,* in which cysts or spores are ingested with food or drink, is the usual method for Coccidia and for intestinal flagellates, amoebae and ciliates.

Transfer by vectors is characteristic of blood parasites. Vectors include blood-sucking flies (*Trypanosoma gambiense*), mosquitoes (malarial parasites), bugs (*Trypanosoma cruzi*), fleas (*Trypanosoma lewisi*), ticks (*Babesia bigemina*), leeches (*Trypanosoma rotatorium*), and apparently vampire bats (*Trypansoma hippicum*). Transfer by vectors may be a mechanical process during which the parasites undergo no significant changes. In other cases, the parasite passes through a phase of the life-cycle before it is again infective for the final host; this *cyclic,* or infective, transfer is characteristic of malarial parasites and various trypanosomes. Some vectors inoculate the parasites directly into the tissues of the host during feeding. In contrast to this method, *Trypanosoma cruzi* is voided from the hind-gut of its vector and reaches the tissues of the vertebrate by contamination of a wound or invasion of a mucous membrane.

The case of *Histomonas meleagridis,* which causes "blackhead" in turkeys, seems to be unique in that the flagellates are said to be transferred in the eggs of an *intestinal nematode, Heterakis gallinae* (94).

Congenital infections may follow placental or ovarian transfer of parasites. Placental transfer, involving the passage of parasites through the placenta, has been reported for *Plasmodium vivax, P. malariae,* and *P. falciparum* of man, and occasionally also for certain trypanosomes in experimentally infected laboratory animals. Ovarian transfer, involving the direct invasion of eggs by parasites, occurs in such invertebrates as female ticks infected with *Babesia bigemina.*

Lacteal transfer, from females to suckling young, has been described in a few trypanosome infections, and this possibility should be considered in interpreting cases of supposedly placental transfer.

GEOGRAPHICAL DISTRIBUTION OF PARASITES OF MAN

The protozoan parasites of man include species which invade the vascular, epithelial, and other tissues, and also a number which live in the lumen of the digestive tract. The digestive tract is parasitized by six species of flagellates—*Trichomonas tenax (buccalis)* of the mouth; *Giardia lamblia* of the small intestine; and *Chilomastix mesnili, Retortomonas (Embadomonas) intestinalis, Tricercomonas intestinalis,* and *Pentatrichomonas hominis* of the colon—and six species of amoebae—*Entamoeba gingivalis* of the mouth; *Entamoeba coli, E. histolytica* (which sometimes invades other organs), *Dientamoeba fragilis, Endolimax nana,* and *Iodamoeba bütschlii* of the colon. One ciliate, *Balantidium coli,* sometimes invades the colon, while a coccidian, *Isospora hominis,* apparently is a parasite of the small intestine. The urogenital tract may harbor *Trichomonas vaginalis,* which is often found in the vagina and urethra in the female, and in the urethra and prostate in the male. Parasites of the blood and other tissues include species of *Leishmania* (*L. brasiliensis, L. donovani, L. tropica*), *Trypanosoma* (*T. cruzi, T. gambiense, T. rhodesiense*), and *Plasmodium* (*P. falciparum, P. malariae, P. ovale, P. vivax*). The status of *Toxoplasma* as a natural parasite of man is somewhat uncertain, in view of the apparent rarity of human infections and the low degree of host-specificity exhibited by these organisms.

The intestinal Protozoa of man are probably worldwide in distribution and are fairly common parasites. The malarial parasites, although most abundant in tropical areas, extend into the temperate zones. The trypanosomes of sleeping sickness, on the other hand, seem to be limited to central Africa by the geographical distribution of their vectors. Species of *Leishmania* are much more widely distributed, and *Trypanosoma cruzi* has an extensive range in the western hemisphere.

The Americas

In North America the usual intestinal Protozoa are to be expected. The incidence of *E. histolytica,* for example, ranges from about 0.2 to 50 per cent of the population in different parts of the United States, with an average possibly approaching 20 per cent (26a). Malaria remains an important problem only in the southeastern United States (3). *Trypanosoma cruzi* occurs at least as far north as central California, although Chagas' disease has not been found in man.

In Mexico and other Central American countries intestinal Protozoa are probably no less common than they are in North America. Malaria is important in lowland areas, both coastal and interior, and Costa Rica and Panama in particular have suffered considerably. Sporadic cases of Chagas' disease have appeared within this area, and both cutaneous and visceral leishmaniasis are known from scattered localities.

In the Caribbean area, malaria remains a public health problem in Jamaica, Haiti, the Dominican Republic, Puerto Rico, and Trinidad. Most of Cuba is free from endemic malaria although there are some areas in which the disease is still important. Among the smaller islands, malaria occurs endemically in the Caymans and is common in some of the Leeward and Windward Islands and in Tobago. To the north of Cuba, malaria has been reported in some of the southern Bahama Islands but is uncommon.

In South America, endemic malaria extends along the western coast from Columbia through Ecuador and Peru into northern Chile. Eastward, malaria is widely distributed in Venezuela, the Guianas and Brazil, except for highland areas. Southward, through Brazil, malaria is endemic in much of Bolivia and Paraguay and extends well into Argentina. Chagas' disease apparently occurs throughout much of South America. The data on incidence are quite incomplete, but recent surveys have shown that this disease is much more common than was formerly suspected. Cutaneous leishmaniasis also is scattered throughout much of South America and occasional cases of visceral leishmaniasis have been reported from Argentina northward to Venezuela. Infections with intestinal Protozoa are presumably as common in South America as they are in Central and North America.

The Mediterranean area

Malaria (particularly benign and malignant tertian) is still of some importance in Spain, Italy, Yugoslavia, Albania, Greece, Turkey, the Levant States, Transjordan, and Palestine, and has been a serious problem in the eastern area within the last few decades. Within this period there have been years in which Greece and Albania, for example, reported a malarial incidence of about 25 per cent. Along the southern shore of the Mediterranean, malaria extends westward through climatically favorable areas to Morocco. Visceral leishmaniasis has been reported occasionally in Spain, Sicily, Malta, Greece, Albania, Yugoslavia, Turkey, Transjordan, Syria, and Lebanon, while dermal leishmaniasis extends from eastern Egypt into Palestine and the Levant States, southern Turkey, and several provinces of Greece. Infections with *E. histolytica* and other intestinal Protozoa are known to be common in some parts of the Mediterranean area and are probably far from rare in other regions for which data are unavailable.

Europe north of the Mediterranean area

Malaria extends along the western shores of Europe from Portugal to the Baltic Sea, and in recent years, has occurred also in Finland. Although malaria is a disease of minor importance in northern Europe, benign tertian is still fairly common in the coastal regions of Holland. Malaria occurs also around the Black Sea, where both malignant and benign tertian may be found, and has extended northwestward for some distance along the Danube River. Infections with intestinal Protozoa are widely distributed and their incidence seems to vary considerably in different areas.

Central and southern Africa

Except for such climatically unfavorable areas as the Sahara, malaria extends throughout most of the continent into the Union of South Africa. The incidence is high in many regions and a native with no malarial experience is a rarity in the Belgian Congo and various other parts of tropical Africa. The distribution of the major types of malaria varies with the region. Benign tertian is apparently less common than malignant tertian in the Belgian Congo, Nigeria, the Gold Coast, and Togo, for example, but may represent 20-30 per cent of the cases in the Union of South Africa. Quartan malaria is fairly common in Togo, less common than benign tertian in Nigeria, rare in Kenya Colony and the Cameroons, and rare or absent in Bechuanaland. Trypanosomiasis (African sleeping sickness) extends from Gambia and French West Africa eastward to Kenya and as far south as Southern Rhodesia. Kala-azar has occurred sporadically along the border of the Sudan and Ethiopa but apparently has not extended westward or southward. Available data indicate that amoebiasis and other intestinal infections are very common in many parts of tropical Africa and apparently less common in others. Madagascar, off the southeastern coast of Africa, is a center of endemic and widely distributed malaria, malignant tertian being important. Amoebiasis is at least as common in Madagascar as in most parts of the mainland.

Southern and southeastern Asia

Malaria extends from the shores of the Red and Caspian seas across Asia to southern and eastern China, and farther inland, from the Caspian Sea well into southern Russia. For most of this area, the real incidence of malaria is unknown. Incomplete data suggest that an estimate of 2,000,000 cases a year, about a third of them malignant tertian, would be fairly conservative for India. Malaria also is important in Thailand, which has experienced a malarial death rate of 3 to 4 per thousand more than once within the past thirty years. Kala-azar extends from Turkey and Iraq eastward into India, Burma, Thailand, Indo-China, and China. The disease is considered an important health problem in India and China but is apparently rare in Thailand and Indo-China. Oriental sore extends from Turkey, Arabia, and Iran into India. Amoebiasis is probably common throughout the area.

The Pacific area

In Australia, malaria is endemic along the northern coast but not elsewhere. Amoebiasis is probably general in distribution, along with other intestinal Protozoa. Malaria is widely distributed and of common occurrence in Sarawak, New Guinea, Borneo, and other parts of the East Indies and amoebiasis also is known to be common throughout the region. In Melanesia, malaria is generally distributed in the New Hebrides and Solomon Islands. In the Philippines, malaria (perhaps more than a third of it malignant tertian) is common enough to be an important health problem, and the incidence of amoebiasis also seems to be fairly high. North of the Philippines, malaria extends into southern Japan.

LITERATURE CITED

1. Alexeieff, A. 1912. *Arch. Zool. Exp. Gén.* **10** (N. et R.): 73.
2. Andrews, J. M. 1927. *J. Parasit.* **13**: 183.
3. —— 1948. *Proc. 4th Intern. Congr. Trop. Med. & Malaria* **1**: 903.
4. Ball, G. H. 1943. *Amer. Nat.* **77**: 345.
5. Beauchamp, P. de 1911. *Arch. Zool. Exp. Gén.* **6** (N. et R.): 52.
6. Becker, E. R. 1923. *J. Parasit.* **10**: 25.
7. —— 1932. *Quart. Rev. Biol.* **7**: 282.
8. —— 1933. *Amer. J. Trop. Med.* **13**: 505.
9. —— and R. C. Everett 1930. *Amer. J. Hyg.* **11**: 362.
10. ——, J. A. Schulz and M. A. Emmerson 1930. *Iowa St. Coll. J. Sci.* **4**: 215.
11. Bozler, E. 1924. *Arch. f. Protistenk.* **49**: 163.
12. Brumpt, E. and G. Lavier 1924. *Ann. Parasitol.* **2**: 248.
13. —— and —— 1935. *Ann. Parasitol.* **13**: 439.
14. Caullery, M. 1922. *Le parasitisme et la symbiose* (Paris: Doin).
15. Chang, S. L. 1945. *J. Inf. Dis.* **76**: 126.
16. Chatton, E. 1920. *Arch. Zool. Exp. Gén.* **59**: 1.
17. —— and E. Biecheler 1934. *C. R. Ac. Sci.* **199**: 252.
18. —— and A. Lwoff 1923. *C. R. Soc. Biol.* **88**: 749.
19. Cleveland, L. R. 1924. *Biol. Bull.* **46**: 178.
20. —— 1926. *Quart. Rev. Biol.* **1**: 51.
21. —— 1928. *Biol. Bull.* **54**: 231.
22. ——, S. R. Hamm, E. P. Sanders and J. Collier 1934. *Mem. Acad. Arts & Sci.* **17**: 185.
23. Codreanu, M. and R. Codreanu 1928. *C. R. Soc. Biol.* **99**: 1368.
24. Drbohlav, J. J. 1925. *Amer. J. Hyg.* **5**: 580.
25. Duboscq, O. and P. Grassé 1927. *Arch. Zool. Exp. Gén.* **66**: 452.
26. —— and —— 1934. *Arch. Zool. Exp. Gén.* **75**: 615.
26a. Faust, E. C. 1942. *Amer. Soc. Trop. Med.* **22**: 93.
27. Fiveiskaja, A. 1929. *Arch. f. Protistenk.* **65**: 275.
28. Geiman, Q. M. and H. L. Ratcliffe 1936. *Parasitol.* **28**: 208.
29. Ghosh, E. 1925. *Parasitol.* **17**: 189.
30. Gojdics, M. 1939. *Trans. Amer. Micr. Soc.* **58**: 241.
31. Gönnert, R. 1935. *Arch. f. Protistenk.* **86**: 113.
32. Grassé, P. P. 1926. *Arch. Zool. Exp. Gén.* **65**: 345.
33. —— 1938. *Bull. Soc. Zool. Fr.* **63**: 110.
34. —— and P. de Boissezon 1929. *Bull. Soc. Zool. Fr.* **54**: 187.
35. Hall, S. R. 1931. *Biol. Bull.* **60**: 327.
36. Hegner, R. 1923. *Biol. Bull.* **45**: 162.
37. —— 1927. *Host-parasite Relations Between Man and His Intestinal Protozoa* (New York: Century).
38. —— 1937. *J. Parasit.* **23**: 1.
39. Hofker, J. 1931. *Arch. f. Protistenk.* **75**: 315.
40. Hood, C. L. 1927. *Biol. Bull.* **52**: 79.
41. Howland, R. B. 1928. *Science* **68**: 37.

42. Hsiung, T. S. 1930. *Iowa St. Coll. J. Sci.* **4**: 356.
43. Hungate, R. E. 1938. *Ecology* **19**: 1.
44. ——— 1942. *Biol. Bull.* **83**: 303.
45. ——— 1943. *Biol. Bull.* **84**: 157.
45a. ——— 1950. *Ann. Rev. Microbiol.* **4**: 53.
46. Jahn, T. L. 1933. *Arch. f. Protistenk.* **79**: 349.
47. Janda, V. and O. Jirovec 1937. *Mem. Soc. Zool. Tchekosl. Prague* **5**: 34.
48. Kirby, H. 1926. *Univ. Calif. Publ. Zool.* **29**: 25.
49. ——— 1927. *Quart. J. Micr. Sci.* **71**: 189.
50. ——— 1928. *Quart. J. Micr. Sci.* **72**: 355.
51. ——— 1932. *Univ. Calif. Publ. Zool.* **37**: 349.
52. ——— 1936. *Quart. J. Micr. Sci.* **79**: 309.
53. ——— 1937. *Univ. Calif. Publ. Zool.* **41**: 189.
54. ——— 1938. *Univ. Calif. Publ. Zool.* **43**: 1.
55. ——— 1938. *Quart. J. Micr. Sci.* **81**: 1.
56. ——— 1941. "Relationships Between Certain Protozoa and Other Animals" in *Protozoa in Biological Research* (New York: Columbia Univ. Press), pp. 890-1008.
57. ——— 1941. "Organisms Living on and in Protozoa" in *Protozoa in Biological Research* (New York: Columbia Univ. Press), pp. 1009-1113.
58. Kofoid, C. A. and R. F. MacLennan 1933. *Univ. Calif. Publ. Zool.* **39**: 1.
59. ——— and O. Swezy 1919. *Univ. Calif. Publ. Zool.* **20**: 1.
60. Kudo, R. 1924. *Ill. Biol. Monogr.* **9**: 3.
61. Lavier, G. 1935. *Ann. Parasitol.* **13**: 351.
62. Levine, N. D. and E. R. Becker 1933. *Iowa St. Coll. J. Sci.* **7**: 83.
63. Loefer, J. B. 1936. *Amer. Nat.* **70**: 184.
64. Lucas, M. S. 1934. *J. Roy. Micr. Soc.* **54**: 79.
65. Lwoff, A. 1924. *C. R. Ac. Sci.* **176**: 928.
66. Lynch, J. E. and A. E. Noble 1931. *Univ. Calif. Publ. Zool.* **36**: 97.
67. MacArthur, W. P. 1922. *J. Roy. Army Med. Corps* **38**: 83.
68. MacKinnon, D. L. and H. N. Ray 1931. *Quart. J. Micr. Sci.* **74**: 439.
69. MacLennan, R. F. 1935. *Arch. f. Protistenk.* **86**: 191.
70. Manwell, R. D., F. Coulston, E. C. Binckley and V. P. Jones 1945. *J. Inf. Dis.* **76**: 1.
71. Mattes, O. 1924. *Arch. f. Protistenk.* **47**: 413.
72. Metcalf, M. M. 1923. *Bull. U. S. Nat. Mus.* **120**: 1.
73. Mitchell, J. B. 1928. *Trans. Amer. Micr. Soc.* **47**: 29.
74. Nigrelli, R. F. 1936. *Zoologica* **21**: 129.
75. Packchanian, A. 1934. *Amer. J. Hyg.* **20**: 135.
76. Parker, R. C. 1926. *J. Exp. Zool.* **46**: 1.
77. Pascher, A. 1929. *Jahrb. wiss. Bot.* **71**: 386.
78. Penard, E. 1922. *Études sur les infusoires d'eau douce* (Genève: Georg).
79. Poisson, R. 1929. *C. R. Soc. Biol.* **102**: 637.
80. Powers, P. B. A. 1935. *Publ. Carneg. Inst.* **452**: 293.
81. Pringsheim, E. G. 1928. *Arch. f. Protistenk.* **64**: 289.
81a. Ratcliffe, H. L. and Q. M. Geiman 1938. *Arch. Pathol.* **25**: 160.
82. Reynolds, B. D. 1936. *J. Parasit.* **22**: 48.
83. Riegel, B., D. W. Stanger, D. M. Wikholm, J. D. Mold and H. Sommer 1949. *J. Biol. Chem.* **177**: 7.
84. Rodhain, J. 1934. *C. R. Soc. Biol.* **117**: 1195.
85. Roskin, G. 1927. *Arch. f. Protistenk.* **59**: 350.
86. Sassuchin, D. N. 1934. *Quart. Rev. Biol.* **9**: 215.
87. Sommer, H., W. F. Whedon, C. A. Kofoid and R. Stohler 1937. *Arch. Pathol.* 24: 537.
88. Stabler, R. M. and T.-T. Chen 1936. *Biol. Bull.* **70**: 56.
89. Steuer, A. 1928. *Arch. f. Protistenk.* **60**: 501.
90. Taylor, A. B. and R. L. King 1937. *Trans. Amer. Micr. Soc.* **56**: 172.
91. Trager, W. 1932. *Biochem. J.* **26**: 1762.
92. ——— 1934. *Biol. Bull.* **66**: 182.
93. Treillard, M. and A. Lwoff 1924. *C. R. Ac. Sci.* **178**: 1761.

94. Tyzzer, E. E. 1934. *Proc. Amer. Acad. Arts & Sci.* **69**: 189.
95. Valkanov, A. 1928. *Arch. f. Protistenk.* **63**: 419.
96. Weineck, E. 1934. *Arch. f. Protistenk.* **82**: 169.
97. Wenrich, D. H. 1924. *Biol. Bull.* **47**: 149.
98. ―――― 1935. *Proc. Amer. Philos. Soc.* **75**: 605.
99. ―――― 1935. *Univ. Penn. Bull.* **35** (No. 58): 23.
100. Wenyon, C. M. 1926. *Protozoology* (London: Ballière, Tindall & Cox).
101. Winogradow, M., T. Winogradowa-Federowa and A. Wereninow 1930. *Zentralbl. f. Bakt.*, II, **81**: 230.

XI

Protozoa of the Digestive and Urogenital Tracts

PROTOZOA OF THE HUMAN MOUTH

T HE HUMAN MOUTH is in some respects a fairly rigorous environment for Protozoa. Foods and drinks vary widely in temperature and chemical nature, and the disturbances involved in the practice of dental hygiene add further complications. Nevertheless, a flagellate (*Tricho-*

544

monas tenax) and an amoeba (*Entamoeba gingivalis*) manage to infect a significant proportion of the population.

The life-cycles of these two parasites do not include cysts, so that infections are spread by the transfer of trophozoites. Under experimental conditions, a trace of moisture has kept *E. gingivalis* alive long enough for droplet transfer, and for transfer by way of contaminated cups and other utensils (93). Transfer by direct oral contact entails much less risk for the parasite.

Trichomonas tenax

This flagellate probably was first described as *Cercaria tenax* by O. F. Müller in 1774 (94). Many years later, the organism was found again and described as *Tetratrichomonas buccalis* Goodey (65). *T. tenax* (Fig. 11: 1, A-C) shows a size range of about 5-21 x 3.8-7.6µ. The undulating membrane is usually rather short and the membrane-flagellum may not extend beyond the membrane. Autotomy occasionally pro-

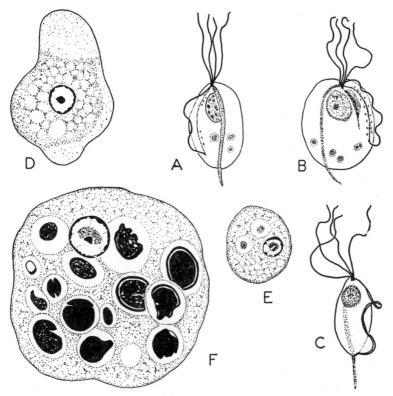

Fig. 11. 1. A-C. *Trichomonas tenax,* parabasal body shown only in B; x2530 (after Wenrich). D-F *Entamoeba gingivalis:* small specimen free from inclusions (D), a smaller rounded form (E), and a large specimen with many food vacuoles; x2000 (after Kofoid and Swezy).

duces forms with projecting axostyles and disproportionately long membranes (71). Mitosis has been described by Hinshaw (71), and *T. tenax* has been compared with other trichomonads of man by Wenrich (175).

Although rarely present in the healthy mouth, infection with *T. tenax* may approach an incidence of 90 per cent in cases of advanced pyorrhea (13, 72, 76). However, a casual relationship to pyorrhea has not been established (95, 97). In addition to their occurrence in the mouth, the flagellates have been found occasionally in pus from infected tonsils and, rarely, in material from the lungs.

Entamoeba gingivalis

This species, described as *Amoeba gingivalis* by Gros in 1849, evidently was the first amoeba reported from man. The specific name, *Endamoeba buccalis,* was proposed later by Prowazek (133) who had overlooked the paper by Gros. Several detailed descriptions have been published more recently (30, 78, 99, 104), and mitosis has been described by Stabler (155a) and Noble (128a). Literature on the species has been reviewed by Kofoid (95).

The amoeba measures 6-60µ in length, usually shows clear pseudopodia, and may contain a number of food vacuoles containing leucocytes, or less commonly, bacteria (Fig. 11. 1, D-F). The amoebae ingest living leucocytes and consequently are not mere scavengers (30). In cultures, both leucocytes and red corpuscles are ingested (78). The nucleus, 2-6µ in diameter, often shows a central clump of granules, as well as a zone of coarse granules near the nuclear membrane.

The incidence of infection apparently increases with age, although the healthy mouth rarely harbors *E. gingivalis*. In cases of pyorrhea, the incidence is high and may exceed 90 per cent (72). Such a coincidence is tempting but there is no conclusive proof of pathogenicity (97). This amoeba seems to be a natural parasite of monkeys (68, 90, 99) as well as of man, and experimental infections are possible in dogs with a preexisting gingivitis (74).

FLAGELLATES OF THE HUMAN INTESTINE

The small intestine is invaded only by *Giardia lamblia*, whereas the colon may contain *Retortomonas intestinalis, Tricercomonas intestinalis, Chilomastix mesnili* and *Pentatrichomonas hominis*.

Retortomonas intestinalis
(Wenyon and O'Connor) Wenrich

This flagellate, often known as *Embadomonas intestinalis* (Wenyon and O'Connor) Chalmers and Pekkola, has been reassigned to *Retortomonas* by Wenrich (165) on the basis that *Embadomonas* Mackinnon is a synonym of *Retortomonas* Grassi. Objections to this conclusion have been presented by Bishop (17).

R. intestinalis (Fig. 11. 2, H, I) is a small (4-9 x 3-4μ) organism with two unequal flagella. The longer flagellum extends anteriorly, the other anterolaterally from a pit (the "oral pouch" or "cytostome"). Shape varies somewhat although the anterior end is usually rounded. The cytoplasm often contains food vacuoles. Binary fission has been described by Bishop (17).

The cyst (Fig. 11. 2, F, G), which measures 4.5-7.0 x 3.0-4.5μ, is ovoid

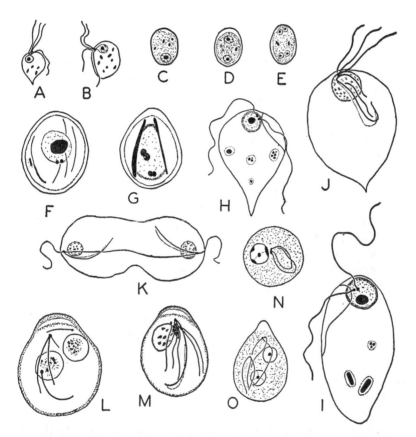

Fig. 11. 2. A-E. *Tricercomonas intestinalis:* flagellate stages (A, B); uninucleate (C), binucleate (D), and tetranucleate (E) cysts; x1600 (after Dobell and O'Connor). F-I *Retortomonas intestinalis:* flagellates from cultures at 37° (H) and 17-20° (I); cysts (F, G); x3600 (after Bishop). J-O. *Chilomoastix mesnili:* flagellate showing cytostomal fibril and cytostomal flagellum (J), x3000 (after Geiman); late fission, new cytostomal fibrils present (K), x2850 (after Geiman); uninucleate (L) and binucleate (M) cysts from *Macaca irus,* x2850 (after Geiman); polar view of uninucleate cyst from man (N), x1600 (after Kessel); binucleate cyst, nuclei joined by a paradesmose (O), x1600 (after Kessel).

to pear-shaped and contains one nucleus; nuclear division apparently does not occur (17).

Tricercomonas intestinalis
Wenyon and O'Connor

This species may or may not be identical with *Enteromonas hominis* Fonseca. This question has been discussed by Dobell and O'Connor (52) and by Wenyon (178), and the latter has pointed out that *Enteromonas hominis* was described with only three flagella.

Flagellated stages (Fig. 11. 2, A, B) have three anterior flagella and a fourth which may seem to lie within the cytoplasm and emerge at or near the posterior end of the body. The size range is 4-10 x 3-6μ. The cysts (Fig. 11. 2, C-E) measure 6-8 x 3-4μ and contain 1-4 nuclei (22). A flagellate apparently identical with *T. intestinalis* has been found in monkeys (46).

Chilomastix mesnili
(Wenyon) Alexeieff

This flagellate (Fig. 11. 2, J-O) seems to be specifically identical with one in apes and monkeys (64). The active stage, 6-20μ in length, has three anterior flagella and a shorter fourth which usually lies in the cytostomal groove, a depression extending obliquely from near the anterior end to about the middle of the body. A second groove often arises near the left anterior margin of the cytostomal cleft and extends posteriorly in one or two spiral turns. Solid food is ingested through a cytostome at the posterior end of the cytostomal groove (178). Just beneath the surface, a cytostomal fibril of uncertain significance extends along the cytostomal groove. Fission has been described by Geiman (64) and by Boeck and Tanabe (24).

Encysted stages (Fig. 11. 2, N, O) measure 7-10 x 4.5-6.0μ, contain one or two nuclei, and often granules and fibrils representing the blepharoplasts, cytostomal fibrils and possibly flagellar axonemes. Mitosis has been described in encysted stages (67, 100).

Pentatrichomonas hominis
(Davaine) Kirby

Two flagellates from the human colon are described in the literature as *Trichomonas hominis* (Davaine) Leuckart, with four anterior flagella, and *Hexamitus ardin-delteili* (44), later transferred to the genus *Pentatrichomonas* (103, 105) on the basis of its fifth free flagellum. In confirming observations of Wenrich (171), Kirby (91) concluded that *T. hominis* normally has a fifth free flagellum and that the two supposedly distinct flagellates should be recognized as *Pentatrichomonas hominis.* Trichomonads apparently identical with *P. hominis* have been found in monkeys, cats, dogs, and rats (171).

The flagellate (Fig. 11. 3, A-C) measures 8-15 x 3-5μ. The undulating membrane is about as long as the body and there is usually a free posterior portion of the membrane-flagellum. The fifth flagellum, which may be trailed posteriorly, beats in a rhythm different from that of the other four anterior flagella (103). A costa extends beneath the base of the undulating membrance and the axostyle usually projects beyond the posterior end of the body. Encysted stages are unknown.

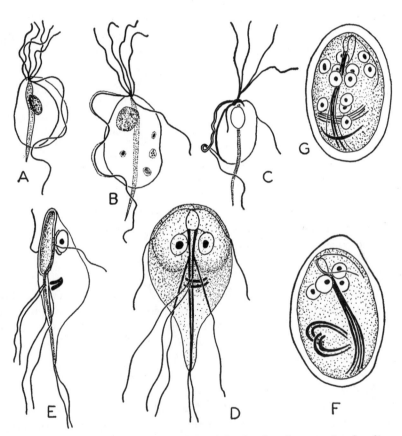

Fig. 11. 3. A. *Pentatrichomonas hominis,* showing five anterior flagella, membrane flagellum, nucleus, axostyle and costa; x2530 (after Wenrich). B. *P. hominis,* larger specimen with several food vacuoles; costa not shown; x2400 (after Wenrich). C. Bodian silver preparation of *P. hominis,* showing pelta anterior to the nucleus and a dorsal filament extending posteriorly from the pelta, between the costa and the nucleus; x2040 (after Kirby). D-G. *Giardia lamblia:* dorsal view (D), ventro-lateral view (E) of flagellate; cysts with four (F) and twelve (G) nuclei; x2560 (after Kofoid and Swezy).

Giardia lamblia
Stiles

This flagellate, described by Lambl in 1859 as *Cercomonas intestinalis,* probably was first seen by Leeuwenhoek in 1681. Although the organism is often referred to as *Giardia intestinalis,* Lambl's name had already been used for a parasite of Amphibia and the correct specific name is *Giardia lamblia.* Nuclear division and fission have been described (101).

The flagellate (Fig. 11. 3, D, E) measures 9-21 x 5-11μ. The body is flattened dorso-ventrally with a rather convex dorsal surface and a more flattened ventral surface, the anterior part of which forms a concave "sucker." Two flagella emerge from the posterior pole, while three other pairs extend from the lateral and antero-lateral surfaces. The paired axostyles, which may appear fused in stained preparations, extend to the posterior end of the body. Two parabasal bodies, sometimes fused together, lie near the axostyles in the posterior third of the body.

The cysts (Fig. 11. 3, F, G) measure 8-14 x 6-10μ and may contain 2-16 nuclei, axostyles, parabasal bodies, and fibrils which are possibly flagellar axonemes. The cyst is the stage most commonly found in stool examinations, since the flagellated forms are discharged primarily during attacks of diarrhea.

Although it was suspected, at one time, that rodents may serve as reservoirs, this suspicion has not been confirmed. Experimental infection of rats has been reported (8), but such infection has been temporary and has not led to production of cysts.

Flagellosis

The effects of flagellate infections have been evaluated primarily by correlating clinical observations with incidence of infection. On such a basis, there is no evidence that *Retortomonas intestinalis* and *Tricercomonas intestinalis* are harmful. *Chilomastix mesnili* has been associated with abnormal stool frequency often enough to arouse suspicion, but there is no reason for considering this species a serious parasite.

Pentatrichomonas hominis has been found in diarrheic patients (150) and *"Pentatrichomonas ardin-delteili"* was first observed (44) in patients with dysentery and later in cases of dysentery and chronic diarrhea (105). Therefore, it is often assumed that *P. hominis* is occasionally a causative or contributary factor in digestive disturbances. Invasion of tissues— agonal (110) and possibly postmortem (176)—has been reported, but probably does not occur in the usual infection.

Infection with *Giardia lamblia* is frequently correlated with digestive disturbances, although there is no invasion of tissues. Heavy infections might interfere with normal absorption, since the flagellates adhere to the mucosa. Symptoms include chronic diarrhea, attacks of diarrhea alternating with constipation, chronic stomachache, occasional cramping and colic, nausea, abdominal tenderness, loss of appetite, chronic headaches, and irritability (61, 111, 178).

Chemotherapy

The treatment of flagellate infections is a less pressing problem and has attracted less attention than the treatment of amoebiasis. Some of the drugs used for *Entamoeba histolytica* have been tried also in flagellate infections, but the results are not always directly comparable. Atebrin has been used effectively for elimination of *Giardia lamblia,* although occasional infections are not cured. Giardiasis in children also has been treated with bismuth-salicylate, followed by treparsol (111), and with acranil (16). Diodoquin is said to be active against *P. hominis,* and good results with gentian violet in combination with argyrol enemas also have been reported.

AMOEBAE OF THE INTESTINAL LUMEN

The human colon may be invaded by *Endolimax nana, Dientamoeba fragilis, Entamoeba coli,* and *Iodamoeba bütschlii.* In addition, natural infection with *Entamoeba polecki,* a parasite of monkeys, has been observed (88).

Endolimax nana
(Wenyon and O'Connor) Brug

First described as *Entamoeba nana* (179), this species was later transferred to the genus *Endolimax* by Brug in 1918. An apparently identical amoeba has been reported from monkeys (46).

The amoeboid stage (Fig. 11. 4, A), usually observed only in loose stools, is a small (6-15μ) sluggish form with clear pseudopodia and food vacuoles containing bacteria. The stained nucleus often shows no peripheral granules, although such can be demonstrated after adequate fixation (155). The endosome is large, usually irregular but sometimes ovoid or spherical, and may be central or eccentric. Precystic stages have been reported as rounded forms without food vacuoles. Mitosis has been described (49a).

The mature cysts (Fig. 11. 4, B-E), 5-12 x 4-6μ, contain four, or rarely eight, nuclei. The shape is usually ovoid, and one surface is often more convex than the opposite side. Stored glycogen may be present in young cysts but disappears gradually as the cysts mature. Occasionally, small filaments have been reported as possible chromatoid bodies. The nuclei of the mature cyst are appreciably smaller than those of the trophozoite, and the endosome is often eccentric.

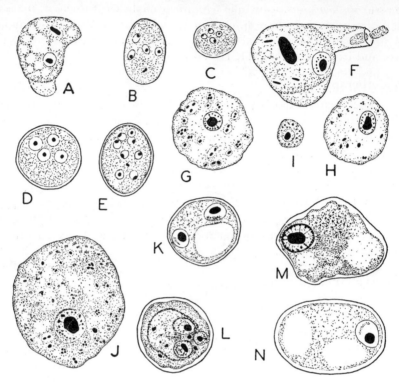

Fig. 11. 4. A-E. *Endolimax nana:* amoeboid stage (A); cysts from naturally infected monkey (B) and from man (C-E); B, x1830; A, C-E, x1600 (after Kessel). F-N. *Iodamoeba bütschlii:* amoboid stage ingesting food through tubular "food-cup" (F), x2400 (after Stabler); small (I), medium (G, H), and large (J) amoeboid stages, periendosomal granules evident in nucleus, x1685 (after Wenrich); binucleate cyst (K), x1600 (after Kessel); cysts with three (possibly four) nuclei (L) and one nucleus (M), x1685 (after Wenrich); uninucleate cyst from naturally infected monkey (N), x1900 (after Kessel).

Iodamoeba bütschlii
(Prowazek) Dobell

This species apparently was described as *Entamoeba bütschlii* by Prowazek (135) and was later transferred to the genus *Iodamoeba* (45). Occasional use of the name, *Iodamoeba williamsi,* is based upon Prowazek's (134) earlier erection of the species *"Entamoeba williamsi"* for a mixture of *Entamoeba coli* and perhaps *I. bütschlii.* Infections with *I. bütschlii* have been reported from apes and monkeys (167) as well as man.

The amoeboid stage (Fig. 11. 4, F-J) measures 4-20μ in length. The organism moves slowly, usually with clear blunt pseudopodia. The stained nucleus is 2.0-3.5μ in diameter and contains a central or slightly eccentric endosome measuring a third to half the nuclear diameter. Nuclear granules may be scattered on a "network" or may lie just within the membrane. The nucleus has been described by Wenrich (167). Precystic stages are rounded amoebae without food vacuoles and either with or without glycogen.

The cyst (Fig. 11. 4, K-N), usually more common than the trophozoite in stool samples, measures 6-16µ and is nearly always uninucleate. For example, only 0.2 per cent of the cysts were binucleate in one series of examinations (159). The cyst may be spherical but is more often irregular. Inclusions resembling chromatoid bodies of other amoebae have been seen occasionally (167), but a large mass of glycogen is characteristic.

Dientamoeba fragilis
Jepps and Dobell

In this amoeba the percentage of binucleate forms has ranged from 9.0 (168) to about 80 (81) in different infections. Occasional specimens contain more than two nuclei (49), sometimes as many as seven (173). Several detailed descriptions have been published (81, 166, 168,

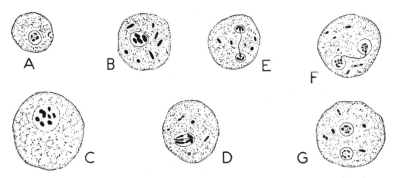

Fig. 11. 5. *Dientamoeba fragilis,* x1600 (after Wenrich). A. Uninucleate form, interphase nucleus. B. A single prophase nucleus with four chromosomes. C. Feulgen preparation, single nucleus with eight chromosomes. D. Single nucleus in anaphase. E. Early telophase, with paradesmose. F. Binucleate form with persisting paradesmose. G. Two nuclei in interphase.

169), and the most recent descriptions of nuclear division are those of Dobell (49) and Wenrich (172). The literature has been reviewed by Wenrich (173).

The diameters of rounded amoebae range from 3.5 to about 20µ. Movement is active, with broad and usually clear pseudopodia. A number of food vacuoles may be present. The nucleus (Fig. 11. 5) usually shows a central group of 4-8 granules, four being the most common number. In mitosis, the division of four chromosomes into eight has been demonstrated (169, 172) and the central group of granules represents these chromosomes. A reticular organization of the nucleus also has been observed occasionally (173). A fibril, similar to the paradesmose of trichomonad flagellates, sometimes joins two nuclei in *D. fragilis* (49).

The ability of *D. fragilis* to encyst remains unproven, although spheroid to ovoid bodies (4-9 x 4-6μ) containing two supposed nuclei have been identified tentatively as cysts of this amoeba (130).

Entamoeba coli
Lösch emend. Schaudinn

This species occurs in monkeys (46, 48) as well as man. The amoeboid stages (Fig. 11. 6, A) vary from 15 to 40μ in diameter, with a common range of 20-30μ. Locomotion is sluggish, with blunt and often granular pseudopodia. Food vacuoles contain bacteria and other material from the intestine but ordinarily no tissue cells. The stained interphase nucleus shows a rather small and normally eccentric endosome, as well as a fairly coarse layer of peripheral granules. In addition, finely granular periendosomal material is stained in the Feulgen technique. The rest of the nucleus is Feulgen-negative (169a). As would be expected, the typical nuclear structure is much modified in mitosis (158).

Spheroid precystic forms usually measure 15-18μ, with a range of 12 to 35μ. There are no food vacuoles and it is sometimes difficult to distinguish precystic *E. coli* from *E. histolytica*.

The cysts (Fig. 11. 6, B-E) range from 10 to 38μ in diameter, although the majority measure 15-20μ. Young cysts contain one or two nuclei and relatively large masses of glycogen. Mature cysts contain eight nuclei, or sometimes 16 or more (48). Chromatoid bodies, visible in the unstained cyst as refractile inclusions, are common in young cysts but have usually disappeared, along with the glycogen, in mature cysts. Chromatoid material may appear as splinters, filaments, irregular clumps of splinter-like bodies, small irregular fragments, or as one or more lobulated masses.

Effects on the host

Pathogenicity of *Endolimax nana* and *Iodamoeba bütschlii* is doubtful and perhaps improbable, although Smithies (150) observed digestive disturbances in all of his patients infected with amoebae. The report of a fatal infection, apparently with *I. bütschlii*, seems to be the only case of its kind on record (43).

Dientamoeba fragilis also is often considered a commensal. However, heavy infection has been associated with definite illness involving digestive disturbances, chronic fatigue, and loss of weight, and both the infection and the symptoms were eliminated by chemotherapy (66). Wenrich also has suggested possible pathogenicity for this species (168), and has reviewed other reports of this nature (173).

Entamoeba coli is another supposedly harmless species, but various gastro-intestinal complaints have been noted in infected patients (150).

AMOEBIASIS

This term is restricted, in the present discussion, to infections with *Entamoeba histolytica* and the resulting effects in man.

The causative organism

Entamoeba histolytica Schaudinn of man apparently is identical with an intestinal amoeba of monkeys (47). The amoeboid forms (Fig. 11. 6, F) usually measure 20-30μ, with a range of about 8.0 to almost 60μ. The size apparently varies in different strains. Locomotion of *E. histolytica* is much more rapid than that of *E. coli,* and the pseudopodia of the former are usually clear. Food vacuoles of *E. histolytica* in stool samples may contain red corpuscles or other tissue elements but rarely bacteria or other material from the lumen of the colon. Feeding activities and digestion have been described by Hopkins and Warner (77). The typical stained nucleus shows a small central endosome and relatively fine peripheral granules near the membrane. The Feulgen technique stains only a zone of small periendosomal granules (169a). Characteristic changes in nuclear structure occur in mitosis (106).

The relatively inactive, rounded precystic forms usually measure 7-20μ. Even before secretion of the cyst membrane, the cytoplasm may contain glycogen and chromatoid bodies. Origin of the chromatoid bodies from cytoplasmic vacuoles or globules has been traced in living material (77). The chromatoid material is usually interpreted as stored food (46).

The approximately spherical cysts (Fig. 11. 6, G-K) measure about 6.0 to 20μ, the range varying in different strains (50, 146, 179). Although the recognition of hereditarily distinct "large" and "small" races seems justified, the transformation of a small race (average, 8.5μ) into a large race (average, 19.0μ) has occurred after maintenance of a strain in the laboratory for six years (122). Small races apparently differ from large races in other respects as well as in size. Small races seem to grow less readily in standard media (146, 152) and seldom or never show ingested red corpuscles (62). Differences in pathogenicity also have been correlated with differences in size.

Chromatoid bodies and glycogen are usually seen in young cysts, but the glycogen and later the chromatoids disappear as the cysts reach maturity. The uninucleate cyst sometimes contains so much glycogen that the nucleus is displaced toward the surface. The chromatoid bodies are typically rod-like, often with rounded ends. Both size and shape are variable, and the inclusions may form clumps instead of being scattered through the cytoplasm. There are commonly a few large (5-10μ) plump rods. At the other extreme, there may be as many as 30 or so small bodies. The mature cysts usually contain four, and rarely eight or more nuclei. After elimination from the intestine, immature cysts apparently do not

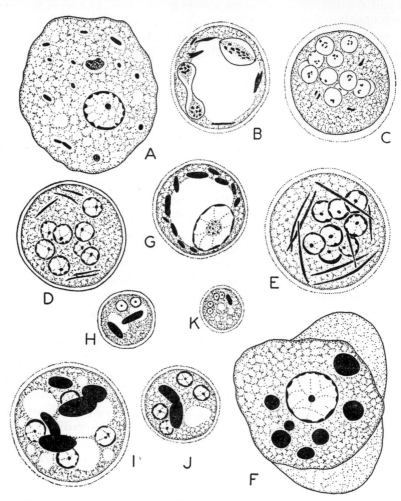

Fig. 11. 6. A-E. *Entamoeba coli:* A. Rounded amoeboid form, numerous food vacuoles, x1600 (after Kessel). B. Cyst with large glycogen vacuole, a few chromatoid bodies, two nuclei in division; x1600 (after Kessel). C. Cyst with twelve nuclei; schematic (after Brooke). D. Typical cyst from naturally infected monkey; x1850 (after Kessel). E. Cyst with eight interphase nuclei and several chromatoid bodies; x1600 (after Kessel). F-K *Entamoeba histolytica:* F. Amoeboid form with ingested red corpuscles; x1600 (after Kessel). G. Cyst with large glycogen "vacuole," several small chromatoid bodies, nucleus in early division; x1600 (after Kessel). H-K. Cysts of various sizes; x1600 (after Kessel).

develop further at room or refrigerator temperature and do not undergo excystment (29a). Cysts of *E. histolytica* are often passed intermittently, sometimes at intervals of a week or so, whereas cysts of *E. coli* are more likely to be found at any examination.

Excystment requires 12-18 hours. The amoeba becomes active and then a small portion of the cytoplasm emerges through a pore in the membrane. Eventually, the organism surges back and forth until it squeezes out as a multinucleate stage (33). The details of growth, nuclear division and plasmotomy vary somewhat, but eight uninucleate amoebae are usually produced from each excysted stage before the normal cycle of fission is resumed (33, 46).

Invasion of tissues by *E. histolytica*

Invasion of the wall of the colon is heaviest in regions where stasis of the contents occurs most frequently (31, 125)—cecum, ascending colon, rectum, sigmoid flexure, and the appendix. In very severe infections the colon may be attacked throughout its length, but no single region is invaded invariably. Consequently, the proctoscopic finding of no rectal ulcers cannot guarantee freedom from amoebae in other parts of the colon.

It is generally assumed that invasion of the tissues may involve mechanical penetration by pseudopodial activity and the destruction of tissue cells by cytolytic enzymes. The relative importance of these two factors has been disputed. Epithelial necrosis with no apparent mechanical penetration has been seen in kittens (118), whereas penetration in monkeys has been attributed primarily to mechanical activities (69). Meleney and Frye (121) concluded that in kittens as well as man, lysis of tissue cells and mechanical penetration are both significant factors, whereas Craig (41) has stressed the cytolytic activity of *E. histolytica* in human amoebiasis. The interpretation of cytolytic activity is based upon the histological appearance of invaded tissues and upon the reported extraction of an active cytolysin from *E. histolytica* in cultures (37).

Development of the amoebic ulcer has been discussed by various workers (41, 52, 69, 136, 137, 140, 178). The amoebae apparently may invade the tissues by crawling into the crypts of Lieberkühn or by attacking the more superficial mucosa. As pictured by Wenyon (178), invasion of an intestinal gland and multiplication of the amoebae is followed by degeneration of gland cells and loosening of the tissues so as to block the duct, and there may be a slight nodular elevation of the mucosa. The earliest lesions reported in human autopsy material are inconspicuous "pinpoint" lesions in individuals reporting no symptoms of amoebiasis (58). The early lesion, if it does not open into the intestinal lumen, may be considered an amoebic abscess which will later rupture to form a small flask-shaped ulcer. After penetrating the epithelium, the amoebae may migrate along the basement membrane or may pass through into the underlying connective tissue. Increase in number of amoebae is accompanied by local necrosis of tissue cells and rupture of capillaries, and the margin of the ulcer is gradually undermined. This ulcer of the colon differs from the typical bacterial ulcer in that there is no tendency for developing fibrous tissue to limit the area of invasion. Instead, there is a gradual transition from the surrounding normal tissue to the completely necrotic tissue at the margin of the ulcer. The amoebae are usually most numerous in the intermediate zone. If secondary bacterial invasion occurs, as is the case fairly often, typical inflammatory reactions modify the histological picture considerably.

Extension of the ulcer may involve increase in depth and in diameter. Penetration may continue through the muscularis mucosae and sometimes even to the serosa, to be followed occasionally by perforation, or by local adhesion of the colon to some adjacent structure. Individual ulcers may heal spontaneously after a time, with a resultant fibrosis of the gut wall and a variable amount of epithelial regeneration. In chronic infections, this fibrosis, primarily of the submucosa and muscularis, may lead to extensive thickening of the colonic wall, either locally or sometimes throughout much of its length.

Complications include perforations of the colon or the appendix, abscesses of the appendix, perirectal abscesses, adhesions of the colon, fistulae of amoebic origin, and sometimes amoebic granuloma of the colon simulating carcinoma. A number of these complications, as encountered in a group of 20,000 patients, have been listed by Musgrave (125).

Secondary sites of infection may be established by migration of *E. histolytica* from the colon into the ileum, or more commonly, by circulatory transportation of the amoebae. Upon entering the capillaries of the portal system, the amoebae would pass first to the liver. From this organ, they might be carried to the heart and to the lungs, and then perhaps back to the heart and out in the systemic circulation.

Amoebic abscess of the liver is the most common secondary lesion, although the incidence has varied from less than 1.0 to about 50 per cent in different groups of patients. Liver abscess may follow acute primary amoebiasis or may develop in patients with no previous history of diarrheic amoebiasis or dysentery. Factors influencing the occurrence of liver abscess are unknown. Such abscesses may be multiple or single, small or large, and occur most frequently in the right lobe of the liver. Complications may result from rupture of a liver abscess into the peritoneal cavity, or following adhesions, into the pleural cavity, into the stomach, or through the body wall. Considerable progress is being made in the recognition of hepatic amoebiasis in its early stages (151), and such early symptoms as hepatic enlargement and tenderness have been correlated with laboratory diagnoses. Since these early conditions seem to be cleared up by chemotherapy, their recognition and characterization represent a real advance in the control of secondary amoebiasis.

A pulmonary abscess may be initiated by rupture of a liver abscess into the pleural cavity, or by transportation of the amoebae through the pulmonary circulation. Other secondary invasions have been reported in the skin (56), lymph glands (96), bone marrow (102), brain, spleen, and urinary bladder. Inflammation of the uterus and vagina, with a bloody mucous discharge containing *E. histolytica* (123), and invasion of the uterine submucosa (142) have also been reported.

Various types of primary amoebiasis

Although some workers still favor the theory that in the asymptomatic individual, *E. histolytica* lives in the lumen of the colon as a commensal (117), there is justification for the opinion that even the "carrier" does not escape at least some damage to the tissues (39, 41, 58, 82). There is still no conclusive proof that *E. histolytica* can live in the human colon without actual invasion of tissue. The status of the so-called small races, which are often believed to have little tendency to invade human tissues (146), remains indefinite in spite of the fact that the small races have not been found in the more severe types of intestinal amoebiasis. The spontaneous transformation of a small race into a large race (122) has added to the uncertainty.

In patients with symptomatic primary amoebiasis, various degrees of severity may be recognized. Many cases are mild in character, others show recurrent diarrhea in addition to symptoms seen in mild cases, and typical amoebic dysentery occurs only in the more severe cases.

The characterization of mild cases, as seen in various geographical areas (26, 27, 40, 41, 125, 145), stresses the variety of symptoms and the confusing clinical picture. Boyers (26) has encountered more than 1,900 complaints in about 700 patients. One very common feature is fatigability, which may develop into a condition of chronic fatigue. Constipation, either recurrent or chronic, is usually more common than diarrhea. Other symptoms include dull headaches, nervousness, irritability, sleepiness during the day, restlessness, aches in the muscles or in the regions of the joints, abdominal distention by gas, "chronic indigestion," and other obscure digestive disturbances. The clinical picture sometimes suggests chronic appendicitis.

In the diarrheic type, recurrent and sometimes prolonged attacks of diarrhea accompany many of the symptoms present in mild cases.

In amoebic dysentery the stools contain appreciable amounts of blood and mucus. Bowel movements may range from five or six to 30 or more per day, so that loss of weight and dehydration become extensive in severe cases. A mild fever may develop, and various symptoms of the diarrheic cases often appear in aggravated form. The onset of acute amoebiasis may be sudden in individuals with no previously recognized symptoms, or there may be a gradual transition from a mild or diarrheic case to typical dysentery. Various complications arise if *E. histolytica* becomes established secondarily in the liver or other organs.

The factors responsible for development of severe amoebiasis have not been determined. Although the appearance of precipitins and complement-fixing antibodies indicates an immunological response, the significance of such factors in the host-parasite relationship is uncertain. Differences in severity of amoebiasis may be correlated with differences in diets (2, 55), but the relation of specific dietary deficiencies to the development of severe amoebiasis remains to be established. The bacterial flora of the colon may be a contributory factor occasionally, as indicated by observations on experimentally infected rats (156) and kittens (33, 126). Such a bacteriostatic agent as penicillin has shown therapeutic activity in infected rats and may also have a prophylactic effect when administered before inoculation with *E. histolytica* (156).

Chemotherapy

Intestinal amoebiasis. Completely effective treatment involves elimination of the infection. Therefore, the results can be determined only by periodic laboratory examination of the patient for at least six months, and preferably a year or more, after treatment. Even an ideal drug would not maintain a perfect record in such tests because it is impossible to eliminate all chances of reinfection. Consequently, the best that can be expected is a high percentage of "permanent" cures.

During treatment and for a short time afterward, the diet of the patient with a mild case should omit roughage and intestinal irritants. The patient with an acute case is usually limited to liquid foods and is preferably kept in bed during treatment. The choice of orally administered drugs varies with the physician. The more commonly used types fall into three groups, arsenicals, quinoline derivatives, and alkaloid derivatives (1, 3, 40, 41). Some of the newer antibiotics form a promising fourth group.

The arsenicals include stovarsol (acetarsone, or acetylamino-hydroxyphenylarsonic acid) and carbarsone (4-carbaminophenylarsonic acid). Carbarsone seems to be the best of various arsenicals (1), whereas stovarsol has been considered somewhat dangerous for routine clinical use (3).

Several quinoline derivatives have given good results. Chiniofon (yatren, quinoxyl, anayodin) is therapeutically satisfactory without producing serious toxic effects (40, 41). Vioform (iodochlorhydroxyquinoline) seems to be more active than chiniofon and produces only minor toxic effects (3). Diodoquin (5,7-diiodo-8-hydroxyquinoline) is a more recently introduced drug which seems to be quite effective.

Widely used alkaloid derivatives include kurchi alkaloids and emetine (the active agent of ipecacuanha). Kurchi alkaloids, from the bark of an Indian tree, show no marked toxicity, but the amoebacidal activity is somewhat less than that of other widely used drugs (3). Emetine-bismuth-iodide, although generally considered therapeutically effective, has acquired such a reputation for toxicity that it is undesirable for treatment of mild amoebiasis (3, 40, 41). However, oral dosage with emetine-hydrochloride in enteric-sealed tablets has given good results in a small group of patients, some of whom were children (149). This method apparently permits dosage with emetine at levels high enough for amoebacidal effectiveness without any serious danger to the patient.

Aureomycin, in contrast to penicillin, seems to be decidedly amoebacidal and has produced apparent cures in cases of intestinal amoebiasis (114). Likewise, terramycin is proving to be effective in treatment of primary amoebiasis (123a). In addition to the usual amoebacidal drugs, supplementary treatment with penicillin or a sulfonamide, such as sulfaguanidine, may be beneficial when intestinal amoebiasis is aggravated by secondary bacterial invasion (1).

Secondary amoebiasis. Treatment of secondary invasions is a more difficult problem than the treatment of intestinal amoebiasis and should be started as early as possible. For hepatic amoebiasis, emetine-hydrochloride apparently is the most effective drug available at present (86), although preliminary results with chloroquine are quite encouraging (34, 116). Many hepatic cases, in which treatment was begun early, have been cured by emetine alone. In more advanced hepatic invasion, aspiration of abscesses may be necessary in conjunction with chemotherapy. Emetine-hydrochloride is injected subcutaneously or intramuscularly, the former method being less painful. The effectiveness of emetine in liver abscess apparently depends upon the rapid concentration and prolonged retention of the drug in the liver following the usual injection (129). Unfortunately, emetine-hydrochloride is highly toxic and its effects are cumulative, so that cautious administration is essential.

The search for new amoebacidal drugs. The need for more effective drugs has led to the testing of many new compounds. Preliminary screening has involved two general procedures: tests for amoebacidal activity in cultures, and tests for therapeutic value in infected laboratory animals. Until pure cultures are available, the results obtained with cultures must be interpreted cautiously. If culture tubes are plugged with cotton, the failure of *E. histolytica* to grow in the presence of a drug might reflect nothing more than a rise in oxidation-reduction potential of the medium following bacteriostasis. Therefore, petrolatum seals, or other devices for maintaining anaerobic conditions, are essential in such tests (28). The use of monkeys (25, 89) in testing amoebicidal drugs has the advantage that these animals often have natural infections with *E. histolytica.* However, *E. polecki,* which also occurs in *Macaca mulatta,* must not be confused with *E. histolytica* in the interpretation of results (88). Dogs maintained on a fish diet are susceptible to experimental infection with

E. histolytica, and there seems to be fairly good correlation between the canine and the human response to known amoebacidal drugs (160). Young rats also have been used to advantage (85).

Problems in control of amoebiasis

The transfer of *E. histolytica* is a simple matter. All that is necessary is for viable stages, voided in the feces of an infected individual, to reach the mouth of another host and be swallowed. The control of intestinal amoebiasis involves nothing more than preventing the completion of this sequence. The fact that no immediate solution of the problem is in sight depends not only upon the biological characteristics of *E. histolytica* but also upon human behavior. That the combination is still beyond control by current public health practice is attested by the widespread distribution of *E. histolytica.*

The encysted stage of *E. histolytica* is well adapted to its normal method of transfer. At temperatures below 22° cysts may remain viable for 1-6 weeks under favorable conditions, with time of survival showing an inverse relationship to temperature (29a). Cysts also are viable for at least several hours after ingestion by flies and passage through the insects (131, 179). Pollution of the soil with cysts is an important source of infection whenever human excrement is used as fertilizer. Under suitable experimental conditions, cysts remain alive in soil for at least eight days at 28-34° (14). Consequently, uncooked vegetables from contaminated soil are potentially dangerous. Treatment of such vegetables with dilute acetic acid may be an effective prophylactic measure (15).

The infected individual may distribute cysts widely, as in the "general pollution of the environment" noted in a revealing survey of a children's home (79). Cysts were recovered from the hands of children, from soiled clothing, from the bottom of a laundry chute, from damp sand in a play-box, from a wading pool, and from the floor of the pool after drainage. In general, any conditions under which sanitary precautions are relaxed or neglected will contribute to infection. Crowding in asylums, prisons, and other institutions may be a contributory factor, especially when coupled with carelessness or ignorance. A recent outbreak in an eastern state hospital is illustrative. Investigation showed that a toilet used by kitchen attendants was without soap and paper, that attendants caring for amoebic patients spent part of their time working in the kitchen, and that carriers of *E. histolytica* had been serving as cooks and kitchen helpers.

Since cysts may remain viable for 15-45 minutes under the fingernails (4), the infected food-handler has often been considered a major source of infection (40, 41), both within the family and in hotels and restaurants. Although there are no adequate data and at least one statistical study has failed to support such transmission (147), the burden of proof would seem to lie upon those who wish to consider this factor unimportant in the epidemiology of amoebiasis. Whether or not it can be assumed that food-handlers are important, the control of amoebiasis at this point would require laboratory examinations at intervals, as well as rigid enforcement of sanitary regulations. The sheer numbers of individuals involved in handling food, the time required for thorough examinations, and the scarcity of experienced laboratory personnel make even a single survey of all food-handlers an utter impossibility. This situation leaves educational measures as the only practical supplement to adequate sanitary codes.

A source of pure drinking water is another important requirement. That amoebiasis can be spread through polluted water was demonstrated in the Chicago hotel outbreak of 1933 (29), although faulty plumbing rather than inadequate purification of drinking water was involved. In the purification of municipal water supplies, rapid sand filtration after preliminary chemical coagulation and sedimentation is reasonably effective in removing cysts of *E. histolytica* (12). Although it is not certain that filtration is completely protective, an efficiently operated filtration plant is probably the best safeguard for a large population. The efficiency of chlorination alone varies with the concentration of free chlorine, with temperature and pH of the water, and with the amount of organic matter present. Varied results have been obtained on experimental scales. Stone (157) found cysts of *E. histolytica* no more resistant than *Escherichia coli*, being killed within 20 minutes by chlorine at 4-10 ppm, whereas Morton (124) believes that even under ideal conditions, chlorine at 30 ppm for 30 minutes would be necessary to kill all cysts. Conservative opinion holds that routine chlorination, as currently practiced, cannot prevent the spread of amoebiasis by water supplies. Treatment with high concentrations ("superchlorination"), followed by removal of enough chlorine to restore potability, is recommended (128).

BALANTIDIOSIS

Balantidium coli
(Malmsten) Stein

This ciliate is the only one definitely known to be parasitic in man. The active stage (Fig. 11. 7, A, B), measures 30-200 x 20-70μ. The cytostome is well developed and functional, as are the two contractile vacuoles. Food vacuoles may contain bacteria and other material from the colon, or sometimes red corpuscles and other tissue elements. A cytological study of *B. coli*, with special reference to the fibrillar system, has been published by McDonald (113).

The cysts (Fig. 11. 7, C), which reach a diameter of 60-65μ, are the largest ones encountered in human stools. Food vacuoles are usually eliminated and the most conspicuous feature is the macronucleus. Cysts containing two ciliates have been seen occasionally, but their significance is uncertain. Conjugation, but not encystment, has been observed in cultures (80).

The infection is usually localized in the colon, although invasion of

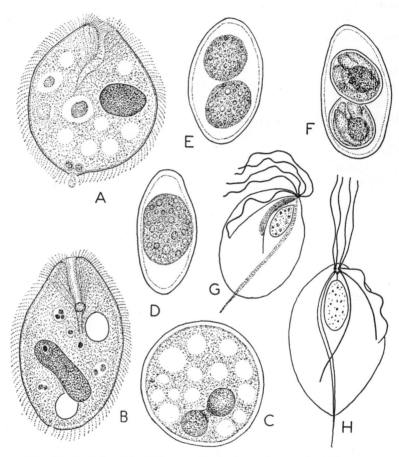

Fig. 11. 7. A-C. *Balantidium coli:* A. Somewhat contracted specimen from a stained preparation, showing macronucleus, several food vacuoles, fibrils extending from gullet to cortex; material apparently being discharged from the cytopyge; x520. B. A more elongated specimen, showing two contractile vacuoles and other structures; x600 (after Wenyon). C. Cyst (stained preparation), bilobed macronucleus; x520. D-F. *Isospora hominis:* oocysts with undivided zygote (D), with two sporoblasts (E), and with two spores containing developing sporozoites; x1030 approx. (after May). G. *Trichomonas vaginalis,* typical undulating membrane, costa, axostyle, nucleus, parabasal body, and parabasal filament; x2400 (after Wenrich). H. *T. vaginalis,* showing group of blepharoplasts and other structures (except parabasal body); schematic (after Powell).

the ileum occurs occasionally. Both active ciliates and cysts may be expected in stool samples. The incidence of infection seems to vary widely in different parts of the world and is apparently quite low in the United States (163, 180). Host-specificity is evidently less rigid than that of various other intestinal Protozoa. This ciliate apparently occurs in the pig, as well as in man and various other primates, and it has been suggested that *B. coli* may be a natural parasite of the pig.

Effects on man

In some cases, the symptoms are insignificant enough to suggest a pseudo-carrier condition. At the other extreme, there may be recurrent attacks of diarrhea, and in severe infections, a chronic dysentery. The stools may contain much mucus and sometimes blood and pus. General symptoms include colic, loss of appetite, occasional nausea, general weakness, and fatigability. In long-standing cases, loss of weight may be noticeable. Ulceration of the colon, which may be extensive in acute cases, resembles that produced by *E. histolytica*. The ciliates penetrate the mucosa where they often occur in groups; in deeper ulcers they may even invade the muscle layers. Perforation of the colon and extension of the infection from the colon to the lower ileum also have been reported. The ciliates have been seen in blood and lymph vessels of the gut and also in adjacent lymph glands, but secondary foci of infection apparently are not established.

Chemotherapy

A number of drugs have been tried in balantidiosis, often with unpredictable results. Carbarsone, however, has been effective in a number of cases (163, 180, 181).

COCCIDIOSIS

Although other species have been reported in rare instances, *Isospora hominis* (Rivolta) Dobell (45a) is the only coccidian known as a frequent parasite of man. The name, *Isospora belli,* also has been proposed for this coccidian (177). Human coccidiosis was formerly considered rare and more than half of the earlier cases had been reported from the Mediterranean area, especially along the eastern shores and in the Balkan countries (108, 115). During World War II, *Isospora hominis* was found to be widely distributed, particularly in tropical areas. Cases have been reported in Indo-China, India, Dutch East Indies, the Philippines, Japan, Hawaii, China, Tonkin-China, southern Russia, Palestine, Argentina, Brazil, Uruguay, Venezuela, Mexico, and Cuba, as well as in the Mediterranean region. The incidence of infection in U. S. troops evacuated from Okinawa was about 0.75 per cent (108).

Isospora hominis

The life-cycle has not been traced completely although developmental stages, possibly of *I. hominis,* were described by Virchow in 1860 and by Eimer in 1870. Oocysts also have been recovered from the small intestine by aspiration through Miller-Abbott tubes (108).

The oocyst (Fig. 11. 7, D-F) measures 25-33 x 12-16μ. In freshly passed stools, the zygote is usually undivided. A dividing zygote or two sporoblasts may be seen occasionally, and in cases of constipation, oocysts may be passed with sporoblasts enclosed in spore membranes (108). The number of oocysts passed in the stools may increase and decrease in irregular cycles of several days each (10), or the number may increase gradually to a maximum and then decline steadily to zero (119). Development of sporozoites, four in each of the two spores, has been observed in stools kept at room temperature for 24-48 hours (120), although maturation may require 60-72 hours at 70° F. (10). Passage of oocysts, which usually begins as symptoms are abated, may continue for several weeks and sometimes for two months or longer (108, 120).

Effects on man

Since intestinal Coccidia invade epithelial cells, tissue destruction is inevitable. Although some cases are so mild that specific symptoms are not evident (120), infection often leads to digestive disturbances with a diarrhea persisting for several weeks. Symptoms in severe cases may include abdominal cramping, nausea, and lack of appetite (10). A typical case, accidentally contracted in the laboratory, showed an incubation period of six days, diarrhea for 22 days, and then normally formed stools at the end of another week (35). A similar course has been described for an experimentally induced infection (119). No relapses have been reported.

Chemotherapy

No adequate treatment has been described. Recent data indicate that standard courses of emetine, atebrin, quinine, carbarsone, tetrachlorethylene, chiniofon, and diodoquin have no significant effect on duration of the infection (10, 108). However, the therapeutic and prophylactic activity of sulfamerazine and sulfaguanidine in *Eimeria tenella* infections of chickens (57) might suggest the possible value of such drugs in human coccidiosis.

TRICHOMONAS OF THE UROGENITAL TRACT[1]

Trichomonas vaginalis Donné was the first trichomonad flagellate to be described from man. Cytological descriptions have been published by Reuling (141) and Powell (132), and the species has been compared with other trichomonads of man by Wenrich (170). The flagellate (Fig. 11. 7, G, H) measures 10-30 x 5-15μ. In material fresh from the vagina, occasional flagellates contain leucocytes or more rarely bacteria, but the majority show no food vacuoles. Food vacuoles are common, however, in flagellates from bacterized cultures (132). The undulating membrane usually does not extend into the posterior third of the body except after autotomy (18, 132). In view of the evidence that *T. vaginalis* is morphologically distinct from *P. hominis* of the intestine (170), it is interesting that agglutinin tests have failed to demonstrate antigenic differences (112).

Pure cultures of *T. vaginalis* have been available for a number of years and are being used to advantage in the study of growth requirements and physiological characteristics of the flagellate (Chapter VIII).

Effects on man

Trichomonas vaginalis seems to be absent or else rarely present in the normal vagina but is to be expected in many cases of vaginitis. It is probable that this flagellate is one of the causative factors in vaginitis and that infections may be correlated also with increased morbidity after childbirth (19, 20). Infection is often accompanied by a definite leucorrhea and a vaginal condition resembling that in acute gonorrheal vaginitis. Infections induced by inoculation of pure cultures also have led to vaginal irritation and abnormal discharges (161). Although the evidence for pathogenicity may not be entirely conclusive, it is strong enough to justify prompt treatment of the patient, especially in pregnancy.

In the male, infection with *T. vaginalis* commonly accompanies a non-gonorrheal urethritis. The incidence of infection, which has approached 37 per cent in some groups (60), is higher than was formerly suspected. Present indications are that the male is an important transmitter of *T. vaginalis* and that the female may become a reservoir for venereal infection.

---

[1] Morphology and biology of *Trichomonas vaginalis,* growth requirements and culture media, clinical aspects of infections, and therapeutic measures have been reviewed in the following monograph: Trussell, R. E. 1947. *Trichomonas vaginalis* and trichomoniasis (Springfield: Thomas).

LABORATORY DIAGNOSIS OF
INFECTION[2]

Protozoa of the mouth

The examination of fresh smears and stained preparations will often demonstrate infections with *Entamoeba gingivalis* and *Trichomonas tenax,* although culture methods seem to be much more reliable. Several satisfactory media have been described for *E. gingivalis* (54, 78, 92, 98) and for *T. tenax* (13, 72, 73, 76, 109).

Protozoa of the intestine

Wet preparations. Material to be examined for active stages should be reasonably fresh, preferably stools passed in the laboratory shortly before examination. Survival of trophozoites of *Entamoeba histolytica* shows an inverse relationship to temperature—2-5 hours in stools stored at 37°, 6-16 hours at 22-25°, and 48-96 hours at 5°. Cysts can survive for longer periods, while *Pentatrichomonas hominis* may live as long as two weeks at 22° (162).

Microscopic examination of fresh material, especially on a warm stage, is useful for detection of amoeboid forms and may serve for complete identification of active flagellates. For encysted flagellates and amoebae, temporary staining techniques are widely used. Lugol's iodin solution, undiluted or in 1:5 dilution (52), Donaldson's iodin-eosin stain (53), and D'Antoni's stabilized iodin stain (7) have given satisfactory results. In addition, a rapid stain which differentiates amoeboid stages in wet preparations has been introduced by Velat, Weinstein, and Otto (164).

Permanent preparations. Although experienced workers may have no serious difficulty in identifying most intestinal Protozoa by means of fresh smears and the iodin stain or comparable techniques, permanent preparations are useful for purposes of confirmation and for permanent records. In addition, physicians without laboratory facilities, or without experience in identification of Protozoa, may find it convenient to fix smears made directly from stool samples and then ship the smears to a laboratory for staining and diagnosis. One of the various hematoxylin techniques is usually preferred for permanent preparations.

Concentration methods. Although direct smears are satisfactory for routine examinations, it is advantageous to concentrate the Protozoa when their presence only in small numbers is suspected. A portion of the stool may be mixed with physiological salt solution and then filtered through cheesecloth. The filtrate is centrifuged, the supernatant liquid is discarded, and the sediment is mixed with fresh salt solution and again

---

[2] Adequate descriptions and evaluations of laboratory techniques will be found in Craig's (42) comprehensive monograph.

centrifuged. Washing is continued until the supernatant fluid is clear. The sediment is then examined for Protozoa. For concentration of cysts only, the zinc-sulphate flotation method (59) is useful.

Culture methods. In the detection of mild infections, culture methods may be successful when direct examination of stools is negative. A variety of culture media[3] have been developed and a number of them have proven useful in diagnosis. Craig (40) has pointed out that in the use of culture media for *E. histolytica,* individual experience with a medium probably counts as much in the long run as the particular type of culture medium.

The effectiveness of culture methods for detecting *E. histolytica* in stools containing cysts has been increased by adding streptomycin to the medium. The retardation of bacterial growth, as well as that of *Blastocystis hominis,* apparently facilitates growth of the amoebae after excystment (153). Perhaps the most satisfactory diagnostic medium will prove to be one which inhibits growth of bacteria more or less completely. The development of such a medium should be possible when more is known about the growth requirements of the intestinal amoebae and flagellates.

Complement-fixation. The practical application of complement-fixation to diagnosis of amoebiasis was first reported by Craig (37, 38). Following the introduction of a commercially prepared antigen, this test is being used on a progressively wider scale. Complement-fixation seems to be of value in the diagnosis of mild primary amoebiasis, and with certain modifications, in the detection of early hepatic amoebiasis (Chapter 14).

Trichomonas vaginalis

The examination of an ordinary wet preparation or hanging-drop is often adequate for the detection of *T. vaginalis.* In the diagnosis of mild infections, in following the effects of treatment, and in detecting trichomonads in centrifuged urine specimens, culture methods (18, 109, 148) are more efficient. Some of the more recently developed media (83, 84, 154, 161) are designed for growth of *T. vaginalis* in bacteria-free cultures. The medium of Kupferberg, Johnson, and Sprince (107), now available commercially, requires only the addition of serum and penicillin for diagnostic use.

LITERATURE CITED

1. Adams, A. R. D. 1946. *Trop. Dis. Bull.* **43:** 613.
2. Alexander, F. D. and H. E. Meleney 1935. *Amer. J. Hyg.* **22:** 704.
3. Anderson, H. H. and A. C. Reed 1934. *Amer. J. Trop. Med.* **14:** 269.

[3] Satisfactory culture media have been described for the following intestinal Protozoa of man: flagellates—*Chilomastix mesnili* (9, 21, 24, 63, 70, 75), *Retortomonas intestinalis* (17, 70, 75), *Pentatrichomonas hominis* (9, 63, 70, 75, 148, 174), *Tricercomonas intestinalis* (70); amoebae—*Dientamoeba fragilis* (9, 49); *Endolimax nana* (9, 51), *Entamoeba coli* (9, 48, 51, 148), *E. histolytica* (9, 23, 32, 36, 51, 63, 127, 138, 144, 148), *Iodamoeba bütschlii* (9); ciliates—*Balantidium coli* (11, 80, 139, 148).

4. Andrews, J. M. 1934. *Amer. J. Trop. Med.* **14:** 439.
5. ——— 1942. *S. Med. J.* **35:** 693.
6. ———, C. M. Johnson and S. C. Schwartz 1933. *Amer. J. Trop. Med.* **13:** 591.
7. D'Antoni, J. S. 1937. *Amer. J. Trop. Med.* **17:** 79.
8. Armaghan, V. 1937. *Amer. J. Hyg.* **26:** 236.
9. Balamuth, W. 1946. *Amer. J. Clin. Pathol.* **16:** 380.
10. Barksdale, W. L. and C. F. Routh 1948. *Amer. J. Trop. Med.* **28:** 639.
11. Barret, H. P. and N. Yarbrough 1921. *Amer. J. Trop. Med.* **1:** 161.
12. Baylis, J. R., O. Gullans and B. K. Spector 1936. *Publ. Health Rep.* **51:** 1567.
13. Beatman, L. H. 1933. *J. Dental Res.* **13:** 339.
14. Beaver, P. C. and G. Deschamps 1949. *Amer. J. Trop. Med.* **29:** 189.
15. ——— and ——— 1949. *Amer. J. Trop. Med.* **29:** 193.
16. Berberian, D. A. 1945. *Amer. J. Trop. Med.* **25:** 441.
17. Bishop, A. 1934. *Parasitol.* **26:** 17.
18. Bland, P. B., L. Goldstein, D. H. Wenrich and E. Weiner 1932. *Amer. J. Hyg.* **16:** 492.
19. ———, D. H. Wenrich and L. Goldstein 1931. *Surg., Gynecol. Obstet.* **53:** 759.
20. ———, ——— and ——— 1931. *J. Amer. Med. Assoc.* **96:** 157.
21. Boeck, W. C. 1921. *J. Exp. Med.* **33:** 147.
22. ——— 1924. *Amer. J. Trop. Med.* **4:** 519.
23. ——— and J. Drbohlav 1925. *Amer. J. Hyg.* **5:** 371.
24. ——— and M. Tanabe 1926. *Amer. J. Hyg.* **6:** 319.
25. Bond, V. P., W. Bostick, E. L. Hansen and H. H. Anderson 1946. *Amer. J. Trop. Med.* **26:** 625.
26. Boyers, L. M. 1933. *Calif. & West. Med.* **39:** 397.
27. ———, C. A. Kofoid and O. Swezy 1925. *J. Amer. Med. Assoc.* **85:** 1444.
28. Bradin, J. L., Jr. and E. L. Hansen 1950. *Amer. J. Trop. Med.* **30:** 27.
29. Bundesen, H. N., I. D. Rawlings, A. E. Gorman, G. W. McCoy and A. V. Hardy 1936. U. S. Treas. Dept.: *Nat. Inst. Health Bull. No. 166,* 187 pp.
29a. Chang, S. L. 1943. *J. Inf. Dis.* **72:** 232.
30. Child, H. J. 1926. *Univ. Calif. Publ. Zool.* **28:** 251.
31. Clark, H. C. 1925. *Amer. J. Trop. Med.* **5:** 157.
32. Cleveland, L. R. and B. Collier 1930. *Amer. J. Hyg.* **12:** 606.
33. ——— and E. P. Sanders 1930. *Arch. f. Protistenk.* **70:** 223.
34. Conan, N. J. 1948. *Amer. J. Trop. Med.* **28:** 107.
35. Connal, A. 1922. *Trans. Roy. Soc. Trop. Med. Hyg.* **16:** 223.
36. Craig, C. F. 1926. *Amer. J. Trop. Med.* **6:** 333.
37. ——— 1927. *Amer. J. Trop. Med.* **7:** 225.
38. ——— 1929. *Amer. J. Trop. Med.* **9:** 277.
39. ——— 1932. *Amer. J. Trop. Med.* **12:** 285.
40. ——— 1934. *Amebiasis and Amebic Dysentery* (Springfield: C. C. Thomas).
41. ——— 1944. The etiology, diagnosis and treatment of amebiasis (Baltimore: Williams and Wilkins).
42. ——— 1948. *Laboratory Diagnosis of Protozoan Diseases* (Philadelphia: Lea and Febiger).
43. Derrick, E. H. 1948. *Trans. Roy. Soc. Trop. Med. Hyg.* **42:** 191.
44. Derrieu, G. and M. Raynaud 1914. *Bull. Soc. Path. Exot.* **7:** 571.
45. Dobell, C. 1919. *The Amoebae Living in Man* (London: John Bale, Sons and Danielsson).
45a. ——— 1919. *Parasitol.* **11:** 147.
46. ——— 1928. *Parasitol.* **20:** 357.
47. ——— 1931. *Parasitol.* **23:** 1.
48. ——— 1938. *Parasitol.* **30:** 195.
49. ——— 1940. *Parasitol.* **32:** 417.
49a. ——— 1943. *Parasitol.* **35:** 134.
50. ——— and M. W. Jepps 1918. *Parasitol.* **10:** 320.
51. ——— and P. Laidlaw 1926. *Parasitol.* **18:** 283.
52. ——— and F. W. O'Connor 1921. *The Intestinal Protozoa of Man* (New York: William Wood).

53. Donaldson, R. 1917. *Lancet* **1**: 571.
54. Drbohlav, J. 1925. *Ann. Parasitol.* **3**: 361.
55. Elsdon-Dew, R. 1949. *Amer. J. Trop. Med.* **29**: 337.
56. Engman, M. F. and H. E. Meleney 1931. *Arch. Dermatol. Syph.* **24**: 1.
57. Farr, M. M. and E. E. Wehr 1945. *J. Parasitol.* **31**: 353.
58. Faust, E. C. 1941. *Amer. J. Trop. Med.* **21**: 35.
59. ———, J. S. D'Antoni, V. Odom, M. J. Miller, C. Peres, W. Sawitz, L. F. Thomen, J. Tobie and J. H. Walker 1938. *Amer. J. Trop. Med.* **18**: 169.
60. Feo, L. G. 1944. *Amer. J. Trop. Med.* **24**: 195.
61. Filho, E. S. and E. L. Castro 1948. *Rev. Brasil. Med.* **5**: 12.
62. Frye, W. W. and H. E. Meleney 1938. *Amer. J. Hyg.* **27**: 580.
63. ——— and ——— 1939. *Science* **89**: 564.
64. Geiman, Q. M. 1935. *J. Morph.* **57**: 429.
65. Goodey, T. 1917. *Parasitol.* **9**: 554.
66. Hakansson, E. G. 1936. *Amer. J. Trop. Med.* **16**: 175.
67. Hegner, R. 1923. *Amer. J. Hyg.* **3**: 349.
68. ——— 1929. *Science* **70**: 539.
69. ———, C. M. Johnson and R. M. Stabler 1932. *Amer. J. Hyg.* **15**: 394.
70. Hill, C. McD. 1926. *Amer. J. Hyg.* **6**: 646.
71. Hinshaw, H. C. 1926. *Univ. Calif. Publ. Zool.* **29**: 159.
72. ——— 1926. *Proc. Soc. Exp. Biol. Med.* **24**: 71.
73. ——— 1927. *Univ. Calif. Publ. Zool.* **31**: 31.
74. ——— 1928. *Proc. Soc. Exp. Biol. Med.* **25**: 430.
75. Hogue, M. J. 1921. *Amer. J. Trop. Med.* **1**: 211.
76. ——— 1926. *Amer. J. Trop. Med.* **6**: 75.
77. Hopkins, D. L. and K. L. Warner 1946. *J. Parasitol.* **32**: 175.
78. Howitt, B. 1925. *Univ. Calif. Publ. Zool.* **28**: 65.
79. Ivanhoe, G. L. 1943. *Amer. J. Trop. Med.* **23**: 401.
80. Jameson, A. P. 1927. *Parasitol.* **19**: 411.
81. Jepps, M. W. and C. Dobell 1918. *Parasitol.* **10**: 352.
82. Johnson, C. M. 1941. *Amer. J. Trop. Med.* **21**: 49.
83. Johnson, G. 1942. *J. Parasit.* **28**: 369.
84. ———, M. Trussell and F. Jahn 1945. *Science* **102**: 126.
85. Jones, W. R. 1946. *Ann. Trop. Med. Parasitol.* **40**: 130.
86. ——— 1948. *Proc. 4th Intern. Congr. Trop. Med. & Malaria* **2**: 1088.
87. Kessel, J. F. and H. G. Johnstone 1949. *Amer. J. Trop. Med.* **29**: 311.
88. Kessel, J. F. and H. G. Johnstone 1949. *Amer. J. Trop. Med.* **29**: 311.
89. ——— and F. Kaplan 1949. *Amer. J. Trop. Med.* **29**: 319.
90. Kirby, H. 1928. *Proc. Soc. Exp. Biol. Med.* **25**: 698.
91. ——— 1945. *J. Parasit.* **31**: 163.
92. Koch, D. A. 1926. *Univ. Calif. Publ. Zool.* **29**: 241.
93. ——— 1927. *Univ. Calif. Publ. Zool.* **31**: 17.
94. Kofoid, C. A. 1920. *Univ. Calif. Publ. Zool.* **20**: 145.
95. ——— 1929. *J. Parasit.* **15**: 151.
96. ———, L. M. Boyers and O. Swezy 1922. *J. Amer. Med. Assoc.* **78**: 1604.
97. ———, H. C. Hinshaw and H. G. Johnstone 1929. *J. Amer. Dental Assoc.* **16**: 1436.
98. ——— and H. G. Johnstone 1929. *Amer. J. Publ. Health* **19**: 549.
99. ——— and ——— 1930. *Univ. Calif. Publ. Zool.* **33**: 379.
100. ——— and O. Swezy 1920. *Univ. Calif. Publ. Zool.* **20**: 117.
101. ——— and ——— 1922. *Univ. Calif. Publ. Zool.* **20**: 199.
102. ——— and ——— 1922. *J. Amer. Med. Assoc.* **78**: 1602.
103. ——— and ——— 1923. *Univ. Calif. Publ. Zool.* **20**: 373.
104. ——— and ——— 1924. *Univ. Calif. Publ. Zool.* **26**: 165.
105. ——— and ——— 1924. *Amer. J. Trop. Med.* **4**: 33.
106. ——— and ——— 1925. *Univ. Calif. Publ. Zool.* **26**: 331.
107. Kupferberg, A. B., G. Johnson and H. Sprince 1948. *Proc. Soc. Exp. Biol. Med.* **67**: 304.
108. Liebow, A. A., N. T. Milliken and C. A. Hannum 1948. *Amer. J. Trop. Med.* **28**: 261.
109. Lynch, K. M. 1922. *Amer. J. Trop. Med.* **2**: 531.

110. ——— 1932. *Amer. J. Trop. Med.* **12**: 247.
111. McClendon, S. J. 1931. *Calif. & West. Med.* **34**: 266.
112. MacDonald, E. M. and A. L. Tatum 1948. *J. Immunol.* **59**: 309.
113. McDonald, J. D. 1922. *Univ. Calif. Publ. Zool.* **20**: 243.
114. McVay, L. V., R. L. Laird and D. H. Sprunt 1949. *Science* **109**: 590.
115. Magath, T. B. 1935. *Amer. J. Trop. Med.* **15**: 91.
116. Manson-Bahr, P. 1949. *J. Trop. Med. Hyg.* **52**: 91.
117. ——— and W. J. Muggleton 1948. *J. Trop. Med. Hyg.* **51**: 23.
118. Martin, D. L. 1930. *Arch. Pathol.* **10**: 349.
119. Matsubayashi, H. and T. Nozawa 1948. *Amer. J. Trop. Med.* **28**: 633.
120. May, E. L. 1947. *Amer. J. Trop. Med.* **27**: 323.
121. Meleney, H. E. and W. W. Frye 1934. *Amer. J. Hyg.* **20**: 84.
122. ——— and L. K. Zuckerman 1948. *Amer. J. Hyg.* **47**: 187.
123. Morse, E. M. and S. P. Seaton 1943. *Amer. J. Trop. Med.* **23**: 325.
123a. Most, H. and F. Van Assendelft 1951. *Amer. J. Trop. Med.* **31**: 284.
124. Morton, T. C. St. C. 1948. *Trop. Dis. Bull.* **45**: 377.
125. Musgrave, W. E. 1931. *Amer. J. Trop. Med.* **11**: 469.
126. Nauss, R. W. and I. Rappaport 1940. *Amer. J. Trop. Med.* **20**: 107.
127. Nelson, E. C. 1947. *Amer. J. Trop. Med.* **27**: 545.
128. Newton, W. L. 1950. *Amer. J. Trop. Med.* **30**: 135.
128a. Noble, E. R. 1947. *Univ. Calif. Publ. Zool.* **53**: 263.
129. Parmer, L. G. 1948. *Proc. Soc. Exp. Biol. Med.* **68**: 362.
130. Piekarski, G. 1948. *Ztschr. f. Hyg. Infektionskr.* **127**: 496.
131. Pipkin, C. A. 1949. *Amer. J. Hyg.* **49**: 255.
132. Powell, W. N. 1936. *Amer. J. Hyg.* **24**: 145.
133. Prowazek, S. v. 1904. *Arb. Kaiserl. Gesundh.* **21**: 42.
134. ——— 1911. *Arch. f. Protistenk.* **22**: 345.
135. ——— 1912. *Arch. f. Protistenk.* **25**: 26.
136. Ratcliffe, H. L. 1931. *Amer. J. Hyg.* **14**: 337.
137. ——— 1934. *Amer. J. Hyg.* **19**: 68.
138. Reardon, L. V. and C. W. Rees 1940. *J. Parasitol.* **26**: 25.
139. Rees, C. W. 1927. *Science* **66**: 89.
140. ——— 1929. *Arch. Pathol.* **7**: 1.
141. Reuling, F. 1921. *Arch. f. Protistenk.* **42**: 347.
142. Riedmüller, F. 1921. *Centralbl. Bakt. Parasit. Infekt.* **108**: 103.
143. Rivas, D. de 1944. *Amer. J. Trop. Med.* **24**: 185.
144. St. John, J. H. 1932. *Amer. J. Trop. Med.* **12**: 301.
145. Sapero, J. J. 1939. *Amer. J. Trop. Med.* **19**: 497.
146. ———, E. G. Hakansson and C. M. Louttit 1942. *Amer. J. Trop. Med.* **22**: 191.
147. ——— and C. M. Johnson 1939. *Amer. J. Trop. Med.* **19**: 255.
148. Schaffer, J. G., F. W. Ryden and W. W. Frye 1949. *Amer. J. Hyg.* **49**: 127.
149. Shrapnel, B. C. 1947. *Amer. J. Trop. Med.* **27**: 527.
150. Smithies, F. 1926. *Amer. J. Trop. Med.* **6**: 1.
151. Sodeman, W. A. 1950. *Amer. J. Trop. Med.* **30**: 141.
152. Spector, B. K. 1936. *Amer. J. Publ. Health* **26**: 813.
153. Spingarn, C. L. and M. H. Edelman 1948. *Amer. J. Trop. Med.* **28**: 825.
154. Sprince, H. and A. B. Kupferberg 1946. *J. Bact.* **53**: 435.
155. Stabler, R. M. 1932. *J. Parasit.* **18**: 278.
155a. ——— 1940. *J. Morph.* **66**: 357.
156. Stewart, G. T. and W. R. Jones 1948. *Ann. Trop. Med. Parasitol.* **42**: 33.
157. Stone, W. S. 1937. *Amer. J. Trop. Med.* **17**: 539.
158. Swezy, O. 1922. *Univ. Calif. Publ. Zool.* **20**: 313.
159. Taliaferro, W. H. and E. R. Becker 1922. *Amer. J. Hyg.* **2**: 188.
160. Thompson, P. E. and B. L. Lilligren 1949. *Amer. J. Trop. Med.* **29**: 323.
161. Trussell, R. E. and E. D. Plass 1940. *Amer. J. Obstet. Gynec.* **40**: 883.
162. Tsuchiya, H. 1945. *Amer. J. Trop. Med.* **25**: 277.
163. ——— and B. Kenamore 1945. *Amer. J. Trop. Med.* **25**: 513.
164. Velat, C. A., P. P. Weinstein and G. F. Otto 1950. *Amer. J. Trop. Med.* **30**: 43.
165. Wenrich, D. H. 1932. *Trans. Amer. Micr. Soc.* **51**: 225.

166. ——— 1936. *J. Parasitol.* **22:** 76.
167. ——— 1937. *Proc. Amer. Philos. Soc.* **77:** 183.
168. ——— 1937. *J. Parasit.* **23:** 183.
169. ——— 1939. *J. Parasit.* **25:** 43.
169a. ——— 1941. *J. Parasit.* **27:** 1.
170. ——— 1944. *Amer. J. Trop. Med.* **24:** 39.
171. ——— 1944. *J. Morph.* **74:** 189.
172. ——— 1944. *J. Morph.* **74:** 467.
173. ——— 1944. *J. Parasit.* **30:** 322.
174. ——— 1946. *J. Parasit.* **32:** 40.
175. ——— 1947. *J. Parasit.* **33:** 177.
176. Wenyon, C. M. 1920. *J. Trop. Med. Hyg.* **23:** 125.
177. ——— 1923. *Ann. Trop. Med. Parasitol.* **17:** 231.
178. ——— 1926. *Protozoology* (London: Ballière, Tindall, & Cox).
179. ——— and F. W. O'Connor 1917. *Human Intestinal Protozoa in the Near East* (London: Wellcome Bur. Sci. Res.).
180. Young, M. D. 1939. *J. Amer. Med. Assoc.* **113:** 580.
181. ——— and R. Burrow 1943. *Publ. Health Rep.* **58:** 1272.

XII

The Blood Flagellates

LEISHMANIASIS

THE FLAGELLATES causing human leishmaniasis belong to the genus *Leishmania* Ross. To this genus there have been assigned also certain flagellates of reptiles. Among these are *L. chamaeleonis,* which is an intestinal parasite retaining the leptomonad form (71), and also *L. ceramodactyli* (5) and *L. hemidactyli* (66), which are blood parasites of gekkos and infect sandflies. *L. ceramodactyli* develops in the posterior station. *L. hemidactyli* develops in the anterior station like the species found in mammals, and this is the case also for *L. tarentolae* (6a) from the blood of gekkos.

The three parasites of man are usually given specific rank: *L. donovani* of visceral leishmaniasis, *L. tropica* of oriental sore, and *L. brasiliensis* (*L. peruviana, L. tropica* var. *americana*) of muco-cutaneous or American leishmaniasis. The lack of obvious morphological differences has led some workers to the opinion that all three parasites are merely strains

574

or races of a single species (31). On the other hand, the specific status of the three types has been defended on the grounds that the clinical, pathological and epidemiological differences seem to be genetically stable (34a).

Visceral leishmaniasis

Distribution. In the Eastern Hemisphere, kala-azar has occurred endemically in certain parts of India, southern U.S.S.R., Burma, Indo-China, Central China, Turkestan, Iraq, along the Mediterranean shores, and in the Sudan. Cases have occurred also in the Western Hemisphere —various parts of Brazil (55), Argentina, Bolivia, Colombia, Paraguay, Peru, and Venezuela. In American areas, visceral leishmaniasis has been reported in both infants and adults. Both young and old are susceptible in India also, while in the Mediterranean area, children under four years have been attacked almost exclusively.

The causative organism. Kala-azar was at various times considered an unusual malaria and a serious type of hookworm disease before the causative organism was discovered. *L. donovani* seems to have been observed by Cunningham in 1885, by Firth in 1891, and by Borowsky in 1892. Although Borowsky recognized the organisms as Protozoa (30a, 54), his observations remained unknown to Leishman and Donovan who described the parasites independently in 1903. After various assignments to the Sporozoa, the affinities of *L. donovani* were demonstrated when Rogers (56a) found the flagellate stage in cultures.

L. donovani occurs in the mammalian host primarily as leishmanial stages in lymphoid-macrophage (reticulo-endothelial) cells of the spleen, liver, bone marrow, intestine, and lymph glands. Occasionally, leishmanial forms occur also in mononuclear and polymorphonuclear leucocytes in the blood. The leishmanial stage may be ovoid or approximately spherical (Fig. 12. 1, I, J). The spherical forms are usually 1-3μ in diameter. Ovoid stages generally measure 2.0-5.0 x 1.5-2.5μ. Identification is based upon the presence of both nucleus and kinetoplast. The latter is often elongated and may be more or less perpendicular or sometimes tangential to the nucleus. In well-stained specimens, an axoneme sometimes can be traced from the kinetoplast to the periplast.

Leishmanial stages multiply in the macrophages, which eventually rupture to release the parasites. Most of them apparently are picked up by macrophages, but some reach the blood stream from which they can be ingested by the vector, a species of *Phlebotomus*. Surviving leishmanial forms change into leptomonad stages in the insect. These multiply in the midgut, and after several days, appear also in the foregut. The leptomonads of the foregut are believed to be infective for man.

The growth of *L. donovani* in cultures is similar to that in the sandfly. After inoculation into a suitable medium the leishmanial stage grows,

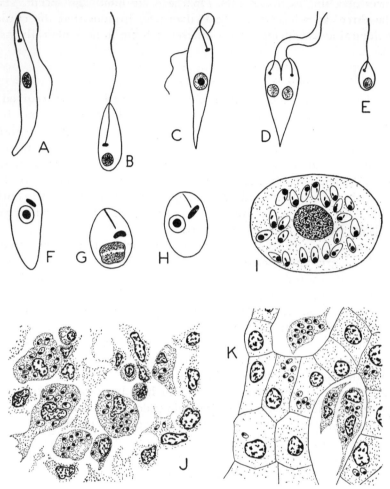

Fig. 12. 1. A-E. Flagellated forms of *Leishmania donovani* from cultures; x2500; (A, B after Laveran; C-E, after Wenyon). F-H. *Leishmania tropica*, leishmanial forms from sores; x5500 (after Wenyon). I. *L. donovani* in large mononuclear cell; from blood, x1350 (after Laveran). J. *L. donovani* in spleen; semidiagrammatic, x1035 (after Nattan-Larrier). K. *L. donovani* in liver; semidiagrammatic, x1035 (after Nattan-Larrier).

develops a flagellum, and becomes a leptomonad form (Fig. 12. 1, A-C) measuring 7-20µ in length. Active leptomonads are usually abundant in cultures after 48-72 hours at 22-25°. Old cultures may contain non-flagellated stages resembling the original leishmanial forms.

The organism causing American cases of visceral leishmaniasis, found in dogs and cats as well as in man, has been considered a new species, *L. chagasi* (14). However, the flagellate may be identical with *L. donovani* of kala-azar (2, 59).

Symptoms and pathology. Kala-azar is a chronic or sub-acute disease characterized by enlargement of the liver and spleen and by an irregular fever, anemia, and leucopenia. Mortality is high in untreated cases. The disease is more severe in epidemic outbreaks than in intervening periods, and effects on a population may be aggravated by famine and by other diseases. The incubation period varies from about 10 days to two or three months as a rule (10), although incubation periods in U. S. troops during World War II ranged from three weeks to 19 months (42).

A common early symptom is a high fever preceded by rigors. The fever may become continuous or may be intermittent and irregular. Early enlargement of the liver and spleen is typical, and the swelling usually increases during the course of the disease. After emaciation becomes marked in children, splenomegaly often produces a swollen protruding abdomen. Grayish discoloration of the skin, especially over the forehead and temples and sometimes around the mouth, is characteristic of chronic cases. Eventually, a low fever becomes more or less continuous and extensive loss of weight occurs.

The spleen, liver, and bone marrow are affected in practically all cases. The extent to which other organs are involved is determined by length and severity of the infection. Normal splenic tissues may be partly replaced by macrophages, and fibrous tissue of the reticulum may increase. Effects on the liver are similar. Küpffer's cells, which increase in number, are often loaded with leishmanial forms, and there may be an increase in fibrous tissue with marked cirrhosis in chronic cases. In the bone marrow, as much as three-fourths of the normal tissue may be replaced by packed macrophages, so that the production of blood cells is greatly reduced. Consequently, some degree of anemia is to be expected, although the red cell count seldom falls below 2,500,000. In addition, there is frequently a leucopenia with a count well below 4,000, and a granulopenia also has been noted. In the intestinal mucosa, multiplication of macrophages sometimes distends the villi.

Multiplication of macrophages in the lymph glands, kidneys, testes, lungs, heart, and adrenals is usually not extensive; accordingly, the parasites are to be expected primarily in isolated phagocytes. However, adrenocortical hypofunction, presumably a result of tissue destruction, has been observed and may be correlated with skin pigmentation and low blood pressure (15).

Skin nodules, similar to non-ulcerating lesions of oriental sore, sometimes appear in treated patients about two years or so after clinical recovery (1, 9). The nodules, usually small, appear most commonly on the face and neck. Beneath the thin epithelium there is an oedematous dermis showing atrophy of connective tissue. Surrounding this area there is a zone of fibroblasts and multiplying macrophages, the latter often containing parasites. Such lesions may form a lasting reservoir of infection and may explain the sporadic occurrence of kala-azar year after year in households and other small groups (48).

In summary, the essential pathological characteristic of kala-azar in man, monkeys and hamsters (40) is the increase in lymphoid-macrophage cells. The macrophages ingest *L. donovani* but are unable to prevent their multiplication after ingestion. Consequently, it is uncertain "whether the reticulo-endothelium is valuable, as the only defense the body has, imperfect as it is, or deleterious, as being the most suitable location for the parasites" (70).

Oriental sore

Distribution. Classical oriental sore, as seen in Eurasia and Africa, is a widespread type of leishmaniasis. In Europe, the disease has been known in Spain, Italy, Greece, and rather rarely in France. In Africa, oriental sore has been fairly common in Egypt, the Sudan, Algeria, French Congo, and Nigeria. In Asia, the disease seems to be endemic in Arabia, Asia Minor, Mesopotamia, Persia, subtropical parts of the U.S.S.R., and parts of India.

The causative organism. *L. tropica* was recognized as the causative organism when Wright described the parasites in 1903. Morphologically, this flagellate (Fig. 12. 1, F) is essentially identical with *L. donovani.* Like the latter, it is usually found inside macrophages in man.

The invertebrate phase of the cycle, as traced in *Phlebotomus papatasii,* is initiated by metamorphosis of the ingested leishmanial forms into leptomonads in the midgut. With continued multiplication, the infection gradually extends into the pharynx and mouth cavity. In at least a few sandflies, the flagellates eventually reach the anterior part of the epipharynx. The last step apparently is essential for transfer to man.

Symptoms and pathology. The incubation period ranges from a few days to several months, and sometimes even three or four years. The skin lesion begins as a small pimple, resembling the swelling which sometimes follows insect bites. The pimple grows and may eventually develop into a nodule an inch or more in diameter. Clinically, the non-ulcerating nodule, the superficial flat ulcer, and the deeper boil may be distinguished. The non-ulcerating lesion, after a year or so, dries up to a scab which drops off, leaving a scar. More commonly, the surface of the nodule breaks down to form an ulcer. Secondary invasion by bacteria usually occurs, and the ulcer may grow to a diameter of several inches. Sections through a sore show an oedematous dermis with many macrophages, pressure from which may cause local destruction of hair follicles and sweat glands. Patients often show only one or two lesions, although sometimes more (even a dozen or so). There is usually little constitutional disturbance. However, lymph glands near sores may become swollen, and fever sometimes occurs.

Muco-cutaneous leishmaniasis

Distribution. Muco-cutaneous leishmaniasis, generally more severe than classical oriental sore, has been reported from Argentina, Bolivia, Brazil, British Honduras, Colombia, Costa Rica, Ecuador, French Guiana, Panama, Paraguay, Peru, Uruguay, and Venezuela.

The causative organism. L. brasiliensis is very similar to *L. tropica* in morphology and likewise is found mainly in macrophages in man. The insect phase of the cycle is similar to that in *L. tropica.*

Symptoms and pathology. The skin lesion develops much as in oriental sore. The non-ulcerating type grows from the primary papule into a slightly elevated reddened area with a rough surface from which a liquid oozes and dries into a crust. This liquid usually contains parasites and thus may start a new sore on contact with a break in the skin. The ulcerating lesion becomes excavated centrally and secondary invasion by bacteria often occurs. Neighboring lymph glands are often swollen, and general symptoms may include fever, chronic headaches and aches in the joints. The mucous membranes also are sometimes involved. Ulcers may develop in the nose and mouth and, more rarely, in the vagina. An ulcer originating in the nose may spread downward over the upper lip into the oral cavity, or the nostrils may become plugged and the nasal septum progressively destroyed. Depending upon their location, mucosal lesions may eventually destroy the sense of smell or hearing, or may cause blindness.

Transmission of leishmaniasis

Transmission of oriental sore by direct contact has long been known. In fact, natives of certain regions in India formerly made a practice of inoculating material from sores into the skin of young children. This crude vaccination led to development of a sore on an unexposed part of the body and, it was hoped, to prevention of more conspicuous sores later in life. The general opinion is that *L. tropica* may invade a sound mucous membrane but cannot penetrate unbroken skin, and it is likely that *L. brasiliensis* has similar abilities. Contact transfer of kala-azar also may be possible, since the flagellates have been demonstrated in nasal secretions of patients.

Bedbugs, fleas, mosquitoes, lice, houseflies, and ticks have all been suspected, at one time or another, of transmitting leishmaniasis to man. There is no convincing evidence that any one of them normally serves as a true host. However, occasional mechanical transfer may be possible, as in the transmission of *L. tropica* by *Stomoxys calcitrans* in Lebanon. Investigations on sandflies have been more successful. By 1924 it was known that *Phlebotomus argentipes* develops a flagellate infection after feeding on kala-azar patients. In 1927, hamsters were infected by inoculation with flagellates from sandflies (29). In the same year, it was found that flagellates from naturally infected sandflies induced typical oriental sore when inoculated into man (4). After feeding upon these lesions, sand-flies developed flagellate infections. These flagellates, in turn, induced typical sores upon inoculation into man. The second crop of sores again was infective for sandflies. In later work on kala-azar, hamsters were in-fected by oral introduction of *L. donovani* (63) and later by ingestion of infected sandflies (65). In 1931, *L. donovani* was transferred to a hamster by the bite of a sandfly under experimental conditions (64). Some of the earlier difficulties in producing heavy infections of sandflies have been largely eliminated by better diets for the flies, and kala-azar can now be transferred readily to hamsters (67, 68). Such techniques also have made possible the vector transfer of kala-azar to human volunteers (69). Similarly, the experimental transfer of *L. tropica* by sandflies has been facilitated by adding salt to the diet of the flies (3).

Diagnosis

Blood films, and smears of other tissues (splenic pulp, bone mar-row, liver, lymph glands) obtained by puncture methods, may be ex-amined directly for *L. donovani*. Spleen smears are probably positive in at least 80 per cent of the actual infections, and sternal puncture is equally reliable (49). The results of the two methods agree closely (30), and sternal puncture has the advantage of being less dangerous. Thick blood smears are somewhat less reliable than smears from the spleen and bone marrow. In any case, diagnosis may be difficult in early stages of kala-azar, and prolonged search of smears may be necessary. In diagnosis of dermal leishmaniasis, the parasites are best detected in material aspi-rated from the periphery of the lesion, from the tissues just beneath the ulcer, or from non-ulcerated nodules. *L. brasiliensis* is most abundant in the early lesions of the skin and mucosa and may be found also in lymph glands adjacent to sores. It is usually difficult to recover the flagellates from old bacterized sores.

Culture methods, for the experienced worker, are generally more reli-able than tissue smears in diagnosis of kala-azar and may be preferable where facilities are available. Aseptic precautions are required, and for best results, blood agar slants may be inoculated with leucocytes centri-fuged from 5-10 ml of blood. Upon incubation at 22-25° C., a heavy growth of flagellates may be expected within 72 hours. With the addition of penicillin for the control of bacteria, culture methods also appear to be satisfactory for demonstrating *L. tropica* in bacterially contaminated lesions (43). This technique may prove useful likewise in diagnosis of kala-azar.

Several indirect tests for kala-azar are based upon the characteristic increase in serum globulins. In Brahmachari's test the addition of 2-3 volumes of distilled water to one of kala-azar serum precipitates the globulins. In Napier's aldehyde test a positive serum forms an opaque coagulum upon addition of a small amount of formalin. Chopra's antimony test is a ring test in which a flocculent precipitate develops in the zone of contact between a positive serum and a solution of urea stibamine. Although such tests are no substitute for demonstration of the parasites, they have been useful as presumptive tests in field surveys. A non-specific complement-fixation test, using an antigen prepared from a human strain of *Mycobacterium tuberculosis*, has given good preliminary results with kala-azar, although false positives may be expected occasionally in pulmonary tuberculosis (60, 61).

Chemotherapy

Prior to 1915 there was no reliable cure for kala-azar and untreated cases had shown a mortality of about 90 per cent in India. Following the introduction of tartar emetic (11), there was a marked change for the better. Introduction of urea stibamine by Brahmachari in 1922 led to further improvement. By 1925, the death rate in India had dropped to about 10 per cent of the cases; in 1928, to about 7 per cent. Neostibosan, introduced a few years after urea stibamine, is more or less comparable in effectiveness. Several more recently tested drugs appear to have real value. Stibatin (sodium antimony gluconate) has given satisfactory results and has fairly low toxicity. Stilbamine seems to be effective against relapsing kala-azar, although its rather high toxicity is an undesirable feature. Stilbamidine, unfortunately too toxic for routine use, has produced clinical cures in about 98 per cent, with a relapse rate of only about 4 per cent. This drug is useful in antimony-resistant and antimony-sensitive cases. Pentamidine isothionate is comparatively harmless to the patient but is not quite so effective as stilbamidine—about 94 per cent clinical cures, with relapses in about 16 per cent. Penicillin has given satisfactory results with "cancrum oris" (noma), a sort of oral gangrene which is a frequently fatal complication of kala-azar.

In dermal leishmaniasis, intravenous or intramuscular injection of leishmanicidal drugs is usually combined with local treatment for control of bacteria. Since the lesions of oriental sore often tend to heal spontaneously, it is difficult to evaluate the effects of chemotherapy.

Control of leishmaniasis

The usual vectors of leishmaniasis are small Diptera belonging to the genus *Phlebotomus*. These sandflies, or owl midges, are active mainly in twilight and darkness. The females are blood-suckers, usually attacking warm blooded animals. Four or five days after a blood meal, the eggs are laid in moist shaded locations—animal burrows, caves, crevices among rocks, cracks in the soil, or at the bases of hollow trees. The eggs hatch in about a week, and two months or more are required for development.

Sandflies are found throughout the year in the tropics. In the cooler climates, the adults apparently do not live through the winter. Instead, hibernation presumably occurs in the last larval instar. The control of sandflies by widespread attacks on breeding places is not, for obvious reasons, a practical method of control. However, the use of residual DDT sprays on suspected shelters and breeding places has produced striking results on a limited scale (27). Similar treatment of buildings with DDT is an effective protection (28). In addition, sleeping nets, fine-mesh screening and insect repellents are useful in preventing contact of sandflies with human beings.

The importance of animal reservoirs is uncertain. Natural infections with flagellates resembling *L. donovani* have been reported in dogs, cats, horses, and sheep. *L. tropica* also occurs naturally in dogs, and the canine strain is infective for man (6). Certain rodents (gerbils, sousliks), found infected in Middle Asia (U.S.S.R.), also may serve as reservoirs (32). Although these lower mammals obviously are reservoirs, it is not known how extensive a part they play in the maintenance of endemic leishmaniasis.

TRYPANOSOMIASIS

Species of *Trypanosoma* are found in fishes, amphibia, reptiles, birds, and mammals, and the great majority appear to be non-pathogenic in their natural hosts. The trypanosomes of mammals include a few pathogens, such as *T. brucei* of nagana, *T. equinum* of mal de caderas, *T. equiperdum* of dourine, *T. evansi* of surra, and the types which attack man—*T. cruzi* of Chagas' disease, and *T. gambiense* and *T. rhodesiense* of sleeping sickness. Life cycles and methods of transfer differ within this small group. Metacyclic, or infective, stages of *T. cruzi* develop in the hindgut ("posterior station") of the vector and are deposited on the skin of the vertebrate by a visiting insect. The flagellates may become established in the vertebrate if they reach a mucous membrane or a break in the skin. Such species as *T. cruzi* and the non-pathogenic *T. lewisi* are probably the most primitive of the mammalian trypanosomes, since the invertebrate phase of the cycle resembles that of the presumably ancestral herpetomonad flagellates. Metacyclic stages of *T. gambiense, T. rhodesiense,* and *T. brucei* develop in the salivary glands of the vector and are transferred to the mammalian host by inoculation. On such bases, these species are believed to be more highly evolved than the *T. lewisi* group. Mechanical transfer by tabanid and stomoxid flies is characteristic of *T. evansi* and *T. equinum,* which are apparently related to the *T. brucei* group. Differentiation of these species may have followed their introduction into regions free from their natural vectors. Such a possibility is not too remote, because mechanical transfer of *T. gambiense* is considered possible for a short time after the flagellates are ingested by the insect host. *T. equiperdum,* possibly evolved through a similar accident of distribution, is now transmitted through direct contact in coitus.

Current differentiation of species is based, in some cases, upon host relationships instead of conventional morphological features. For example, *T. brucei, T. gambiense,* and *T. rhodesiense* are morphologically indistinguishable. The same is true for *T. equiperdum* and *T. evansi.* In such cases, the homologues could be, and probably should be, considered specialized strains of a single species (31).

The range in pathogenicity of trypanosomes has interested various workers in possible explanations for pathological effects. The sugar consumption theory (58) assumed that the consumption of sugar by trypanosomes might reduce the blood sugar of the host too rapidly for the liver to maintain a normal blood level. The resultant strain was supposed to cause a breakdown of liver function, leading to fatal intoxication. In spite of a few cases in which blood sugar levels have been low consistently (56), marked reduction in sugar levels generally occurs only in the last days or hours of a lethal infection.

Another theory (7) holds that death of the host is caused by asphyxiation, supposedly the result of a pulmonary oedema following partial obstruction of capillaries by agglutinated trypanosomes. A third suggestion (35) is that lactic acid, produced from sugars by trypanosomes, interferes with normal tissue oxidations. The lactic acid concentration of the blood usually does show an increase during the terminal stages of a fatal infection, but the concentrations reported are considered too low for appreciable injury to the host. Approximate doubling of the serum potassium level has been reported before death of rats infected with *T. equiperdum* (78), while in other cases no correlation has been observed between the time of survival and the tolerance to potassium (57a). Trypanosomal toxins also have been suggested as an explanation for pathogenicity. Although there is no evidence that trypanosomes produce true exotoxins, it is possible that endotoxins (in the bacteriological sense) might harm the host.

African sleeping sickness

Distribution. There are two varieties of this disease, Gambian and Rhodesian. The Gambian variety has ranged from about 15° N. to 15° S. latitude but is more common in the western than in the eastern part of this zone in Africa. Within its range, the disease occurs primarily along rivers and near lakes, in correlation with the distribution of its major vector, *Glossina palpalis.* In the eastern part of its range, Gambian sleeping sickness extends into the territory of the Rhodesian variety. The latter, which is less widely distributed, has been known in North and South Rhodesia, Portugese East Africa, Nyasaland, Tanganyika Territory, northeastern Mozambique, Uganda Protectorate, and the southern

Sudan. Within these areas, high temperatures (75-85° F.) favor development of the trypanosomes in tsetse flies, while temperatures below 70°
are unfavorable. A few outbreaks of epidemic proportions have been
recorded, but the disease is generally sporadic in occurrence.

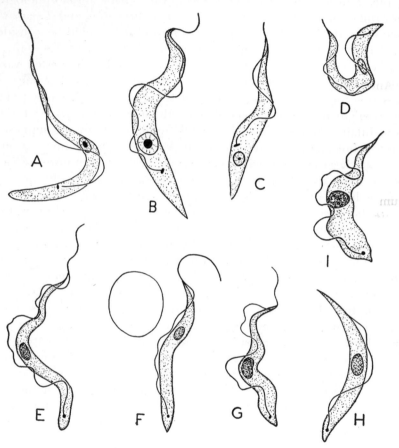

Fig. 12 2. *Trypanosoma gambiense.* A-D. Stages in *Glossina palpalis*
(x3300, after Robertson): A. Stage in mid-gut after two days; B. Stage in
gut after 2-3 weeks; C. Crithidial stage in salivary glands; D. Metacyclic
trypanosome in salivary glands. E-I. Stages in blood of man; x2200 approx.: E. Slender form (after Laveran); F. Slender form (after Bruce);
G. Intermediate form (after Bruce); H. Broad form (after Laveran); I.
Broad form (after Bruce).

The causative organisms. Trypanosoma gambiense Dutton, first seen
by Forde in 1901, is the causative organism of Gambian sleeping sickness;
T. rhodesiense Stephens and Fantham, of the Rhodesian type. Although
the two parasites differ in virulence, and to a considerable extent in
geographical distribution, they cannot be distinguished with certainty
from each other or from *T. brucei*. Some workers believe that *T. rho-*

desiense is a more virulent strain of *T. gambiense* (17), and there have been suggestions that the two types are interconvertible (26).

T. gambiense (Fig. 12.2) measures 10-40µ. in length and contains a small spherical kinetoplast. Three forms have been described: slender flagellates with a long flagellum, intermediate forms with a short flagellum, and broad forms with no free flagellum. It has been suggested that such polymorphism is correlated with sexual phenomena, but the evidence is inconclusive (Chapter II). In man, trypanosomal stages appear in the blood, where they undergo fission. Eventually the flagellates may get into the cerebrospinal fluid, the invasion often bringing on "sleeping sickness."

Glossina palpalis is the major vector, but *G. tachinoides* is important in some parts of West Africa. The fly sucks the trypanosomes into the gut along with a meal of blood. For a few hours, at least, the trypanosomes apparently remain unchanged. If conditions are favorable, the flagellates survive and undergo fission, but only a small percentage of the tsetse flies actually become infected after ingesting *T. gambiense*. After about two weeks, the digestive tract contains many slender trypanosomes. The infection gradually extends into the foregut and some of the flagellates usually reach the salivary glands by the end of the third week. Here the trypanosomes become attached, change into the crithidial stage (Fig. 12.2) and divide rapidly for two or three days. The flagellates then develop into metacyclic trypanosomes infective for the vertebrate host. The insect phase of the cycle lasts from three to five weeks, depending upon environmental conditions.

In the transfer from tsetse fly to vertebrate, two methods are possible: mechanical transfer of the flagellates shortly after ingestion; and cyclic transfer, in which the flagellates pass through developmental stages in the vector before they are again infective for the vertebrate. Within a day or so after ingestion, completion of the insect cycle becomes essential for infection of the vertebrate.

The life cycle of *T. rhodesiense* is quite similar to that of *T. gambiense*. However, the insect phase of the cycle—in the usual vector, *Glossina morsitans*—requires only about two weeks for completion.

Symptoms and pathology. In Gambian sleeping sickness, the bite of an infected fly often causes a local irritation which normally disappears after a few days. Following an incubation period, ranging from two weeks to a year or more, an irregular recurrent fever usually is the first noticeable symptom. Although the fever is sometimes mild, temperatures of 105-106° may be observed. After a time, physical weakness becomes marked and other symptoms include anemia, rapid pulse, severe headaches, enlargment of the cervical lymph glands ("Winterbottom's sign"), and loss of weight. Itchy skin eruptions are fairly common, although less noticeable in natives than in foreigners. Enlargement of the liver and spleen is said to increase with rise in temperature and to decrease as the temperature falls. In some cases, the disease may seem to end at this stage. However, the frequency of spontaneous recovery—if it actually occurs—is uncertain, since there are indications that the infection sometimes becomes latent.

On the basis of later history, three general types have been distinguished (39). In a mild variety, an equilibrium seems to be established with the patient in poor physical condition. In view of the lowered resistance to other diseases, even this mild form contributes significantly to depopulation. A severe acute type is characterized by marked toxemia and often by oedema and may lead to death without involvement of the central nervous system. The third type is the classical form with a sleeping sickness stage. The second and third types become predominant in epidemics, whereas the mild type is otherwise the most common. In later stages of the third type, invasion of the central nervous system is followed by sleeping sickness. This stage often develops in untreated cases after a more or less prolonged period, sometimes several years. Physical weakness and languor become more and more pronounced and loss of weight is often striking. The patient falls asleep at irregular intervals. Convulsive movements of the limbs, sometimes followed by temporary paralysis, become evident. Mania may develop, and mental and physical symptoms sometimes resemble those of paresis. The spells of sleep gradually become more frequent, and death is usually the outcome in untreated cases.

Anemia is a common feature and becomes more marked in later stages. Leucopenia, with a relative increase in mononuclears, is common, but a leucocytosis may occur instead. Red corpuscles in fresh blood smears may undergo agglutination at room temperature, a phenomenon attributed to an increase in "autoagglutinin." Swelling of the lymph glands is often produced, even in early stages, by multiplication of lymphocytes in the germ centers. Multiplication of cells may occur also in the endothelium of lymph channels. Hemorrhages frequently develop, and the degeneration of lymphatic tissue may be followed by invasion of fibrous tissue. Enlargement of the spleen is more or less proportional to the degree of anemia and to the parasitemia. Endothelial proliferation, increase in number of phagocytes, increase in thickness of the capsule, and some degeneration of splenic tissue have been observed. Endothelial proliferation also has been observed in vessels of the lungs, liver and kidneys, sometimes leading to obliteration of capillaries in the lungs and kidneys. Lymphocytic infiltration has been noted in the heart, pericardium, liver, digestive tract and skin. Aggregates of macrophages, sometimes found in the skin, may contain ingested trypanosomes.

The typical lesions depend upon the presence of trypanosomes in the tissues. Extravascular distribution of the flagellates in experimental infections has been noted in the kidney, brain, inner ear, fetal heart, lymph glands, wall of the stomach, and the choroid plexus. Chronic inflammation of the brain is not observed until after the trypanosomes have reached the cerebrospinal fluid. Capillary hemorrhages sometimes occur, and there is a proliferation of neuroglia and endothelial cells, the latter sometimes even in the arteries. Some of the neurons may degenerate and atrophy of dendrities is observed occasionally. The spinal cord is usually affected less severely than the cerebral cortex.

Rhodesian sleeping sickness is similar in many respects to the Gambian variety but is generally more acute. Fever is more evident in early stages, while early enlargement of lymph glands is less common than in the Gambian variety. Also, the mortality is higher in Rhodesian sleeping sickness, although mild cases supposedly of the Rhodesian type have been reported occasionally.

Diagnosis. During the acute phase, laboratory diagnosis is comparatively easy. The trypanosomes can usually be detected in fresh or stained blood films and in material obtained by puncture of enlarged lymph glands. In later stages fewer flagellates are present in the blood, so that examination of several blood films, or preferably thick smears, may be necessary to detect the parasites. Smears from centrifuged blood may be positive when thin films or thick smears are negative. During the sleeping sickness stage, blood examination is much more likely to be negative. Therefore, the examination of cerebrospinal fluid, obtained by lumbar or cisternal puncture, may be necessary if other methods fail.

Chemotherapy. A number of drugs have been used in treatment of Gambian sleeping sickness, some with fair success and others with good results. In the experience of Kellersberger (34) with more than 9,000 cases, Bayer 205 was effective in early stages but useless after the central nervous system was involved. Atoxyl also was not curative in later stages. Tryparsemide showed more activity in early stages and also was the most effective drug in later stages, even arresting a few apparently moribund cases. However, this drug is quite toxic and dosage is usually spread over a period of two or three months. In treatment of early cases, p-arsenophenyl butyric acid (24), germanin and pentamidine all seem to be fairly effective. Orsanine seems to be active in cases showing involvement of the central nervous system. Good results have been obtained also with melarsen oxide which may be given orally or by injection and has shown low toxicity and relatively rapid action. The trypanocidal activity of tryparsemide, mapharsen and stilbamine involves effects on hexokinase and other enzymes of trypanosomes (16).

Chemotherapy has been less successful in Rhodesian sleeping sickness. In recent years, apparent cures have ranged from 16 to 48 per cent during various outbreaks in Tanganyika Territory. Particular drugs may differ in their activity against *T. rhodesiense* and *T. gambiense*. Bayer 205 seems to be more effective against *T. rhodesiense,* while the reverse apparently is true for tryparsemide and atoxyl.

An important complication of chemotherapy has been the tendency of trypanosomes to develop a resistance to arsenicals or antimonials (Chapter IX). However, the terms, "arsenic-fastness" and "antimony-fastness," sometimes applied to such phenomena, may not be entirely accurate. Resistance may be developed against substituted phenyl groups rather than against arsenic or antimony as such.

Control of sleeping sickness. Man apparently is the main source of infection with *T. gambiense,* and in many areas, the human reservoir is more than adequate for the maintenance of sleeping sickness. In various parts of British West Africa, for instance, a general incidence of 1-6 per cent has been observed and some villages show a much higher percentage of infection. Distinct reduction in the incidence of human infection has been obtained in West Africa by surveys and treatment of populations. In addition, pentamidine has shown some promise in mass prophylaxis, but there are serious practical difficulties in carrying out such programs on a wide scale.

Lower animals also may serve as a source of human infection. Domestic and wild animals apparently become infected with *T. gambiense* occasionally and may act as reservoirs, but there is little evidence that wild mammals are especially important in this respect. However, it appears that various types of game, particularly antelopes, may serve as reservoirs for *T. rhodesiense,* and cattle (72) also are known to become infected. Recent progress in chemotherapy and prophylaxis, on a practical scale, seems to promise not only elimination of the reservoir problem in domestic animals, but also the general control of trypanosomiasis in cattle and other domesticated herbivores.

Direct attack on tsetse flies helps to control sleeping sickness and also to reduce the incidence of nagana, a serious disease which is caused by *T. brucei* and has prevented the maintenance of domestic animals in densely infested areas. Measures effective in controlling the flies vary with the haunts and habits of the different species.[1] Four species are known to be important in transmission of sleeping sickness. The Gambian variety is spread by *Glossina palpalis,* and in some areas at least, by *G. tachinoides.* Rhodesian sleeping sickness is transmitted by *G. morsitans* and *G. swynnertoni. Glossina palpalis* is seldom found far from water, unless carried off while feeding on some animal (33), and *G. tachinoides* has similar habits. Consequently, these species can be controlled in some areas by clearing out bushes and low trees along rivers in the vicinity of villages and river crossings. Such a cleared strip, extending for a half mile or more on each side of a bridge or ford, offers fairly good pro-

[1] The literature of the past forty years, dealing with ecological relationships, feeding habits and breeding habits of tsetse flies, has been reviewed by Jackson (33a).

tection. Certain other species, such as *G. morsitans* and *G. swynnertoni,* have a wide range over bush land and must be controlled by other methods. Destroying or driving out game may be effective, with reduction in numbers or even practical elimination of tsetse flies in the area. This method has been practiced successfully in Southern Rhodesia for the control of *G. morsitans.* Aside from the decrease in sleeping sickness, the reduction in incidence of nagana has favored the maintenance of cattle. The local use of DDT sprays also seems to have some value. The spraying of domestic animals not only protects them from flies, but may help also in reducing the numbers of tsetse flies. In addition, the spraying of DDT from airplanes has been effective in practical tests over bushy areas of a few square miles.

A rather interesting delayed effect on the tsetse fly population may be produced by hybridization. It seems that mating will occur readily between subspecies or species in certain combinations, leading to hybrid offspring which are often sterile or of low fertility. Biological warfare of this type has been suggested as a possibility in controlling tsetse flies.

Chagas' disease

Distribution. This disease was first described by Chagas (12) in Minas Geraes, Brazil, and for many years this appeared to be the only area in which cases were at all common. Prior to 1937, only 113 cases had been reported outside Brazil, although these were distributed through Argentina, Guatemala, Panama, Peru, El Salvador, and Venezuela (77). Increasing interest, coupled with the extensive use of xenodiagnosis and complement-fixation tests, has revealed that the disease is far from rare in South America. In Chile (50), xenodiagnosis has shown an incidence of 12 per cent in 12,581 individuals; complement-fixation tests, 17 per cent in 8,142. Surveys of smaller groups have indicated a comparable or higher incidence in other areas: Argentina, 23-42 per cent; Bolivia, 6-31 per cent; Brazil, 15-51 per cent; Uruguay, 6 per cent; Venezuela, 27-46 per cent. Cases also have been reported in Colombia, Ecuador, Mexico, and Paraguay. Such data accentuate the need for intensive surveys throughout the known range of *Trypanosoma cruzi.* Perhaps Chaga's disease, once considered geographically as well as historically Brazilian, will prove to be more nearly an all-American disease.

The causative organism. Trypanosoma cruzi is unusual in that, in the vertebrate, the trypanosomal form invades various tissue cells in such organs as the heart, striated muscles, central nervous system, thyroid and lymph glands, bone marrow, ovaries, and testes. Invasion is followed by metamorphosis into the leishmanial stage. Repeated fission then occurs, so that the host cell is distended into a relatively thin membrane ("cyst") enclosing leishmanial stages (Fig. 12.3), the number of which varies with size of the host cell (41). Metamorphosis into trypanosomal forms, through an intermediate crithidial stage, is followed by rupture of the "cyst" to liberate the flagellates into the body fluids. A minimum of four or five days is required for this phase of the cycle.

In tissue-culture infections (38, 41, 57), trypanosomes of the type usually seen in the blood also have been observed about the fifth day after inoculation with *T. cruzi*. Muniz and de Freitas (47), using peritoneal fluid as a culture medium, have obtained stages similar to those normally seen in the vertebrate. The presence of tissue cells apparently is not necessary for transformation of the trypanosomal into the leishmanial form. On the other hand, metamorphosis into the trypanosomal stage, observed in whole peritoneal fluid, does not occur in cell-free fluid. Regular intervention of a crithidial stage between the leishmanial and the trypanosomal forms in the vertebrate has been questioned by Elkeles (25) who failed to find crithidial forms in his material. Also interesting is the report that crithidial stages from cultures mostly disintegrate in normal serum, while leishmanial and trypanosomal forms are not affected (44). However, all stages in the classical vertebrate cycle have been observed in chick embryo tissue cultures (41).

Trypanosomal stages in vertebrate blood are ingested by an insect vector and apparently change into leishmanial forms in the midgut. Fission of leishmanial forms may occur, but metamorphosis into crithidial forms takes place within a day or two. In the crithidial phase, multiplication occurs for some time before small metacyclic trypanosomes are derived from crithidial stages in the hindgut. Completion of the insect cycle requires about two weeks. In cultures, transformation of trypanosomal into crithidial stages seems to depend upon some substance present in washed erythrocytes, peptone and meat infusion. Hematin apparently is not the significant factor (46). This "metamorphosis-inducing factor" presumably would be required also in the digestive tract of the vector.

Transfer of the parasites to the vertebrate host involves discharge of metacyclic trypanosomes from the hindgut as the bug ingests another meal of blood. Large numbers of flagellates, sometimes as many as 2,500/mm³ (21), are deposited in the fecal material. If the trypanosomes reach a break in the skin or the wound made by the insect, infection may result. Or infection may follow contamination of intact mucous membranes (the conjunctiva and the oral, rectal, and vaginal mucosae). In addition to the usual transfer by vectors, rodents are known to eat triatomids and may acquire the infection in this way. Such transfer would be favored by the occasional survival of *T. cruzi* for several weeks in dead insects (75). Carnivores probably can become infected by eating infected rodents. Other direct methods apparently include lacteal and placental transfer in mammals (23). Furthermore, there is always a possibility of transferring the flagellates by blood transfusion in man.

Vectors and reservoir hosts. The reported range of *T. cruzi* extends from 41° S. (Patagones, Buenos Aires, Argentina) to 38° N. latitude (Pinole, California). Within this range, the trypanosome has been reported from a number of mammalian hosts and from a variety of insects. In addition to *Trypanosoma cruzi*, the similar *T. rangeli* has been reported from man, dogs, and reduviid bugs in South America (55a).

Panstrongylus megistus (*Triatoma megista*) was the first insect identified as a vector of *T. cruzi* (12). Since 1909, more than 30 species of

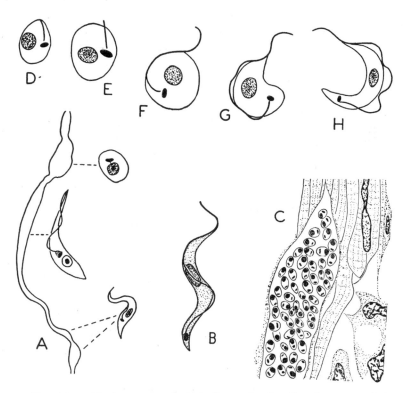

Fig. 12. 3. *Trypanosoma cruzi*. A. Stages in the digestive tract of the vector; schematic (after Lent). B. Trypanosomal stage from blood, x2800 (after Wenyon). C. Leishmanial forms in heart muscle, semidiagrammatic, x1150 approx. (after Chagas). D-H. Metamorphosis of the leishmanial into the trypanosomal form, semidiagrammatic, x2300 approx. (after Wenyon).

triatomid bugs—belonging mostly to the genera *Panstrongylus, Rhodnius,* and *Triatoma*—have been found naturally infected, the incidence ranging from 16 to 92 per cent in different areas. Infected insects have been observed in Argentina, Bolivia, Brazil, Chile, Colombia, Ecuador, French Guiana, Guatemala, Honduras, Mexico, Panama, Paraguay, Peru, El Salvador, Uruguay, Venezuela, and also in Arizona, California, and Texas. In the United States, insect infection was first reported for "*Trypanosoma triatomae*" in *Triatoma protracta* of California. Subsequently, infections have been reported in *T. uhleri* (37), *T. longipes* (74, 76), *T. protracta* (76) and *Paratriatoma hirsuta* (76) from Arizona, and in *T. gerstaeckeri* (51), *T. protracta* (74) and *T. heidemanni* (53) from Texas. The incidence of infection has approximated 33 per cent in representative triatomids of Texas (68a). The strain of *T. cruzi* from *T. heidemanni* is infective for man under experimental conditions (53).

The vectors of practical importance are the bugs which have become adapted to life in association with man. Such bugs infest the primitive huts and cabins common in rural South and Central America. During the day the triatomids normally hide in cracks in walls, in bedding and in furniture, as well as outdoors in piles of rubbish. Feeding on man or other accessible mammals is usually a nocturnal activity.

The ecological distribution of most infected triatomids indicates that *T. cruzi* is a natural parasite of various wild mammals which constitute a permanent and extensive reservoir. The cat was the first reservoir host to be recognized (12). Natural infections have since been reported in anteaters, armadillos, bats, dogs, ferrets, foxes, opossums, porcupines, and squirrels in various parts of Central and South America. In the United States, the San Diego wood rat of California was the first recognized reservoir (73). More recently, armadillos, house mice, opossums, and wood rats have been found infected in Texas (52); wood rats and white-footed mice, in Arizona (76).

Symptoms and pathology. Chagas' disease[2] may occur in either an acute or a chronic form. The acute type is most common in children under 10 years of age. The chronic form is the predominant type in adults, and perhaps 70 per cent of these cases occur in the age group, 20-50.

Following an incubation period, which has lasted 10-12 days in experimental human infections (13), characteristic symptoms appear. The acute case usually begins with a fever which is often moderate and may be irregular or remittent. Another common early symptom is facial oedema, sometimes accompanied by a conjunctivitis so severe that one eye cannot be opened. This effect has been attributed to invasion of *T. cruzi* by way of the conjunctiva. In severe cases, the oedema may become extensive, involving the extremities and sometimes most of the body. Adenitis is characteristic and often includes the submaxillary, preauricular, cervical, inguinal, and axillary glands. There is usually a detectable swelling of the liver and spleen, especially the former. A progressive anemia and a rapid pulse are commonly noted. Physical weakness, loss of appetite, diarrhea and headaches are frequently noted in children. Occasional cases, usually fatal, show symptoms of acute meningoencephalitis. The cardiac signs are usually not well defined and do not show the marked changes in rhythm reported for many chronic cases. However, there is

---

[2] A comprehensive discussion of symptoms and treatment has been published by Laranja, Dias, and Nobrega (38a).

sometimes an acute myocarditis which may lead to heart failure. Mortality in this form of Chagas' disease often exceeds 10 per cent.

The acute form of the disease runs a fairly short course. In surviving patients, the trypanosomes usually disappear from the blood after a few weeks and the oedema and other symptoms gradually subside. The temperature often drops to normal. However, a low fever may persist for some time after termination of the acute phase. Although there may appear to be clinical recovery, the infection may persist, even for as long as 16 years (22). In other words, a patient may simply progress from the acute into the chronic form of the disease.

The usual chronic case is the cardiac type and, for practical purposes, almost every chronic case may be considered a potential heart patient. Symptoms vary with the extent of damage to cardiac muscle. While myocardial damage is progressive, it is usually so slow that several years may be required to produce indications of heart failure. Symptoms may be mild or almost unnoticeable, the only evidence of cardiac damage being that obtained with the electrocardiograph. Commonly, however, such symptoms as dyspnea, palpitation, and abdominal pain in the upper right quadrant are observed. Cardiac enlargement is often noticeable, and irregularities in heart rhythm are common. Prognosis of the cardiac case depends upon progress of the infection. Patients with slight or moderate enlargement of the heart may be expected to live for several years. For those with marked enlargement, the outlook is rather uncertain. Mortality in chronic cases approaches 10 per cent, and the majority of deaths occur before the age of fifty.

Pathological effects include degeneration of the invaded cells as well as a cellular infiltration and eventual fibrosis of the invaded tissues. Lesions of the heart, brain and liver are most characteristic, although the flagellates have been found in most organs of the body in acute cases. The heart shows a diffuse myocarditis. Among the muscle fibres there is extensive infiltration of lymphocytes and macrophages, sometimes with wide separation of the individual fibres, some of which show fragmentation and degeneration. Groups of leishmanial forms may be found either in the muscle fibres or in large mononuclear cells and monocytes. Cellular infiltration of the epicardium and endocardium is noted occasionally. Multiplication of *T. cruzi* may also occur in skeletal muscle, which shows much the same changes as cardiac muscle. Damage to the brain is observed in some cases. Parasites may be found in neuroglia cells and in large mononuclears in centers of inflammation scattered through the nervous tissue. In the liver, the flagellates have been found in Küpffer cells. Fatty degeneration of liver tissue is sometimes noticeable and enlargement of the liver is fairly common. The spleen also may be enlarged to some extent, but parasites have been detected less commonly than in the liver. Leishmanial stages also have been found occasionally in the thyroid, adrenal glands, ovaries, and testes. Enlargement and congestion of lymph glands are common effects but the flagellates seem to be absent or rarely present in lymphatic tissue.

Diagnosis. Microscopic detection of *T. cruzi* is often easy enough in the early acute stage. In addition, the precipitin test is useful in diagnosis of early cases with mild symptoms (43a). In chronic cases, flagellates occur in the blood in small numbers at most and the examination of blood smears is usually negative. Culture methods have been used, and their practical value may be increased by the addition of bacteriostatic agents (penicillin, streptomycin) to suitable media (58a). Inoculation of blood into laboratory animals may give good results, and xenodiagnosis also is often effective. In xenodiagnosis, trypanosome-free insects are allowed to feed upon suspected human cases. The subsequent appearance of *T. cruzi* in the triatomids justifies a positive diagnosis. The success of xenodiagnosis depends upon an adequate number of trypanosomes in the blood, and some workers feel that the results are positive in an unfortunately small percentage of chronic cases. Precipitin tests apparently have little value in chronic cases (43a), but accurate diagnosis is possible with complement-fixation tests (Machado-Guerreiro reaction) in which the test antigen is prepared from cultures of *T. cruzi* (Chapter XIV). Results already obtained in thousands of tests (18, 23, 45, 50) suggest that complement-fixation is superior to other diagnostic procedures and should be the method of choice for suspected chronic cases.

Therapy and control. Chemotherapy has been generally ineffective and the problems of treatment are complicated by the usual occurrence of the most acute cases in young children. A quinaldine compound, Bayer 7602 Ac, is one of the few which have shown some activity against *T. cruzi*. The drug has been tried in acute cases, but the results are scarcely extensive enough for accurate evaluation. General methods of treatment are those used for heart patients—rest, dietary control, and other methods indicated for relief of heart failure.

Control of Chagas' disease is essentially an economic problem. Prevalence of the disease in rural areas of Central and South America is mainly attributable to the infestation of native cabins and huts with triatomid bugs. Long range control must depend upon improvements in rural housing, since well built houses with adequate screening are effective barriers to the vectors. In short-term control, the persistent use of insecticides, although only an emergency measure at best, can be reasonably effective on a limited scale.

LITERATURE CITED

1. Acton, H. W. and L. E. Napier 1927. *Ind. J. Med. Res.* **15**: 97.
2. Adler, S. 1940. *Mem. Inst. Oswaldo Cruz* **35**: 179.
3. ——— and M. Ber 1941. *Ind. J. Med. Res.* **29**: 803.
4. ——— and O. Theodor 1927. *Ann. Trop. Med. & Parasitol.* **21**: 89.
5. ——— and ——— 1929. *Trans. Roy. Soc. Trop. Med. & Hyg.* **22**: 343.

6. ———— and ———— 1930. *Ann. Trop. Med. & Parasitol.* **24**: 197.

6a. ———— and ———— 1935. *Proc. Roy. Soc. London* (B) **116**: 543.

7. Andrews, J., C. M. Johnson and V. J. Dormal 1930. *Amer. J. Hyg.* **12**: 381.

8. Bovet, D. and G. Montezin 1937. *Bull. Soc. Pathol. Exot.* **30**: 68.

9. Brahmachari, U. N. 1922. *Ind. J. Med. Res.* **10**: 948.

10. Brooke, R. 1927. *Amer. J. Trop. Med.* **7**: 27.

11. Caronia, G. 1930. *Amer. J. Trop. Med.* **10**: 261.

12. Chagas, C. 1909. *Mem. Inst. Oswaldo Cruz* **1**: 158.

13. Chagas, E. 1935. *C. R. Soc. Biol.* **118**: 290.

14. ————, M. da Cunha, G. O. Castro, L. C. Ferreira and C. Romana 1937. *Mem. Inst. Oswaldo Cruz* **32**: 324.

15. Chakravarty, N. K. 1947. *The Adreno-cortical and Hepatic Dys-function in Kala-azar and Their Role in the Morbid Processes of the Disease* (Calcutta).

16. Chen, G. 1948. *J. Inf. Dis.* **82**: 226.

17. Corson, J. F. 1946. *Trop. Dis. Bull.* **43**: 167.

18. Davis, D. J. 1943. *Publ. Health Rep.* **58**: 20.

19. ———— 1946. *Publ. Health Rep.* **61**: 1083.

20. Dias, E. 1932. *C. R. Soc. Biol.* **110**: 203.

21. ———— 1934. *Mem. Inst. Oswaldo Cruz* **28**: 1.

22. ———— 1938. *C. R. Soc. Biol.* **129**: 430.

23. ———— and F. S. Laranja 1948. *Proc. 4th Inter. Congr. Trop. Med. & Malaria* **2**: 1159.

24. Earle, H. 1946. *Publ. Health Rep.* **61**: 1019.

25. Elkeles, G. 1945. *Amer. J. Trop. Med.* **25**: 141.

26. Fairbarn, H. and E. Burtt 1946. *Ann. Trop. Med. & Parasitol.* **40**: 270.

27. Hertig, M. and G. B. Fairchild 1948. *Amer. J. Trop. Med.* **28**: 207.

28. ———— and R. A. Fisher 1945. *Bull. U. S. Army Med. Dept., No.* **88**: 97.

29. Hindle, E. and W. S. Patton 1927. *Nature* **119**: 460.

30. Ho, E. A., T. H. Soong and Y. Li 1948. *Trans. Roy. Soc. Trop. Med. & Hyg.* **41**: 629.

30a. Hoare, C. A. 1938. *Trans. Roy. Soc. Trop. Med. & Hyg.* **32**: 67.

31. ———— 1943. *Biol. Rev.* **18**: 137.

32. ———— 1944. *Trop. Dis. Bull.* **41**: 331.

33. Hunt, A. R. and J. F. E. Bloss 1945. *Trans. Roy. Soc. Trop. Med. & Hyg.* **39**: 43.

33a. Jackson, C. H. N. 1949. *Biol Rev.* **24**: 174.

34. Kellersberger, E. R. 1933. *Amer. J. Trop. Med.* **13**: 211.

34a. Kirk, R. 1929. *Parasitol.* **39**: 263.

35. Kligler, I. J., A. Geiger and R. Comaroff 1929. *Ann. Trop. Med. & Parasitol.* **23**: 325.

36. Kofoid, C. A. and I. McCulloch 1916. *Univ. Calif. Publ. Zool.* **16**: 113.

37. ———— and B. G. Whitaker 1936. *J. Parasitol.* **22**: 259.

38. ————, F. D. Wood and E. McNeil 1935. *Univ. Calif. Publ. Zool.* **41**: 23.

38a. Laranja, F. S., E. Dias and G. Nobrega 1948. *Mem. Inst. Oswaldo Cruz* **46**: 473.

39. Lester, H. M. O. 1938. *West Africa Med. J.* **10**: 2.

40. Meleney, H. E. 1925. *Amer. J. Pathol.* **1**: 147.

41. Meyer, H. and M. X. de Oliveira 1948. *Parasitol.* **39**: 91.

42. Most, H. and P. H. Lavietes 1947. *Medicine* **26**: 221.

43. Mukerjee, S. 1945. *Ann. Biochem. & Exper. Med.* **5**: 95.

43a. Muniz, J. 1947. *Mem. Inst. Oswaldo Cruz* **45**: 537.

44. ———— and A. Borriello 1945. *Rev. Brasil. Biol.* **5**: 563.

45. ———— and G. de Freitas 1944. *Mem. Inst. Oswaldo Cruz* **41**: 303.

46. ———— and ———— 1945. *Rev. Brasil. Med.* **2**: 995.

47. ———— and ———— 1946. *Rev. Brasil. Biol.* **6**: 467.

48. Napier, L. E. 1931. *Ind. J. Med. Res.* **19**: 295.

49. ————, P. C. Sen Gupta and G. N. Sen 1942. *Ind. Med. Gaz.* **77**: 321.

50. Neghme, A. and J. Roman 1948. *Amer. J. Trop. Med.* **28**: 835.

51. Packchanian, A. 1939. *Publ. Health Rep.* **54**: 1547.

52. ———— 1942. *Amer. J. Trop. Med.* **22**: 623.

53. ———— 1943. *Amer. J. Trop. Med.* **23**: 309.

54. Pawlowsky, E. 1931. *Centralbl. f. Bakt., Orig.* **123:** 14.
55. Penna, H. A. 1934. *Brasil. Med.* **48:** 949.
55a. Pifano, F. 1948. *Bull. Soc. Path. Exot.* **41:** 671.
56. Poindexter, H. A. 1935. *J. Parasitol.* **21:** 292.
56a. Rogers, L. 1904. *Quart. J. Micr. Sci.* **48:** 367.
57. Romana, C. and H. Meyer 1942. *Mem. Inst. O. Cruz* **37:** 19.
57a. Scheff, G. J. and J. S. Thatcher 1949. *J. Parasitol.* **35:** 35.
58. Schern, K. 1925. *Centralbl. f. Bakt., Orig.* **96:** 356.
58a. Seneca, H., E. Henderson and M. Harvey 1949. *Amer. J. Trop. Med.* **29:** 41.
59. Senekjie, H. A. 1944. *J. Parasit.* **30:** 303.
60. Sen Gupta, P. C. 1943. *Ind. Med. Gaz.* **78:** 336.
61. —— 1943. *Ind. Med. Gaz.* **78:** 537.
62. —— and N. K Chakravarty 1945. *Ind. Med. Gaz.* **80:** 542.
63. Shortt, H. E., A. C. Craighead, R. O. A. Smith and C. S. Swaminath 1929. *Ind. J. Med. Res.* **17:** 335.
64. ——, R. O. A. Smith, C. S. Swaminath and K. V. Krishnan 1931. *Ind. J. Med. Res.* **18:** 1373.
65. ——, R. O. A. Smith and C. S. Swaminath 1931. *Ind. J. Med. Res.* **19:** 351.
66. —— and C. S. Swaminath 1928. *Ind. J. Med. Res.* **16:** 241.
67. Smith, R. O. A., K. O. Holder and I. Ahmed 1940. *Ind. J. Med. Res.* **28:** 585.
68. ——, —— and —— 1941. *Ind. J. Med. Res.* **29:** 799.
68a. Sullivan, T. D., T. McGregor, R. B. Eads and D. J. Davis 1949. *Amer. J. Trop. Med.* **29:** 453.
69. Swaminath, C., H. E. Shortt and L. A. P. Anderson 1942. *Ind. J. Med. Res.* **30:** 473.
70. Taliaferro, W. H. 1929. *The Immunology of Parasitic Infections* (New York: Century).
71. Wenyon, C. M. 1926. *Protozoology* (London: Ballière, Tindall & Cox).
72. Wilde, J. K. H. and H. M. French 1945. *J. Comp. Pathol. & Therap.* **55:** 206.
73. Wood, F. D. 1934. *Proc. Soc. Exp. Biol. & Med.* **32:** 61.
74. Wood, S. F. 1941. *Amer. J. Hyg.* **34,** C: 1.
75. —— 1944. *Bull. S. Calif. Acad. Sci.* **42:** 115.
76. —— 1949. *Amer. J. Trop. Med.* **29:** 43.
77. Yorke, W. 1937. *Trop. Dis. Bull.* **34:** 275.
78. Zwemer, R. L. and J. T. Culbertson 1939. *Amer. J. Hyg.* **29,** C: 7.

XIII

Malaria

INTRODUCTION

For MANY CENTURIES malaria[1] has been man's most important protozoan disease. In spite of recent progress in malariology, the current toll involves millions of cases annually, and malaria remains a serious hindrance to economic and social development in various parts of the world. In the eastern hemisphere, the history of malaria has included most of Africa, southern and southeastern Asia, northern Australia, southern Russia, England, and the European mainland bordering the Mediterranean and Atlantic. Outbreaks have occurred as far north as Finland. In the islands of the Pacific area, malaria extends southward from Japan into the New Hebrides. In the western hemisphere malaria has been prevalent from the central portions of South America to southernmost Canada. Within this tremendous potential range, malaria has been almost completely suppressed in a few regions and is gradually being

[1] An encyclopedic review of malaria in all its phases, recently published under the editorship of M. F. Boyd (13), will be invaluable to all who are interested in the subject.

597

brought under control in others. At the opposite extreme, there are still areas in which perhaps 90 per cent of the population have malarial infections every year. The history of malaria in North America (11, 44, 119) illustrates the results which may be expected from more or less systematic efforts to control the disease.

The origin of malaria in North America is uncertain. Some authorities suspect that the disease did not exist in the Americas before their discovery by Europeans. Others think that malaria was already endemic when Europeans first reached America. At any rate, malaria has played an important part in the history of North America for more than four centuries. Introduction of slaves from Guinea into the West Indies was begun about 1518 and the subsequently developed slave trade did much to spread malaria, especially malignant tertian.

The early Spanish and French expeditions to the Gulf and south Atlantic coasts probably brought malaria to North America, but some time elapsed before the disease became important here. The settlers who reached Roanoke Island in 1585 apparently were not troubled by malaria. However, those who came to Jamestown in 1607 had been recruited mostly from the London area where malaria was then endemic. Within four months more than 40 per cent of the settlers had died in what was possibly an outbreak of malaria. By 1619, the slave trade also was beginning to influence the malaria situation in Virginia. Along the Carolina and Georgia coasts, malaria gradually increased with the establishment of rice plantations, since the practice of flooding the fields provided breeding grounds for anopheline mosquitoes. The cultivation of rice was gradually extended southward. As a result, malaria flourished and the prosperous coastal region soon became the most intensely malarial. The disease also spread northward to New England, producing outbreaks in Massachusetts in 1647, 1650, and 1668. Thus, a century before the outbreak of the American Revolution, malaria had become established along the Atlantic coast from Massachusetts to Georgia. The Revolutionary War introduced susceptible foreign troops into the malarial regions along the coast and probably helped to spread the disease in the southeastern area.

The close of the Revolution ended restrictions on migration. The result was a westward movement of native easterners and immigrants. Malaria accompanied the early migrants over the Appalachians and beyond the Alleghenies to become endemic along the trails. Later settlers passed through these malarial regions on their way westward and helped to extend the disease into new territory. By 1850 most of the United States—with the exception of the western plains and deserts, northern Minnesota and Wisconsin, and the Appalachian and Rocky Mountain highlands—was afflicted with malaria. The disease extended from the Atlantic to the Pacific and from the Gulf of Mexico to the

Canadian shores of Lake Erie. On the eastern coast, malaria was still common in the Hudson River valley and along the shores of Long Island Sound. Although it is uncertain when malaria reached the Pacific, the early migrants evidently brought the disease overland to the lower Columbia River valley and the Sacramento-San Joaquin valley in California. An outbreak of chills and fever, possibly malaria, appeared among the Indians of the Fort Vancouver region in 1829. Within three years, about 90 per cent of the Indians had been exterminated. Another severe epidemic, thought to have been malaria, attacked the California Indians in 1833. The discovery of gold, which stimulated overland migration, accelerated the introduction of new malarial strains.

In most of these malarial areas, epidemic outbreaks occurred only during the warmer months of the year, but the situation in the southern and southeastern states was more serious. The status of malaria in the southern states is reflected in the fact that, from 1841 to 1847, 25.8 per cent of the patients admitted to Charity Hospital in New Orleans were suffering from malaria.[2] For the United States as a whole, malaria seems to have reached a peak about 1855, and the next few years showed a gradual decline in incidence.

The Civil War interrupted this trend by introducing relatively susceptible Federal troops into malarial regions of the South. Movements of the Confederate armies also contributed to the spread of malaria. Information concerning malaria in the Confederate armies is scanty, but it is known that the white Federal troops developed 1,163,184 cases of malaria from May, 1861, to June, 1866.

Immediately after the Civil War, outbreaks of malaria increased in some parts of the South, and it is likely that Federal troops also took southern strains of the parasites home with them. Malaria broke out in Connecticut, for example, and spread into Rhode Island and Massachusetts, the outbreak reaching a peak in 1881. In the South, increased incidence of malaria was favored by unsettled conditions. Failure of drainage systems extended the breeding grounds for mosquitoes, and the partial failure of southern agriculture led to much undernourishment with increased susceptibility to malaria. During the period, 1870-1900, malaria was still important in many areas now more or less free from the disease—Indiana, southern and northern Illinois, southeastern Kansas, Ohio and Michigan along the shores of Lakes Erie and Ontario. Cases were still fairly common in Philadelphia, on Manhattan Island, and in Massachusetts.

Toward the close of the century, the incidence of malaria once more began to drop. This trend has continued, and the recession has been marked by the almost complete disappearance of malaria north of the

[2] By way of contrast, malaria accounted for only 0.58 per cent of admissions to the same hospital for the period, 1933-1940.

Ohio River and by its general restriction to the so-called "malarial belt." This area extends eastward from the plains of Texas and Oklahoma and includes the lower Mississippi valley and the Gulf Coast. Even within this area, where malaria is mainly a rural disease, reduction in incidence has been marked and continued reduction is to be expected with the extension and improvement of control measures now in operation (1). At present, however, endemic malaria in the southeastern states remains a local problem of some importance as well as a potential threat to other North American regions.

THE MALARIAL PARASITES OF MAN

Malarial parasites apparently were first seen by Meckel in 1847. Their significance was not recognized until Laveran reported, in 1880, that he was able to find them only in corpuscles of malaria patients. Five years later, Marchiafava and Celli produced apparently the first cases of experimental malaria by inoculating human volunteers with blood containing the parasites.

Four species of *Plasmodium* are now generally recognized as parasites of man: *P. vivax,* causing tertian (benign tertian) malaria; *P. falciparum,* causing malignant tertian (subtertian, aestivo-autumnal) malaria; *P. malariae,* causing quartan malaria; and *P. ovale,* causing a comparatively mild tertian type.

The relative incidence of these malarias varies in different parts of the world. Benign tertian is primarily a disease of temperate and subtropical areas and, while widely distributed throughout the tropics, it is apparently uncommon in some tropical countries. Malignant tertian is predominantly tropical, although extending into temperate regions where it is generally much less common than *vivax* malaria. Quartan malaria is widely distributed but is usually a second-rate problem in comparison with the dominant type (*vivax* or *falciparum* malaria) in any given region. However, there are exceptions, such as the Belgian Congo, in which quartan malaria is especially prevalent. *P. ovale* produces a malaria resembling but appreciably milder than benign tertian. Latent infections tend to develop early and are less liable to relapse than in the other malarias (103). *P. ovale* was observed by Craig (32) in American troops returning from the Philippines, and was described later (33) as a variety of *P. vivax* with a strong resemblance to *P. malariae.* The specific name, *P. ovale,* was proposed by Stephens in 1922 after careful study of the parasites (105). This species has since been investigated in additional material (55, 77, 103, 108, 122). Strains have retained their characteristics in passage through paretics (103, 122) and through mosquitoes (55, 103). Examination of stained preparations convinced Craig (34) that *P. ovale* is the same species which he had observed earlier. Infections have been reported from certain parts of Africa (Belgian Congo, East Africa, Gold

Coast, Nigeria, Sierra Leone, Uganda, West Africa), from Palestine, western South America, and the Philippines. However, *ovale* malaria seems to be rare wherever it has been found. The ecology of the *Plasmodium-Anopheles* complex is not yet known well enough to explain these differences in distribution, although the biothermal range of the parasites may be a factor in some cases. *P. vivax,* for instance, apparently does not develop in *Anopheles quadrimaculatus* at temperatures much above 30° (111), whereas such temperatures seem to be satisfactory for *P. falciparum.*

The evolutionary relationships of human malarial parasites and those of apes are suggested by the apparent morphological identity of *P. vivax, P. falciparum,* and *P. malariae* with *P. schwetzi* Brumpt, *P. reichenowi* Sluiter and Swellengrebel, and *P. rodhaini* Brumpt. In fact, it is debatable whether these parasites of apes are specifically different from those of man. Apparent physiological differentiation does indicate that *P. vivax* and *P. falciparum* and their homologues in apes are distinct strains. *P. schwetzi* (85, 88, 89) and *P. reichenowi* (6, 88) have failed to infect artificially inoculated men, and *P. falciparum* has not infected chimpanzees under similar conditions (71). *P. vivax,* upon inoculation into chimpanzees, occasionally produces a subpatent infection which persists for several weeks without loss of virulence for man (85). The differentiation of *P. malariae* and *P. rodhaini* seems to be less marked. Inoculation of *P. rodhaini* into man has led to mild symptoms of quartan malaria and the appearance of parasites showing the characteristics of *P. malariae* (86). Strains of *P. malariae* also have proven infective for chimpanzees, in which they retain their virulence for man (87).

THE LIFE-CYCLE OF MALARIAL PARASITES

Exo-erythrocytic phase

For many years protozoologists were puzzled by the failure to find malarial parasites early in an infection. The rather abrupt appearance of parasites later on led to a suspicion, expressed clearly by Grassi in 1900 and later by James (54), that sporozoites develop outside the blood before invading erythrocytes. The confirmatory evidence is now conclusive.

Experimental inoculations have indicated that parasites disappear from the blood soon after introduction of sporozoites, are absent for some time, and then suddenly reappear. Blood transfusions, within 7-30 minutes after inoculation of sporozoites, have transferred *P. vivax* and *P. falciparum* to the recipients. Transfusions made after more than 30 minutes have given negative results (42). The blood does not become infective again until about the eighth day with *P. vivax* (25, 42) and the sixth or seventh day with *P. falciparum* (23, 42). Likewise, *P. cathemerium* disappears from the blood of canaries within an hour after inoculation and does not reappear until the end of the third day (118). Coatney, cited by Sapero (90), has found also that large volumes of blood from latent cases of *vivax* malaria fail to infect the recipients. The latent phase thus resembles the prepatent period in that the blood contains no demonstrable parasites. That the parasites are actually present in the host is indicated by the subsequent relapse or primary attack.

The accumulation of morphological data, culminating in the observations of Shortt and his colleagues on primate malaria, gradually brought to light this previously unknown exo-erythrocytic (E-E) phase

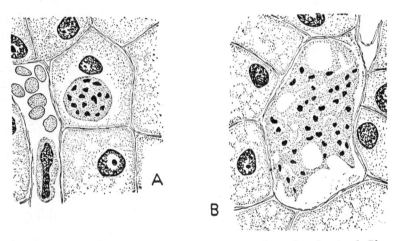

Fig. 13. 1. Exoerythrocytic schizonts (preerythrocytic phase) of *Plasmodium cynomolgi* in hepatic cells of *Macaca mulatta;* schematic (after Shortt). A. Stage recovered on fifth day after inoculation by mosquitoes; diameter of schizonts, 10-11μ. B. Vacuolated schizont recovered on the seventh day of the infection.

(Fig. 13.1). Non-pigmented E-E stages were perhaps first reported by Raffaele (81), who found them in bone marrow endothelium of birds infected with *P. elongatum* and suggested (82) their origin from sporozoites. Raffaele (83) later described non-pigmented *P. vivax* in human bone-marrow five days after inoculation with sporozoites. From other laboratories, E-E stages have been reported in *P. gallinaceum* infections (53, 57) and tissue cultures (48, 61), in tissue cultures of *P. lophurae* (115), in canaries infected with *P. cathemerium* (121), in *P. relictum* (31), in *P. mexicanum* of lizards (113), in monkeys infected with *P. cynomolgi* (95, 97, 100), and from human liver early in a *P. vivax* infection (95, 99).

After inoculation of monkeys (*Macaca mulatta*) with sporozoites of *P. cynomolgi*, E-E stages undergo growth and merogony in hepatic parenchyma cells. By the fifth day the schizont approaches 11μ in diameter and at maturity, on the eighth or ninth day, measures 35-60μ. (95, 100). Merogony results in about 1,000 merozoites, averaging 1.1μ in diameter (98). Some of these merozoites presumably enter red corpuscles at the end of the prepatent period. The E-E cycle is continued in the liver, where schizonts have been found in the fourth month of infection and after a month of latency (97). Thus, for the first time in the history of malaria, a complete description of the life-cycle became available for a species parasitic in a mammal (96). Preliminary observations (95, 99) have indicated that the E-E cycle of *P. vivax* closely resembles that of *P. cynomolgi.*

The E-E stages of avian parasites have been observed mainly in lymphoid-macrophage (reticulo-endothelial) cells. E-E stages of *P. elongatum* develop primarily in wandering lymphoid-macrophage cells. Such species as *P. gallinaceum* (53) and *P. relictum* (31) are found principally in capillary endothelial cells, Küpffer cells of the liver, and other fixed cells lining sinuses of the bone marrow, lungs, and spleen. *P. mexicanum* of lizards develops in both fixed and wandering cells (113). Two varieties of E-E schizonts are found in *P. relictum* and *P. gallinaceum.* Microschizonts may produce about a thousand micromerozoites which are believed to enter erythrocytes. Macroschizonts produce fewer and larger macromerozoites which apparently invade lymphoid-macrophage cells and continue the E-E cycle.

This E-E phase in malaria offers a logical explanation for prepatent and postpatent periods, latency, and repopulation of the blood in relapses. The direct invasion of tissue cells other than erythrocytes by the inoculated sporozoites leads to a pre-erythrocytic cycle of growth and merogony. This explains the failure to demonstrate parasites in the blood during the prepatent period. However, the development of E-E stages does not depend exclusively upon the introduction of sporozoites in avian malaria. Inoculation of blood containing trophozoites of *P. gallinaceum,* for example, may be followed by the appearance of E-E stages in lymphoid-macrophage cells after 4-6 days (116). In fact, inoculation of a single trophozoite into a chick has produced infections showing E-E stages (39). Factors which eliminate erythrocytic stages, as the primary attack passes into a latent phase in relapsing malarias, usually do not eliminate the E-E stages. Accordingly, the E-E cycle continues throughout latency and may persist for a long time, as indicated by occasional relapse after a prolonged latency. It is more likely that invasion of the blood is attempted periodically, only to fail under the action of a stimulated malaricidal mechanism, than that the production of "micromerozoites" destined for red corpuscles is completely suppressed during latency. Sooner or later, however, the blood is repopulated in relapsing malaria. The most logical explanation for the occurrence of relapses is based upon immunological relationships (Chapter XIV).

The erythrocytic phase

General features. The erythrocytic phase in a natural infection normally is initiated by merozoites derived from E-E schizonts. Once inside the red corpuscle, the young parasite usually develops a vacuole which displaces the nucleus to the periphery, producing a "signet-ring" stage. The ring, or young trophozoite, soon begins to grow. Binary fission of ring stages has been suggested for *P. vivax* (3) and *P. falciparum* (50), but this interpretation is not generally accepted. During growth, hemoglobin is split into its protein component, which is used as food, and hematin (76). As indicated by chemical and spectroscopic examination (38, 47, 102), hematin is deposited in the refractile pigment granules of erythrocytic stages. As estimated in infections of *Macaca mulatta* with *P. knowlesi,* the hematin from about three-fourths of the corpuscular hemoglobin is converted into pigment by the average parasite (74).

Nuclear division begins toward the end of the growth period. The result is a multinucleate schizont, which undergoes merogony. The resulting merozoites, with some residual cytoplasm containing the pigment, are released into the blood stream. The pigment and other residual material are ingested by phagocytes. Hence, the presence of pigment in such cells indicates a malarial infection with a current or recently terminated erythrocytic phase. The liberated merozoites which do not undergo phagocytosis enter fresh red corpuscles, or sometimes reticulocytes, and repeat the cycle of growth and merogony. The time required ranges from about 24 to 72 hours in different species, with some variation among strains of a single species. Length of the cycle in the St. Elizabeth strain of *P. vivax* has averaged 43.4 hours; in the New Hebrides strain, 45.7 hours; and in the Baltimore strain, 41.5 hours (123).

During growth of the parasite, the corpuscle may undergo changes which vary with the species of *Plasmodium.* Invaded corpuscles may become enlarged, be distorted, become paler than the normal corpuscle, undergo changes in reaction to the usual blood stains, or may show little or no effect. Invaded corpuscles also tend to clump together in certain malarial infections, such as *P. knowlesi* in monkeys (60). At the beginning of the patent period, each corpuscle invaded by *P. knowlesi* becomes coated with a thin self-adherent precipitate. As a result, such corpuscles stick together. Since this coating substance is selectively ingested by phagocytes, parasitized cells are rapidly ingested at this stage. As the parasite-density increases, a fluffy precipitate forms, binding both invaded and normal corpuscles into large masses. The blood now becomes thick and sludge-like. Resistance of the larger masses causes the blood to flow more slowly through the capillaries. Some of the smaller clumps, containing both normal and invaded corpuscles, are ingested at this stage. Later on, many of the larger clumps are broken up against the forks of arterioles into fragments small enough for phagocytosis. This leads to substantial destruction of red corpuscles, parasitized and normal alike.

After several erythrocytic cycles of merogony, two types of gametocytes normally appear in the peripheral blood, macrogametocytes usually being more abundant than microgametocytes. Gametocytes may be expected, in a primary attack, some time after a definite fever develops. In experimental *vivax* malaria gametocytes are often present on the fifth day of the patent period, usually persist during the clinical attack, and may still be present for some time after the fever disappears. Infection of mosquitoes may be possible even after the blood contains less than 10 gametocytes/mm³. In laboratory-induced *falciparum* infections, gametocytes are observed about the tenth day of the patent period and sometimes not until after the primary attack subsides. A gametocyte density of 60/mm³ is believed to be the minimum for infection of mosquitoes, and results have usually been negative with less than 100/mm³ (15, 26). In natural infections with *P. falciparum,* gametocyte densities ranging from 1/mm³ to 90/mm³ have proven infective for mosquitoes (125).

The factors responsible for differentiation of gametocytes are unknown. Strains of *P. vivax* vary in the numbers of gametocytes usually produced, and the ability to produce gametocytes may decline during transmission by blood inoculation exclusively (5). In addition, the ability to produce gametocytes may be lost in an unnatural host. For instance, a strain of *P. elongatum,* isolated from a sparrow and maintained in canaries and ducks, stopped producing gametocytes at the fourteenth canary and the fifteenth duck transfer. A return to sparrows failed to reverse the change (72). Any strain undergoing such a change under natural conditions would necessarily perish at the end of its current infection. However, the mere production of gametocytes in the vertebrate host does not insure perpetuation of a strain. Mature gametocytes have a rather short life in the vertebrate, perhaps only a day or so in the case of *P. vivax* (7), and both types must be ingested by a suitable mosquito if the life-cycle is to be completed.

The various stages in the erythrocytic cycle—rings, growth stages, mature schizonts, stages of merogony, and gametocytes—differ morphologically from species to species and furnish the major criteria for differentiation of malarial parasites (36, 118a).

Erythrocytic phase in P. vivax (Fig. 13.2). The earliest stage in the red corpuscle is a discoid form with a small nucleus. After development of the usual vacuole, the ring measures about 2μ in diameter and generally contains a single chromatin mass, although sometimes two. A corpuscle usually contains only one ring, occasionally two or three. Growing parasites appear as larger rings, and later on, as irregular amoeboid forms. Refractile light brown pigment granules are deposited in the parasite during growth. These inclusions show brownian movement in fresh

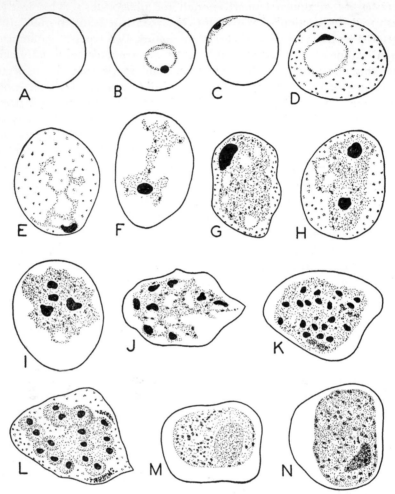

Fig. 13. 2. *Plasmodium vivax,* semidiagrammatic: A. Uninvaded red corpuscle, in outline. B. Young ring. C. Marginal form. D. Older ring stage; Schüffner's dots indicated in cytoplasm of the corpuscle. E-G. Growth stages. H-K. Binucleate, tetranucleate and multinucleate schizonts. L. Formation of merozoites. M. Microgametocyte. N. Macrogametocyte.

preparations. With continued growth of the parasite, the corpuscle is gradually enlarged to about 2-4 times the normal size and may be distorted. Invaded corpuscles are usually decolorized and may show small eosinophilic granules, *Schüffner's dots,* possibly derived from the granules of reticulocytes. The percentage of corpuscles showing Schüffner's dots may vary from patient to patient—for example, from 13.2 to 36.4 per cent in specific cases (51). By the end of 36 hours, growth has practically ceased and nuclear division is under way. At this point, the schizont almost fills the enlarged corpuscle. After about 46 hours or less, depending upon the strain, 12-24 daughter nuclei are present. After merogony, rupture of the corpuscle liberates the merozoites, and the survivors enter fresh corpuscles.

After a time, mature gametocytes appear in the peripheral blood. The cytoplasm of the larger (8-10μ) macrogametocyte usually stains a fairly deep blue (Wright's stain); that of the smaller (7-8μ) microgametocyte, a pale blue. The nucleus of the former is comparatively small and stains a rather deep red, or sometimes bluish-red. The larger nucleus of the microgametocyte is stained light red or pink. Numerous small brownish pigment granules are distributed throughout the cytoplasm of the micro-gametocyte. The larger and fewer pigment granules of the macrogameto-cyte are often concentrated in the peripheral cytoplasm. Both types of gametocytes practically fill the enlarged corpuscle at maturity.

Erythrocytic phase in P. falciparum (Fig. 13.3). Merogony is usually

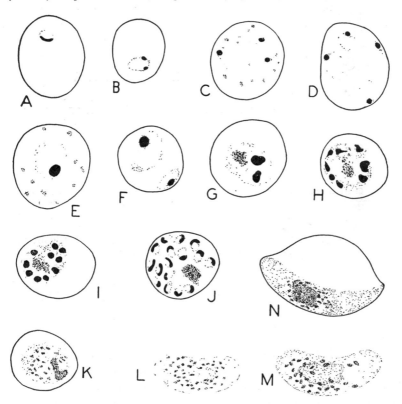

Fig. 13. 3. *Plasmodium falciparum,* semidiagrammatic: A. Young ring. B. Ring with two masses of chromatin. C. Double invasion of a corpuscle in which Maurer's dots are indicated. D. Corpuscle with four young para-sites. E. Older ring; corpuscle shows Maurer's dots. F. Two growth stages in a corpuscle. G-I. Binucleate and multinucleate schizonts. J. Merozoites. K. Undifferentiated gametocyte. L, M. Microgametocytes. N. Macrogameto-cyte.

completed in the visceral capillaries. Hence, the young rings, formed shortly after merozoites invade fresh corpuscles, are normally the youngest stages seen in blood smears. A characteristic feature is the fairly common appearance of several, sometimes as many as six, small rings in one corpuscle. The young ring usually measures not more than one-sixth the diameter of the corpuscle. A thin film of cytoplasm encloses the vacuole and the nuclear material is often seen as a small granule apparently projecting from the outer surface of the ring. Occasionally, the chromatin mass is rod-shaped, or there may be two or more small granules instead of one. Early growth stages develop a thicker cytoplasmic layer, become somewhat irregular in outline, and deposit dark brown or black pigment granules. These larger and somewhat irregular rings, less amoeboid than in *P. vivax*, are probably comparable to half-grown forms of the latter.

The invaded corpuscle does not become enlarged, does not show Schüffner's dots, and may stain a little more intensely than the normal corpuscle. Relatively coarse irregular eosinophilic granules (*Maurer's dots*) are seen rather rarely, but small basophilic granules (*dots of Stephens and Christopher*) may be expected somewhat more frequently.

In severe cases, particularly those with an unfavorable prognosis, all stages of development may be found in blood smears. Ordinarily, however, growth stages remain in the peripheral circulation for about 24 hours and then drop out in the capillaries of the spleen, bone marrow, and other internal organs where merogony is completed. Late stages of growth and merogony have been observed also in dermal tissue smears from children (79). This characteristic lagging of the older stages in visceral capillaries is possibly the result of an acquired adhesiveness of the invaded corpuscles, which tend to stick together and to the capillary endothelium.

In the later stages the vacuole disappears and the cytoplasm appears denser. This compact stage, shortly before nuclear division begins, is not much larger than the largest rings seen in the peripheral blood. The mature schizont, in which the pigment may occupy almost a third of the cytoplasm, usually measures not more than two-thirds the diameter of the corpuscle. Merogony produces 8-24 merozoites which measure 1.0μ or less.

The early development of gametocytes occurs typically in the visceral capillaries. As it reaches the peripheral circulation, the mature gameto-cyte varies in form, even within a single strain (58, 59). Most commonly, both types of gametocytes are sausage-shaped rather than crescentic. As a rule, the two show fairly distinct differences, but there may be some intergradation between gametocytes which are not quite mature. The mature microgametocyte usually shows a fairly large, lightly stained nucleus. The smaller nucleus of the macrogametocyte stains a little more deeply. The cytoplasm of the macrogametocyte stains a rather deep blue;

that of the microgametocyte, usually pale blue or lavender (Wright's stain). The golden-brown pigment of the microgametocyte is usually arranged rather loosely around or near the nucleus. The darker and sometimes greenish-black pigment of the macrogametocyte usually forms a compact aggregate partly or completely surrounding the nucleus. When the gametocytes appear in the peripheral blood, the ring stages usually

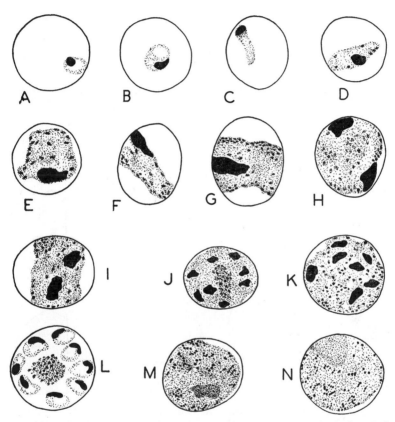

Fig. 13. 4. *Plasmodium malariae,* semidiagrammatic: A. Young ring. B-G. Stages in growth. H-K. Binucleate and multinucleate schizonts. L. Merozoites. M. Macrogametocyte. N. Microgametocyte.

decrease in number and it is not uncommon to find gametocytes as almost the only stages in blood smears. Mature gametocytes are believed to live for only a few days in the blood (114). In some patients gametocytes may disappear completely after a time, and new ones are seen only after a few more cycles of merogony (19).

Erythrocytic phase in P. malariae (Fig. 13. 4). This species differs from *P. vivax* and *P. falciparum* in its longer asexual cycle and in the smaller number of merozoites (usually 6-12) produced in merogony. The young rings, measuring from one-fourth to one-third the diameter of the corpuscle, are similar to those of *P. vivax*. Although the cytoplasm and chromatin are slightly coarser and the cytoplasm may stain a little more intensely than in *P. vivax*, it is difficult or impossible to distinguish the two at this stage. After a few hours of growth, the vacuole disappears and the cytoplasm becomes compact. *P. malariae* rarely shows pseudopodia.

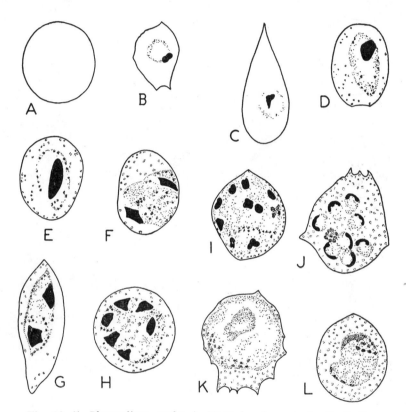

Fig. 13. 5. *Plasmodium ovale:* A. Normal red corpuscle. B, C. Young parasites. D, E. Stages in growth; stippling of corpuscles indicated. F-I. Binucleate and multinucleate schizonts. J. Merozoites. K. Microgametocyte. L. Macrogametocyte. Semidiagrammatic.

Pigment is deposited early and is appreciably more abundant than in the other parasites of man. Even half-grown parasites may show as many as 30-50 dark or almost jet-black granules. Older growth stages may form bands, stretching more or less completely across the corpuscle. Such bands are usually considered a diagnostic feature because they are so much more common in *P. malariae* than in the other species. In addition to the bands, growth stages are often seen as compact masses without pseudopodia. The mature schizont approximates the diameter of the corpuscle.

The invaded corpuscle is not enlarged and usually retains its normal shape, color, and staining reaction.

The cytoplasm of the mature microgametocyte stains a light blue to pale lavender (Wright's stain); that of the macrogametocyte, a fairly deep blue. The nuclear material of the microgametocyte stains a light pink and may occupy half the diameter of the parasite; that of the macrogametocyte is more compact and is usually stained a bright red or purple. The dark brown, or greenish brown, pigment granules are usually scattered through the cytoplasm in the microgametocyte; more or less restricted to the peripheral cytoplasm in the macrogametocyte. Each gametocyte almost fills the unenlarged corpuscle.

Erythrocytic phase in P. ovale (Fig. 13.5). The small ring stages (108) are usually coarser and stain more deeply than those of *P. falciparum*. Both young and later growth stages resemble those of *P. malariae* in their compact form, but are larger and contain slightly lighter, finer, and less abundant pigment granules. The corpuscle is somewhat enlarged and is sometimes oval, occasionally rounded at one end and tapering at the other, or often irregular or ragged in outline. Schüffner's dots are often distinct and numerous, may be present even with early growth stages, and may stain more intensely than in *P. vivax* infections. The mature schizont is usually rather rounded and measures about three-fourths the diameter of the corpuscle. Merogony often produces 8-10, but sometimes as many as 14 merozoites.

The gametocytes are similar to those of *P. vivax* and *P. malariae* and are usually not found in oval corpuscles. Enlargement of the corpuscle and the presence of Schüffner's dots distinguish the gametocytes of *P. ovale* from those of *P. malariae*. Since they fill only about three-fourths of the corpuscle, they are distinctly smaller than the gametocytes of *P. vivax*.

The mosquito phase[3] (Fig. 13.6)

Although gametocytes establish infections only in the natural hosts, maturation will take place even *in vitro*. Maturation of the microgametocyte (*exflagellation*) involves nuclear division and budding to form uniflagellate microgametes, the number of which is small—4-8 in *P. vivax* (84), 4-8 in *P. falciparum* and 2-5 in *P. malariae* (124), according to various reports. Exflagellation *in vitro* can usually be seen within 5-20 minutes after withdrawal of blood from a patient. The macrogametocyte merely ruptures the enclosing corpuscle and then rounds up. The possible occurrence of meiosis at this stage is suggested by observations of MacDougall (62a). Fertilization is accomplished when a microgamete penetrates the rounded macrogamete.

The zygote soon becomes an active *ookinete* which passes through

[3] Recent descriptions of the mosquito phase have been published for *P. malariae* (65) and for *P. vivax* and *P. falciparum* (64).

the epithelium and rounds up beneath the outer layer of the mid-gut within a period of 24-48 hours. Here the zygote begins to grow, apparently enclosed in a thin "oocyst" membrane. Several to many oocysts may develop in a single mosquito, usually without any appreciable effect on the host. The rate of growth varies with the species of *Plasmodium* and *Anopheles* and among different oocysts in the same mosquito, and is influenced also by the external environment. Oocysts of *P. vivax* may reach a diameter of 50μ or more in 1-2 weeks under favorable conditions. Oocysts of *P. falciparum* reach a comparable size in two weeks or so,

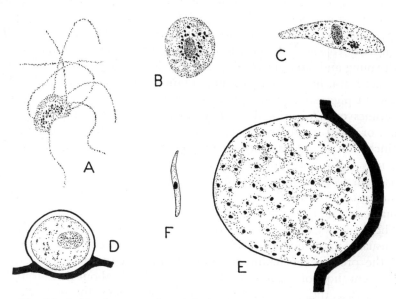

Fig. 13. 6. Development of a malarial parasite in the mosquito; diagrammatic: A. Microgametogenesis, or "exflagellation." B. Macrogamete. C. Ookinete. D. Zygote encysted on the wall of the stomach. E. Multinucleate oocyst some time before the formation of sporozoites. F. A sporozoite.

while those of *P. malariae* grow a little more slowly (69). During growth, rapid nuclear division occurs and sporogony finally produces thousands of sporozoites. Eventual rupture of the "oocyst" releases the sporozoites into the tissue spaces and some of them reach the mouth-parts of the mosquito.

The time required for completion of the mosquito phase varies considerably with environmental conditions. Under comparable laboratory conditions, *P. vivax* and *P. falciparum* have required less than three weeks and *P. malariae* about four (70), but these periods are shorter in more favorable environments.

The sporozoites of *P. vivax* (25) and presumably the other species are able to penetrate the tissues of man after inoculation by a mosquito. Within a short time, perhaps half an hour (42), they have entered tissue cells to initiate the pre-erythrocytic phase.

TRANSFER OF MALARIAL PARASITES

The relation of mosquitoes to malaria apparently was first suspected by Lancisi, who stated in 1717 that marshes cause malaria through the transformation of minute worms into mosquitoes which infuse a poisoned liquid into the wounds they inflict. In 1883, Krieg and King again suggested that malaria might be spread by mosquitoes, and this same opinion was held by Laveran, Manson, Pfeiffer, and others. The theory was confirmed for bird malaria by Ross in 1898, and later in the same year, by Grassi and his colleagues for *P. falciparum*. By the end of 1899, Grassi and his associates had demonstrated similar cycles in *P. malariae* and *P. vivax* and had transferred malaria to man from infected mosquitoes.

Aside from the dubious possibility that apes may serve as reservoirs, the source of mosquito infection is a human reservoir with both types of gametocytes. Young children are often the major source in tropical countries. For example, in Central African areas where malaria is endemic, adults usually show only trophozoites of *P. falciparum,* or rarely a few gametocytes of this species, whereas the gametocytes of all three major species may be expected in children (92).

The ability to transmit human malaria is limited to anophelines. Of these mosquitoes, only the "domesticated" types are usually important because they are most likely to become infected. Once they have acquired *P. falciparum,* mosquitoes may remain highly infective for about 10 days after sporozoites appear but are no longer infective to man after 40 days (27). The period of infectivity is somewhat longer for *P. vivax* (24). If malaria is to be maintained in a human population, suitable mosquitoes must be present in at least a minimal density. Hence, climatic conditions, which affect both mosquito breeding and development of the parasites in mosquitoes, exert an important influence on transfer of malaria.

Seasonal variations in incidence are more or less noticeable in malarial regions. In general, *vivax* malaria is most common in the early spring and through mid-summer in temperate regions. Initial attacks of malignant tertian rarely occur before early summer and are usually to be expected in late summer and early autumn. Quartan malaria is more likely to reach its peak in late autumn and early winter. The rainy and dry seasons in the tropics are obviously major influences on seasonal incidence. In temperate climates, however, changes in temperature may be more important. For example, the biothermal range for *P. vivax* in *Anopheles quadrimaculatus* is about 15-30°, with an optimum near 28°. At temperatures above 30° development is inhibited, and the parasites are usually eliminated after 24 hours at 37.5°. *P. vivax* is more resistant to low temperatures and arrested oocysts may pass the winter in mosquitoes and complete their development in the following spring (111).

In any season, a combination of circumstances may lead to a severe outbreak of malaria, as opposed to the more common endemic condition. Favorable climatic changes, permitting a marked increase in the anopheline density, may produce such a result in a susceptible population containing enough gametocyte carriers. An unusually wet season may serve the purpose in an area normally too dry for dangerously heavy mosquito densities. An unusually dry period might exert the same effect by converting rapidly flowing streams into isolated pools suitable for mosquito breeding. Importation of a prolific vector into new malarial territory offering little hindrance to breeding may be followed by a severe outbreak of malaria. Human activities, such as the migration of gametocyte carriers into anopheline territory, also may start an outbreak in a population relatively free from malaria.

Congenital transfer of malaria has been reported occasionally under conditions which eliminate other possibilities, but there are no adequate data for estimating the frequency of such transfer. Mechanical transfer by inoculation of blood is a routine measure in malarial therapy of syphilis and has occurred occasionally in blood transfusions. Storage of blood in a blood bank for a week is not a complete safeguard against the transfer of parasites in transfusions (94). Erythrocytic stages of *P. vivax* may be stored, at −70°, in citrated or defibrinated blood for at least five months without eliminating infectivity upon inoculation (91). Mechanical transfer also may be accomplished by drug addicts through common use of a hypodermic needle (75).

THE HUMAN MALARIAS

The incubation period

The number of sporozoites introduced is probably the most important influence on length of the incubation period (9, 16). The minimum for establishment of human infections is unknown, although inoculation of single trophozoites has produced infections with *P. knowlesi* in *Macaca mulatta* (30) and with *P. cathemerium* in canaries (104). Relative susceptibility of the individual ranks next in importance. In addition, the incubation period may vary with the strain of malarial parasites. Climatic conditions also may have some significance, since incubation periods in *falciparum* malaria may be relatively short from October through December and relatively long during the winter months (14).

The usual incubation periods are 14-18 days, with a common range of 5-35 days, for *P. vivax;* 18-21 days for *P. malariae;* and 9-12 days for *P.*

falciparum. In unusual cases symptoms may appear after much longer periods. For example, mosquito inoculation of *P. vivax* has produced a primary attack after 10 months (21). Likewise, under natural conditions, autumnal mosquito inoculations sometimes do not lead to primary attacks of *vivax* malaria until the following spring (101). A more unusual case, involving an apparent "incubation" period of 19 years, has been reported for *P. malariae* (78). Such cases may be considered latent infections and presumably involve an unusually prolonged pre-erythrocytic phase. Somewhat similar to these latent infections, occasional cases show very mild symptoms; unless treated, these may develop into typical cases.

Mixed infections may introduce complications. In experimental mixtures of *P. vivax* and *P. falciparum* (19), the latter was the first to populate the blood and the early symptoms were those of *falciparum* malaria. *P. vivax* later increased in number, while the population of *P. falciparum* decreased rapidly, and a typical attack of benign tertian occurred next.

Prodromal symptoms

In a typical primary attack of *vivax* malaria, mild symptoms appear a day or so before the patent period. These include nausea, loss of appetite, constipation, apathy, and sometimes insomnia. The mouth often feels dry and the tongue may be thickly coated. Headache, muscular pains, and aches in the joints soon develop, and there may be sensations of chilliness. Comparable early symptoms may appear in quartan malaria, but usually not before parasites are detectable. Such prodromal symptoms are sometimes seen in *falciparum* cases but are often so insignificant that the attack shows a sudden onset, particularly in partially resistant individuals.

The paroxysm

Prodromal symptoms are followed by a series of paroxysms, the length of the series varying with the patient and the type of malaria. A clinical reaction may occur in naturally induced *vivax* malaria when the parasite density approximates $10/\text{mm}^3$ (8), whereas recognizable symptoms may accompany the first appearance of parasites in the peripheral blood in *falciparum* malaria (23). The complete paroxysm includes the *rigor* (cold stage, chill), the *fever stage,* and the *sweating stage.*

The rigor usually begins with a chilly sensation, in the hands and feet at first and more general later on. Acute shivering may follow, with cyanosis of the lips and fingers tips. Rapid pulse and respiration, and sometimes severe headaches, may be expected. Nausea and vomiting also are fairly common. A rigor rarely initiates the first paroxysm in *vivax* malaria, may not occur until after several days of intermittent fever, and seldom precedes a peak temperature of less than 102° F. Appearance of a rigor in the first paroxysm suggests previous experience with malaria or else a relapse. As the infection progresses, duration of the *vivax* rigor may increase from 5-10 minutes to 1-3 hours. In quartan malaria, rigors usually begin with temperatures of less than 100° F., although a temperature of 103-104° sometimes follows the first one. However, a rigor is not always present in the quartan paroxysm. The paroxysm of malignant tertian is often initiated by a sensation of chilliness, and in perhaps less than a third of the cases, by a definite rigor. The factors inducing the rigor are not definitely known. The appearance of specific toxins has not been demonstrated, and similar symptoms can be induced by intra-

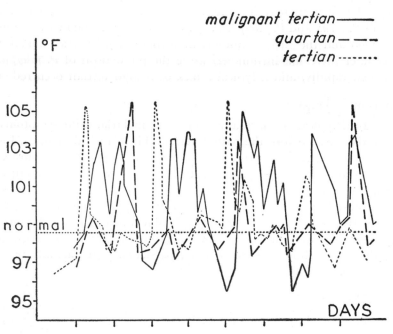

Fig. 13. 7. Diagrammatic comparison of temperature curves in malignant tertian, quartan, and tertian malarias.

venous injection of foreign proteins or denatured normal serum. The merozoites and residual protoplasm released at merogony presumably could serve as such foreign proteins.

The fever stage overlaps the rigor. The temperature begins to rise well before the end of the chill, or even near its beginning. As a result, the patient soon feels hot instead of cold. Although duration of the fever is variable, most of the surviving merozoites have penetrated corpuscles before the fever disappears. In the *vivax* paroxysm, the fever may last for 3-6 hours and the temperature curve (Fig. 13.7) generally shows an abrupt rise, a sharp peak and a fairly rapid decline. A progressive decrease in the temperature peaks may be expected toward the end of a clinical attack. In infants and young children with *vivax* malaria the fever is commonly continuous or remittent, without showing the periodicity characteristic of the adult case. The fever stage in quartan malaria is similar to that in tertian but the quartan temperature curves typically show a steeper rise and fall. In malignant tertian a fever of 12-24 hours is not uncommon. The temperature curves usually show fairly broad peaks, sometimes broken by partial remission of the fever. In general, the paroxysms are less clearly defined than in benign tertian and quartan malaria and temperatures may remain above normal for as long as two days or so.

The sweating stage of the tertian paroxysm sets in after the temperature has started to drop and may last 2-4 hours. The patient usually improves rapidly and feels fairly comfortable within a few hours. The sweating stage in quartan malaria is similar, but fails to bring such rapid improvement. A subnormal temperature may persist for a day or two. Sweating is usually less noticeable in malignant tertian, but the stage is accompanied by subnormal temperatures as in the other malarias.

A tertian periodicity, with paroxysms on alternate days, is characteristic of uncomplicated infections with *P. vivax, P. ovale,* and *P. falciparum.* A quartan periodicity, with paroxysms at intervals of about 72 hours, occurs in *P. malariae* infections. The exact periodicity may vary within a species, however, and average intervals of 43.4, 45.7 and 41.5 hours have been noted for three strains of *P. vivax* (123). Periodicity is influenced also by the occurrence of double or multiple infections. A double infection, for instance, may include strains undergoing merogony on alternate days and producing quotidian paroxysms. In experimental tertian malaria, quotidian paroxysms may occur even after a single inoculation (10). Such a course may change abruptly into a tertian one, or a new cycle may develop in a tertian course to produce quotidian paroxysms. Similarly, a double quartan course may become quotidian, or a quotidian periodicity may revert to a quartan series. Naturally infected patients, in contrast to those with induced malaria, show fewer of these irregularities in quartan and tertian malaria. In malignant tertian, on the other hand, changes and irregularities are common, and temperature curves sometimes suggest the lack of any basic organization. A simple tertian course in *falciparum* malaria may even indicate some degree of resistance. The origin of these irregularities is uncertain. The appearance of a new cycle in a tertian or quartan course might be attributed to fresh invasion from an exo-erythrocytic reservoir, but the change from a quotidian to a simple tertian or quartan series is another problem.

Some characteristic effects of the malarias

Anemia is inevitable in clinical attacks and normal red cell counts are not to be expected except perhaps during the early erythrocytic phase. A marked anemia may occur within a few days, especially in malignant tertian in which the parasitemia has reached 925,999/mm³ in extreme cases (109). There is sometimes a temporary increase in leucocytes during a paroxysm but such an increase, if it occurs at all, is followed by a reduction. After some days in an uncomplicated infection there is usually a leucopenia (3,500-4,500 leucocytes/mm³, or sometimes less). The accumulation of pigment in leucocytes, mostly the large mononuclears, is characteristic. Ingested pigment is to be expected also in the lymphoid-macrophage cells in the viscera.

Enlargement of the spleen is another characteristic effect, so much so that the "splenic index" has been used to advantage in malaria surveys. Enlargement of the spleen in *vivax* malaria usually is not evident in white adults until after a week or so of the patent period (110), but the splenic response is more rapid in infants and young children. Splenomegaly is much less noticeable in quartan than in tertian malaria, usually develops rather slowly in whites, and may be absent in negro patients. Jaundice is fairly common and may be marked in some malignant tertian cases. The condition may be expected in acute *vivax* malaria with a red cell count dropping below 2,000,000 during the first week or ten days, but is seen less frequently in slowly developing cases.

In contrast to the other types, *falciparum* malaria may be considered potentially lethal, although some patients seem tolerant to fairly heavy infections and may show comparatively mild attacks. In the simpler *falciparum* cases, no particular organ system is extensively involved. Even without localization, however, the parasites may multiply rapidly enough to overwhelm the patient unless the infection is checked.

Localized, or *pernicious,* malignant tertian occurs primarily in the tropics and in areas where the disease is highly endemic. Pernicious cases are generally severe and their development is favored by malnutrition, fatigue, heat prostration, drug addiction, and the like. The *cerebral* varieties involve localization in the nervous system. Effects include delirium, convulsions, failure of muscular coordination, amnesia, difficulties in speech, partial paralysis, indications of meningitis, or simulation of acute intoxication. The clumping of invaded corpuscles may lead to thrombus formation in cerebral capillaries, sometimes with resulting coma or death. The *visceral* (or *algid*) types of pernicious malaria involve localization in the digestive and circulatory systems primarily. The surface of the body feels cold. Symptoms may suggest acute appendicitis, bacterial dysentery, cholera, gastritis, peritonitis, or typhoid fever. Circulatory involvement often leads to angina-like pains and symptoms of thrombosis, with indications of heart failure. However, fatal cases may be the result of vascular collapse more often than of cardiac failure (67). The adrenal glands may be invaded, sometimes with degenerative changes in the cortex, and adrenal insufficiency has been considered a possible factor in fatal pernicious malaria. Involvement of the respiratory system may lead to indications of bronchitis or pneumonia. Effects on the urogenital system may suggest nephritis, orchitis or oophoritis, and haemoglobinuria or haematuria also may develop.

As complications of pregnancy, the malarias may be blamed for a considerable amount of fetal, neonatal, and maternal mortality. Even benign tertian is important in this respect and malignant tertian is particularly dangerous, both to the mother and to the fetus. The later the *falciparum* infection occurs in pregnancy, the less is the chance of carrying the fetus to term, and if the child is born alive it sometimes lives for only a few days.

Duration of clinical attacks

Duration of the *vivax* attack varies with the strain of parasites, with resistance of the individual, and apparently with the season of the year. Under comparable experimental conditions, July-September cases have shown longer clinical courses than January-March cases (22). Clinical symptoms have mostly disappeared in experimental tertian when the parasite density drops to about 100/mm³. In quartan malaria, duration of clinical attacks has averaged 170 days in naturally inoculated whites and 76 days in negroes. After artificial inoculation, the corresponding averages were 81 and 53 days (9). Duration of attacks in experimental *falciparum* malaria has averaged about 11 days, with a maximum of 36 (14). As in benign tertian, the length of the attack may vary with the season, being relatively long during the fall and shorter during the winter months.

Duration of infections

The duration of untreated infections is uncertain, in view of the occasional occurrence of prolonged latency. Even in induced malaria it is difficult to determine the end-point because failure to find the parasites does not guarantee the absence of a latent infection. In uncomplicated *vivax* malaria, the attacks usually become less and less severe and eventually cease. However, the infection sometimes persists for at least two years after the primary attack. In *falciparum* malaria, there are grounds for believing that infections usually last no more than six months (12, 56). *P. malariae* shows greater persistence and latent infections may last for five years or more after the primary attack (106).

Relapses

Although the tendency of *P. ovale* infections to relapse is comparatively slight (68, 103), relapses are characteristic of the other human malarias. *Recrudescences,* which occur shortly after recovery from a primary attack, are sometimes distinguished from *relapses* following a fairly long period of latency.

The greatest tendency to relapse is noted in tertian malaria. In many experimental infections (18), relapses have occurred after most primary attacks interrupted by small doses of quinine, and after half of the spontaneously terminated primary attacks. The tendency to relapse varies with the strain of *P. vivax* (18). Seasonal factors also may be significant, since July-September cases have shown a greater tendency to relapse than the January-March group (22). The pattern of relapse also varies with the strain (29). The course of tertian malaria often involves a series of "recrudescences" and then a period of latency, which may last 6-12 months before the next relapse occurs. In stubborn cases, this sequence may be repeated for several years after the primary attack. The St. Elizabeth strain (United States) usually does not show marked recrudescence, but a prolonged latent period and eventually a relapse are characteristic. The Chesson strain (New Guinea) usually shows fairly regular renewals of activity without prolonged latency. Relapses of the St. Elizabeth strain seem to coincide approximately with the mosquito season in the southern states. The Chesson strain is native to a region in which mosquitoes are reasonably available throughout the year.

In *falciparum* malaria, renewed activity shortly after the primary attack is generally to be expected, but relapses after long latency are much less common than in benign tertian. The tendency to produce "short-term" relapses may vary with the strain, and the incidence of relapses has ranged from 8.3 per cent (11) to 80.6 per cent (56) in experimental infections.

Although infections with *P. malariae* sometimes last a long time and relapses occur after apparently long periods of latency, little is known about the pattern and incidence of relapses.

Malariologists now believe that relapses involve two different phases in the life-cycle. A reactivation (recrudescence) occurring shortly after the primary attack depends upon renewed multiplication of erythrocytic stages not yet eliminated from the blood. The relapse following a long period of latency involves a persistent exo-erythrocytic infection which eventually supplies the merozoites for repopulation of the blood.

Blackwater fever

Blackwater fever occurs most frequently in individuals coming from malaria-free areas into a region where malaria is highly endemic. The specific cause is unknown. When it occurs, blackwater fever follows prolonged cases of malaria which have been imperfectly treated, and there is good evidence that *P. falciparum* is always, or nearly always, the only species involved. Inadequate dosage with quinine is not essential to development of the condition, since blackwater fever has followed treatment with other drugs such as atebrin. The onset is often marked by rigors, bilious vomiting, jaundice, black urine, and general prostration. The characteristic feature is intravascular hemolysis, followed by passage of hemoglobin in the urine. The pathological effects are essentially those of severe chronic malaria, with the complication of sudden and extensive hemolysis. The only known preventive is adequate treatment of patients in areas where blackwater fever is known. An extensive treatise on blackwater fever has been published by Stephens (107).

Laboratory diagnosis of malaria

Final diagnosis depends upon the detection of parasites in material from the patient.[4] Although certain serological techniques (Chapter XIV) seem to be useful, they are not yet adequate substitutes for direct demonstration of the parasites. Smears of bone marrow, obtained by sternal puncture, have been used for diagnosis of chronic malaria, but blood films are the preparations usually examined.

Both thick and thin films are often prepared for examination. Most routine descriptions of the parasites are based upon thin-film preparations. The thick film, in which a large drop of blood is spread over a small area of the slide, is the more efficient, both in saving time and in insuring detection of the parasites. Since the thick-film techniques—the rapid method of Field (45), the method of Barber and Komp (2), and others—destroy the corpuscles, the technician must depend upon careful microscopy and morphology of the parasites. With either type of films, it may be necessary to examine slides prepared at successive intervals if parasites are not detected at first. In any case, it is not sound practice to base a negative report upon examination of thin films alone if malaria is suspected.

Chemotherapy

Although malariologists seem to agree that *P. falciparum* should be eliminated promptly, opinions have differed concerning the treatment of quartan and benign tertian cases. Advocates of the "short-term" treatment have disapproved attempts to eradicate *P. vivax* and *P. malariae* during primary attacks, preferring clinical prophylaxis and suppressive treatment during residence in malarial territory. Such recommendations are based upon the assumption that individuals with sub-clinical infections will gradually develop an effective immunity, whereas prompt elimination of the parasites will leave the individual susceptible to reinfection. In presenting objections to the short-term treatment, Craig (35) has stressed the shortcomings of active immunization in India, where the

[4] Comprehensive discussions of laboratory diagnosis have been published by Craig (36) and Wilcox (118a).

native population has had many generations in which to practice "premunition" relatively undisturbed by chemotherapy.

From the practical standpoint, malarial therapy faces two problems (90): suppression of the erythrocytic phase in both clinical prophylaxis and clinical cure of primary attacks and relapses; and the elimination of exo-erythrocytic stages. Solution of the second problem is much the more difficult, but there is no true cure until exo-erythrocytic stages have been eradicated. Suppressive therapy brings relief to the patient, and by eliminating erythrocytic stages for the moment, temporarily eliminates a source of infection for mosquitoes. However, effective suppressive treatment is often followed by relapse, especially in *vivax* malaria. In terms of modern concepts, such a suppressant has been ineffective against exo-erythrocytic stages.

Quinine, the traditional malaricidal drug, is a good suppressant, although its activity may vary with the strain of parasites and especially so in *falciparum* malaria. Atebrin (atabrine, mepacrine, quinacrine) is active against erythrocytic stages of all species, and is valuable also in clinical prophylaxis. Both atebrin and quinine cause morphological changes in trophozoites of *P. vivax*, as seen in blood films a few hours after treatment (65a), but neither has any marked action on exo-erythrocytic stages. Chloroquine, which is well tolerated even by infants and is an effective suppressant for *vivax, falciparum,* and quartan malaria (4, 40), also has little effect on exo-erythrocytic stages. Pentaquine, although a poor suppressant, shows apparent activity against E-E stages (62). Plasmochin (pamaquine, plasmoquine) is just a fairly satisfactory suppressant for tertian and quartan malaria, but seems to be active against E-E stages (62). However, the effects of plasmochin may vary with the strain, in view of its failure to prevent relapse in mosquito-induced infections with the Chesson strain of *P. vivax* (37). In fairly heavy dosage, plasmochin is said to be an effective prophylactic against *P. vivax* and *P. falciparum* (93), but the toxicity of the drug would seem to limit its usefulness for this purpose. Paludrine (proguanil, chloroguanide), which seems to be a fairly good suppressant for *vivax* and *falciparum* malaria and is particularly active against pre-erythrocytic forms of *P. falciparum* (63, 66), has an interesting delayed effect on both species. Gametocytes mature in the treated patient and syngamy occurs after ingestion of gametocytes by the mosquito. However, the resulting oocysts fail to mature in the vector (43, 63). Camoquin, another new drug, seems to be about as good a suppressant as chloroquine and has given excellent results when administered in a single dose for moderate to heavy infections with *P. vivax* and *P. falciparum* (49). The advantages of effective treatment with a single oral dose are obvious.

The ideal malaricidal drug would be one harmless enough for use in infants, active enough for the prompt suppression of acute infections, and effective enough against exo-erythrocytic stages to insure complete prophylaxis and true cure. The search for such a drug is still in progress.[5] At present, the closest approach to the desired effects has been obtained with combinations of drugs. For example, the combination of quinine and pentaquine produces a low relapse rate in tertian malaria (73, 112). Likewise, quinine and plasmochin, as well as quinine and paludrine, have real value in clearing up relapsing cases (73). Such combinations as paludrine and atebrin, paludrine and chloroquine, and atebrin and chloroquine also have been used in malignant tertian.

Control

Mass treatment and prophylaxis, with an ideal drug administered to a docile or thoroughly cooperative population, probably could eliminate malaria from a given area without disturbing the local mosquitoes. Since the perfect drug is not yet available and the human factor is rather unpredictable, the most effective method for completely controlling malaria involves the reduction of anophelines to such a low density that the disease cannot be maintained in a given area. Successful results within the shortest possible time would require a combination of mosquito control and suppressive chemotherapy.

Long range measures, such as drainage of marshy areas and the stocking of natural and artificial lakes with fish which eat mosquito larvae, are effective deterrents to the breeding of mosquitoes. Treatment of stagnant pools and marshes with larvicides can be very effective where local conditions permit such measures. Adequate screening of houses tends to prevent contact of mosquitoes with man. In addition, some of the newer insecticides promise striking results in the direct attack on adult mosquitoes. For instance, residual DDT spray has been tested in several districts of Bombay Province with a population of about 1,600,000. After one year of spraying human and animal shelters at intervals of 6-8 weeks, the apparent incidence of malaria was reduced by 40-70 per cent in different areas (117). Practical tests in several tropical towns have shown that malaria can be controlled to a satisfactory degree by combining the use of DDT with suppressive chloroquine therapy (41). With the systematic application of available methods based upon sound knowledge of anopheline ecology, the practical elimination of human malaria now seems to be a distinct possibility. Attainment of this goal is retarded mainly by economic factors.

LITERATURE CITED

1. Andrews, J. M. and W. E. Gilbertson 1948. *J. Nat. Malar. Soc.* **7:** 167.
2. Barber, W. A. and H. W. Komp 1929. *Publ. Health Rep.* **44:** 2330.
3. Beach, T. de V. 1936. *Amer. J. Trop. Med.* **16:** 147.

[5] A fairly recent survey of antimalarials has been edited by Wiselagle (120); a later one has been published by Coatney (28).

4. Berberian, D. A. and E. W. Dennis 1948. *Amer. J. Trop. Med.* **28**: 755.
5. Bijlmer, J. and H. Kraan 1948. *J. Trop. Med. Hyg.* **51**: 222.
6. Blacklock, B. and S. Adler 1922. *Ann. Trop. Med. & Parasit.* **16**: 99.
7. Boyd, M. F. 1935. *Amer. J. Trop. Med.* **15**: 605.
8. ———— 1938. *Amer. J. Trop. Med.* **18**: 497.
9. ———— 1940. *Amer. J. Trop. Med.* **20**: 279.
10. ———— 1940. *Amer. J. Trop. Med.* **20**: 749.
11. ———— 1941. *Amer. J. Trop. Med.* **21**: 223.
12. ———— 1941. "A Symposium on Human Malaria." *Amer. Assoc. Adv. Sci. Publ. No. 15*, p. 163.
13. ———— (Editor). 1949. *Malariology: A Comprehensive Survey of All Aspects of This Group of Diseases from a Global Standpoint* (Philadelphia: W. B. Saunders).
14. ———— and S. F. Kitchen 1937. *Amer. J. Trop. Med.* **17**: 213.
15. ———— and ———— 1937. *Amer. J. Trop. Med.* **17**: 253.
16. ———— and ———— 1937. *Amer. J. Trop. Med.* **17**: 437.
17. ———— and ———— 1937. *Amer. J. Trop. Med.* **17**: 849.
18. ———— and ———— 1937. *Amer. J. Trop. Med.* **17**: 833.
19. ———— and ———— 1937. *Amer. J. Trop. Med.* **17**: 855.
20. ———— and ———— 1938. *Amer. J. Trop. Med.* **18**: 515.
21. ———— and ———— 1938. *Amer. J. Trop. Med.* **18**: 729.
22. ————, ———— and H. Muench 1936. *Amer. J. Trop. Med.* **16**: 589.
23. ———— and C. B. Matthews 1939. *Amer. J. Trop. Med.* **19**: 69.
24. ———— and W. K. Stratman-Thomas 1934. *Amer. J. Hyg.* **19**: 539.
25. ———— and ———— 1934. *Amer. J. Hyg.* **20**: 488.
26. ————, ———— and S. F. Kitchen 1935. *Amer. J. Trop. Med.* **15**: 485.
27. ————, ———— and ———— 1936. *Amer. J. Trop. Med.* **16**: 157.
28. Coatney, G. R. 1949. *Bol. Off. Sanit. Pan-Americana* **28**: 27.
29. ———— and W. C. Cooper 1948. *Proc. 4th Intern. Congr. Trop. Med. & Malaria* **1**: 629.
30. Coggeshall, L. T. 1938. *J. Exp. Med.* **68**: 29.
31. Coulston, F. and C. G. Huff 1947. *J. Inf. Dis.* **80**: 209.
32. Craig, C. F. 1900. U. S. Army: *Report of Surgeon General.*
33. ———— 1914. *J. Parasit.* **1**: 85.
34. ———— 1933. *Amer. J. Trop. Med.* **13**: 539.
35. ———— 1940. *Amer. J. Trop. Med.* **20**: 239.
36. ———— 1948. *Laboratory Diagnosis of Protozoan Diseases* (Philadelphia: Lea and Febiger).
37. Craige, B., Jr., R. Jones, Jr., C. M. Whorton, T. N. Pullman, A. S. Alving and L. Eichelberger 1947. *Amer. J. Trop. Med.* **27**: 309.
38. Devine, J. and J. D. Fulton 1942. *Ann. Trop. Med. & Parasit.* **36**: 167.
39. Downs, W. G. 1947. *Amer. J. Hyg.* **46**: 41.
40. Earle, D. P. and R. W. Berliner 1948. *Proc. 4th Intern. Congr. Trop. Med. & Malaria* **1**: 724.
41. Elmendorf, J. E., Jr. 1948. *Amer. J. Trop. Med.* **28**: 425.
42. Fairley, N. H. 1945. *Trans. Roy. Soc. Trop. Med. & Hyg.* **38**: 311.
43. ———— 1946. *Trans. Roy. Soc. Trop. Med. & Hyg.* **40**: 105.
44. Faust, E. C. 1945. *Amer. J. Trop. Med.* **25**: 185.
45. Field, J. W. 1941. *Trans. Roy. Soc. Trop. Med. & Hyg.* **35**: 35.
46. Garnham, P. C. C. 1948. *Trop. Dis. Bull.* **45**: 831.
47. Ghosh, B. N. and J. A. Sinton 1934. *Rec. Malar. Surv. India* **4**: 43.
48. Hawking, F. 1945. *Trans. Roy. Soc. Trop. Med. & Hyg.* **39**: 245.
49. Heokenga, M. T. 1950. *Amer. J. Trop. Med.* **30**: 63.
50. Hingst, H. E. 1934. *Amer. J. Trop. Med.* **14**: 325.
51. ———— 1936. *Amer. J. Trop. Med.* **16**: 679.
52. Huff, C. G. 1947. *Ann. Rev. Microbiol.* **1**: 43.
53. ———— and F. Coulston 1944. *J. Inf. Dis.* **75**: 231.
54. James, S. P. 1931. *Trans. Roy. Soc. Trop. Med. & Hyg.* **24**: 477.
55. ————, W. D. Nicol and P. G. Shute 1932. *Ann. Trop. Med. & Parasitol.* **26**: 139.
56. ————, ———— and ———— 1932. *Proc. Roy. Soc. Med.* **25**: 1153.

57. —— and P. Tate 1937. *Nature* **139**: 545.
58. Kitchen, S. F. and P. Putnam 1943. *Amer. J. Trop. Med.* **23**: 163.
59. —— and —— 1943. *Amer. J. Trop. Med.* **23**: 189.
60. Knisely, M. H., W. K. Stratman-Thomas, T. E. Eliot and E. H. Bloch 1945. *J. Nat. Mal. Soc.* **4**: 285.
61. Lewert, R. M. 1948. *Science* **107**: 250.
62. Loeb, R. F. 1946. *J. Amer. Med. Assoc.* **132**: 321.
62a. MacDougall, M. S. 1947. *J. Nat. Mal. Soc.* **6**: 91.
63. Mackerras, M. J. and Q. N. Ercole 1947. *Trans. Roy. Soc. Trop. Med. & Hyg.* **41**: 365.
64. —— and —— 1948. *Austral. J. Exp. Biol. Med. Sci.* **26**: 439.
65. —— and —— 1948. *Austral. J. Exp. Biol. Med. Sci.* **26**: 515.
65a. —— and —— 1949. *Trans. Roy. Soc. Trop. Med. & Hyg.* **42**: 443.
66. Maegraith, B. G. 1948. *Proc. 4th Intern. Congr. Trop. Med. & Malaria* **1**: 742.
67. —— 1948. *Trans. Roy. Soc. Trop. Med. & Hyg.* **41**: 687.
68. Malaria Commission 1933. *Quart. Bull. Health Org. League Nat.* **2**: 181.
69. Mayne, T. B. 1932. *Publ. Health Rep.* **47**: 1771.
70. Mer, G. 1933. *Ann. Trop. Med. & Parasit.* **27**: 483.
71. Mesnil, F. and E. Roubaud 1920. *Ann. Inst. Pasteur* **34**: 466.
72. Micks, D. W. 1947. *J. Parasit.* **33**: 499.
73. Monk, J. F. 1948. *Brit. Med. J.,* 1221.
74. Morrison, D. B. and H. A. Jeskey 1948. *J. Nat. Mal. Soc.* **7**: 259.
75. Most, H. 1940. *Amer. J. Trop. Med.* **20**: 551.
76. Moulder, J. W. and E. A. Evans 1946. *J. Biol. Chem.* **164**: 145.
77. Mühlens, P. 1934. *Arch. Schiffs-u. Tropenhyg.* **38**: 369.
78. —— 1937. *Muench. Med. Woch.* **84**: 5.
79. Peel, E. and L. van Hoof 1948. *Ann. Soc. Belge Med. Trop.* **28**: 273.
80. Porter, R. J. and C. G. Huff 1940. *Amer. J. Trop. Med.* **20**: 869.
81. Raffaele, G. 1934. *Riv. di Malariol.* **13**: 331.
82. —— 1936. *Riv. di Malariol.* **15**: 309.
83. —— 1937. *Riv. di Malariol.* **16**: 413.
84. —— 1939. *Riv. di Malariol.* **18**: 141.
85. Rodhain, J. 1939. *C. R. Soc. Biol.* **132**: 69.
86. —— 1940. *C. R. Soc. Biol.* **133**: 276.
87. —— 1948. *Amer. J. Trop. Med.* **28**: 629.
88. —— and G. Muyelle 1938. *C. R. Soc. Biol.* **127**: 1467.
89. —— and —— 1939. *C. R. Soc. Biol.* **131**: 114.
90. Sapero, J. J. 1947. *Amer. J. Trop. Med.* **27**: 271.
91. Saunders, G. M., D. W. Talmadge and V. Scott 1948. *J. Lab. Clin. Med.* **33**: 1579.
92. Schwetz, J. 1949. *Trans. Roy. Soc. Trop. Med. & Hyg.* **42**: 403.
93. Shannon, J. A. 1948. *Proc. 4th Intern. Congr. Trop. Med. & Malaria* **1**: 714.
94. Sharnoff, J. G., J. Geiger and I. Selzer 1945. *Amer. J. Clin. Pathol.* **15**: 494.
95. Shortt, H. E. 1948. *Proc. 4th Intern. Congr. Trop. Med. & Malaria* **1**: 607.
96. —— 1948. *Trans. Roy. Soc. Trop. Med. & Hyg.* **42**: 227.
97. —— and P. C. C. Garnham 1948. *Brit. Med. J.,* 1225.
98. —— and —— 1948. *Trans. Roy. Soc. Trop. Med. & Hyg.* **41**: 785.
99. ——, —— and G. Covell 1948. *Brit. Med. J.,* 547.
100. ——, —— and B. Malamos 1948. *Brit. Med. J.,* 192.
101. Shute, P. G. 1939. *J. Trop. Med. & Hyg.* **42**: 201.
102. Sinton, J. A. and B. N. Ghosh 1934. *Rec. Malaria Surv. India* **4**: 205.
103. —— and P. G. Shute 1939. *Trans. Roy. Soc. Trop. Med. & Hyg.* **32**: 751.
104. Stauber, L. A. 1939. *J. Parasitol.* **25**: 95.
105. Stephens, J. W. W. 1922. *Ann. Trop. Med. & Parasitol.* **16**: 383.
106. —— 1924. *Ann. Trop. Med. & Parasitol.* **18**: 127.
107. —— 1937. *Blackwater Fever* (Liverpool: University Press).
108. —— and D. U. Owen 1927. *Ann. Trop. Med. & Parasit.* **21**: 293.
109. Strahan, J. H. 1948. *Trans. Roy. Soc. Trop. Med. & Hyg.* **41**: 669.
110. Stratman-Thomas, W. K. 1935. *Amer. J. Trop. Med.* **21**: 361.
111. —— 1940. *Amer. J. Trop. Med.* **20**: 703.

112. Strauss, B. and J. Gennis 1948. *Bull. N. Y. Acad. Med.* **24**: 395.
113. Thompson, P. E. and C. G. Huff 1944. *J. Inf. Dis.* **74**: 48.
114. Thomson, J. G. and A. Robertson 1935. *Trans. Roy. Soc. Trop. Med. & Hyg.* **29**: 31.
115. Tonkin, I. M. and F. Hawking 1947. *Trans. Roy. Soc. Trop. Med. & Hyg.* **41**: 407.
116. Tullis, J. L. 1947. *Amer. J. Trop. Med.* **27**: 21.
117. Viewanthan, D. K. and T. R. Rao 1947. *Ind. J. Malariol.* **1**: 503.
118. Warren, A. J. and L. T. Coggeshall 1937. *Amer. J. Hyg.* **26**: 1.
118a. Wilcox, A. 1943. "Manual for the Microscopical Diagnosis of Malaria in Man." *Nat. Inst. Health Bull.* **180**, pp. 1-39.
119. Williams, L. L. 1941. "A Symposium on Human Malaria." *Amer. Assoc. Adv. Sci. Publ.* No. **15**, p. 365.
120. Wiselagle, F. Y. (Editor) 1947. *A Survey of Antimalarials, 1941-1945* (Ann Arbor: J. W. Edwards).
121. Wolfson, F. 1940. *Amer. J. Hyg.* **31** (C): 26.
122. Yorke, W. and D. U. Owen 1930. *Ann. Trop. Med. & Parasit.* **24**: 593.
123. Young, M. D. 1944. *J. Nat. Malar. Soc.* **3**: 237.
124. ―― and G. R. Coatney 1941. "A Symposium on Human Malaria." *Amer. Assoc. Adv. Sci. Publ.* No. **15**, p. 25.
125. ――, N. F. Hardman, R. W. Burgess, W. C. Frahne and C. W. Sabrosky 1948. *Amer. J. Trop. Med.* **28**: 303.

XIV

Immunity and Resistance

NATURAL RESISTANCE

JUST AS THERE ARE natural infections with Protozoa, so there appear to be natural immunities to protozoan parasites, immunities which probably should be attributed to biological incompatibility. A natural immunity may be absolute, or it may be a relative immunity which can be overcome by massive inoculation or by debilitating factors.

The degree of natural resistance to a given parasite commonly varies with the host and may vary widely even within a single genus, as demonstrated in *Peromyscus* (128). In highly susceptible species of *Peromyscus,* infection with *Trypanosoma brucei* is usually fatal within a week. In another group of species, the infection is subacute and survival of the mice averages about three months. In a third group, the infection runs a chronic course and most of the mice apparently recover.

Within a single species, racial differences in natural resistance may exist, although little is known about this aspect of immunity against Protozoa. Differences between the apparent resistance of Europeans and that of natives to tropical diseases have often been emphasized as examples of racial differences in immunity. These differences also have been attributed to selection. Thus, native children may acquire endemic diseases at an early age, with resulting death of the weakest. Consequently, the survivors in each generation represent a selected group with a resistance greater than that of the average incoming foreigner. So far as malaria is concerned, some authorities believe that differences in the immune status of racial groups depend primarily upon frequency of infection. Whether this explanation accounts for the relatively high resistance of American Negroes, perhaps even young children (32), to *Plasmodium vivax* has been questioned. However, if there actually is such a racial difference in resistance, it apparently does not extend to Pacific strains of *P. vivax* since the susceptibility of American Negroes to Pacific *vivax* malaria does not differ significantly from that of American whites (38). Nevertheless, an apparently valid racial difference in susceptibility to *Plasmodium knowlesi* has been reported by Milam and Coggeshall (115). Experimentally infected Negroes showed appreciably longer incubation periods than whites and their blood remained infective to monkeys for a shorter time.

Individual variations in natural resistance also have been reported, particularly in the induction of therapeutic infections with malarial parasites. If the possibility of previous experience with the parasites can be eliminated, refractory individuals presumably exhibit an effective degree of natural resistance.

The factors influencing occurrence and degree of natural resistance are mostly unknown, since only a few cases have been investigated from this standpoint. In some instances, body fluids of the host play an important part in the fate of incoming parasites. Thus, coccidian oocysts pass unchanged through the digestive tract of a naturally immune animal, whereas hatching is apparently facilitated by the digestive fluids in a susceptible animal (4). Occasionally, resistance may depend upon parasiticidal properties of the body fluids. For example, after inoculation into various cold-blooded vertebrates, *Trypanosoma evansi* fails to appear in the blood of such animals as the eel, the serum of which destroys the flagellates *in vitro* (104). An analogous factor presumably is responsible for resistance of chickens to *Plasmodium cathemerium*. Immersion of sporozoites in hen's blood for 30 minutes or more greatly reduces their infectivity for canaries (21), which are normally susceptible to this parasite.

For individual organisms, age is an important factor in resistance. In general, young animals are more easily infected and usually show more severe symptoms than older animals. *Trypanosoma lewisi*, for instance, is frequently lethal in young rats but normally produces mild and self-terminating infections in adult hosts (60, 64). *T. cruzi* also produces lethal infections in young rats and comparatively mild infections in mature animals (100). Comparable differences have been noted even in chick embryos of different ages. Embryos are highly susceptible to infection with *T. evansi* at 8-14 days of incubation, but are quite resistant at 15-17 days (23). Susceptibility to invasion by a particular route also may vary with age of the host. Oral inoculation of rats with *T. cruzi* is usually possible up to 12 days of age but becomes increasingly more difficult in older animals (102).

Diet, and particularly the vitamin supply, may influence individual resistance to infection. A well balanced diet is a predisposing factor in human resistance to amoebiasis (2). Conversely, birds on a generally deficient diet suffer abnormally severe attacks of malaria, with greater tendency to relapse than in control animals (36). Certain high-protein diets decrease the severity of flagellosis in rats (133), amoebic infections in mice (134) and dogs (73), and balantodiosis in rats (150). Such effects of proteins have been attributed to modification of the intestinal flora, producing an environment unfavorable to Protozoa. In other cases, particular constituents of the diet, such as vitamins, may exert an important influence.

Vitamin K, as a dietary supplement, protects chicks against *Eimeria tenella,* reducing mortality from about 70 to 10 per cent (10). Likewise, supplementary riboflavin (13), thiamine, or a combination of thiamine and pyridoxine (14) decreases the intensity of coccidiosis in rats. A protective influence of ascorbic acid has been reported for *Trypanosoma brucei* infections in guinea pigs (130). A low-biotin diet favors abnormally high parasite densities in chickens and ducks infected with *Plasmodium lophurae* and in ducks infected with *P. cathemerium* (189, 190). A biotin deficiency also prolongs and intensifies *Trypanosoma lewisi* infections in rats, and even a moderate deficiency may lead to death (39, 40). Lack of folic acid increases the severity of *P. lophurae* infections in chickens (152). A pantothenic acid deficiency, in rats infected with *T. lewisi,* results in unusually high parasite densities, continued multiplication of the flagellates beyond the usual period, and death of the host in extreme cases (20). Even an inorganic supplement—e.g., copper added to the diet of rats infected with *T. equiperdum* (129)—may increase resistance of the host.

In contrast to such instances in which an adequate supply of a vitamin enhances resistance of the host or a deficiency lowers resistance, there are cases in which development of the parasite is stimulated by a particular vitamin in favorable concentrations. Such a relationship of vitamins to coccidiosis of rats is indicated in a series of papers from Becker's laboratory. Preliminary observations (18) showed that dietary factors are directly related to the intensity of infections with *Eimeria nieschulzi.* Addition of yeast to the diet stimulated production of oocysts to a maximum, while certain other supplements were somewhat less stimulatory. Subsequent experiments showed that the yield of oocysts is increased by supplementary pyridoxine (14) or pantothenate (19). Comparable findings have been reported for malarial parasites. A riboflavin deficiency, in chickens infected with *Plasmodium lophurae,* reduces the parasitemia to less than one-fifth that in birds on a high-riboflavin diet (151). Pantothenic acid shows a similar influence on *P. gallinaceum.* Chickens with a pantothenate deficiency develop much less severe trophozoite-induced infections than controls on a normal diet. Oral dosage with analogues of pantothenic acid produces much the same effect as pantothenate deficiency, the most active analogue (pantoyltauramido-4-chlorobenzene) being at least four times as active as quinine (34).

The relative resistance of a particular host is influenced also by virulence of the parasite, which may vary within a species. Such differences in virulence are apparent in strains of avian malarial parasites (135), in *Plasmodium cynomolgi, P. inui,* and *P. knowlesi* of monkeys (160), and in malarial parasites of man (25, 82). Some strains of *P. vivax* have such low virulence that they are of no value in malarial therapy. Differences in virulence may be correlated with rates of reproduction. The relatively virulent Madagascar strain of *P. vivax* averages 17-18 merozoites at merogony; the less virulent Dutch strain, only 12-13. Strains of *Entamoeba histolytica* also may vary in virulence, as indicated by their effects on kittens (112), and strains retain their general characteristics in cultures (114). Experimental reduction of virulence may be possible. For example, a human passage strain of *P. knowlesi,* a species normally lethal to certain monkeys, has produced a mild chronic infection in these animals (93). Likewise, virulence may be increased experimentally. A typical strain of *Trypanosoma gambiense,* after seven passages through young rats, caused death of adult rats in 4-7 days. Survival of adults infected with the original strain ranged from 25 to 95 days (145). In similar fashion, two strains of *E. histolytica* showed increased virulence for kittens after seven passages through dogs. Upon return of the strains to cultures, however, virulence dropped to approximately the original levels after several months (113).

ACQUIRED RESISTANCE

Resistance may be acquired actively, as a result of infection or vaccination, or passively by transfer of antibodies from an actively immunized animal. The resistance which is acquired actively in certain protozoan infections is a resistance to superinfection—"premunition" of Ed. Sergent—and is dependent to a considerable extent upon persistence of a latent infection, as in malaria. However, this resistance may last for some time after apparent elimination of the parasites. In other cases, such as *Trypanosoma lewisi* in the rat and coccidiosis in mammals, the parasites are finally eliminated so that a so-called "sterile" immunity is developed,

Active immunization

Active immunization: Leishmania. Vaccination against oriental sore was practiced empirically long before the causative organism was discovered, and the practical value of this procedure has been confirmed (22). In experimental immunization, results have varied with the host. Monkeys are more readily immunized than dogs, and like man, often become quite resistant to reinfection with *L. tropica.* Mice, on the other hand, acquire practically no immunity. Prophylaxis with killed vaccines has been generally unsuccessful, although such vaccines may have some therapeutic value.

Laboratory animals are sometimes immune after recovery from infection with *L. donovani* (123), and it is generally believed that recovery also leaves man resistant to reinfection. However, no effective method of vaccination has been developed.

Active immunization: Trypanosoma. Development of acquired immunity to a trypanosome was first demonstrated in rats recovering from infections with *T. lewisi* (94). Development of such an immunity is limited to rats more than 25 days old (64), and fails to occur even in adult rats after hypophysectomy (59). The pathogenic trypanosomes are usually lethal to laboratory animals, but sheep and goats sometimes recover from chronic infections with a resulting immunity which lasts for several years (65). Likewise, rats may recover spontaneously from infections with *T. cruzi* and remain resistant to reinfection for at least five weeks (58).

Experimental immunization has followed several methods: inoculation with a living, attenuated strain; inoculation with a virulent strain, followed by adequate chemotherapy; and inoculation with killed trypanosomes. Living attenuated vaccines were first used in attempts to immunize cattle to *T. brucei* (99). Although the procedure apparently was successful with some animals, this interpretation has been questioned on the basis that cattle sometimes recover spontaneously from infection with this trypanosome. However, rats have been immunized to *T. lewisi* with attenuated cultures non-infective even in massive doses (127). Ehrlich and Shiga (72) showed that, after inoculation with virulent trypanosomes and subsequent chemotherapy, mice remain resistant to reinfection for several weeks. These observations have been confirmed in other laboratories, and similar results have been obtained with rats, rabbits, and guinea pigs. Obviously, the practical value of this method is dubious. Most attempts to use killed vaccines have been unsuccessful. However, such vaccines have immunized adult rats against *T. lewisi* (57, 126), although vaccinated nurslings may succumb as readily as controls of the same age (57). A few positive results have been reported for pathogenic trypanosomes (35, 138, 148). Rats have been immunized against *T. equinum*, to the extent that vaccinated animals always outlived the controls after inoculation with a virulent strain, but absolute immunity was rarely produced (138).

Active immunization: Babesia. Smith and Kilbourne (162) noted that cattle surviving an attack of Texas fever possessed an immunity associated with a persisting low-grade infection. Such infections, with concomitant immunity, may last as long as 12 years (149). Resistance of the host is not absolute, since relapses may follow environmental or other disturbances to the equilibrium.

Active immunization: Plasmodium. In areas where malaria is endemic, many natives have the disease as children and the survivors seem to develop a resistance to malaria. This resistance is believed to accompany low-grade infections and to disappear gradually after the infections are terminated.

Active immunization to *P. vivax* has been produced repeatedly under experimental conditions (30, 31, 92, 198). Recovery from attacks is accompanied by an immunity which often prevents clinical attacks upon reinoculation with the homologous strain (27). However, there is little or no protection against other strains (heterologous strains). Infection with homologous trophozoites is frequently inhibited, although the introduction of homologous sporozoites may lead to a subclinical infection (26). The exact duration of immunity to *P. vivax* is unknown. However, immunity may persist for six or seven years, as indicated by light infections with mild symptoms or none at all following reinoculation with the homologous strain (29). A comparable immunity, developed against *P. falciparum,* often aborts a second clinical attack, although some multiplication of the parasites may follow reinoculation (33). Inoculation of a heterologous strain may induce a new clinical attack almost as severe as the first but an increased tolerance is sometimes indicated by a shorter attack and a lower parasitemia (28). In the case of *P. ovale,* the immunity is usually more effective against heterologous strains than it is in *P. falciparum* or *P. vivax* (161).

The phenomenon of relapse, although apparently less common in *P. ovale* infections (109), is characteristic of other human malarias. Relapses in *falciparum* malaria are usually of the "short-term" type, occurring within a few weeks after apparent recovery from the original attack. Relapses in *vivax* malaria, and especially in quartan malaria, are often "long-term." Cases of the former many relapse after 6-12 months, and quartan after even longer periods. The occurrence of relapse is sometimes attributed to factors which lower resistance of the host—adverse climatic changes, prolonged fatigue, surgical shock, pregnancy, inadequate diet, and the like. However, an adequate immunological explanation for this recurrence of symptoms, after a specific immunity presumably has been developed, is highly desirable. Certain experimental data are suggestive. For example, a relapse in monkeys infected with *P. knowlesi* is preceded by a decrease in titre of the protective antibody, while a rise in titre occurs after recovery from the relapse (47). Furthermore, superinfection with the homologous strain (St. Elizabeth strain of *P. vivax*) is possible after prolonged periods of latency (49). This indicates a gradual relaxation of the defensive mechanism during latency. On such grounds, it has been suggested (172) that antigenic stimulation during primary attacks with *P. vivax* and *P. malariae* usually induces a temporary low-grade immunity. This immunity wears off after the disappearance of erythrocytic stages. The result is a relapse. Relapses bring further antigenic stimulation, producing an immunity which may eventually become potent enough to eliminate the parasites.

Homologous immunities, similar to those in the human malarias, are developed against parasites of monkeys (160) and of birds (171). In avian and simian, as well as in human malaria, the immunity is believed to be primarily a resistance to superinfection in animals carrying a low-grade infection with the homologous strain. Such an immunity may persist for some time, in diminishing degree, after elimination of the infection. The immunity of canaries to *P. cathemerium* decreases gradually from the first to the sixth month after cure and is no longer detectable after eight months (80). Man also develops an apparently sterile immunity to *P. knowlesi* (115). A similar temporary immunity to *P. knowlesi* has been obtained by chemotherapeutic elimination of latent infections in monkeys (43, 107) and also against *P. vivax* in man by dosage with pentaquine (48, 197a). This residual immunity against *P. vivax* varies in intensity with the number of relapses rather than duration of the infection, and is lost rather rapidly after elimination of the parasites.

In a few instances, resistance to *Plasmodium* has been induced with killed vaccines. Resistance of canaries to *P. cathemerium* has been increased by vaccination with formalin-killed parasites (79), and similar vaccines have immunized ducks to *P. cathemerium* and *P. lophurae* (187). Striking results have been obtained in rhesus monkeys vaccinated with killed *P. knowlesi,* emulsified in paraffin oil containing killed *Mycobacterium tuberculosis* (76). Although *P. knowlesi* is usually lethal, inoculation of the vaccinated animals resulted in mild infections of short duration. However, vaccination of man against *P. vivax* has produced no significant protection (87).

Different stages in the life-cycle may vary in their susceptibility to antibodies. Apparently normal pre-erythrocytic stages, but few or no erythrocytic, have appeared after heavy inoculation of immunized chickens with sporozoites of *P. gallinaceum* (90). In addition, chickens vaccinated with inactivated sporozoites of *P. gallinaceum* are partially immune to sporozoites but not to erythrocytic stages (143).

Active immunization: Coccidia. Andrews (3), with his observations that dogs and cats remain immune at least seven months after recovery from infections with *Isospora,* was one of the first to demonstrate immunization against Coccidia. Similar results have been obtained with other mammals (9) and with chickens (191, 192) by feeding Coccidia in small doses. The severity of the infection is correlated with the degree of acquired immunity, and very light infections may induce no appreciable resistance. Immunity against Coccidia is a sterile immunity which prevents development of the homologous parasites. Thus, sporozoites of *Eimeria tenella* may invade intestinal cells of immune chickens but soon disintegrate (192).

Vaccination with non-viable parasites has been unsuccessful in chickens (191), rabbits (9), and rats (12). These unpromising results, and the ineffectiveness of antiserum prophylaxis, led Becker to suggest that immunity to coccidiosis cannot be explained on the basis of a generalized response of the host's tissues. Instead, resistance may involve a tissue immunity which spreads from centers of infection over the remaining epithelial layer (12).

Passive immunization

Passive immunization: Trypanosoma. In certain host-parasite combinations, antiserum from a recovered animal, or from one with a chronic or subacute infection, is protective when inoculated simultaneously with pathogenic trypanosomes (e.g., *T. brucei, T. cruzi, T. equiperdum*). Serum prophylaxis against *T. cruzi,* although not preventing infection, does induce a mild type of trypanosomiasis in rats (58). Passive immunization likewise is effective against *T. lewisi* (167) and *T. duttoni* (170). Lacteal transfer of antibodies, from actively or passively immunized females to nurslings, has been demonstrated with *T. lewisi* (55, 56) and *T. cruzi* (102) in rats. During the first 24 hours, a newborn rat can receive enough antibodies in milk to protect it against an inoculum of 1,000,000 *T. lewisi.* The results with *T. cruzi* are usually an abortive infection and survival of the nursling. Placental transfer of antibodies appears to be insignificant in these cases, as indicated in the exchange of litters between immunized and normal females.

Serum therapy has been more or less beneficial in some instances. Upon treatment with antiserum, goats infected with *T. congolense* have developed mild infections with recovery after three months, while controls have died (144). Beneficial effects of antiserum have been obtained also with *T. equinum* in mice (176). Such treatment of *T. cruzi* infections in rats induces an incomplete crisis in the blood, but a relapse occurs soon after the last injection of serum (58).

Passive immunization: Plasmodium. Although the results are of uncertain practical value, favorable effects of antiserum in human malaria have been reported occasionally (95, 106, 163). Sera from monkeys with chronic *P. inui* or *P. knowlesi* infections also are beneficial to monkeys with the homologous infection (46, 47). Likewise, serum therapy has protected canaries against *P. cathemerium* (86) and *P. circumflexum* (110) and chickens against *P. lophurae* when adequate dosage was continued over a long enough period (180).

In certain parts of Africa, the comparative incidence of malaria in infants and in older children has suggested to some workers that passive immunization may be important in man. Cases of malaria are relatively rare in young infants but become more and more common toward the end of the first year. On this basis, it has seemed possible that resistant mothers transmit to their infants an immunity which is rather effective during the first few months after birth and then gradually disappears.

FACTORS INVOLVED IN ACQUIRED RESISTANCE

Antibodies

The development of an acquired immunity may involve both a specific intensification of the host's normal defensive reactions and the appearance of defensive factors not present in the normal animal. The mechanism of resistance may include an increased phagocytic activity, specific for the homologous parasite, as well as the production of specific antibodies affecting the parasite directly. Substances which induce such reactions upon parenteral introduction into an animal are known as antigens. In general, an antigen may be considered a protein which, if it is to show antigenic properties in a particular animal, must be chemically foreign to that animal. Since Protozoa, like other microorganisms, contain more than a single type of antigen, any strain should be considered an antigenic complex rather than a pure antigen. There is probably a certain amount of overlapping among related Protozoa. One or more similar, or possibly identical, antigens (*group antigens*) may occur in several strains or in several species. Other antigens (species-specific or strain-specific) are limited to a single species or a single strain. Among bacteria, strain-specificity may depend upon certain non-protein substances (*haptenes*) which modify the antigenicity of proteins. Such substances have not yet been investigated extensively in Protozoa. However, possibly specific polysaccharides have been reported from leptomonad stages of *Leishmania tropica* (153) and also from *Trypanosoma cruzi*, *Leishmania brasiliensis*, *L. donovani*, *Endotrypanum schaudinni*, *Leptomonas culicidarum*, and *L. oncopelti* (119a). It is interesting that the polysaccharide fractions from *Leptomonas* gave negative precipitin tests with antisera for the other flagellates, while *T. cruzi* showed fairly strong cross-reactions with anti-*Leishmania* sera. It has been suggested that the lipoid fraction, rather than the carbohydrate fraction, is related to the antigenic peculiarities of trypanosomes (97a).

Introduction of an antigen into an animal induces the appearance of antibodies which react specifically with that particular antigen (homologous antigen). Introduction of an antigenic complex (e.g., Protozoa, bacteria) induces the appearance of various antibodies corresponding to the different antigens of the complex. Some of these antibodies will react only with the particular microorganism involved. Others, induced by group antigens, will react also with related microorganisms which contain such antigens. Antigen-antibody reactions of the latter type are often termed *group reactions*. Such group reactions may form the basis of a *cross-immunity*, in which an animal immunized to one strain of parasites shows a detectable immunity to a related strain. Antibodies, which are associated with the globulin fraction of the serum proteins, are evidently proteins. On the basis of their reactions with antigens, they are usually termed *agglutinins, precipitins, lysins,* and *opsonins,* although the unitarian theory holds that a single antibody produces the various reactions under appropriate conditions. True *antitoxins,* comparable to those induced by bacterial exotoxins, have not been demonstrated in animals infected with Protozoa. The complement-fixation reaction, involving "complement-fixing" antibodies, is discussed below.

Under suitable conditions, a particular antibody and its homologous antigen will react in a characteristic fashion. A *precipitin reaction* involves the "precipitation" of a non-cellular antigen by a specific precipitin in the presence of an electrolyte. An *agglutinin reaction* involves agglutination of a cellular antigen (bacteria, Protozoa, etc.) by a specific agglutinin under similar conditions. In agglutination of *Trypanosoma equiperdum,* for example, the flagellates form clumps visible macroscopically (138). Under the microscope, the flagellates appear in characteristic rosettes, since the bodies stick together more readily than the motile flagella. *Lysis,* which also involves a cellular antigen, may bring about disintegration of Protozoa. In lysis of *Bodo caudatus,* motility is first reduced and then the flagellates round up, become transparent and finally disintegrate (140). A lysin, unlike precipitins and agglutinins, acts on the homologous antigen only in combination with *complement.* A heat-labile complex of substances, complement (or alexin) is found in normal serum as well as in serum from immunized animals. An antiserum containing a lysin loses its lytic activity if it is heated (e.g., for 15 minutes at 56° C.). Reactivation is produced by adding a suitable amount of normal serum and thus restoring complement. The *opsonic effect,* also dependent upon complement, is expressed as an increased phagocytic activity against the homologous antigen. More than one of these various antibodies are to be expected in animals infected with a given parasite. Rabbits infected with *Trypanosoma cruzi* develop precipitins, agglutinins, lysins, and complement-fixing antibodies (154). Likewise, monkeys infected with *Plasmodium knowlesi* (69) develop agglutinins, complement-fixing antibodies and so-called protective antibodies (probably opsonins). Precipitins (169) and agglutinins (69, 110) also have been reported in other malarial infections.

Defensive mechanisms in trypanosome infections

While it is possible to observe various antigen-antibody reactions *in vitro,* the composite action on the parasite—the effect of the defensive mechanism as a whole—can be comprehended only by the study of parasite populations during infections. This method has been followed by Taliaferro and his associates (171, 173) who have studied the development of resistance in various host-parasite combinations. Growth of populations has been traced by counting the flagellates in blood samples at intervals throughout the infections. Rate of reproduction has been estimated by computing the coefficient of variation in length of the flagel-

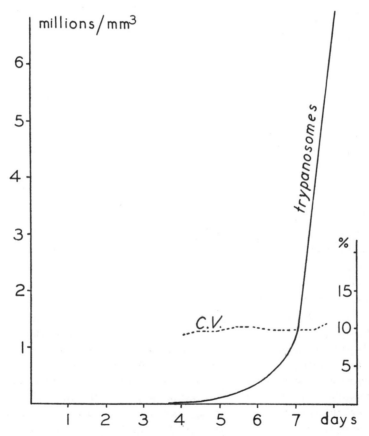

Fig. 14. 1. An acute lethal infection: *Trypanosoma rhodesiense* in a mouse (after Taliaferro and Taliaferro). A relatively constant coefficient of variation (C. V.) indicates a uniform rate of reproduction.

lates at appropriate intervals. This procedure is based upon the premise that in a rapidly dividing population, there is greater variation in length and a larger coefficient of variation than in an adult population of fully grown flagellates. The rate of reproduction may be estimated also by determining the percentage of dividing flagellates (175). Any destruction of parasites may be estimated on the basis of significant decrease in parasite density. Such methods have been applied to the analysis of acute lethal infections, relapsing lethal infections, and infections with non-pathogenic species.

Acute lethal infections (Taliaferro's "continuous fatal" type) are the simplest type, showing merely an incubation period and then a sharp

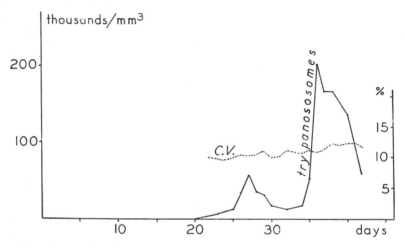

Fig. 14. 2. A relapsing lethal infection: *Trypanosoma rhodesiense* in a guinea pig (after Taliaferro and Taliaferro).

increase in the parasite population. In mice infected with *T. rhodesiense* (178), the flagellates are detectable about four days after inoculation, and they continue to multiply until the host dies on the seventh or eighth day (Fig. 14. 1.). The coefficient of variation remains fairly constant, indicating a uniform fission-rate, and there is no significant break in the growth-curve. The obvious conclusion is that the mouse develops no appreciable resistance to *T. rhodesiense.*

Relapsing lethal infections (Taliaferro's "intermittent fatal" type) are produced in a number of host-parasite combinations—*T. brucei, T. gambiense,* and *T. rhodesiense* in guinea pigs, rabbits, and rats; *T. equinum* and *T. evansi* in rats; *T. rhodesiense* in man and the cat. With *T. rhodesiense* in the guinea pig (178), there are irregular increases and decreases in parasite density (Fig. 14. 2.). The decreases are referred to as *crises;* the subsequent increases in parasite population, as *relapses.* Very few flagellates are present during the first three weeks. A week or so later, the population reaches a moderate density and then undergoes a crisis in which most of the flagellates are destroyed. During the succeeding chronic phase the survivors, as the *relapse strain,* multiply at the normal rate in the presence of a trypanolysin to which they seem to be no longer susceptible. The resulting increase in trypanosomes produces the first relapse, which is followed by a second crisis. This crisis presumably involves a new lysin, the appearance of which is induced by the antigenically modified relapse strain. The action of the second lysin on

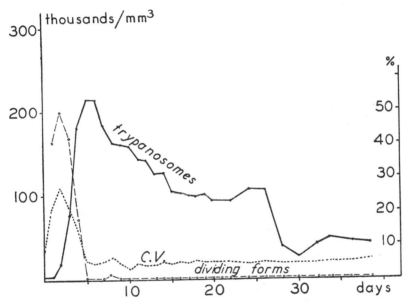

Fig. 14. 3. A non-lethal infection: *Trypanosoma lewisi* in a rat (after Taliaferro and Pavlinova). Early cessation of reproduction is indicated by marked decreases in the coefficient of variation (C. V.) and the percentage of dividing forms.

the relapse strain is comparable to that of the first on the original, or *passage strain.* The typical infection shows only a few crises and relapses, and death of the host usually occurs during the second month. Since fission-rate remains practically constant, as indicated by the coefficient of variation, the acquired immunity is expressed primarily through the action of lysins which produce the crises.

Trypanosoma lewisi in the rat (178) produces a non-lethal infection. After a short incubation period, the parasite density rises rapidly (Fig. 14. 3), usually without killing the adult rat. During the second week, the trypanosomes begin to decrease in number. This decrease may be quite rapid in some rats (178), somewhat more gradual in others (Fig. 14. 3).

In either case, reproduction of the flagellates (as indicated by the coefficient of variation and the percentage of divising forms) is rapid at first but shows a sharp decline after the first few days and has practically ceased within two weeks. Throughout the rest of the infection, there seems to be no further reproduction, although the persisting flagellates remain infective for normal rats (171a).

This inhibition of reproduction is attributed to the appearance of an antibody, *ablastin,* which prevents fission without destroying the trypano-

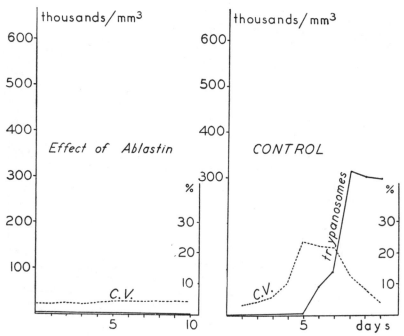

Fig. 14. 4. The effect of ablastin on development of *Trypanosoma lewisi* in the rat. The experimental animal was inoculated with *T. lewisi* suspended in serum containing ablastin; the control, with a comparable inoculum of trypanosomes from the same source but suspended in normal serum.

somes. Ablastin serum, transferred to non-immune rats (Fig.14. 4) produces the same effect (167). The importance of ablastin in defence against reinfection has been questioned by Augustine (5), who observed dividing flagellates in immune rats after massive intraperitoneal inoculation with *T. lewisi.* If these dividing flagellates were not present in the inocula of 200-900 million *T. lewisi,* or if there was a significant increase in dividing forms after inoculation, it would appear that ablastin is relatively inactive against reinfection by this route. On the other hand, the data of Becker and Lysenko (16) are in accord with the view that ablastin and trypanolysin are separate antibodies. At any rate, ablastin (or the ablastin effect) appears after about four days in a primary infection and the titre increases almost explosively toward the end of the first week (50). The ability to produce ablastin is well marked in animals of 25 days or older. Young rats apparently produce little or no ablastin and often die with *T. lewisi* infections (60). Production of ablastin also may depend upon the diet of the host. A pantothenate deficiency almost doubles the period of multiplication in *T. lewisi* infections (17, 20), and a biotin deficiency likewise delays the production of ablastin as well as trypanolysin (40). Irradiation of rats with X-rays (120) and dosage with sodium salicylate (15) also delay the ablastin effect.

The first crisis is caused by a lysin, which upon passive transfer to rats with early infections, induces a crisis within a few hours (51). The second crisis, according to different suggestions, depends primarily upon the action of a new lysin (167), mainly upon phagocytosis (137), or perhaps upon both factors.

The relative importance of cellular mechanisms in resistance to trypanosomiasis is uncertain, but the possible significance of phagocytes in general has been considered by various workers. Phagocytosis has been reported *in vitro* and *in vivo*. Ingested flagellates are sometimes seen in circulating leucocytes, chiefly the large mononuclears, and also in fixed tissue phagocytes. Furthermore, rabbits which survive infections with *T. brucei* show an increase in percentage and in total number of monocytes just before the first crisis. Rats and non-resistant rabbits show no such increase (81). An absolute monocytosis also occurs about the time of the first crisis in rats which survive *T. lewisi* infections, but not in those which are to die (64). In addition to any possible importance in phagocytosis, the lymphoid-macrophage cells have been considered as a source of ablastin—for example, by Regendanz and Kikuth (137) who noted that splenectomy usually delayed the ablastin effect for several days and was sometimes followed by death. Others (175) have failed to detect any marked effect of splenectomy on the production of ablastin. A possible relation of lymphoid-macrophage cells to formation of lysins also has been considered. Denison (63), for instance, has traced the effects of blockade with trypan blue upon the production of *T. cruzi* lysin in rats. In hanging-drop preparations, antiserum from infected normals produced lysis much more rapidly than that from blockaded animals, and the antibody titre was higher in the former serum.

Defensive mechanisms in malaria

Early investigations on bird malaria (reviews: 168, 171) showed that the incubation period—in canaries infected with *Plasmodium cathemerium,* for instance—is followed by an acute stage in which 30-50 per cent of the corpuscles are invaded. If the bird survives, the acute phase is terminated by a crisis which eliminates most of the parasites

(Fig. 14. 5). There follows a chronic phase of a week or more, during which a few parasites can be detected in blood smears. The chronic phase gradually fades into a latent stage, during which the parasites cannot be found in the blood. Subsequently, relapses may occur. Each relapse, checked by another crisis, is followed by a new latent period.

Taliaferro and his associates concluded that the bird acquires no resistance during the incubation period and early acute phase. The first crisis was attributed to a stimulated malaricidal mechanism, which from an early stage of the infection, was already destroying the majority

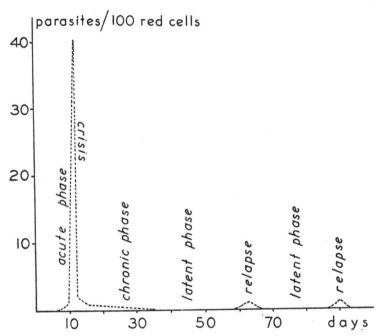

Fig. 14. 5. A typical malarial infection in a canary (after Taliaferro).

of merozoites—approximately 67 per cent at each merogony in specific cases (166). Accumulation of carbon dioxide in the blood, in unfavorable concentration, also has been suggested as a factor contributing to the crisis (139). It was believed that the high malaricidal rate prevented repopulation of the blood during latency, although reproduction continued at the original rate. A relapse was assumed to involve temporary relaxation of the malaricidal mechanism. This concept of the malarial infection in birds was modified slightly by Boyd (24) in observations on *P. cathemerium* in canaries. During the first day, division-rate was high (16.3 and 16.0 merozoites at merogony in two of the birds). During the next couple of days, while the parasite density was increasing enormously, the rate of reproduction dropped 25-50 per cent before the first crisis. After the crisis, the division-rate rose again and became fairly constant, but usually failed to reach the original level (Fig. 14. 6). The malaricidal rate also varied. During the first day, 50-60 per cent of the parasites were destroyed after each merogony. Three or four days later, the rate reached 90 per cent or higher and then remained at about this level. In similar fashion, the malaricidal rate in *P. knowlesi* infections in monkeys in-

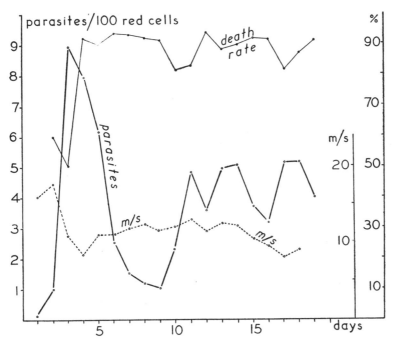

Fig. 14. 6. *Plasmodium cathemerium* in a canary (after G. H. Boyd). The rate of reproduction is indicated by the average number of merozoites produced by each schizont (m/s). The death rate is expressed as percentage of parasites destroyed in each merogonic cycle.

creases from about zero to approximately 90 per cent in acute infections (183a).

The primary factor in the malaricidal mechanism is phagocytosis; the lymphoid-macrophage, or "reticulo-endothelial," cells play the dominant role. Although it was once believed that phagocytes are mainly scavengers in malaria, the evidence indicates that normal parasites are ingested (174, 188). Indirect evidence also has been obtained by splenectomy and by blockade of the tissue phagocytes. The latter procedure involves the injection of material which is ingested by phagocytes and subsequently interferes with phagocytosis of parasites. Splenectomy in monkeys with chronic or latent infections is often followed by relapse, very severe with some species of *Plasmodium*. In other cases, a natural tolerance may be eliminated by splenectomy. Much the same effects have been produced by blockading techniques.

In natural resistance—that is, in the normal animal—phagocytosis appears to be non-specific. Circulating phagocytes seem to take little part in destruction of the parasites and the macrophages show only sluggish phagocytosis. In the early stages of infection, the phagocytes possibly ingest only moribund parasites (78, 84).

As the infection progresses, some degree of immunity is developed. Previous experience of monkeys with malaria, involving activation of lymphoid-macrophage cells, apparently facilitates the development of immunity against a new strain (118). Cellular responses in the spleen of monkeys (177) include both multiplication of lymphocytes in the splenic nodules, followed by their migration into the red pulp, and later multiplication of lymphocytes and their transformation into macrophages in the pulp. The result is a marked increase in the number of phagocytes. The reproduction of macrophages as such apparently occurs only to a minor extent. As would be expected, such agents as X-rays in heavy dosage (185) and nitrogen mustard (183), which destroy lymphocytes, retard the development of immunity.

In addition to the increase in number of phagocytes, the phagocytosis of homologous parasites is specifically stimulated. This response suggests the influence of an opsonin (47, 199). It is now widely believed that the appearance of such opsonins, or "protective antibodies," is characteristic of malarial immunity. In monkeys, corpuscles invaded by *P. knowlesi* become coated with a precipitate which is selectively ingested by phagocytes (98a.) This phenomenon implies stimulation of phagocytes rather than a harmful action of opsonins on the parasites. Phagocytosis occurs principally in regions where the blood flows relatively slowly and comes into close contact with the phagocytes. Such regions are represented particularly by the liver, bone marrow, and spleen. Acquired immunity to malaria, in the phraseology of Taliaferro, is thus expressed primarily as an intensified and specific phagocytosis in such strategically located organs as the spleen. The sluggish and non-specific phagocytosis of the normal animal usually can not prevent establishment of an infection, but the development of immunity increases phagocytosis to such an extent that the infection is brought more or less under control.

The malaricidal mechanism, particularly after development of a potent immunity, probably plays a significant part in the net results of chemotherapy. This conclusion is indicated, for example, by the results of splenectomy in chickens infected with *P. gallinaceum* (184). Direct interference with the lymphoid-macrophage cells throws more than the usual load on a malaricidal drug in the elimination of infections. A similar situation may exist in therapy following a low-grade immunological response to a mild infection or in the early chemotherapeutic suppression of primary attacks. Conversely, artificial stimulation of the defensive mechanism in conjunction with administration of malaricidal drugs may intensify effects on the parasites. As reported by Garcia (77a), injections of tetanus toxoid following atebrin or chloroquine therapy have reduced the relapse rate with *P. vivax* from an average of 90 to 9.5 per cent and that with *P. falciparum* from 90 per cent to zero.

SEROLOGICAL DIAGNOSIS OF INFECTION

Diagnosis of a protozoan infection is usually based upon detection of the parasites in body fluids or other materials. This method works well enough when the parasites are present in reasonably large numbers. In early infections and in chronic and latent stages, however, the usual laboratory examination becomes time consuming and often fruitless. Such difficulties have stimulated attempts to apply antigen-antibody reactions to diagnosis of protozoan infections. These tests are based upon the principle that the infected animal will sooner or later develop antibodies which react specifically with the causative organism.

In the usual procedure, a suitable antigen—a suspension of the parasites for an agglutinin test, or an extract for a precipitin or a complement-fixation test—is prepared from the suspected organisms. Serum from the infected animal is then tested with this antigen. A positive reaction, after elimination of possible group reactions, indicates that the host has developed antibodies against the particular parasite. A positive test, with corroboratory clinical evidence, may thus be considered presumptive evidence of infection.

Agglutinin tests

A suspension of the parasite in physiological salt solution is mixed with dilute serum from the suspected host. Agglutination becomes increasingly significant as the dilution of the serum is increased. Agglutination at a low dilution may represent merely a group reaction. Since group agglutinins are usually present in concentrations lower than those of antibodies specific for the homologous parasite, they are gradually eliminated with increasing dilution of the serum. A positive test at high titre thus indicates that the host has produced specific agglutinins for the test antigen.

The results obtained with kala azar have been contradictory. Some tests have been fairly successful, while others have not been clear cut. Caronia (41) demonstrated agglutinins in children infected with *L. donovani,* but concluded that the titre was too low for diagnostic purposes. More recently, however, Row (141) has obtained well marked agglutination of flagellates from cultures. Agglutination of trypanosomes was first demonstrated with sera from rats infected with *T. lewisi* (103). Practical application has been fairly successful in the diagnosis of dourine in horses. Although the diagnostic value of the reaction has not been determined, erythrocytic stages of avian malarial parasites (110) and *P. knowlesi* of monkeys (79) are agglutinated by homologus antisera.

Precipitin tests

The test antigen is usually prepared as an extract of the suspected parasite. Various dilutions of the antigen, in physiological salt solution, are then tested with serum from the host. Group reactions may be eliminated by increasing the dilution of the antigen. Consequently, a reaction with the antigen in high dilution has the same general significance as agglutination with high dilution of the test serum. In addition to demonstrating specific antibodies in the blood of the host, the test also may detect antigens of the parasite in body fluids of the host, as in *Trypanosoma equiperdum* infections of laboratory animals (131). In this case, a known antiserum is tested with material from the host, serving as the test antigen.

The precipitin reaction has been applied to diagnosis of dourine in horses, and has been tried also in diagnosis of human trypanosomiasis (119, 158, 159). Muniz (119) has found the test reliable for active cases of Chagas' disease, although much less sensitive than the complement-fixation reaction in chronic cases. Precipitin tests have proved positive for well developed *Entamoeba histolytica* infections in cats, although negative for early infections and dying animals (194). Good results have been reported also for malaria (142, 169). Group reactions, common to sera from patients with *P. falciparum* and *P. vivax,* have been noted. However, more intense reactions are obtained with the homologous antigen (142).

Complement-fixation tests

Specific complement-fixation depends upon the fact that an antigen and its homologous complement-fixing antibody will "fix," or combine with complement. If either the antigen or the homologous antibody is absent, complement is not fixed. The results are read in terms of an indicator, the so-called hemolytic system. In carrying out such a test, measured quantities of the test antigen, the test serum (heated to inactivate the complement), and complement (in normal guinea pig serum) are added, in physiological salt solution, to a serological test tube. After incubation, a suspension of red corpuscles and an appropriate amount of inactivated serum containing homologous hemolysin are added to the tube. The red corpuscles and the hemolytic serum constitute the "hemolytic system." The complete mixture is incubated and later examined for effects on the red corpuscles. A settling out of the corpuscles without hemolysis indicates that complement was fixed in the test reaction, since there was none available for the hemolytic reaction. Absence of hemolysis thus indicates that the test serum contains antibodies homologous for the test antigen. On the other hand, the occurrence of hemolysis, indicating that complement was not fixed in the test reaction and hence was free to combine with the red corpuscles and hemolysin, demonstrates that the test serum does not contain the homologous antibodies. In the usual procedure, the test is checked with various control tubes containing no test antigen, no test serum, neither test antigen nor test serum, or only red corpuscles, as well as with complete systems containing known positive and negative test sera.

Complement-fixation has sometimes shown good correlation with other methods for diagnosis of leishmaniasis. Using *L. donovani* antigen prepared from spleens of infected hamsters, Hindle, Hou, and Patton (89) obtained good results with sera from kala-azar patients. Comparable and more significant results have been reported for antigens prepared from cultures (6, 61, 77, 124). The test is positive in early cases and seems to be highly specific (77). The usual procedure also has been reversed by using antiserum from immunized rabbits to detect *Leishmania* antigens in human blood (121). Complement-fixation has been useful in the diagnosis of dourine because tests are positive at an early stage, and in spite of group reactions with *Trypanosoma evansi,* seem to be reliable. Complement-fixation also has been used extensively in the diagnosis of Chagas' disease (122). With antigens prepared from cultures of *T. cruzi,* the test is dependable and apparently is not complicated by cross-reactions with Wassermann sera (96). A polysaccharide fraction prepared from *T. cruzi* also has proven effective as a test antigen (119a).

Izar (91) and Scalas (146) apparently were the first to report success with complement-fixation in amoebiasis. Subsequently, the results of Craig (52, 53, 54) and later workers, with antigens prepared from cultures of *E. histolytica,* indicated the practical value of this test in mild intestinal amoebiasis. The important handicap to wider application seems to have been the difficulty of preparing effective test antigens. Establishment of *E. histolytica* in cultures with one strain of bacteria (136) and the current availability of commercially prepared antigen should eliminate certain variables caused by uncontrolled bacterial flora. However, one modification of the test, carried out with commercially produced materials, seems to be useful for diagnosis of hepatic but not intestinal amoebiasis (90a).

Application of complement-fixation to diagnosis of malaria was not successful at first because sensitivity of the tests was too low. More recently, reasonably good results have been obtained with antigens prepared from parasitized human or monkey blood (44, 45, 62, 67, 71, 83, 98, 111, 164, 165) and from chicken blood containing *P. gallinaceum* (83, 98). Such tests also will detect malarial antigens, in the blood of the host, which fix complement in the presence of antiserum (70). Although complement-fixation with *P. knowlesi* or *P. gallinaceum* antigen in human malaria is a group reaction and false reactions are sometimes obtained with syphilitic sera (7, 83), its practical value as a supplementary method in diagnosing mild infections with *P. vivax* seems to have been demonstrated (68). However, the test seems to have no value in latent *vivax* malaria. An interesting outgrowth of these investigations is the demonstration that *P. gallinaceum* antigen is effective in complement-fixation tests for *Haemoproteus columbae* in pigeons (197). Perhaps the relationship between *Plasmodium* and *Haemoproteus* is closer than is generally believed.

Tests with human sera from known and suspected cases of toxoplasmosis have indicated that complement-fixation may be useful in diagnosis of active toxoplasmosis (196). Complement-fixation tests may be positive also in animals infected with Coccidia (8, 42) but the diagnostic value is uncertain.

In addition to specific complement-fixation, in which the reaction is dependent upon the presence of a particular antigen and its homologous antibodies, *non-specific* complement-fixation tests have been used extensively in serological diagnosis. In these tests, the test "antigen" bears no apparent relation to the parasite causing the infection under consideration. The best known example is the Wassermann reaction, in which the test "antigen" is extracted from normal ox heart. A comparable non-specific test has been tried in diagnosis of kala azar (155, 156), the "antigen" being prepared from a human strain of *Mycobacterium tuberculosis*. Although occasional false positives have been obtained in pulmonary tuberculosis, this test for kala azar seems to be fairly reliable.

Skin tests

Diagnostic skin tests depend upon a cutaneous inflammatory reaction induced by an antigen, introduced either by intradermal injection or by the scratch method, into an animal containing homologous antibodies. A positive reaction in man usually involves both immediate and delayed reactions. In lower animals which react at all, an inflammatory reaction usually develops the day after inoculation. The minute reddened area of a negative reaction is readily distinguished from a positive test.

Skin reactions to *Leishmania* have been obtained in rabbits immunized to *L. donovani* and *L. tropica* (193) and also in human cases of dermal leishmaniasis (117, 153). Positive tests have been reported also in rabbits immunized to *Trypanosoma cruzi* (154), in human amoebiasis (147), and in guinea pigs for several weeks after recovery from coccidiosis (88). Preliminary experience with an intradermal test for human malaria has been promising. With antigen prepared from *Plasmodium gallinaceum*, the test compares favorably with examination of blood films (108).

Adhesion tests

Adhesion, or "adhesin," tests, in diagnosis of trypanosomiasis, involve mixing citrated blood from the host with a suspension of the suspected parasites. A positive test, in which red corpuscles and sometimes blood platelets stick to the flagellates, indicates that the blood contains antibodies specific for the trypanosomes. The reaction apparently depends upon the presence of complement (195). Adhesion tests have been applied to diagnosis of trypanosomiasis in man and other animals (37, 66, 132, 179, 195) as well as infections with *Leishmania tropica* (116).

SEROLOGICAL DIFFERENTIATION OF SPECIES

In the differentiation of species by means of serological reactions, microorganisms are tested with known antisera. A positive reaction, such as agglutination, indicates that the antiserum contains antibodies homologous for the test organism. This establishes the identity of the strain, provided group reactions have been eliminated. The specificity of an agglutin test can be increased by preliminary absorption of the antiserum with appropriate heterologous antigens so as to eliminate some or most of the group antibodies. Even the quantitative interpretation of group reactions may throw some light on degrees of taxonomic relationship (85, 186). Serological tests have some value in differentiating morphologically similar organisms, but the data must be interpreted cautiously because the tests are so sensitive. For instance, agglutinin tests have distinguished between strains of trypanosomes derived from one original stock but maintained in different host species (138).

Agglutinin tests have given good results in differentiating types of *Leishmania*. Bandi (11), who was interested in the status of *"Leishmania canis,"* found that either *L. canis* or *L. donovani* agglutinin would react with either strain in titres up to 160. Neither agglutinin was active against *L. tropica* in titres above 70. *L. canis* and *L. donovani* thus seemed to be serologically identical, while both were distinct from *L. tropica*. More recently, agglutinin tests have indicated that *L. donovani, L. tropica,* and *L. brasiliensis* are serologically distinct (74, 97, 125), although group reactions may be expected with low dilutions of agglutinating sera. Group agglutination is eliminated in higher dilutions, while homologous agglutination may still be detectable at titres of 2,560-2,580 (157). Adler and Theodor (1) used agglutinin tests in identifying an invertebrate host of *L. tropica* with their demonstration that *"Herpetomonas papatasii,"* an intestinal flagellate of sandflies, is serologically identical with *L. tropica*.

Specific lysins also have been tried in the identification of Trypanosomidae. By inoculating flagellates into culture media to which known lytic antisera had been added, da Fonseca (75) was able to distinguish *Leishmania brasiliensis* from *L. tropica*. Growth of *L. brasiliensis* was inhibited by anti-*brasiliensis* lysin but not by anti-*tropica* lysin. The results were the reverse with cultures of *L. tropica*. Neither antiserum prevented growth of *L. donovani* in cultures. There are also indications that species of *Trypanosoma* may be differentiated by lysis *in vitro* (105), although there may be difficulties with group reactions.

LITERATURE CITED[1]

1. Adler, S. and O. Theodor 1926. *Ann. Trop. Med. & Parasitol.* **20**: 355.
2. Alexander, F. D. and H. E. Meleney 1935. *Amer. J. Hyg.* **22**: 704.
3. Andrews, J. M. 1926. *Amer. J. Hyg.* **6**: 784.
4. ——— 1927. *J. Parasitol.* **13**: 183.
5. Augustine, D. L. 1943. *Proc. Amer. Acad. Arts & Sci.* **75**: 85.
6. Auricchio, L. 1927. *Pediatria* **35**: 745.
7. Babin, F. and A. D. Dulaney 1945. *Amer. J. Hyg.* **42**: 167.
8. Bachman, G. W. 1930. *Amer. J. Hyg.* **12**: 624.
9. ——— 1930. *Amer. J. Hyg.* **12**: 641.
10. Baldwin, F. M., O. B. Wiswell and H. A. Jankiewicz 1941. *Proc. Soc. Exp. Biol. & Med.* **48**: 278.
11. Bandi, I. 1913. *J. Trop. Med. & Hyg.* **16**: 50.
12. Becker, E. R. 1935. *Amer. J. Hyg.* **21**: 389.
13. ——— 1942. *Proc. Iowa Acad. Sci.* **49**: 503.
14. ——— and R. I. Dilworth 1941. *J. Inf. Dis.* **68**: 285.
15. ——— and P. L. Gallagher 1947. *Iowa St. Col. J. Sci.* **21**: 351.
16. ——— and M. G. Lysenko 1948. *Iowa St. Col. J. Sci.* **22**: 239.
17. ———, M. Manresa and E. M. Johnson 1943. *Iowa St. Col. J. Sci.* **17**: 431.
18. ——— and N. F. Morehouse 1936. *J. Parasitol.* **22**: 60.
19. ——— and L. Smith 1942. *Iowa St. Col. J. Sci.* **16**: 443.
20. ———, J. Taylor and C. Fuhrmeister 1947. *Iowa St. Col. J. Sci.* **21**: 237.
21. Beckman, H. 1948. *Proc. Soc. Exp. Biol. & Med.* **67**: 172.
22. Berberian, D. A. 1939. *Trans. Roy. Soc. Trop. Med. & Hyg.* **33**: 87.
23. Berghe, L. van den 1943. *Ann. Soc. Belge Méd. Trop.* **23**: 113.
24. Boyd, G. H. 1939. *Amer. J. Hyg.* **29** (C): 119.
25. Boyd, M. F. 1940. *Amer. J. Trop. Med.* **20**: 69.
26. ——— and S. F. Kitchen 1936. *Amer. J. Trop. Med.* **16**: 317.
27. ——— and ——— 1936. *Amer. J. Trop. Med.* **16**: 447.
28. ——— and ——— 1945. *J. Nat. Malar. Soc.* **4**: 301.
29. ——— and C. B. Matthews 1939. *Amer. J. Trop. Med.* **19**: 63.
30. ——— and W. K. Stratman-Thomas 1933. *Amer. J. Hyg.* **17**: 55.
31. ——— and ——— 1933. *Amer. J. Hyg.* **18**: 482.
32. ——— and ——— 1933. *Amer. J. Hyg.* **18**: 485.
33. ———, ——— and S. F. Kitchen 1936. *Amer. J. Trop. Med.* **16**: 139.
34. Brackett, S., E. Waletsky and M. Baker 1946. *J. Parasit.* **32**: 453.
35. Braun, H. and E. Teuchmann 1912. *Deutsch. med. Wchnschr.* **38**: 107.
36. Brooke, M. M. 1945. *Amer. J. Hyg.* **41**: 81.
37. Brown, H. C. and J. C. Broom 1938. *Trans. Roy. Soc. Trop. Med. & Hyg.* **32**: 209.
38. Butler, F. A. and J. J. Sapero 1947. *Amer. J. Trop. Med.* **27**: 111.
39. Caldwell, F. E. and P. György 1943. *Proc. Soc. Exp. Biol. & Med.* **53**: 116.
40. ——— and ——— 1947. *J. Inf. Dis.* **81**: 197.
41. Caronia, G. 1913. *Ztschr. f. Immunitätsforsch., Orig.* **20**: 174.
42. Chapman, M. J. 1929. *Amer. J. Hyg.* **9**: 389.

[1] For detailed reviews of the earlier literature, see: (a) Taliaferro, W. H. 1929. The immunology of parasitic infections (New York: Century); (b) Culbertson, J. T. 1941. Immunity against animal parasites (New York, Columbia Univ. Press).

43. Coggeshall, L. T. 1938. *Amer. J. Trop. Med.* **18**: 715.
44. ——— 1941. *Proc. Indiana Acad. Sci.* **50**: 1.
45. ——— and M. D. Eaton 1938. *J. Exp. Med.* **67**: 871.
46. ——— and H. W. Kumm 1937. *J. Exper. Med.* **66**: 177.
47. ——— and ——— 1938. *J. Exp. Med.* **68**: 17.
48. ———, F. A. Rice and E. H. Yount 1948. *Proc. 4th Intern. Congr. Trop. Med. & Malaria* **1**: 749.
49. Cooper, W. C., G. R. Coatney and D. S. Ruhe 1947. *Amer. J. Hyg.* **46**: 141.
50. Coventry, F. A. 1925. *Amer. J. Hyg.* **5**: 127.
51. ——— 1930. *Amer. J. Hyg.* **12**: 366.
52. Craig, C. F. 1927. *Amer. J. Trop. Med.* **7**: 225.
53. ——— 1928. *Amer. J. Trop. Med.* **8**: 29.
54. ——— 1937. *Amer. J. Publ. Health* **27**: 689.
55. Culbertson, J. T. 1938. *J. Parasitol.* **24**: 65.
56. ——— 1939. *J. Parasitol.* **25**: 182.
57. ——— and W. R. Kessler 1939. *Amer. J. Hyg.* **29** (C): 33.
58. ——— and M. H. Kolodny 1938. *J. Parasit.* **24**: 83.
59. ——— and N. Molomut 1938. *Proc. Soc. Exp. Biol. & Med.* **39**: 28.
60. ——— and R. M. Wotton 1939. *Amer. J. Hyg.* **30** (C): 101.
61. Cunha, A. M. and E. Dias 1938. *C. R. Soc. Biol.* **129**: 991.
62. Davis, B. D. 1948. *J. Immunol.* **58**: 269.
63. Denison, N. 1943. *Proc. Soc. Exp. Biol. & Med.* **52**: 26.
64. Duca, C. J. 1939. *Amer. J. Hyg.* **29** (C): 25.
65. Duke, H. L. 1928. *Parasitol.* **20**: 427.
66. ——— and J. M. Wallace 1930. *Parasitol.* **22**: 414.
67. Dulaney, A. D. and D. B. Morrison 1944. *Amer. J. Trop. Med.* **24**: 323.
68. ——— and R. B. Watson 1945. *Amer. J. Trop. Med.* **25**: 473.
69. Eaton, M. D. 1938. *J. Exper. Med.* **67**: 857.
70. ——— 1939. *J. Exp. Med.* **69**: 517.
71. ——— and L. T. Coggeshall 1939. *J. Exp. Med.* **69**: 379.
72. Ehrlich, P. and K. Shiga 1904. *Berlin. klin. Wchnschr.* **41**: 329.
73. Faust, E. C. and E. S. Kagy 1934. *Amer. J. Trop. Med.* **14**: 235.
74. Fonseca, F. da 1932. *Amer. J. Trop. Med.* **12**: 453.
75. ——— 1933. *Amer. J. Trop. Med.* **13**: 113.
76. Freund, J., K. J. Thomson, H. E. Sommer, A. W. Walter and T. M. Pisani 1948. *Amer. J. Trop. Med.* **28**: 1.
77a. Garcia, E. Y. 1948. *Ann. N. Y. Acad. Sci.* **50**: 171.
77. Ghosh, H., N. N. Ghosh and J. C. Ray 1945. *Ann. Biochem. & Exp. Med.* **5**: 153.
78. Gingrich, W. 1934. *J. Parasitol.* **20**: 332.
79. ——— 1941. *J. Inf. Dis.* **68**: 46.
80. ——— 1948. *J. Nat. Malar. Soc.* **7**: 109.
81. Gowe, D. F. 1937. *Amer. J. Trop. Med.* **17**: 401.
82. Hackett, L. W. 1937. *Malaria in Europe* (London: Oxford Univ. Press).
83. Harris, A. D. and L. M. Reidel 1948. *Amer. J. Trop. Med.* **28**: 787.
84. Hartman, E. 1927. *Amer. J. Hyg.* **7**: 407.
85. Heathman, L. 1932. *Amer. J. Hyg.* **16**: 97.
86. Hegner, R. and L. Eskridge 1938. *Amer. J. Hyg.* **28**: 367.
87. Heidelberger, M., W. A. Coates and M. M. Mayer 1946. *J. Immunol.* **53**: 113.
88. Henry, D. P. 1932. *Univ. Calif. Publ. Zool.* **37**: 211.
89. Hindle, E., P. C. Hou and W. S. Patton 1926. *Proc. Roy. Soc.*, B, **100**: 368.
90. Huff, C. G. and F. Coulston 1946. *J. Inf. Dis.* **78**: 99.
90a. Hussey, K. L. and H. W. Brown 1950. *Amer. J. Trop. Med.* **30**: 147.
91. Izar, G. 1914. *Arch. f. Schiffs-u. Tropenhyg.* **18**: 36.
92. James, S. P. 1931. *Trans. Roy. Soc. Trop. Med. and Hyg.* **24**: 477.
93. Jolly, A., M. Lavergne and D. Tanguy 1937. *Ann. Inst. Pasteur* **58**: 297.
94. Kanthack, A. A., H. E. Durham and W. F. H. Blandford 1898. *Proc. Roy. Soc. London* **64**: 100.
95. Kauders, O. 1927. *Centralbl. f. Bakt., Orig.* **104**: 158.
96. Kelser, R. A. 1936. *Amer. J. Trop. Med.* **16**: 405.

97. Kligler, I. J. 1925. *Trans. Roy. Soc. Trop. Med. & Hyg.* **19**: 330.
97a. —— and L. Olitzki 1936. *Ann. Trop. Med. Parasit.* **30**: 287.
98. —— and M. Yoeli 1941. *Amer. J. Trop. Med.* **21**: 531.
98a. Knisely, M. H., W. K. Stratman-Thomas, T. S. Eliot and E. H. Bloch 1945. *J. Nat. Malar. Soc.* **4**: 285.
99. Koch, R. 1901. *B. z. Deutsch. Kolonialbl.* 12, No. **24**.
100. Kolodny, M. H. 1939. *Amer. J. Hyg.* **29** (C): 13.
101. —— 1939. *Amer. J. Hyg.* **29** (C): 155.
102. —— 1939. *Amer. J. Hyg.* **30** (C): 19.
103. Laveran, A. and F. Mesnil 1900. *C. R. Soc. Biol.* **52**: 939.
104. —— and A. Pettit 1909. *C. R. Ac. Sci.* **149**: 500.
105. Léger, A. and J. Ringenbach 1912. *C. R. Soc. Biol.* **72**: 267.
106. Lorando, N. and D. Sotiriades 1937. *Trans. Roy. Soc. Trop. Med. & Hyg.* **31**: 227.
107. Maier, J. and L. T. Coggeshall 1944. *J. Exp. Med.* **79**: 401.
108. Makari, J. G. 1948. *Proc. 4th Intern. Congr. Trop. Med. & Malaria* **1**: 818.
109. Malaria Commission, League of Nations 1933. League of Nations: *Quart. Bull. Health Org.*, **2**: 181.
110. Manwell, R. D. and F. Goldstein 1940. *J. Exp. Med.* **71**: 409.
111. Mayer, M. and M. Heidelberger 1946. *J. Immunol.* **54**: 89.
112. Meleney, H. E. and W. W. Frye 1933. *Amer. J. Hyg.* **17**: 637.
113. —— and —— 1937. *Amer. J. Hyg. Dis. Nutr.* **4**: 37.
114. ——, —— and W. S. Leathers 1939. *Amer. J. Hyg.* **29** (C): 61.
115. Milan, D. F. and L. T. Coggeshall 1938. *Amer. J. Trop. Med.* **18**: 331.
116. Mills, E. A. and C. Machattie 1931. *Trans. Roy. Soc. Trop. Med. & Hyg.* **25**: 205.
117. Montenegro, J. 1926. *Arch. Dermat. Syph.* **13**: 187.
118. Mulligan, H. W., T. Somerville and C. S. Swaminath 1940. *J. Malar. Inst. India* **3**: 563.
119. Muniz, J. 1947. *Brasil-Medico 61*, Nos. **29-30**, p. 3.
119a. —— and G. de Freitas 1944. *Rev. Brasil. Biol.* **4**: 421.
120. Naiman, D. N. 1944. *J. Parasitol.* **30**: 209.
121. Nattan-Larrier, L. and L. Grimard 1935. *Bull. Soc. Path. Exot.* **28**: 658.
122. Neghme, A. and J. Román 1948. *Amer. J. Trop. Med.* **28**: 835.
123. Nicolle, C. and C. Anderson 1925. *Arch. Inst. Pasteur Tunis* **14**: 278.
124. Niyogi, A. K. and J. C. Ray 1942. *Ann. Biochem. & Exp. Med.* **2**: 47.
125. Noguchi, H. 1926. *J. Exp. Med.* **44**: 327.
126. Novy, F. G. 1907. *Proc. Soc. Exp. Biol. & Med.* **4**: 42.
127. Novy, F. G., W. A. Perkins and R. Chambers 1912. *J. Inf. Dis.* **11**: 411.
128. Packchanian, A. 1934. *Amer. J. Hyg.* **20**: 135.
129. Perla, D. 1934. *J. Exp. Med.* **60**: 541.
130. —— 1937. *Amer. J. Hyg.* **26**: 374.
131. Poindexter, H. A. 1934. *J. Exp. Med.* **60**: 575.
132. Raffel, S. 1930. *Amer. J. Hyg.* **19**: 416.
133. Ratcliffe, H. L. 1928. *Amer. J. Hyg.* **8**: 910.
134. —— 1929. *J. Parasit.* **16**: 75.
135. Redmond, W. B. 1939. *J. Inf. Dis.* **64**: 273.
136. Rees, C. W., J. Bozicevich, L. V. Reardon and F. Jones 1942. *Amer. J. Trop. Med.* **22**: 581.
137. Regendanz, P. and W. Kikuth 1927. *Centralbl. f. Bakt., Orig.* **103**: 271.
137a. Rein, C. R., S. C. Bukantz, J. F. Kent, W. C. Cooper, D. S. Ruhe and G. R. Coatney 1949. *Amer. J. Hyg.* **49**: 374.
138. Reiner, L. and S. S. Chao 1933. *Amer. J. Trop. Med.* **13**: 525.
139. Rigdon, R. H. 1947. *Amer. J. Hyg.* **46**: 254.
140. Robertson, M. 1934. *J. Pathol. & Bact.* **38**: 363.
141. Row, R. 1931. *Ind. J. Med. Res.* **19**: 641.
142. —— 1931. *Trans. Roy. Soc. Trop. Med. & Hyg.* **24**: 623.
143. Russell, P. F., H. W. Mulligan and B. N. Mohan 1942. *J. Malar. Inst. India* **4**: 311.
144. Saceghem, R. van 1922. *C. R. Soc. Biol.* **86**: 515.
145. Sandground, J. H. 1947. *Ann. Trop. Med. & Parasitol.* **41**: 293.
146. Scalas, L. 1921. *Riforma med.* **37**: 103.

147. ——— 1923. *Riforma med.* **39**: 967.
148. Schilling, C. 1912. *Deutsch. med. Wchnschr.* **36**: 13.
149. Schroeder, E. C. and W. E. Cotton 1907. *22d Ann. Rep. Bur. Anim. Industry,* p. 71.
150. Schumaker, E. 1930. *Amer. J. Hyg.* **12**: 341.
151. Seeler, A. O. and W. H. Ott 1944. *J. Inf. Dis.* **75**: 175.
152. ——— and ——— 1945. *J. Inf. Dis.* **77**: 82.
153. Senekjie, H. A. 1941. *Amer. J. Hyg.* **34** (C): 63.
154. ——— 1943. *Proc. Soc. Exp. Biol. & Med.* **52**: 56.
155. Sen Gupta, P. C. 1943. *Indian Med. Gaz.* **78**: 336.
156. ——— 1943. *Indian Med. Gaz.* **78**: 537.
157. Shi Lu Chang and W. O. Negherbon 1947. *J. Inf. Dis.* **81**: 209.
158. Sice, A. 1929. *Bull. Soc. Path. Exot.* **22**: 912.
159. ——— 1930. *Bull. Soc. Path. Exot.* **23**: 459.
160. Sinton, J. A. 1937. *Rec. Malar. Surv. India* **7**: 85.
161. ———, E. L. Hutton and P. G. Shute 1939. *Trans. Roy. Soc. Trop. Med. & Hyg.* **33**: 47.
162. Smith, T. and F. L. Kilborne 1893. *Bur. Anim. Ind. Bull. 1,* 301 pp.
163. Sotiriades, D. 1917. *Grèce Méd.* **19**: 27.
164. Stratman-Thomas, W. K. and A. D. Dulaney 1940. *Amer. J. Trop. Med.* **20**: 717.
165. ——— and ——— 1940. *J. Immunol.* **39**: 257.
166. Taliaferro, L. G. 1925. *Amer. J. Hyg.* **5**: 742.
167. Taliaferro, W. H. 1924. *J. Exp. Med.* **39**: 171.
168. ——— 1926. *Quart. Rev. Biol.* **1**: 246.
169. ——— 1928. *Amer. J. Publ. Health* **18**: 793.
170. ——— 1938. *J. Immunol.* **35**: 303.
171. ——— 1941. "The Immunology of the Parasitic Protozoa" in Calkins and Sumners, *Protozoa in Biological Research* (New York: Columbia Press), p. 830.
171a. ——— 1941. *Amer. Nat.* **75**: 458.
172. ——— 1948. *Proc. 4th Intern. Congr. Trop. Med. & Malar.* **1**: 776.
173. ——— 1948. *Bact. Rev.* **12**: 1.
174. ——— and P. R. Cannon 1936. *J. Inf. Dis.* **59**: 72.
175. ———, ——— and S. Goodloe 1931. *Amer. J. Hyg.* **14**: 1.
176. ——— and T. L. Johnson 1926. *J. Prev. Med.* **1**: 85.
177. ——— and H. W. Mulligan 1937. *Ind. Med. Res. Mem.,* No. 29.
178. ——— and L. G. Taliaferro 1922. *Amer. J. Hyg.* **2**: 264.
179. ——— and ——— 1934. *J. Immunol.* **26**: 193.
180. ——— and ——— 1940. *J. Inf. Dis.* **66**: 152.
181. ——— and ——— 1944. *J. Inf. Dis.* **75**: 1.
182. ——— and ——— 1947. *J. Inf. Dis.* **80**: 78.
183. ——— and ——— 1948. *J. Inf. Dis.* **82**: 5.
183a. ——— and ——— 1949. *J. Inf. Dis.* **85**: 101.
184. ———, ——— and F. E. Kelsey 1948. *Science* **107**: 460.
185. ———, ——— and E. L. Simmons 1945. *J. Inf. Dis.* **77**: 158.
186. Tanzer, C. 1941. *J. Immunol.* **42**: 291.
187. Thomson, K. J., J. Freund, H. E. Somer and A. W. Walter 1947. *Amer. J. Trop. Med.* **27**: 79.
188. Thomson, J. G. 1933. *Trans. Roy. Soc. Trop. Med. & Hyg.* **26**: 483.
189. Trager, W. 1943. *J. Exp. Med.* **77**: 557.
190. ——— 1947. *J. Exp. Med.* **85**: 663.
191. Tyzzer, E. E. and E. E. Jones 1929. *Amer. J. Hyg.* **10**: 269.
192. ———, H. Theiler and E. E. Jones 1932. *Amer. J. Hyg.* **15**: 319.
193. Wagener, E. H. 1923. *Univ. Calif. Publ. Zool.* **20**: 477.
194. ——— 1924. *Univ. Calif. Publ. Zool.* **26**: 15.
195. Wallace, J. M. and A. Wormall 1931. *Parasitol.* **23**: 346.
196. Warren, J. and A. B. Sabin 1942. *Proc. Soc. Exp. Biol. & Med.* **51**: 11.
197. Yoeli, M. 1948. *Amer. J. Trop. Med.* **28**: 387.
197a. Yount, E. H., Jr. and L. T. Coggeshall 1949. *Amer. J. Trop. Med.* **29**: 701.
198. Yorke, W. and J. W. S. Macfie 1924. *Trans. Roy. Soc. Trop. Med. & Hyg.* **18**: 13.
199. Zuckerman, A. 1945. *J. Inf. Dis.* **77**: 28.

Index

Numbers in italics refer to pages on which figures occur. In the text, names of authors are cited mostly by numbers referring to papers listed at the end of each chapter. Accordingly, the names of relatively few authors are listed separately in the index.

654

658   Index